THE SELECT READER

THE SELECT
READER

TORONTO · NEW YORK

Editor:	Noel Rae
Senior Editors:	David Dunbar
	Mary Kirby
	Janetta Lee
Assistant Editor:	Amy Peck

CONTENTS

THE FRUIT PALACE

CHARLES NICHOLL

Comic and foolhardy, The Fruit Palace *is a hugely enjoyable adventure that Charles Nicholl, to our benefit and delight, actually survived—but just barely.*

Arriving in Colombia in the early 1970s, Nicholl had his first brush with the country's cocaine smugglers at a dingy cafe known as the Fruit Palace. Twelve years later, having won from his publisher the impossible assignment of penetrating this dangerous world, he returned to write "The Great Cocaine Story."

Following the billion-dollar cocaine pipeline, he visited mountain towns, muddy jungle villages, tumbledown seaports and glittering resorts. Before long, Nicholl was meeting the fixers and smugglers, the "cooks" and the "mules." The Fruit Palace *is the harrowing and hilarious adventure story of a spunky writer who managed to explore the drug capital of the world—and lived to laugh about it.*

"This book is not a tract for or against the trafficking of drugs," writes Nicholl. "It is simply a story. I know that I owe some sort of apology to the people of Colombia, because like everyone I talk of little else but their mala fama. *I can only say that the book grew—if at an odd angle—out of my love for Colombia, and for the warmth, wit and honesty of its people."*

PREFACE

It is raining in Europe. There are no windows in this narrow, strip-lit room, but I know it's still raining, as it was when the plane landed two, maybe three hours ago. One of the customs officers has just come back in. "It's pissing down out there," he says. The shoulders of his blue, vaguely naval uniform are wet. The other officer, the Scot, the one who asks all the questions, turns to me and says, "Looks like we're doing you a favor after all."

They have looked up my record, looked up my rectum, searched me from the heel of my boot to the lining of my hat. They have sifted through my baggage like archaeologists. There remains the possibility that I'm body-packing—carrying cocaine inside my stomach, packaged up in condoms or the fingers of surgical gloves—but they are inclined to doubt it. They are dealing with a nuisance, an eccentric, a fool, but not a smuggler.

So the only problem is this handful of greenish-brown leaves, sitting on the pinewood desk in front of me, spilling out of a couple of pages of last Wednesday's edition of *El Bogotano*. They are coca leaves. To be precise, they are the leaves of *Erythroxylum coca novogranatense*, the subspecies of *Erythroxylum coca* that grows in the temperate mountain valleys of Colombia. I have explained it all carefully. I'm just a writer returning home from an assignment. I brought the leaves back as a souvenir. They were given to me by the Arhuacos, the mountain Indians of the Sierra Nevada. I stretch the point a little and say they were a "ceremonial" gift. No, I was not aware they were illegal here. Yes, of course I knew that cocaine was extracted from coca leaves, but look, the leaves are old and stale. They are spotted with white mildew—*coca caspada*, they call it, dandruffy coca. Any self-respecting coca user would throw them away.

My two interrogators, the dark Scot and his soft-spoken, curly-haired backup, would probably let the whole thing go. It has been an interesting morning for them. They had pulled a thousand people with Colombian stamps in their passport, but they had never seen a coca leaf before. "Most instructive," says the droll Scot. But the Senior Officer, one Liggett, has been summoned, and he has no doubts whatever. The law clearly states that the coca leaf is a Controlled Substance, a Class A drug as defined in Schedule Two of the Misuse of Drugs Act, 1971. I am consequently under arrest.

The Scot licks his finger, turns a new page of his notebook. "Right. Let's run through this story of yours from the beginning, shall we?"

CHAPTER ONE

At the Fruit Palace

If these things have a beginning I suppose this began at the Fruit Palace, some twelve years ago. The Fruit Palace was a small, whitewashed café, much like thousands of others in Colombia. It stood a couple of blocks up from the waterfront in Santa Marta, a hot, scruffy seaport on the northern coast. The wooden sign outside read, *EL PALACIO DE LAS FRUTAS, Cafetería Refresquería Residencias*, the letters painted in bright, naive colors, with a small study in fruit—oranges, mangoes, a half-sliced pineapple—in the bottom corner. The speciality of the house was *jugo*, or tropical fruit juice, but you could also get the usual range of cheap meals, and of course the ubiquitous *tinto*, the small cup of black coffee that fuels the nation.

The Fruit Palace was always open and never crowded. I think Julio, who owned and ran it, actually preferred business slow. He had dreams of getting rich, but they were quite divorced from his day-to-day life. Whisking *jugos* was something to do while he waited for the big one to turn up. "With a little bit of sweet and a little bit of sour," he said, "a man is happy."

Julio was in his mid-thirties, but he looked older. He was not a Samario, as the natives of Santa Marta are known, but one of the town's floating population. Santa Marta is a honey-trap for hopeful prospectors from the interior, drawn by the promise of the good life by the Caribbean Sea, and of the rich pickings to be had from the town's various forms of contraband, mainly—but by no means exclusively—drugs. Julio was from Boyacá, 500 miles south in the Eastern Cordillera of the Andes. With his black stubble, bad teeth, sideburns and faded check shirts, he had the typical look of the Colombian *criollo*, the mixed Spanish-Indian type that forms the majority of the country's people. But he had something else—a certain finesse, a dapperness of manner and philosophy. His pointed nose and thick, slightly twirled mustache gave him an oddly *belle époque* air, a minor French dandy somehow adrift down a South American back street.

Julio's contribution to Santa Marta's black economy was a little modest dealing in emeralds. Whenever a new gringo face turned up at the Fruit Palace, it was not long before the talk was steered around to the fabulous virtues of the Colombian gem emerald, *la más famosa en el mundo*. Out would come the little fold of tissue paper, with a pair of stones winking inside. He would rock them gently in his palm, like tiny dice. "*Mire, mire, el fuego verde!*" Look at the green fire in it. His prices were always good, even by black market standards. I wondered if he sometimes sold fakes—he certainly spoke expertly about counterfeiting—but it wouldn't have done to ask him.

Also living at the Fruit Palace was a girl called Miriam, who did the cooking and the cleaning. Julio had a wife and a little daughter, but they were somewhere else for a while—the vagueness was Julio's—and in the meantime he was sharing his bed with Miriam. She was a plump, moody girl in her twenties. She wore tight skirts and a man's wristwatch. As she worked she rendered current hit songs in a tuneless, hissing kind of whistle—her favorite was a tearjerker entitled "*Volver, Volver, Volver*." She was no great beauty, but she had a certain flash every time she smiled. She flirted slyly with all the gringos. She visited me in my dreams, her breasts syncopating softly as they did when she danced to the songs on the radio. The quiet glint of machismo in Julio's eye was enough to keep it at that.

There was a small back room behind the café which Julio rented out— this was the *residencias* advertised on the sign outside. I had stumbled into the café one day for a beer, straight off the train from Barrancabermeja, a fifteen-hour haul across the Magdalena plains. The room was vacant. Too tired to look for a hotel, I took it for the night. The profound nonchalance of Santa Marta stole over me, and I was still there three months later. The bed had once belonged to Julio's grandmother and had a carved cedarwood headboard of which he was very proud, but it was bone-hard to lie on, and after a while I slept in the hammock out in the yard. When the tiny rent Julio charged for the room grew too onerous, I actually rented the hammock off him for something like 10 pesos a night, and shared the yard with a small contingent of animals. Down at the end by the kitchen lived the hen, immured by night in its miniature shack of old fruit boxes. There was a guard dog pacing on the neighbor's roof, there were rats beneath the concrete walkway, and there was the cockroach—one of many, but definitely *the* cockroach, sleek and fat and shiny brown.

Julio was delighted with this new arrangement. It had the magic smack of something for nothing. I paid less, he got more, the back room now being free for other gringos. There were always gringos in town. The better class stayed at the seafront hotels, or out at Rodadero, the modern hotel development hidden around the headland. They certainly didn't stay down on 10th Street, where the Fruit Palace stood. This was really the last of the "safe" streets. After that you were on your own, in the shantytown *barrio* of San Martín, which sprawled up the dusty hills above the docks. Only the more dubious, low-rent travelers, or those who had special reasons for being near the docks, sought their lodgings here. In those days there were plenty who fell into one or both of those categories, and Julio's back room was seldom vacant for long.

When I think now of the Fruit Palace I remember especially the sweet-scented nights. Julio always bought his fruit overripe. This was both cheaper and better for making *jugos*, yet another instance of those secret financial harmonies he loved to observe. The musk of sweating tropical fruit pervaded the café. By day it had to compete with the oily aromas of

Miriam's cuisine, but at night, as I swayed in my hammock in the yard, the sweet smell of corruption lay over me like a blanket.

It was at the Fruit Palace that I had my first taste of the Colombian drug trade. Illegal drugs were, and still are, the economic and cultural heartbeat of Santa Marta. In the early 1970s, when I was there, this still primarily meant marijuana. Colombian grass is considered by many connoisseurs to be the finest in the world, and nine times out of ten this means one of the strains from the Sierra Nevada southeast of town—Santa Marta Gold, Blue Sky Blonde, Punto Rojo (Red Dot), etc. But in those days the vast marijuana market in the United States was mainly supplied by Mexican grass. It wasn't until the late 1970s, after a massive American herbicide campaign had wiped out many Mexican plantations, that Colombian marijuana reigned supreme. The profits were big, but they weren't yet in megabuck units. And so the resourceful Samario *contrabandista* was becoming increasingly involved in another illicit chemical: cocaine.

Santa Marta's involvement in the cocaine trade is a simple matter of geography. The town stands precisely placed between the major producers and the major consumers of cocaine, between the *cocales*, or small hillside terraces, of Peru and Bolivia where the coca plant is intensively cultivated, and the United States where the refined end product is snorted up by the truckload. There are plenty of side doors along the way, but the basic route, then and now, is for the drug to be funneled north across the mainland to the Caribbean coast of Colombia, and from there to be shipped or flown to the United States and Europe. In the phrase of a former president of Colombia, Santa Marta is "a victim of its privileged geographic position."

These were still the early days of the great cocaine boom. In America and Europe coke was the chic new chemical toy, and down in Colombia the big smuggling syndicates were beginning to emerge, but there was still plenty of room for independent operations, for the local cowboys and the gringo casuals and the small-time dealers.

So, what with the dope and the coke, this part of the Colombian coast, and three towns in particular—the industrial port city of Barranquilla to the west, Santa Marta in the middle, and Riohacha out on the Guajira peninsula—were fast becoming world centers for drug smuggling. In Santa Marta everyone seemed to have a finger in the pie. The town had the feel of a tropical smugglers' den. It was a rakish, seedy, avaricious little place, but somehow exhilarating in the way it lived according to its own laws. The whole thing felt like a game. It was hard to imagine Santa Marta as the world center for anything. But often at night, lying in my hammock, I would hear the sound of freight trucks backfiring, and I would hold my breath because sometimes there followed a kind of shock wave, a pattern of silence and shouts, that meant it was gunfire.

A few of the gringos who stayed at the Fruit Palace were putting together small deals of some sort. The coolest of these was Nancy. She was a swan-necked girl from Toronto, who always wore sunglasses. She had me fooled all the way. She was supposedly on the coast to buy and export pre-Columbian gold pieces. She spent a lot of time with a big man called Luis, who seemed to have a bottomless supply of golden figurines and pendants, no doubt looted from Tairona burial sites in the Sierra. This is another of Santa Marta's stocks-in-trade.

Nancy came and went a lot, but she kept the room paid up even when she wasn't there. Julio was transfixed by her. This exquisite *gringuita*, paying twenty-eight days in advance, was like a holy vision to him. One day Nancy said she was going to Cartagena on business, would I perhaps like to meet up with her there in a week or so? My mouth dropped open with delight. She was a beautiful girl, and Cartagena was a beautiful town. Of course I'd like to meet up with her.

A few days later a telegram arrived for me at the Fruit Palace. It was from Nancy. "PLEASE FIND OUT PRICE AND CONDITION OF LUIS'S GOLD FROGS DISCREETLY LET ME KNOW WHEN YOU COME ROOM 32." I dutifully sought out Luis. "Tell her I've got ten frogs, ready to go," he said. He named a price per frog.

"Is that in pesos or dollars?"

"She'll know."

I took the bus to Cartagena, tingling with hopes of romance in the old white city. When I got there she seemed more interested in Luis's figures than in me, and to my disappointment she left the hotel early that evening and didn't return. The next I saw of her was two weeks later at the Fruit Palace. It was only then that she told me. The gold "frogs" had really been kilos of Santa Marta Gold and I had unwittingly couriered information for a drug run out of Cartagena.

I was aghast. How could she use me like that? *Why* had she used me like that? She shrugged. "Timing. Security. I often use guys like you, places like this. It's like they say—innocence is the best cover."

Thanks a bunch, Nancy. I still have the telegram she sent me, a souvenir of something, I don't quite know what. You would think I might have learned my lesson, but just a few weeks later I found myself mixed up in another drug move. It was cocaine this time, where the stakes are higher, the people crazier, and the comebacks nastier. From this night of folly I have no souvenirs, except the occasional flashback when my nerves are bad.

CHAPTER TWO

A Night with Captain Cocaine

It was a Saturday night in April, the hot, slack month before the brief rainy season. Soon after dark I left the Fruit Palace and made for the seafront, thinking to get a beer or two at the Pan-American, where they usually had a band playing on Saturday nights. A fat orange moon, two days past the full, squatted over the low hills inland.

The Pan-American was Santa Marta's smartest café. It had white tables laid out under a blue awning, and the words *Aire condicionado* emblazoned in scrolly red neon. Featured that night on the little stage in the corner was a Barranquilla trio, Bruno y su Jazz. Bruno was a squat, check-shirted local with an old Gibson electric guitar. His combo consisted of a ferrety bass man in beret and sunglasses, and an energetic black drummer in a sleeveless blue shirt already soaked in sweat. Slightly off to one side, self-invited, an old black in a hat was playing the wooden rhythm stick called a *guacharaca*. The waiters wanted to get rid of him, but he stood just inside the charmed circle of the music and they couldn't touch him.

Sitting alone at one of the tables was a gringo I didn't recognize—a "pure" gringo from the United States, I guessed, as opposed to the hybrid European variety. He was smartly dressed in lightweight gear, musta-chioed, bulky, balding, age indeterminate. He was sitting over a beer with his back to the music. He glanced fitfully over the magazine in front of him; it was obvious he was waiting for someone. I took a seat at the next table, and when the song finished we got talking. He was from New York City, I learned. No, he'd never been in Colombia before, in fact he'd never been farther south than Phoenix, Arizona, before yesterday. Yes, he was just here on vacation. He had a high-pitched voice, aggressive in the New York way, and rather catarrhal. Quite a crowd had gathered for the music, and he craned nervously for a view of the sidewalk.

"You're waiting for someone?" I asked.

"Goddamn right I am," he replied, with an irritated check at his watch. "He said he'd be here at six."

His watch said nearly eight. "At a guess," I bantered, "you're waiting for a Colombian. They're not the best time-keepers in the world."

"*Mañana*, huh?"

I ordered two more beers. We formalized our meeting with a hand-shake. His palm was cold and damp. His name was Harvey. He had been in Santa Marta twenty-four hours, he said, and the whole goddamn place seemed crazy.

We drank and smoked, discussed Colombia, and eyed the *costeñas*, the stunning local girls, in their Saturday best. I was showing off, full of tips and lore and knowing the ropes. I would get my comeuppance soon enough. Harvey ordered more beers, in English. One of the things he didn't like about Colombia, hc implied, was the Spanish language. He was getting a bit drunk now. He had been through three bottles of Aguila beer before I arrived. An unhealthy dew of sweat lay on his forehead.

Bruno brought a long guitar solo to a climax of high, gull-like notes, then a dramatic pause before the final bar. This was spoiled somewhat by the old man with the *guacharaca*, who kept hammering the stick on the neck of his rum bottle, dancing away with his eyes tight shut and a huge, oblivious grin on his face.

It was in the lull after this number that Harvey leaned conspiratorially across the table. He was glad he had met me, he said, because he had this problem.

This did not entirely surprise me. In Santa Marta two and two do not infallibly make four, but a nervous, catarrhal gringo fresh into town almost certainly spells "cocaine." Sure enough. "I'm not really here on vacation," he explained. "I've come down for a bit of business. You know—" he touched the side of his nose with his finger "—Cousin Charlie."

I nodded understandingly, but said nothing.

"Just a quick in and out job," he added sharply. His look suggested that the way out was not at this moment quite clear.

"So there's a problem?" I said. He nodded, looked around, and leaned still closer. In anticipation of a long and delicate story I said, "Why don't we pay, and go for a walk along the beach?"

The story Harvey told me was simple enough. For a couple of years now, since arriving in New York from some backwoods in Wisconsin, he had been doing a bit of small-time cocaine dealing. He loved the stuff dearly, and the dealing was mainly to keep himself in "candy" and make back the money his habit was costing him. He was living in Queens, which has a large population of Colombian immigrants. Connections were easy.

"For a time it was great," he said wistfully. "Plenty of candy, plenty of bread. Then you start getting greedy. You're doing two, three grams a night, seven nights a week. When you start getting greedy, it's trouble time. You can't walk away from it anymore. That's when you're going to take a fall."

Harvey indeed took a fall. He started selling larger quantities, and one day a Lexington Avenue street dealer "pulled out a piece and spat in my eye"—robbed him, in other words, at gunpoint. Net result: half a kilo of cocaine, as yet unpaid for, "down the john." Fortunately for Harvey, the owner of the cocaine did not exact any violent retribution—"like they drop you in the river twice and pull you out once." Instead he offered Harvey an arrangement. He needed someone to take care of a shipment from the

Colombian end. If Harvey would look after it for him, he would forget about this unpleasant business of the missing half kilo.

"I was fifteen adrift, man," Harvey whined. Fifteen thousand dollars was what a half kilo was worth in New York in the early seventies. "I had no way of paying up. The man could cut me up into any shape he liked. He offers me a deal. No way I could refuse.

"It all seemed pretty tight. He gives me Air Florida tickets, New York-Miami-Barranquilla-Santa Marta. He tells me where to go and who to deal with. He gives me a false-bottom suitcase with a stack of hundreds in it, plenty of spending money, and an ounce of free candy over the top when I get home. All I got to do is deliver the money, check the gear for quantity and quality, and see it onto the boat. Then I fly home, clean as a bone."

We reached one end of the town beach. In the sand near the water's edge were black drifts of mica. Specks of pyrite, fool's gold, glinted in the diffuse, mauvish light of the town. A station wagon lurched noisily off the beach drag onto 22nd Street. It stopped outside a lit doorway where a knot of people were lounging. Two men got out and lifted a third, wrapped in a blanket, out of the back of the car. Another patient was being admitted to the emergency ward of the town's hospital.

Harvey asked what was going on. When I told him he said, "Christ Jesus!" softly, and rubbed his hands up and down his white arms as if he were cold. We set off back up the beach.

Everything had gone fine, he said, until yesterday afternoon. He was supposed to meet his contact in the bar of his hotel at six o'clock. The contact, he had been assured, would have everything arranged, and he spoke perfect English. Harvey waited, but no one came. Then the barman brought him the phone—"a call for you, *señor*"—and someone was jabbering at him in Spanish. The caller eventually got the gist of the message across. Harvey's contact was no longer in on the deal; Harvey was to take a taxi into town the next morning; he was to go to the Hotel Venezuela and ask for someone called Manolo.

The following morning, the morning of this Saturday, Harvey did as he had been instructed. He met Manolo, "a little jerk in shades," at the Venezuela. Manolo told him the coke would be ready that night, and wanted to see the money. Harvey said the money was back at his hotel. Manolo said to bring all his stuff over, there was a room for him here at the Venezuela, the *portero* would look after him, and so on. Harvey did not like this arrangement. Communication was difficult. They agreed to meet at the Pan-American at six.

Harvey's second six o'clock in Colombia came and went like the first, waiting for a "friend" who did not come, and so it was that a couple of hours later I had seen this balding gringo, casting a worried eye up and down the sidewalk outside the Pan-American.

This, broadly, was Harvey's account of the business so far. From what I knew about the cocaine racket, it sounded like the usual cloak-and-dagger stuff. So what exactly was the "problem" he had mentioned, the problem that I—I suspected—was in some way supposed to solve? I asked him.

"The problem?" he snapped. "The goddamn problem is that I got to *do* it!"

"I'm sorry, I don't understand."

"Look, Charlie. Everything about this score smells wrong. First my connection vanishes and I'm dealing with this little hood Manolo instead. Now *he* doesn't show. It all smells wrong. OK, ninety-nine times out of a hundred you walk away. No score, no nothing. Don't need a weatherman to know which way the wind blows, right? But this one's different. Number one hundred. I owe it to the man. I'm plumbed right into it."

I murmured sympathy. We were sitting with our backs to a beach hut. Harvey was looking at me thoughtfully. "So what's your next move?" I asked.

"It's all a question of how we handle Manolo...."

"Just a minute, Harvey, *we* aren't...."

"I can read that guy like a clock, man! He's just aching to finger the money. What I got to do is make sure I get the candy in return. If he can't take the money and run, he'll come up with the gear. I'm sure of it. What I need is muscle."

"Well, don't look at me, chum," I said firmly. I am not what you would call "muscle." Surely Harvey could see that.

"I don't mean strong-arm stuff, man. I mean negotiating muscle." He gripped my arm. The cards, at last, were landing on the table. "I need two things, Charlie, and you can supply them both. First thing, I need space. I'm not doing any deal at the Venezuela. This place of yours, this Fruit Castle, sounds just about right. There'll be you, me and that guy of yours, Julio, all nice and cozy. We'll put the flake on the table, the money on the table, five-o five-o and no monkey business.

"The second thing I need is someone who can speak the lingo. I need an interpreter, Charlie. What you say, man?"

Harvey was glinting and glistening at me. Whether or not he had convinced me, he had certainly convinced himself. He was Harvey the street-wise superfly, the veteran of a hundred daring deals. I could see the fantasy gleam in his bulbous eye. All right, I thought, he wants to play Captain Cocaine, but do I want to play his bloody Batman? Sitting here years later, with the benefit of hindsight, it is easy to say I should have told Harvey politely but firmly to find someone else. But the night was hot, and these things have a logic of their own. There were risks, of course, but there were undeniable attractions. First, the carrot: $250 on the nail for me, the same for Julio. Second, the story: I was supposed to be some kind of journalist, wasn't I? Third, the general scenario: suitcases stuffed with bank notes, lashings of someone else's cocaine. In short, greed battled with fear, and greed won. "Why not?" I said, and thus with a handshake I became the smallest of small-time accomplices in the cocaine trade.

From that point on everything clicked ominously into place. We headed back to the Pan-American. I skulked on the beach while Harvey scanned the tables from the promenade. He loped back clumsily through the sand. "He's there, man!" he hissed. "We're in business." The next step was for me to consult with Julio. Harvey would meanwhile "keep the little creep happy" at the Pan-American. Back at the Fruit Palace Julio listened patiently. He then said he didn't like *coco*, he didn't like Manolo, he didn't want trouble, and consequently he couldn't let his place be used for a trifling 250. He wanted 500.

Back I toiled to the Pan-American. Manolo rose suavely to shake hands, a little man with a thin smile and gold in his teeth. His slicked-back hair shone like wet coal. I told Harvey of Julio's price. He grumbled but, as Julio had doubtless divined, he was in no position to refuse.

"OK, OK," he said. "Now, Charlie, I want you to explain it all to our friend here, nice and gentle. You tell him he does the deal our way or not at all. We meet at the Fruit Palace at—" he checked his watch "—at midnight. He comes alone, with the gear. Five kilos, as arranged. Any monkey business and the deal's off. OK?"

Manolo listened blandly to my polite schoolboy Spanish. It's all right, I thought. He'll simply say "No" and the whole business will be over. But it was a night for wrong decisions, and what he finally said, with a last lingering look at both of us and a light shrug, was: "OK, I'll be there."

Midnight found the four of us—Julio, Harvey, Manolo and myself—sitting around the "private table" at the Fruit Palace. The air was hot and sweet. A single light shone down on the table: coffee cups, ashtrays, a half-empty bottle of Medellín rum. The street door was shut and bolted. A passerby might have seen the light under the door, but he would have kept on walking, because at midnight on 10th Street the rule was always to keep on walking.

Harvey had arrived by taxi an hour before, stumbling in with two suitcases, one of them containing $50,000. While we waited Julio tried to sell him some emeralds, but Harvey's mind was elsewhere and his palms were sweating, and he kept dropping the stones. Now Manolo had just turned up—without the five kilos, but with a small *muestra*, a sample, instead.

Harvey did not like this. "Where's the deal, man?" he whined. "I want to see the deal."

I translated, nervously formal. *"Harvey quiere ver toda la mercancía."*

"I can get it. No problem. Half an hour." Manolo spoke smoothly, with flashes of gold from his teeth. "Doesn't Señor Harvey trust me?"

Harvey said, "Shit, man. I don't even trust myself."

"Harvey is a little nervous," I relayed reassuringly.

"Why doesn't he try the *muestra*? It's real good stuff. Ninety-eight percent pure."

Harvey caught the last phrase, *"pureza de noventa y ocho por ciento,"* and snorted tetchily. "I've heard *that* up in Spanish Harlem. I didn't believe it then and I don't believe it now."

I told him to cool down and try the sample. Manolo pushed the small, rectangular fold of paper over to him. It was cheap lined paper from a letter pad. Harvey took it. Grumpily, but with gentle care, he opened it up and inspected the small, flattened heap of cream-colored cocaine inside. He nodded abstractedly. It seemed to please him. He dabbed a bit on the end of his forefinger and tasted it. Again he nodded. Now he wet his finger and took another dab, and watched while the powder dissolved. He held the finger out to me. There was a trace of gray, fluffy dust on it. "The cut," he murmured. This is a fallible test, I'm told—many "cuts," or adulterants, are quite as soluble as the coke itself—but right then it seemed impressive enough. Harvey looked every inch the professional. He was on home ground at last.

Julio, slightly out of the arc of light, rocked back on the thin-legged café chair. He looked poised and philosophical, as always, but his brown eyes didn't miss a trick. Hardly moving a muscle, he called out for coffee. *"Hay tinto, Miriam?"* A sulky, droned *"Sí"* came out of the bedroom, and Miriam plodded kitchenward, scraping her flip-flop sandals on the floor. She did not look at us as she passed. She did not approve of *narcotráfico*.

"Looks OK to me," said Harvey. He took out a small knife with a retractable blade, and began to dice up some of the cocaine on the table. He cursed when grains of crystal jumped away from the blade. I saw that his hands were trembling. He fashioned a small pile of coke into thin lines. Manolo unhooked a coke spoon from a silver neck chain under his shirt, but Harvey shook his head—"Uh-uh"—and took out a crisp $100 bill. He rolled it neatly into a thin pipe. "I take it Wonder Warthog style," he chuckled. The imminent pleasure of the cocaine hit was sweeping aside all his grumbles and paranoias, clearing his mind like a runway for takeoff. He hunched over the table and hoovered up a line through the bill with a single deep snort. He winced a little and jerked his head back. His nose stuck up like a shark's fin. He emitted a long, slow hiss of pleasure, as if the cocaine had gone in like a spike and let out all the stale air in him. "Nice," he sighed, "nice," then "Hmmmm," and an odd, girlish giggle. He bent back down to repeat the procedure via the other nostril, then pressed some leftover dust off the melamine tabletop, and massaged it into his gums.

He handed me the little pipe. I took a hit, rather smaller than Harvey's. I felt my nostril scorch, my mouth freeze, my veins hum all the way down to my feet. I had tasted coke before, but this felt lethal. Simple case of motor stimulation, I reminded myself. Heart racing, adrenal secretions, everything hastening to some unknown crescendo. Purely pharmaceutical, of course. Not *really* on a big dipper at all. Not falling, not flying, not swooping through the room like a white owl over a dark field.

My hand was waving the rolled-up bill at Julio. He shook his head. "I'm thinking of getting some sleep tonight." Manolo also declined it. Instead he stuck his coke spoon straight into the *muestra*, and sniffed up two level spoonfuls with a practiced, haughty movement, like a coffee-house fop taking snuff. Harvey lit a cigarette with trembling hands. The smoke eddied under the light. His face had a sheen, a chilly polish.

"Pheeee-ew!" he went. "White line fever!" I felt the first bitter tang of mucus coming down the back of my throat, and Miriam came in with a trayful of *tintos*.

It must have been about three in the morning when Manolo at last came back with "the deal." It was in a big cardboard box tied up with packing string. Harvey's eyes were out on stalks by now. He was chain-smoking and jiggling his knees up and down under the table. He had seen off the rest of the *muestra* more or less single-handed, with rum and coffee on the side. He had talked till he was hoarse and now he was apparently trying to grind all the enamel off his teeth.

The box was on the table, Manolo's jeweled fingers resting on it. "So this is it, huh?" said Harvey, with a pitiful, lockjawed attempt at a smile. "Let's take a look." He moved to take the box, but Manolo's pressure on it hardened.

"La plata?" he said politely.

Harvey sat back, with a baffled, half-focused stare at Manolo.

"He means the money, Harvey," I hissed.

The money—a good touch—was in the smaller, flimsier suitcase, the tartan zip-up rather than the stouter Revelation piece. Harvey fumbled up the top section—shirt, socks—and there they were. Ten neat wads, so fresh you could almost smell the ink, each one containing fifty $100 bills.

"There she blows, man! Fifty grand. Five kilos at nine apiece makes forty-five, and five over for the boat."

I stored these figures away and later worked on them. Harvey's man would sell his merchandise pretty quickly, but he would almost certainly "step on" it a little before he did. Even if he only put a light hit on it— turned five kilos of pure into seven or eight of adulterated—he still stood to clear, I reckoned, something approaching $200,000. Not a bad margin from one fairly modest run, with someone else doing all the sweating.

Harvey held open the tartan money bag; Manolo nursed the box of cocaine. Like swapping captured agents on a frontier, neither party wanted to be the first to surrender its bargaining piece.

The money had straightened Harvey up. "I want to check the stuff he's brought," he said.

"Quiere verlo."

Manolo shrugged and smiled. He took a thin, black-handled switchblade from his back pocket, held it thoughtfully in his delicate fingers. The blade sprang out like a snake's tongue. He cut the string around the carton and sliced down the adhesive tape along the top flaps. Inside were folds of sacking, and under them the plastic kilo bags, each about the size of a small pillow. "Which one?" he asked. Harvey shrugged. Manolo tossed one of the bags onto the table and nicked a slit in it to expose the cocaine inside. Harvey took some on his knife and, as before, he poked and sifted, tasted and tested, and finally snorted some of the specimen, frowning all the while with concentration. He said nothing.

We waited in the silence, the smoke, the hot, stale air of the small hours cloying with the rank smell of fruit. I wished fervently I was somewhere else, not in this stuffy little room with two knives sitting on the table.

Harvey had digested his hit. He said softly, "You goddamn little creep!" Manolo raised an inquiring eyebrow at me. I felt Julio stiffen beside me.

Harvey's voice was low and fierce. "Tell him, Charlie. Tell him this shit's been stepped on so hard it's flat as a fucking Frisbee."

"God, Harvey, are you sure?"

"Sure I'm sure. Looks different, tastes different. It's the oldest trick in the book, the beginner's rip-off. They hit you with a sample of heavy and sell you a crock of shit while you're flying. You tell him, man."

I told Manolo, as if he didn't know, that Harvey did not like the *coco*. He stiffened into an exaggerated air of surprise and regret, shoulders up in a shrug, eyebrows up toward the brilliantined hairline. Can this be true, *señor*? He actually said nothing.

"Tell him it's crap, Charlie."

"No, no," said Manolo. "It's real good *perico*, very pure."

"Ask him if it's the same stuff as before."

Manolo chose his words with care. "No. It is not the same. It is better!" I groaned inwardly. He can go on lying all night, I thought. I hardly had the heart to tell Harvey of this latest pitch.

Harvey was looking very bad now. His face was white as paper and wet with sweat. His cigarette, one of Julio's untipped Pielrojas, was falling apart as he smoked it. He began to rock back and forth, spitting flakes of tobacco off his lips and saying, "Oh no! Oh no!" He turned to Manolo and said two of his few words of Spanish: *"No quiero."* I don't want it.

"Sí," said Manolo steelily. "It is all agreed." They glared at one another across the table.

It was at this moment of impasse that things began to get seriously out of control. Out of the silence, with just a faint rustle of warning, came a sudden loud knock at the street door. Harvey leaped up, a gargle of fear in his throat. "It's the cops!" he shouted. "It's a fucking burn!" He grabbed the tartan case and, holding it under his arm, blundered past me into the backyard. I called after him, but he raced down to the end, pushing aside my hammock, looking for a way out. Seeing none, he made a flying leap on to the henhouse and began to scale the end wall. The henhouse promptly collapsed, with much indignant squawking from within. "Oh Jesus, God, please," Harvey wailed. He started scrambling up the side wall by the kitchen door, but the guard dog on the neighbor's roof came snarling and snapping at him from the other side of the parapet. Harvey let go with a yelp and crashed back down, splintering wood and scattering feathers. He lurched across to the other wall. He jumped to grab the top of it and screamed in pain as his hands closed over a serried line of broken glass, put there for some such occasion as this. He crumpled back into the henhouse and lay still, whimpering faintly, clutching his money bag to him like a teddy bear.

"Tell him to shut up," said Julio. They had stowed the drugs in Julio's bedroom. The Fruit Palace was just a room full of smoke and rum glasses: a quiet evening among friends. He went to the door and called, "Who is it?" A voice answered from the other side. Julio swore softly, and called back to us to relax. He unbolted the door and a very drunken Negro swayed in. It was the old *guacharacero* who had been playing down at the Pan-American.

"What the hell do you want, Jo-jo?"

"Breakfast," said the old-timer, and tacked across to a table.

Soon there came a sudden dawn, and then it was Sunday morning in Santa Marta, another hot day on the way. Julio mixed us a morning-after *jugo*— papaya, lemon-water and crushed ice. In a trancelike calm Harvey paid us our fees. Struck with pity and remorse I made to refuse, but Julio swiftly reminded me of monies owed for food and board.

The last I saw of Harvey was when I put him in a taxi to the airport. His immediate task, unenviable and unprofitable, was carrying $50,000 *back* into the United States—not actually illegal, but prone to awkward questions. Then there was the music to face in New York. We made to shake hands, but he winced and drew back his hand.

"Sorry it didn't work out, Harvey."

"That's showbiz," said Captain Cocaine. The taxi moved off, and I walked on down to the French Corner for some breakfast.

CHAPTER THREE

The Assignment

Twelve years later I was back in Colombia, on what I laughably called an "assignment." I stood blinking in the raw mountain light outside Eldorado airport, Bogotá.

I smelled again that gut-tightening, high-octane Bogotá smell. A pall of fumes, diesel and human, hangs over the shallow dish of mountains in which the city stands. At nearly 9,000 feet the oxygen is scarce and the hydrocarbons never seem to burn up.

I took a *colectivo* taxi into town, jammed up against a plump, smiling woman with great tufts of black hair at her armpits. There were four of us in the back, plus a child on a lap, and two more in front. The skinny driver took our fares as he drove.

At first glance Bogotá hadn't changed much in twelve years. The style of the place seemed still to be locked in a vague composite of old Hollywood movies. The driver's slicked-back black hair was pure James Dean. The marvelous old chrome-flashed cars came straight out of *The Big Sleep*. I saw flower stalls, and huge laden buses with people hanging out the doors. Cows grazed on brilliant emerald grass in vacant lots. The taxi plowed through ruts and potholes filled with black scummy water. The water came up through the floor, and the fat lady lifted up her feet, crying, *"Ay! Mis zapatos!"*

I took a room in a cheap *residencias* in La Candelaria, the old colonial quarter running up from the Plaza Bolívar to the skirts of the Monserrate mountain. It was a big, dusty room with bare floorboards and an iron bed, and a fine view east over the red-tiled roofs to Monserrate. Everything seemed to smell of the porter's hair cream. A thin, mournful woman put fresh sheets on my bed, and told me the window would break if I opened it, but after she left I opened it anyway. The trucks jockeyed in the narrow street below, Paloma Street. At the corner a man in a trilby sat on a piece of sacking, tying up chick-pea plants into bunches. From the little shoe store opposite came the sound of hammering. Music drifted up from a radio. I closed my eyes and listened, and the first *vallenato*, the swirling accordions and plangent harmonies of Colombian Rhythm and Blues, burst over me.

For the first twenty-four hours I took things gently. The altitude is fairly modest by Andean standards, but to the unaccustomed lowlander it can be devastating. The first time I had arrived in Bogotá I had ignored all the rules and crashed badly. On the plane from Panama City I had met a Colombian journalist, Jorge, and he had invited me back to the family house. There I was plied with aguardiente, fried eggs, guava jelly and the rest. I spent the next two days sweating on Jorge's floor, racked with poison headaches, and evacuating out of every orifice into the new flush toilet of which the family was so proud. What I had was Acute Mountain Sickness (AMS), known in the Andes as *soroche*. It was entirely self-inflicted. Any strong drink when you are unused to the altitude is a recipe for disaster, and aguardiente—Colombia's national hootch, an anis-flavored liquor—is the worst of the lot.

This time I stuck to the straight and narrow, and had nothing worse than a few breathless flutters. The worst of these was not *soroche* at all.

Mooching around the bookstalls on 19th Street, I joined the edges of a small crowd. The midday edition of *El Bogotano* had just come out, and they were looking at the front page. There was a color picture of a young man lying dead in the dirt, shirt rucked up to his shoulders to reveal a mess of blood and bullet holes. The headline read, *"MATADO OTRO TRAF-ICANTE DE COCAINA."*

I sat on my hotel bed, wondering how to get this ball rolling, and where the hell it was going to roll to if I did. It had all looked different a few weeks ago, when publisher Malcolm Goodman had telephoned to say he was looking for a book on Colombia. I fondly imagined he was talking about a travel book.

Over lunch the next day the truth dawned. The truth was that Malcolm had discovered cocaine. He pushed aside his platter of *fruits de mer*, and drew forth a wad of clippings and color supplements from his briefcase. "There's been a tremendous amount of publicity," he said. There were articles about the huge popularity—"epidemic proportions"—of cocaine in Europe and the United States; grisly accounts of cocaine-related gang warfare in Miami; a tabloid piece headed "DIARY OF A COKE SMUGGLER." I saw passages lined and asterisked with Malcolm's busy felt-tip. Colombian connection. Colombian mafia.

"It all comes out of Colombia, you know."

"Yes, I know."

"And you're an old Colombian hand, as you yourself said."

"Well, yes."

Once he was on his hobbyhorse there was no stopping Malcolm. He was a man perennially in quest of that grail among publishers, the fabled Right Book at the Right Time. Eyes glinting behind his large, fashionable tortoise-shells, he spoke of the fan-*tas*-tic scope here, how *the* book about the drug trade had yet to be written. He spoke of serial rights, screen treatments, networking. He mentioned sums of money that made me weak at the knees.

I had absolutely no choice. It is the hack's first principle to rush toward every conceivable assignment crying like Molly Bloom, "Yes I will Yes." You may have a hundred misgivings, a hundred reasons for saying "No," but you silence them all. A publisher wants the moon; of course you'll get it. Time enough later to talk him down to the bit of green cheese you come back with. "Inside the Cocaine Underworld," as Malcolm was calling it, sounded nasty, dangerous and downright improbable, but there was no way I could refuse. He ordered another bottle of cheap Frascati. We clinked glasses as if to celebrate. A vision flashed through my head, as clear as day—Harvey sobbing in a broken henhouse, daubed with blood, shit and feathers.

The plan of action, if I can call it that, was to spend a week or two in Bogotá, gathering background material about the cocaine racket, and then to repair up to the coast, to the smuggling centers like Santa Marta and Riohacha. There I would address myself to the main task. "A hard-nosed, on-the-spot report. The who, the how and the why of Colombian cocaine smuggling. That's what we're after!" Malcolm thought up the ideas, provided the cash and fashioned the package. The rest was up to me, the old Colombian hand.

We said a last goodbye in the rain, outside his office near Park Lane. A black cab burbled beside us, ready to whisk him off to some meeting. "And for goodness' sake," he said as we shook hands, "if you're in any kind of trouble, give us a call."

So here I sat, the intrepid reporter on the trail of the Great Cocaine Story. I felt more like a new boy on his first day at school. I gazed blankly at what was—with the exception of the wedge of dollars in my wallet—Malcolm's sole contribution to the logistics of the operation. The Letter of Introduction. *"A Quién Se Interese,"* it boomed, beneath the publisher's tasteful green letterhead. It announced me as a British author, gathering material for a book "on the country and people of Colombia." It was signed, *"Muy atentamente*, Malcolm Goodman, Senior Commissioning Editor."

Malcolm said he wanted to know "the who, the how and the why" of the cocaine racket. I could tell him the "why" without going to Colombia at all. The "why" is money.

Prices fluctuate according to supply, but as cheap thrills go coke is always expensive. In American and European cities, a gram of cocaine, Standard Street Toot, is liable to cost between $70 and $100. That gram— one spoonful of medicine, one long night of fun for four—is not, of course, a gram of pure cocaine. It will have been cut, or "stepped on," at different stages of the pipeline. You will be lucky if it is even half cocaine. Much of it will consist of an inert cut, simply there as make-weight. This might be lactose, mannitol, baking soda, talc, borax—anything that looks like cocaine and has no immediately noticeable side effects. To make up some of the potency lost by adulteration, most street coke also contains an "active" cut. There are two types—speed and freeze—usually a little of both: a lacing of powdered amphetamine (methedrine, sulphate, etc.) to give it an energy kick; and some synthetic, cocaine-related anesthetic like novocaine or benzocaine to simulate the mouth-numbing effects of genuine cocaine. Together these cuts, far cheaper and easier to acquire than the coke itself, give a crude approximation of the true cocaine high.

If you have a really good friend in the smuggling business you may be lucky enough to sample nearly pure coke, off-the-boat quality, and then your nerve ends will feel like they've been bathed in champagne and you will know what all the fuss is about. If you score in a doorway off Dealer Street, you will probably end up with a cocktail of cuts and no cocaine at all. Anywhere in between, it's pot luck. The customs officers' rule of thumb is that retail coke, your average gram, is unlikely to be more than 30 percent pure. Some coke fanciers are so habituated to the cut they are to all intents and purposes speed freaks, paying way over the odds for a bit of crank because it smells sweeter by the name of "coke." Speed kills, but coke is hip, the achievers' drug.

Why is it so phenomenally expensive? First, because it is illegal. It is not the coke that costs, but the high risks of supplying it: the buyer pays the dealers' wages, all down the line. For the actual cocaine in your gram of toot you are paying about 30 times as much as it costs someone to buy it, in bulk, in Colombia. Second: it costs that much because people will pay that much. In a sense people like it expensive. The price is all part of its ritzy mystique.

People will also tell you that the price of the stuff has its comforts, that there is a kind of security in knowing that all the dangers of chronic cocaine abuse—deviated septum, digestive disorders, progression on to the needle, a whole range of psychological disruptions culminating in the paranoid delusions known as "cocaine psychosis"—are simply way out of their price bracket. "A cocaine *problem*? I should be so lucky!"

Every year, more and more people buy more and more cocaine. According to the U.S. drug agency surveys, 20 million Americans have "tried" it, five million are "regular" users (at least once a month), and about half a million are "profoundly dependent" on it. The figures are round and possibly high, but one gets the general picture. Taking cocaine is not confined to some lunatic fringe of degenerate no-hope junkies. It is what millions of affluent young Westerners want to spend their money on. In the United States alone about $35 billion a year is being spent on it.

Cocaine is, in short, one of the great growth industries of the 1980s.

CHAPTER FOUR

The Flying Scotsman

My first move in this game without rules was to drum up some connections from twelve years ago. I pondered my list of old names and addresses. Some of the faces were hazy, but I could never forget Augustus McGregor.

Gus was a half-crazed Scottish newspaperman—I call him Scottish, and he called himself Scottish, but in fact he had been brought up somewhere in the Kentish London suburbs, and his proud assertions of Highland blood were couched in unmistakable South London accents. He had gone to Brazil in the sixties, studying at São Paulo University and working as a stringer for a news agency. Gus was one of those people who disappeared into South America, lost all notion of where he had come from and where he was going. He worked for a while for the *Brazilian Herald*. He was a good journalist, but too long in South America and too many bad drugs had turned him into a compulsive fantasist. By his own account, as I remember, he had wandered the length and breadth of the continent, left a wife in São Paulo and another in Paraguay, narrowly escaped the death squads in Chile, and located the fabled Brotherhood of the Seven Rays in some hidden valley south of Cuzco.

All this was behind him, if anywhere, when I knew him in Bogotá. We worked together for a while on the *Andean Echo*, an English language weekly aimed mainly at the North American commercial and diplomatic community. The *Echo* paid miserable penny-a-line rates, but together with a bit of English teaching he just about scratched a living. He was a tall, gangling, whey-faced man, with long, straggly ginger hair. He was a great favorite with the caretaker at the *Echo*'s offices, who called him *"El Rojo"* on account of his red hair, and was always feeding him fried rabbit and creole potatoes in his little hut behind the office block.

Most of Gus's money went on cocaine—"peach," as he called it. By a fine reverse argument, he blamed this on his alleged Calvinist upbringing. "We're all doomed to the bonfire anyway, so we might as well have some fun on the way." I remember the nights we went up into La Perseverancia to score a gram, which in those days cost around $10. There's a saying about Perseverancia—"Go in walking and come out in an ambulance"— but everyone knew Gus and we never had any trouble. We would score in a little lamp-lit room, two steps straight down off the dark street. I can see Gus now in his gray *ruana*—the Colombian woolen poncho—funneling up a sample off the corner of his Brazilian press card. "The finest peach in town at Alfonso's!" he would say, grinning his gray-toothed, alley-cat grin. If Gus couldn't furnish me with a few leads on the Great Cocaine Story, no one could.

I got on the phone in the hotel lobby and dialed Gus's old number—not actually his own place, he never really had one, but the apartment of a benevolent Italian painter, which he used as a message drop and lodging house. I rang three times, but all I got was an asthmatic sighing in my ear. I tried the number of the *Echo*. A woman curtly told me the paper didn't exist anymore. I was not surprised.

I couldn't remember the name of Gus's mentor, the Italian painter, but I had his address. Perhaps he was still there, under a new phone number. Outside the Avianca building on 7th Avenue, on my way to catch a *buseta* north, I saw a small brown dog lying in the morning sun. Its tail twitched a little as it dozed, and I thought how splendid this was, to slumber in the sun amid the downtown jostle of commuters and hawkers. When I got closer I saw that the dog was dead. It was only the breeze stirring the fine sandy hairs of its tail.

The painter's apartment was on the first floor of a dilapidated red-brick block off 22nd Avenue, in the midtown residential district of San Luis. The venetian blinds were shut on the windows. I pressed the door bell. It made no discernible sound. I knocked twice: nothing. I was about to be on my way, when I heard faint sounds within, shuffling steps down the stairs, a child crying, and then a woman's voice, shrill and aged, saying, "Who is it?" behind the door.

"Good morning, *señora*." There was silence. "I am looking for Señor McGregor."

"Maggegar?"

"Señor McGregor," I enunciated. "The Scotsman. He used to live here."

"Scotsman? I do not know him. He is not here."

I pressed closer to the door, trying to gauge where the old crone's head should be. "He was a friend of the painter, the Italian gentleman. Perhaps *he* is here?"

"No, *señor*. We have no foreigners here." She sounded annoyed. I started to say something else, but her reedy voice cut in. "You must go now. My son will be home soon." She receded, muttering. In a moment of pique I slapped my hand against the door and hissed an English obscenity after her. Unflattening myself from the door, I turned back toward the street and saw a small, rotund policeman staring at me. I felt an obscure pang of guilt.

"You are looking for Señor Bruno?" asked the policeman.

"No, I'm—I mean, yes, yes, of course, Señor Bruno." That was the name of the painter. Alessandro Bruno, the bearded modernist from Bologna.

"He does not live here anymore. He moved nine, ten months ago. I knew him very well."

This was encouraging. Did he perhaps know where Bruno lived now? He pursed his lips and waggled his head, as if to shake the answer loose. *"Más allá,"* he said with an airy gesture. Over that way. "Up north. Unicentro. El Chicó." His truncheon bobbed gently against his thigh as he gestured. It was obvious he didn't really know, but the answer was not quite random. The places he mentioned were upmarket. In place of information he was humoring me with an oblique compliment. These small courtly transactions count for a lot in Colombia. I shook the little policeman's hand, and thanked him.

At the Telecom on 22nd Avenue I found Bruno's name in the directory, and dialed his new number. He answered in his Italian-accented Spanish. Yes, with a little prompting, he remembered me. No, he had not seen Gus for a while, but as far as he knew he was still in town. We talked a bit. Then he said, "Listen, Charlie, I'll tell you because I know you're Gus's friend. I think he's in some kind of trouble. I haven't seen him for weeks. Someone came for his things, a Colombian boy. He had a note from Gus, but all it said was not to worry. Well, I gave up worrying about Gus a long time ago, but this isn't like him."

Other than this all Bruno could give me was a few names. There was a girl Gus knocked around with, Anita. There were some bars and eating houses Gus frequented: he gave me three names and addresses. We were just about to hang up when he remembered one more name, a street dealer called Julio Cesar. "Gus mentioned him a few times. I think he bought his *perico* off him. He used to say that Julius Caesar conquered the English 2,000 years ago, and now he's selling drugs to the Scots."

By the time I entered the Paso Doble, the third of the three bars Bruno had mentioned, I was getting seriously disgruntled. The first two had turned up blank. Sure, they knew Gus but no one had seen him around recently. The names of Anita and Julio Cesar meant nothing to them. It was now about four o'clock. I had been tramping to and fro all day, had got soaked in a thunderstorm, and was about ready to give up.

The Paso Doble was a small, murky café-bar off Caracas Avenue, a bad part of town. Bogotá is laid out on a grid system. As in New York, danger can be mathematically computed, and this was well south of 12th Street, which is one of the demarcation lines. The café was quiet. Three dusty workmen sharing a half of aguardiente, an old woman in black nursing a bowl of milky coffee, a pair of corner boys lounging at the doorway, and the inevitable children running in and out, the dark-eyed grubby children that play around the edge of every scene.

I bought a beer. The barman was stocky and simian, with tight curls of white hair fizzing up out of the neck of his shirt. After a few pleasantries, I trotted out my weary formula. I am looking for Gus, Señor McGregor, El Rojo, the Flying Bloody Scotsman. . . .

"You mean Gustavo," said the barman. "No, I do not know where he is."

"I am his friend. I think he might be in trouble. I have come to help him."

The barman gazed at me. "You are Scottish, no?"

"Of course I am," I lied.

The barman nodded sagely. I seemed to be winning through. We Scots stick together, I told him. He called out over his shoulder, "*Oiga!* Julio Cesar!" and with an almost comic, Punch and Judy promptitude a face poked out from a curtained-off doorway behind the bar. The barman jerked his head at me, and turned away with the air of one washing his hands of the whole business.

Julio Cesar advanced, plausible, false and wary. He looked about eighteen, had a pencil-thin mustache, light brown hair and a black jacket with a diamond pattern picked out in gold. *"Hola, hombre,"* he said, with a firm handshake. We went over to a corner table.

"You want *perico*, basuko, real good grass?" he asked pleasantly.

"No, not really, I—"

"Emeralds?"

"No, I am looking for Gustavo the Scotsman. I'm told you know where to find him."

His patter hiccuped briefly. "Gus? Ah yes, Señor Gus. Yes, I know him. It is very difficult...."

"But you do know where he lives?"

Julio Cesar shrugged, long and slow, hands juggling the possibilities. The classic Colombian gesture: yes and no, *señor*, take your pick. In this case: yes, I know where he lives; no, I'm not going to tell you.

It took two beers, a crisp 100-peso bill and a lot of guff about how Gus was like a brother to me—"my teacher, my *compadre*"—before Julio Cesar admitted that he knew how to get in touch with Gus. Another 100 pesos and he agreed to take him a message from me. I scribbled a note. It was folded away neatly in the sequined top pocket, along with the two bills. He told me to come back the following evening.

I returned to the Paso Doble the following night, as arranged. It was a Friday and the sleepy, dusty bar was full of people. The tables had been pushed to the side, colored bulbs flashed above the bar, and the air was filled with smoke and laughter. A pair of antiquated speakers were bashing out *música tropical* at a tooth-rattling volume.

I could see no sign of Gus or Julio Cesar, but the barman greeted me like an old friend, and poured me a straight shot of aguardiente. It seemed to be the only thing he was serving. "It's my birthday," he explained. I sipped at my drink gingerly, remembering the heightened potency of liquor at high altitude. "No, *hombre*," he cried. "Like this." He drained his glass with a flourish. With an inward shrug of resignation I did likewise. I was still struggling with the spasms when he refilled the glasses. These too were dispatched in unison. He wiped his hand across his mouth and laughed. He called to a woman serving at the other end of the bar. She came over, a large, slow-moving lady, who regarded all the revelry with an imperious air. She seemed, as Colombian *señoras* often do, to be the boss. The barman put his arm around her waist, looking like a little white-haired monkey beside her bulk. "Look, *querida*," he said. "It's the friend of Gustavo I was telling you about. The Scotsman." He filled my glass yet again. She surveyed me through half-closed eyes. She made little tutting sounds, as if what she saw somehow exasperated her.

"So you are Scottish too?" she asked. I nodded brightly: it was too late to turn back on this one. She narrowed her eyes still further. "Is it true what Gustavo says, that the men all wear skirts?"

"Yes," I said uncertainly, "well, some of them do." I did not feel I wanted the idea broadcast around the bar at this moment. "We call them kilts," I added.

I was beginning to feel very drunk. I wanted to get away from this mountainous woman, to slip away and quietly slough off my newfound Scottishness. God knew what nonsense Gus had been spinning. But the crowd hemmed me in tight. The barman came back, poured me more aguardiente. Not to be outdone on the matter of Highland lore, he said, "You like very much the *cornamusa*, no?" This completely stumped me. Seeing my confusion, he had one of those drunken bright ideas. "Wait, I have some here." He fumbled under the bar for a bit, and came up holding a tape-cassette. "It's Gustavo's," he said. "It makes him cry." I guessed then that the *cornamusa* was bagpipes, but it was too late. The *música tropical* was silenced in mid-flow. The new cassette was put in, and my heart sank as a familiar skirling dirge ground out at top volume. It was Andy Stewart singing "A Scottish Soldier." Heads turned in surprise, and some in frank displeasure. I was quickly located as chief suspect in the matter, indeed the barman was cheerily shouting, "*Música escocésa* for our friend here." When the refrain came he wrapped his arm around my shoulder, and I was forced into a dreadful duet, he crooning wordlessly along with the tune, me thinking less of the green hills of home than of how I was going to wring Gus's neck when I found him. I have never known a song to last so long. Another began—"Speed, Bonny Boat," I think—but mercifully there were shouts of protest, and the tape was ejected. The *música tropical* returned, and I lurched away from the bar.

I found a seat and tried to regain some anonymity. I was sweating aguardiente like a squeezed sponge. Looking around, I saw, as I had already dimly realized, that virtually all the women were tarts, all eye-shadow and shiny black boots. One of them was staring at me. I hauled a newspaper out of my jacket: the print swam before my eyes. I looked at the ceiling: the cobwebbed rafters seemed to pulsate to the music. Still the girl was giving me the sultry eye. I lit a cigarette, tried to concentrate on the paper. My heart was pumping too fast. Now she was getting up, bringing her chair with her, leaning her hands on my table, black hair falling over her face, black eyes heavy with mascara. She looked older and more brittle than she had a few yards away through the smoke. She had a black patent-leather handbag slung crosswise. The leather had peeled off the strap where it ran down between her breasts. *"Buenas noches, churro,"* she said. She took some lottery tickets out of her handbag and asked to look at my newspaper: "I think it's my lucky night tonight!" Someone pushing past the table knocked her, and she fell forward, much farther than she needed.

Her hand grabbed my thigh and her face was a few inches from mine, and she was laughing cheap scent, tobacco and liquor in my face. Then she gave a little squawk of surprise. Someone had grabbed her around the waist: a gold-sequined arm. It was Julio Cesar. He sat down on her seat, pulled her on his lap and held her there like a recalcitrant kitten.

Out of his jacket pocket came a crumpled piece of paper. He handed it to me. "There you are, my friend." It was the note I had written yesterday. On the back, in a rickety sloping hand, an address was written. "That's Señor Gus's place," said Julio Cesar. "There's a taxi waiting for you now, at the corner of Caracas. He'll take you to the corner of Gus's street. After that you walk. Ten minutes, no problem. Just keep straight till you find Number 99. Don't talk to anyone on the way."

We went to the bar. I paid for my drinks and bought a bottle of rum to take to Gus. Julio Cesar slipped off behind the curtained door. He came back and slid a little package into my hand. "For Gus," he whispered, closing my hand around it.

CHAPTER FIVE

Welcome to the Crow's Nest

It was drizzling again when I paid off the taxi. I had to hope he knew where we were, because there were no street signs, just a wide, featureless road with most of the streetlights broken, and a dark little side road leading off. This, I hoped, harbored Gus at No. 99. I had tried to take some bearings on the way, but I felt sick and drunk, and I mostly just sat back in a torpor, grateful for the cold air on my face.

With a squeal of rubber the taxi hung a U-turn and roared off back toward town. I set off in silence down the side street. There were no lights, and most of the low-built houses seemed derelict. Empty windows stared like sockets in a skull. Spiky vegetation curled out of doorways. Behind me a car turned into the street. As it lurched over the ruts its lights raked up and down like searchlights. I hid in a doorway till it passed. I was getting jumpy. It was cold and late, and this felt like no-man's-land. As I crossed a small intersection, the character of the street changed. On either side were junk yards, smelling of oil and rust and old tires. Rickety workshops loomed out of the mist. None of the buildings had any numbers that I could see.

A curve in the road ahead was lit with an odd glow, and coming around it I found myself in a stretch of muddy wasteland. Away to my right a huge fire blazed. I saw figures around it, and dogs and children, even a small pig or two. I froze into the shadows. *Gamines? Gitanos?* Street *bandidos* with knives under their rag blankets? The road ran on, a muddy track, through the rubbish and dismembered cars. It would take a minute, perhaps less, to get to the buildings on the other side. Steeling myself, I began to walk. I was halfway across when the dogs caught my scent. They loped barking toward me, rangy sand-colored curs of the kind you see all over Bogotá. A drunken voice called to me from the fireside, *"Venga, hombre, venga!"* I waved vaguely back and quickened my pace. I had just reached the buildings, where the track became a recognizable street again, when a small boy suddenly appeared in front of me. I stopped. One of the dogs came snarling up, but the boy ran at it with a shout, and rapped it across the snout, and it yelped off back toward the fire. I made to walk on, but the boy jumped around in front of me again. He stuck his hand out and asked for pesos. First he used the word *regalo*, asking for a present, but then he added another word, *peaje*, which means "toll," implying that I had better pay up if I wanted to carry on down the road. He was about ten, I guessed, and he looked like he could get a knife between my ribs before I could say "Juancho Robinson." I dug into my pocket for change. He took it silently and backed off into the shadows. In the corner of the building I saw a rough shelter of plastic and old rafter-wood. An old woman was sitting on a box at its entrance. The boy pushed past her into the shelter. She too held out her hand, and I went over and gave her some money.

It really was as if I had paid a toll and crossed a border, for now the street took on a more inhabited air, poor but lived in. In a half-lit room I saw a crucifix on the wall, the flicker of a black-and-white TV. And at last I saw a number: 87, 89. I was just five doors away from Gus's bolt-hole.

No. 99 was an old two-story house with political posters peeling off the façade. It had tall windows, many broken, behind iron grills, and the words *CUIDADO CON EL PERRO* roughly painted beside the door. I knocked but there was no sound. The *perro* was apparently not barking tonight. I pulled open the door by a piece of rope that served for a handle, and came into a dark, evil-smelling passage. This gave on to a courtyard, unexpectedly large, with a rickety balcony all around it. A line of washing was strung between the balconies. Pushing through the sheets on the line came an old woman, wiping her hands on her apron.

"Señor?"

"Good evening, *señora*. This is Number 99?" She nodded. She was small, wrinkled, and with her hair combed up into a tight bun. "I have come to see Señor McGregor," I said. "He is expecting me."

She shook her head and began to disclaim all knowledge. Then suddenly a voice hissed out from somewhere above us. *"Oiga, señora, tranquila!"* And a moment later, in the same stage whisper but now in English, "Up here, mate!"

We both turned. I couldn't see anyone. The old lady gave a stiff little bow of apology, and gestured me toward the corner stairs that led up to the balcony. There were doors and shuttered windows all around the upper story, but I could see no lights, and where the doors were open the rooms looked empty and derelict. Halfway up the steps, I saw a thin, pale hand fluttering in the gloom like a trapped insect. Nothing else, just the hand, apparently coming straight out of the wall. As I walked along the balcony toward it, the hand disappeared. Stooping down, I saw a slit in the wall just beneath the shuttered window. I peered into it, a pair of eyes stared back.

"Gus?"

"Welcome to the crow's nest, mate. Glad you could make it."

The eyes disappeared from the peephole. A key turned. "Door's open!" he called.

The room was narrow and dimly lit. There was a faint reek of damp stone, old food, stale body. Gus was fitting a brick back into his peephole. He looked ghastly. He had lost most of his hair on the top since I had last seen him. The rest, shorter than before, hung around his ears like docked rats' tails. He had scabs down one side of his face, as if he had been scraped along a road. His left leg was bandaged, none too freshly, from the ankle to the knee. "Close the door, for Christ's sake," he said. I pushed it, but it didn't close properly. He hobbled past me and slammed it. A thin shower of plaster floated down. The ceiling was mostly gone, rough cane-stem lath showing through, and wires leading to a single 20-watt bulb. The pitted walls shone cold and moist. There was a hole in the outside wall, stuffed with grimy plastic and newspaper.

Gus lowered himself into an armchair, the only chair. It was positioned next to the wall, so that the peephole was at eye level when he sat. The shutters on the window facing the courtyard were barred and nailed, with rag wadding stuffed into the gaps. The door too had strips of cloth around the edges. I had seen no chinks of light when I was out on the balcony. It was the perfect bolt-hole. Wincing with pain, Gus eased his bandaged leg on to a box of old clothes.

"There," he said, settling with a sigh. He waved in vague apology at the room. "It's not the eighteenth floor at the Tequendama, but ... under the circumstances ..."

I refrained from asking what exactly the circumstances were. Judging from the dust on his scattered belongings, he had been here for some time. There were boxes of papers, tumbled-out suitcases, a tin can brimming with butt ends. On a makeshift table in the corner I saw, suddenly remembering it, Gus's proudest possession—his typewriter, an old black highstanding Underwood, circa 1940, a vintage three-fingers-of-Jack-Daniel's-and-hold-the-front-page model.

He surveyed me from his chair, like a gouty old judge about to pass sentence. I proffered the bottle of rum. "Good boy," he said. "Fetch a couple of cups over, and we'll murder some." He poured out two large slugs. We raised our cups. "Up your crack," he said, and drained his in one. He poured a second.

"So what's the story, Gus?" I asked.

"Yes, well, sorry about all the jiggery-pokery, mate. Got to choose my visitors carefully these days. Keeping a bit of a low profile for a while."

"What happened to your leg?"

"That? Oh, nothing much. Machete accident. Tell you about it later."

"It's OK, isn't it? You shouldn't be seeing someone about it?"

"Well, I've got these pills." He rattled a tin that had once contained Nestlé's Condensed Milk. "The old biddy changes the bandages from time to time. She's Julio Cesar's mother, you see. I pay her for the room and one meal a day. J.C. keeps me in the style to which I'm accustomed—you know, booze and drugs and so on. I'm not *seeing* anyone. That's the whole bloody point of the operation."

"That reminds me," I said, fishing out the little package from my top pocket. "Julio Cesar asked me to give you this."

Gus sat up with a start and a wince. "For Christ's sake, mate," he said, very affronted. "First things first. Give it here."

Inside a fold of newspaper was the familiar toy-town package. But as Gus gingerly opened it, I saw that it was not cocaine. It was a rough powder, peachy-brown, like pancake makeup. This was basuko, dried cocaine base. Basuko is essentially a by-product, a halfway stage between the raw coca leaf and cocaine. A few basic laboratory operations could have converted this gram of basuko into a slightly smaller volume of coke: good base yields up to 90 percent. It is a rougher, milder, and—above all—far cheaper version of coke. Not that it is really an alternative to coke. It is smoked rather than snorted, for one thing. You might feel giddy, benevolent, chattery, vigilant after a *sucito*—a joint of basuko—but you are soothed rather than fired up. It has none of the Ice Nine crystalline quality, the cool fever of the true cocaine high.

Gus sprinkled a few grains into a pile of tobacco, and rolled it up in a bit of paper torn from an old *Time* magazine. He lit up and drew deeply. There were beads of sweat above his lips. The smoke had a sweet, woody tang, faintly sickly but very agreeable. He handed me the joint and I took my first hit of basuko. Into the arms of *la morenita*, the brown-haired girl, sweet little step-daughter to *la blanca*, the white lady.

Shivering a little as the smoke spread through him, Gus gazed at me, palpably mellowed. "So," he said, as if our meeting were at last properly beginning. "It's been a long time, Charlie. What brings you back to Bogotá?" He jokily mispronounced it, *à la gringo*, with the first syllable as in "bogey."

I explained, in so many words, about the Great Cocaine Story. He laughed and said, "Pull the other one, mate. It's got bandages on."

"I'm serious, Gus. It's a bona fide commission. Inside the cocaine underworld, hard-nosed stuff."

His eyes narrowed. "You mean someone's paying you?"

"Yes. Well, they've stumped up with a bit. You know publishers. Actually," I continued, "I was hoping you might be able to give me a few leads. You know—"

He puffed in derision. "Leads? Oh yeah, leads! Look, I'll lend you a bulletproof suit, if you like. That's what you'll need. Course, if they come after you with the old coconut-cleavers, you'll need a whole bloody suit of armor." He hissed out the last bit of basuko smoke, and stubbed out the butt with tense, stabbing movements.

"Hell, Gus. I'm as big a coward as the next man. I don't want anything heavy. Just a few stories, a bit of local detail. You know the recipe."

He leaned forward a few inches. His face was shiny and serious. "Listen, cock," he said quietly. "Why do you imagine I'm sitting here on my jack while my fucking leg rots off? Well, I'll tell you why. It's because the cocaine underworld, as you call it, doesn't like reporters one little bit. They like to keep everything, you know, off the record. Reasonable enough, really."

"Christ, Gus. Do you mean someone's after you for poking your nose in?"

He closed his eyes. "Look down there." He waved wearily toward the table with the old typewriter on it. "See that box? It's all there, the whole sorry story. But take it from me, mate. It just isn't worth it."

I saw a carton stuffed with dog-eared papers, cheap folders held together with rubber bands. "Can I take a look?" I asked.

"No, you bloody well can't."

"Well, what's in it?"

"Everything anyone needs to know about your bloody cocaine underworld, that's what. Names, dates, kitchens, boats. I call it my 'Who's Who.' Every damn hood worth his salt gets a mention in it somewhere. That's why I'm not exactly flavor of the month in certain circles."

"How much have you done?" I asked. "Is it ready to run?"

"You're joking. That's it, there in the box. There's twelve years with my ear to the ground in there. I wouldn't start writing anything until I was a good few thousand miles away from Colombia. Like I said, these people don't like publicity."

All those years of street wisdom in one box. With all the diligent fieldwork in the world, I couldn't accumulate a tenth of it. For now I decided to leave the matter alone. I could see he was getting touchy on the subject. Besides, something else was worrying me.

"Do you really mean, Gus, that someone did *that* to you?" I pointed at his leg.

He nodded. "Two weeks ago, up in Perseverancia."

Since I had first come in and smelled the smell in the room, I had sensed there was something more to it than damp walls and dirty linen. There was a low, crapulent odor I couldn't quite trace. I thought perhaps it was bad food—there were a couple of plates with the congealed remains of chicken and rice on them. Now I was beginning to be sure it was something worse. I went over to him and looked at the leg.

"Is it bad, Gus? You don't smell too good, you know."

"It's not great," he admitted.

"Should I take a look?"

He feigned impatience, but he set to unwrapping the bandages willingly enough. I was right about the smell. Gingerly he drew away the lint to reveal a vertical gash, 10 inches long, up his left calf. A machete had carved away part of his leg like a prime slice of chicken breast. The wound was about the shape and size of a banana peel. It was the color of an Andean sunset, scarlet, yellow and black. At the edges it oozed a malevolent pus. I am no doctor, but it was clear that Gus was in a bad way.

He peered at it with just a hint of pride. "It's getting better," he said unconvincingly. "Hurts like a bitch, but it's definitely on the mend. The old dear puts something on it when she changes the bandages. *Polvo de la Madre Celestina*, she calls it. Some mumbo-jumbo herbal stuff, I don't know."

"You really ought to see a doctor, Gus. I mean, you get gangrene, you lose your leg, that sort of thing."

He gave a wheezy laugh. "Long John Silver, eh?" Then more angrily, "Look, I've told you. I'm a nowhere man just now. The walls have eyes round here, and bloody ears. If someone saw me out and about it wouldn't take 10 minutes. OK, the leg's not great, I know. But it's a whole lot better than what'll happen if they catch up with me again. There'll be no second chance, mate. I'll be dog's meat."

"Who exactly arc thcy, Gus?"

He ignored the question, bandaging himself up. I let it go. We had more rum, another *sucito*, talked of old times. The drink and the drugs took their toll on his wasted frame. He began to doze. I stood up, thinking about leaving. He jerked awake, eyes wide. "Don't go, mate." For a moment it was a plea, but then he covered it. "You'll never get a taxi at this time of night. Streets are bad. You can sleep on the bed."

I shrugged and sat down on the bed. Soon Gus was snoring gently, head tipped forward, ginger hair dangling monkishly from the balding pate. I went and covered him with a blanket. I lay on the gray rumpled bed in a basuko haze. I wondered if the whole thing was a giant paranoid fantasy of Gus's own making. But the machete wound? That was real enough. I could smell it suppurating a few feet away in the darkness.

Somewhere outside—or perhaps it was only in my head—I heard a dog howl, and as I drifted down the tunnel of a fitful sleep, I seemed to see

Gus hobbling along through the lunar streets outside. The hounds were on his trail, just around the corner, and the whores in the doorways were all wearing kilts.

When I woke the room was still dark, but there were chinks of light in the shutters on the outside window. I had a chill in my bones, catarrh in my head. The previous evening's intakes vied biliously in my stomach. Gus was still asleep, sprawled in the armchair, head lolling, mouth wide.

It was a soft tap at the door that had woken me. Now there came another, sharper, and a woman's voice calling tentatively, *"Buenos días, señores."* Gus woke with a start. His eyes ranged around in a moment of plain fear. Then he remembered who he was, who I was, and whose the voice at the door was, and he called back a greeting in reply. He motioned me to the door. I unlocked it, the big key making me think of an English church door, and there stood the old lady with two cups of *tinto*. She asked if I would like some breakfast. Of course I would, Gus answered on my behalf. He hobbled to the door and stood there scratching at his ribs and breathing in the morning air. It was early still. Above the wavering gables of the old house the sky was pinkish-gray. In a corner of the courtyard below, beneath a half-dead almond tree, a man in a vest was shaving.

The *tinto* worked fast. Directed by Gus, I sped down the steps to the bathroom. The man looked up from his shaving and nodded at me as casually as if he'd seen me every day for the last ten years. Sunlight caught the blade of his cutthroat razor. His mirror hung from a nail in the tree trunk. The bathroom was dark and smelly, but newspaper was provided. The lavatory didn't flush. The old lady appeared with a pail of water. We conversed briefly over the top of the wooden door. She said to pour half the water down the pan to flush it. The other half I could use for my *abluciones*. Outside the bathroom, on an oil drum, was a beaten tin dish and a neatly folded cloth for a towel. This simple, graceful hospitality is Colombia's greatest gift to the traveler.

Back upstairs the stale air of Gus's room hit me in the gut. He had opened the shutters on the outside window. The morning was "safe time," Gus said. *They* wouldn't come now. The edginess of the previous night returned to me like a twinge of toothache.

Gus lumbered off to the *baño*. Out of curiosity, I stood on the bed and stretched up to look out of the open square of window. It looked on to a scrap yard. A couple of men were lazily talking, perhaps arguing, in the sun. A small brown dog was licking its rump. Directly below me I saw a pile of rotting old mattresses. I realized that it would be possible to lever yourself straight out of the window, and jump the 15 feet or so on to the mattresses. Difficult, especially with a septic machete wound in your leg, but possible.

So Gus had his back way out, if ever "they" came up the stairs. The manic ingenuity of it all made me nervous.

Breakfast arrived, two enormous oval platters of eggs, plantains, yucca and rice, with bowls of sweet milky coffee. The *señora* hovered for a moment. "Pay the lady, will you, mate?" said Gus pleasantly. I paid her. His eyes furtively appraised my wad of notes.

He set upon his breakfast, shoveling the food into his mouth. He ate like a dog, hasty and mistrustful. I was still halfway through when he pushed his plate aside scraped clean. He gave a loud belch, rolled up a *sucito*, poured out a slug of rum and leaned back in his moth-eaten throne.

"So you want to write a story about the cocaine trade," he said reflectively.

Outside in the street a truck backfired. I saw Gus stiffen and listen. I thought of those nights at the Fruit Palace. It was all just a game then.

He settled back. "Debt and deadly sin, who is not subject to, mate?" he said unexpectedly. "I can handle the deadly sin, but the debt really gets me down. These people have been very good to me, you know, and I just can't pay them. And then there's the nights, when the candyman don't come no more."

For a moment I missed his drift. He was staring at me through the brown-tinged smoke of his *sucito*. It seemed like a look of expectancy, but it was hard to gauge what emotions were playing across that pale, wasted dial. "Come on, cock," he said. "It's obvious, isn't it? Look. I need a bit of cash, you need a bit of information. Normally, of course, I'd be glad to give freely, but..."

This wasn't quite what I'd had in mind when I set out to look Gus up, but under the circumstances it seemed sensible. We made a deal of sorts. All he wanted, to begin with anyway, was "a few blue ones"—a few thousand pesos—and plenty of basuko. I didn't even have to bring the basuko: Julio Cesar would bring it over from the Paso Doble. All I had to do was keep him supplied with pesos. In return he would open up his box of delights, his "Who's Who" of the Colombian cocaine trade. It was another of those offers I couldn't refuse.

CHAPTER SIX

Who's Who

The next day, after dark, I set off once more for Gus's crow's nest. I brought him money, rum, a bagful of bread and fruit and canned food, and some medicaments and bandages. I even offered to change his dressing, but he refused. His hand closed over the fresh 1,000-peso notes. "Cheap at the price, mate. It pays to know what you're up against in this game, believe you me." Then deep into the night I sat at Gus's feet while he discoursed like a guru on the nature and philosophy of the cocaine mafia.

Gus's "Who's Who" was a vast pile of jottings, clippings, photographs and scrawled, arcane organigrams. He had amassed it, haphazardly but doggedly, over the years. It was in part a by-product of his own cocaine habit. He had almost become part of the furniture among the lower echelons of the Bogotá cocaine circuit: Gus in his dirty *ruana*, scoring another little bundle on credit. He traded gossip with the razor-boys, listened in on the Perseverancia street telegraph, drifted through long snowbound raps with other users—and the next morning down it all went in the "Who's Who."

Guided by an invisible cross-referencing system, crouched over the carton like some scabrous old ferret casing a burrow, he hauled out names and dates. Veronica Rivera, the "Cocaine Queen," for example. He had seen her once, short and dark, like a dumpy Colombian housewife, but somehow you could smell the money and the death all around her.

"You'd be surprised at the number of women involved in this business," he said. "The cocaine queens, the money-laundresses, the molls, the mules. Above all the mules. It's a well-known fact that women make the best mules. There's a girl in town I know, Spanish girl, who's carried enough snow through customs to start up a ski resort. You ought to pay her a visit, mate. Tell Julio Cesar you want to see Rosalita. He'll fix you up."

On a new page of my notebook I wrote: Rosalita the Mule. "And of course the biggest Queen Bitch of them all," Gus was saying, "is cocaine itself."

Gus had said he wanted to warn me about what I was "up against," and the gist of his message was that there had been a lot of changes since I was last in Colombia in the early 1970s. Those were "the good old bad old days." It was a free-for-all. There was big money up for grabs, and anyone with a bit of nerve and plenty of luck could get a piece of it.

Now, Gus said, it's all different. "They're not gangs anymore, they're bloody corporations." Now it's all what the economists call "vertical integration," controlling every phase of the operation from raw material to end user, eliminating the middleman, or at least putting him on the payroll and enveloping all his profits. There are still thousands of Colombians involved in the drug trade, but the whole business is ultimately controlled by a score of giant, Mafia-style syndicates. They've got huge production plants where they process the cocaine, either out of raw cocaine paste smuggled up from Peru and Bolivia, or—increasingly—from their own coca plantations. They've got small private armies guarding the plants. A lot of them have formed an unholy alliance with the Colombian guerrilla factions; they pay the guerrillas money and arms in return for protection. The processed coke is ferried northward in private planes, hundreds of kilos at a time, to the wharves and landing strips of the Caribbean coast, especially the Guajira peninsula. There the planes refuel, or the cargo is switched to another plane or boat, and on to the States.

Up in Florida, there's been a long feud between the Cubans and the Colombians for control of the wholesaling network, but the Colombians are on top right now. They've got all the latest gear—computer links, electronic surveillance, helipads and the rest. And they've got people in place all down the line: bent police and customs agents, *representantes* in all the major ports and airports, Colombian travel agents to handle their comings and goings, Colombian realtors to handle their offices and apartments. And underpinning the operation is a brutal army of hit men who are rapidly acquiring a reputation as the meanest sons of bitches in the underworld. The traditional *Mafiosi* might put a .22 bullet through someone's head, and leave a note for his wife saying how much they regretted it, but business is business, *omertà* and all that. The Colombians don't bother. They go in with the "big key"—an axe or sledgehammer—and blow away the whole family with M-16 machine guns.

At this top end of smuggling, the profits are immense. Statistics are hard to substantiate—no one's publishing end-of-year accounts—but the guess-timate is that in the early 1980s about 50,000 kilos, 50 tons of pure cocaine, were leaving Colombia every year, mainly destined for the United States. At a conservative reckoning this earns around $2 billion annually, more than the country's major legitimate export, coffee. With the marijuana trade included, Colombia's entire export earnings, just over $3 billion, are probably matched dollar for dollar by illicit drug earnings.

But money is only the beginning. It is what the money does that counts, the power grip that the drug mafia exerts on Colombia. A lot of drug money never finds its way back into Colombia. It stays in the United States, mainly in Florida, where it is said of the Colombian drug mafia that they don't rob banks, they buy them. But as much as a third, say a billion dollars a year, does flow back into the country. There it supports the fantastical opulence of the drug *capos*. It buys off police, judiciary and administration, flows into legitimate business fronts, becomes a major source of low-interest credit, vastly increases the growth of the country's money supply, and jacks up the inflation rate, currently running at about 30 percent.

Then there are the spin-off effects: the government money diverted, under American pressure, to finance anti-trafficking operations; the increasing bill for food imports, as marijuana and coca plantations swallow up agricultural land; the loss of tourist earnings, as Colombia's gangland reputation scares off the holiday-makers.

These narco-dollars are only a part, though now much the biggest part, of Colombia's subterranean economy, the black market and contraband interests so widespread they are simply known as *la otra economía*, the other economy. Huge quantities of green coffee, sugar, cattle and cement are creamed off for illegal shipment and sale. These "clandestine" exports are said to net about $500 million a year. And then there are emeralds. Official exports of gem emeralds are worth $50 million a year, but at least as much goes out by the back door, smuggled out by Colombians or bought by gringos from the thousands of small-time merchants like Julio at the Fruit Palace. The other side of the "other economy" is the profusion of contraband goods coming *into* the country—cars, cigarettes, whiskey, electrical appliances, any consumer item with high import tariffs. Colombia is a smuggler's paradise. Drug traffic is the big one, but most of the drug *capos* have their fingers in the other pies, and make full use of the ingrained profiteering networks of *la otra economía*.

The influx of blue money into the national economy is deleterious in much the same way as pumping a body full of anabolic steroids. It is a short-term fortifier which in the long term weakens, and one of the most pervasive ways in which it weakens is through the corruption and bribery of officialdom. The corruption percolates through to every level of Colombian political life. In theory, of course, the Colombian government is pledged to fight the drug mafia. In reality, the whole Colombian power base is so deeply implicated, through bribes and kickbacks and drug-related political funds, that any concerted action against the drug racket has a built-in softness, one hand waving a cudgel while the other pockets a share of the proceeds. The big busts are good propaganda, but it is always the small fry who get caught, while *los peces gordos*, the "fat fish," swim on happily in their fortified haciendas and Miami-baroque mansions. The biggest *capos* are well-known, high-profile figures—men like Carlos Lehder, probably the biggest of the lot, who owns his own newspaper, his own neo-Nazi political party and his own island in the Bahamas. Everyone knows about Carlitos, "Joe Leather," who worships John Lennon and Adolf Hitler, just as everyone knows about the other billionaire barons like Pablo Escobar, the Botero brothers, Benjamin "Papa Negro" Herrera, and Gonzalo "El Mejicano" Rodriguez. These people don't need anonymity; they reckon they are untouchable. The removal of mafia capital from the country's banks and businesses would cause economic chaos, the full naming of names on the payroll would tear the entire administration apart, and, as the bottom line, the cocaine mafia has enough arms, airplanes, manpower and high-placed military friends to start another civil war of the kind which dots the country's recent history. This is an extreme scenario, but with the stakes that high it will take a brave politician to call their bluff.

CHAPTER SEVEN

Snow White

This, in broad outline, was Gus's view of today's cocaine trade. It wasn't startlingly original, but on a chill Bogotá night, with the light flickering from bad connections and a blanket of basuko smoke in the air, it struck home. The moral was clear. Forget the Fruit Palace, forget the droll capers of yesteryear. Above all, forget the Great Cocaine Story. The utter naked absurdity of my assignment loomed before me. Inside the Cocaine Underworld! Gus had an answer for that one. "The only way you're going to get inside the cocaine underworld, mate, is after it's chewed you up and swallowed you."

It was very disheartening. But I turned up again the next night, as I had said I would. I found him in good spirits. His leg was freshly bandaged. We talked aimlessly for a while. Then I asked him if he had any particular stories on the boil at the moment. I want something I can get my teeth into, Gus.

He looked at me for a long time, and then he said, "Yes. Yes, I have. One *very* particular story, as a matter of fact." Even as he said it he glanced nervously at the door, and slipped the brick out of the peephole for a quick scan of the courtyard, and I knew that at last I was going to learn why he was holed up here in the back streets like an animal on the run.

Gus's story concerned a new syndicate that was elbowing its way into the Bogotá cocaine market. "It's very big, very streamlined and very secretive," he said. The first thing anyone noticed was the sudden, unexpected appearance of some very good cocaine on the circuit. Casual purchases of coke in Bogotá tend to be as disappointingly dilute as they are in London. "This was stronger and purer than anything we'd seen for years. Mean peach, mate. Everyone sat up and wanted some, but no one seemed quite sure where it came from." Or if they knew, they weren't saying.

There were other hints and traces: new whispers of rivalry, small seismic disturbances from the underworld. To the trained ear like Gus's, the regular fare of gangland killings, kidnappings, rip-offs and run-outs assumes a kind of pattern. "You know who's treading on whose toes. And when you *don't* know, you start to wonder. A gets knocked off his perch, but you know it wasn't B or C. So you turn a new page and you write at the top: 'D.' A new *banda* in town, carving out a patch for itself."

The primo coke and the subterranean rumors continued. Gus persisted with his usual nosiness. And then at last he got something—in fact, the way it sometimes goes, he suddenly got two quite independent leads in as many days. The first was a name. "It was pure luck. I got it from someone

who had no right to know anything. He was just a regular, low-grade cor-
ner-boy on Caracas. I'd never even seen him before. I was drinking with
some friends in this bar. He comes up and asks, did anyone want to score
perico? It was that kind of bar. As a matter of fact I did want to. We went
out back and he gave me a *muestra*. No doubt about it. It was that same
primo peach again." Gus played it rather crafty at that point. He said to
the boy, *"No sirve, no es pura."* This coke's no use. The boy protested—
he knew it was good. Gus again feigned distaste. Then the boy said: *"Sí,
hermano. Esa es el perico de* Snow White." He used the English words,
Snow White. This is Snow White cocaine.

"I didn't know what the hell he meant, of course. But he was very clear
about it. This was cocaine from a source—someone or something—called
Snow White."

Gus tried to get more out of him. Who or what was Snow White? But
the boy was wiser than his years. All he would say was, "You want more
Snow White stuff I'll get it for you." But at least Gus had a name of sorts,
and names are hard to come by in this business.

The very next night he was with an American called Kreitman, who ran
a gold and precious stone shop in the Chapinero district. Kreitman was a
recent addition to Gus's list of eligible gringos, good for an occasional
cadge of dinner, drugs and a night on the sofa. This night Kreitman laid
some *perico* on Gus, and it was once again this *premier cru* peach, which
Gus now knew to be Snow White cocaine. Kreitman was boasting about
his contacts, his savoir faire, his reflected glory from laying such fine stuff
on an old street veteran like Gus. "So I came straight out, put my cards
on the table. I said: 'This is Snow White stuff, right?' No reaction. It didn't
mean anything to him. So much for his contacts."

But Gus did learn something from Kreitman. "Do you know what the
beauty of this stuff is?" said Kreitman. "It's never going to run out. I have
it on *very* good authority, from the man who sells it to me, in fact. These
people are bringing 100 kilos a week into Bogotá. A *hundred* a week."

Gus broke off suddenly. Something clattered down below the outside
window, down where the scrap yard was. He had forgotten his fears while
he was talking: they came back now, like electricity switched on. Then came
a louder noise, and a scattering wail of cats. Gus breathed out heavily. His
hand was shaking as he reached for the rum bottle. After a pause he said,
"Well, that's just about it, really."

I stared at him in disappointment. "You mean that's all you've got?
You've got a name—a nickname really—and you've a figure for how much
they're dealing in. It's not a lot to go on, is it, Gus?"

He looked at me sourly. "Yeah, well, the inquiry got discontinued, didn't
it?"

"You mean your... accident?"

"Right. Comeback from little Snow White, just as quick as if I'd
punched a button. Saturday night, bar in Perseverancia, just a couple of

days after I'd seen Kreitman. There was this guy I knew, small-time hood. I was really hot on this Snow White story, and I was sure, can't quite remember why, that he knew something about it. I started asking a lot of damn fool questions, very indiscreet, broke all the rules. I'd had a skinful.

"So when I leave the bar, they're waiting for me. Two of them, across the street, in the shadows. I didn't really take them in at first: there were other people on the street. But a couple of blocks later, all quiet, I knew they were after me. I started to run. Any minute now they're going to put a bullet in my back. Concentrates the mind wonderfully. I went like a bloody gazelle. I got myself off the street, down an alley, a lane. You know Perseverancia: it's just like a village. Little houses, yards out back. There's nowhere to hide. So of course the alley's a dead end, but there's a door with light behind it. I hammered on the door. Then the apes caught up with me. One of them had a machete—no, it was more like a butcher's knife, anyway it was long and sharp, and he was a big bugger, and he was going to do my throat with it. That was my finest moment, mate. I got him a beautiful kick right in the nuts. He must have sliced my leg then. I didn't feel a thing till afterward. Then this geezer opens the door—about bloody time—and he's standing there in his nightshirt with a Winchester 18-bore rifle in his hands. The double-act pissed off, and that was that. Blood all over the shop, and at least eight of my nine lives used up."

So there it was. Ace McGregor's last story. It was almost three in the morning, and I felt completely dried up. "So what's your plan, Gus?" I asked. "You can't stay here forever."

"Right now I haven't got a lot of choice. You know—no money, one leg, a lot of people with bad attitudes on the lookout for me. Makes travel a little difficult. It's not safe here, but it's as safe as I can get." He jutted his ginger-stubbled chin out, and added, "The long-term plan, of course, is to get back in there and nail them."

"Nail them?"

"Sure. Get the story, name the names. Tell the world about Snow White and the Hundred Kilos. A little Colombian fairy tale."

"And how the hell are you going to do that?"

"Same way as I always do, mate. Look for the weak spots. I've been thinking. Got bugger all else to do all day. I've been putting Snow White into context, you might say."

The Bogotá market isn't what it used to be, Gus explained. There's only the remnants now of the big wholesale market that used to thrive here 10, 15 years ago. Then there were a lot of American dealers in town: at the Tequendama Hotel it was like a permanent convention. And a lot of high-volume purchases were actually physically made in Bogotá. Now the volume tends to go straight up-country, by air, from the processing plants in the south to the export points in the north. There's no need for it to come into Bogotá at all.

"So why the hell is Snow White bringing 100 kilos of the stuff in every week? That's way too much for the domestic market. It's coming in *and* it's going out again, or a lot of it is, anyway. So. Question number one. Where and how do they bring the gear in? Nothing much to go on there, probably on four wheels, rather than by air. Question number two. Where and how is the stuff going out? Answer, almost certainly by air. There's no point in bringing it into town just to take it out again overland. So you've got a big volume going out, regular as clockwork, from one of the airports. The volume's too big for mules to carry through customs. It's going out either dressed up as cargo, or possibly through some scam using air force or army planes. My money's on cargo. Question number three. Where's it going to? I'll tell you my thinking on that one, mate. It's going to Europe. I just don't see it coming into Bogotá if it's going Stateside. They've got so many supply lines going up from the northern seaboard. If I was a smart *capo*, looking for elbow room in a very tight market, I might well be looking at Europe."

He fingered the scabs on his face thoughtfully. "I'd love to nail those bloody apes. If I can just work out the pipeline, how it comes in and how it goes out, I'll put a cracker so far up Snow White's arse he won't know whether to shit or wind his wristwatch!"

"And how do you propose to do that?" I asked. I couldn't believe he was contemplating a second go at them.

"Obvious," he said. "I go back to Kreitman, and try to find out who he buys his *perico* off. Because whoever it is seems to know a few details about Snow White." He looked at me. Thoughtfully he said, "Trouble is, of course, I can't do anything right now. But *you* can, mate. No one knows *your* face. Most natural thing in the world for you to breeze into Kreitman's shop. You're looking for a few expensive souvenirs, he's a very pleasant chap, you'll get talking, he'll lay a line or two on you, and Bob's your uncle."

Alternatively, I thought, Bob's your gorilla up a dark alley with a machete. No thanks, Gus. No kamikaze journalism for me. "I'll think about it," I said.

"Think about it! Christ! I'm offering you the story, cock, mint-fresh. A big new syndicate, pouring hundreds of kilos of snow into Europe. This is your Cocaine Underworld, mate. These stories don't grow on trees round here, you know."

When I left that morning, I had Kreitman's business card in my pocket— *Galería Pecadillo: Daniel y Claudia Kreitman: Oro y Cerámica Precolombinos*—and I kept on thinking: No one's forcing you; you don't *have* to do it.

I decided to let Snow White lie for a while, but the least I could do was look up Rosalita the Mule. I presented myself once more at the Paso Doble. The fat *señora* sat splay-legged on a chair. "Ah!" she sneered. *"El Meester Escocés!"*

Julio Cesar took me over to the corner table. "You see Señor Gus?"

"Yes, I saw him. He's in a bit of a bad way, isn't he?"

"The leg. The leg is not good, but . . ." He trailed off into a shrug.

I told him I would like to meet Rosalita. He darted a quick look over his shoulder. The bandying of names is not encouraged in these circles. "You another damn journalist?" he asked.

It was my turn to shrug. "I've heard she's got some interesting stories to tell."

It was difficult, he said—just as it had been difficult to get in touch with Gus. It was 500 pesos' worth of difficulty this time. He went into the back room to make a phone call. "You're in luck," he said when he came back, flashing a grin. "She says she's lonely tonight."

We took a taxi down Caracas. First we were going to score some *perico* for me to take to Rosalita. "What's she like?" I asked. "You'll see," he said.

On the way we talked about Gus. Julio Cesar said Gus had been very good to him and his family. "A few years ago, when times were hard, when my papa died, Gus lent us money. He put a lot of contacts my way when I started selling the drugs. Gus is special to me. That's why I always get him good stuff for up here—" tapping his head "—and that's why we're helping him now."

"If you really want to help him, you ought to get him to a doctor. He needs to get that leg properly patched up."

Another shrug, another quavering of the pencil mustache. "It's not easy," he said vaguely.

"But surely he could get to a doctor without anyone knowing. Taxi there and back. I mean, is he really in that much danger?"

He looked at me thoughtfully. Chilly, streetwise eyes. Arm resting loosely on the back of the seat, behind my head. He seemed to be sizing me up for something. "Look," he said. "Gus tells you what he wants to tell you. That's OK by me. I don't want to say anything against Señor Gus. But the truth . . . well, in Colombia we say, *la verdad es una puta y hay que pagar*. Truth is a whore and you must pay for her."

I couldn't quite see what he was grappling at. His breath had a sweet, sickly tang: he'd been drinking a *gaseosa*. "Do you mean that Gus isn't really in danger after all?"

"Bogotá is dangerous. Look—" He bent down and flicked up his trouser leg. In his sock, held by a thick rubber band, was a pearl-handled flickknife. "You take good care in Bogotá. OK, Gus asks too many damn questions. He pokes his nose in. But I don't think anyone's wasting much time looking for him."

The taxi suddenly slowed down. There had been an accident. A *buseta* had left the road, and was lying on its side. There was a lot of broken glass and wood, at least three bodies lying in the litter. Two young soldiers were trying to calm a small but volatile crowd. There were no policemen that I could see. The driver leaned out, had a shouted conference with other drivers leaning out, and brought back the news that the *buseta* had killed a man with an ice-cream cart. For the next few minutes, not having spoken a word till then, the taxi driver regaled us with a bitter harangue against *busetas* and their drivers, their speed, their carelessness, their clannishness, and, of course, the way they took customers from good honest cabbies like himself. This in turn shaded into a moving apostrophe on behalf of the dead ice-cream vendor. He finally lapsed into silence, but it was still preying on his mind when we stopped at a red light a minute or two later, and he said to himself, with a little grunt of laughter, *"Helado con sabor de sangre."* Blood-flavored ice cream.

I was digesting this new angle on Gus, a new pointer to old suspicions. But the leg? What about the leg? I asked Julio Cesar.

"I don't know," he said. "Gus told you they came after him with a machete, no? He told you he was sniffing around after some big *coqueros* and they were sent after him?" I nodded. "Well, I don't know. That's what he told me too. Gus says it happened up in Perseverancia. OK. He's been in fights up there before. He's got this girl, his *putita*, up there. She's a really bad girl—set him up, string him along real bad. You want me to tell you what I think happened? OK. It was Saturday night in Perseverancia, someone picked a bad card, it was Gus. Tomorrow you or me, maybe. *Así es en Bogotá.*"

"So if there *isn't* anyone after him," I said, "why the hell can't he go to a doctor?"

He chafed his thumb and forefinger, the universal sign for money. *"Plata, hombre. Falta la plata.* Doctors cost money: 10,000, maybe 15,000 pesos for the treatment. That's just for starters. Señor Gus got nothing."

"Couldn't someone lend him the money?"

"Who? You wanna lend him? Everyone's lent money to Gus. He don't have no more credit. We've given him back that money he gave us twenty times over. We are poor people, *hombre*. You don't understand about Gus, I think. He's been bad for a year or so now. He don't work, he don't do nothing but bum *perico*. He takes too much *perico*, I buy him basuko. If he don't get basuko he starts to go crazy. I see many, many people like this. They don't want to do nothing but sniff and smoke. After a time no one wants them around, you know? We stick by him, even if he is a bit *loco*. But he's got to work it out for himself."

He leaned forward and told the taxi driver to hang a U-turn at the next light. We stopped outside a club called El Gose Pagano. "So what about this Snow White, then?" I asked. He didn't answer. He started to open the door to get out. I grabbed his arm. "What about Snow White?" I repeated.

He looked at my hand on his sequined forearm, then up into my face. He gently removed my hand and said, "I never heard of Snow White from anyone but Señor Gus."

CHAPTER EIGHT

Rosalita

Perhaps it was the tripping lightness of the syllables, perhaps it was the Springsteen song—"Rosalita, jump a little higher, *Señorita*, come sit by my fire"—that made me expect her to be flouncy and bright-eyed and ready to trip a *bambuco* or two by moonlight. She was overweight, tired and puff-faced, with a mouth turned down by the way things had gone. She wore glasses, and slacks that were too tight at the thighs. Somewhere behind it all you could see she had been pretty once, and the sharpness still flashed in her eyes like a zoo animal's memory of the jungle. She lived in a half-finished modern apartment out in Quinta Paredes, toward the airport. It smelled of plaster and oil paint. The new doors had warped and wouldn't close properly.

I gave her the *perico*. This seemed to be my act at the moment: a notebook in one hand, a little package of powder in the other. I explained that I was writing a book about the cocaine trade. She said, "Sure." She followed the first stiff hit of coke with a small chaser, and by the time she was laying out the third rail the sloth had gone from her face and hands, and she wasn't slurring her words anymore. She spoke fluent English in a Spanish-American accent. Her voice was lovely. If you closed your eyes she was beautiful, tough and titillatingly foreign. She was the best in the business, Rosalita the mule, who had walked cocaine through U.S. customs 43 times and never got caught. Then you opened your eyes and you saw a pale, faded woman in a woolen cardigan, huddled beside a single-element electric heater.

She was from Oviedo, a small town in the Cantabrian mountains of northern Spain. Her father was a local lawyer. She had gone to the States in the 1960s. A cousin had made it big in San Francisco, importing clothes from Mexico. He went back to Oviedo once a year, trailing the scent of success, bearing huge vulgar toys for the children. It had always been his promise that one day Rosalita would come and work for him, and she would see the cable cars and bridges and deep blue bay. And one day that's what happened. Cousin Bartolomeo wrote to say he could get her papers, she could come and work as an assistant in one of his Mexican boutiques. She landed in San Francisco in 1967, two days short of her seventeenth birthday. This made her in her early thirties now: she looked ten years older.

The cable cars were fine, and the Golden Gate Bridge was, too, but Cousin Bartolomeo did not come up to expectations. "He was all big talk and shiny suits, but he was real mean. He wanted me because I was cheap. For a year he didn't pay me at all, only room and board. I was just cleaning, and doing odd jobs for him. He tried to get me to do other things too, you know, dirty things...." She raised an inquiring eye at me. My pen hovered foolishly over the notebook. "I was pretty then," she said, fixing me with a hard look that dared me to mumble that she still was.

She was also sharp, and it soon came to her notice that Cousin Bartolomeo had other interests besides peasant-style Mexican dresses. For one thing he was dealing in illegal Mexican immigrants. He was selling passage into the U.S., selling false documentation—that was probably how he'd got papers for Rosalita—and he was setting up cheap illegal labor for his business friends. The other iron, the one which really opened Rosalita's eyes, was pornography: hard-core material produced in Tijuana, smuggled in along Bartolomeo's supply routes, and sold under the counter down Broadway, San Francisco's sex street. "I've seen some things," said Rosalita, "but this was really filthy." Her voice curled like a tendril around the word "feelthy."

"So one day I went to Bartolomeo. I said, 'I want a job and a salary.' And before he could say no, I said, 'If you don't I tell the family back home about the porno.'"

The following Monday morning she was behind the counter in one of Bartolomeo's Mexican clothes shops, the one in chic Sausalito, across the Golden Gate. She got her own apartment, lived smart. She was good at her job, and a couple of years later, when Bartolomeo was expanding his legitimate business front, he put her in charge of a new store. This was selling clothes and weavings from Guatemala. From now on she traveled regularly to Guatemala City.

Up to now she was 100 percent legitimate. Then, in the fall of 1970, she met Chick. Chick was a Colombian boy from Medellín. His real name was Ernesto, but his family had always called him Chico, and he had effortlessly Americanized this into Chick. "That was Chick all over," she said. "He could fit like a glove over any scene. That's why he was one hell of a smuggler." Not that Rosalita knew anything about *that* when this young, handsome, dandified boy came in the shop. They got talking. He became very interested when she told him about her trips to Guatemala. He said he had good contacts in Colombia, who could supply her with the kinds of goods she sold in the shop. The next week he came back with business cards, addresses, lists of arts and crafts shops. He really did seem to have good connections. Rosalita was in love, Cousin Bartolomeo was agreeable, and a couple of months later she made her first trip to Bogotá. The night before she left Chick gave her a beautiful leather traveling case. For good luck, he says, and kisses her sweetly on the cheek.

She flew to Bogotá, met Chick's contacts, bought an impressive selection of moderately priced *ruanas*, dresses, wall-hangings, etc., and flew back to San Francisco. When she got back Chick plied her with questions. How had it been, getting through customs? Had there been any problems clearing the stuff? And so on. In fact, Rosalita said, there had been rather more questions than there were when she came back from Guatemala. This was late 1970: there was only a trickle of cocaine coming up from Colombia, but there was already a lot of marijuana, and Colombia was undoubtedly on the customs list of suspicious provenances.

But they didn't search you? Chick asked. No, of course not, said innocent Rosalita. As a matter of fact she knew the customs man quite well.

Chick danced around, and kissed her, and said, "You're perfect, baby! You've just made us *millonarios*!" He picked up the traveling case he had given her. The four little rubber studs on the bottom unscrewed, the base came away, and there was a neat little compartment inside. For a moment she thought she'd been set up. But there was nothing in it. Chick said, "You just carried thin air into the States from Colombia. Next time, baby, you carry in $25,000."

"You want me to carry in *money*?"

"*Plata de polvo,*" Chick laughed. Powder money.

Rosalita was shocked. She could just about handle dope: some of her friends smoked. But cocaine. That was something she vaguely associated with junkies, blacks, jazz musicians. Chick said, "Trust me," and he also said, "Try some." Rosalita did both. Two months later she flew in from Bogotá with 3 pounds of Huanaco White cocaine packed in a long thin wedge in the underbelly of her traveling case. It was Rosalita's first run, and it went like a dream. "And, you know, I'm not sure which got me higher. That first hit of *perico* Chick gave me, or that first run through customs."

Over a couple of years Rosalita did that run ten times, clearing about twenty grand each time. Overheads were zero, of course. All the expenses of the trips were picked up unwittingly by Cousin Bartolomeo. He for his part was happy with the profits from his Colombian shop, "Andes," on the first floor above the Guatemala shop in Sausalito.

They contemplated broadening their horizons. The other method obviously available to them was to import the cocaine in one of the crates of woolens and weavings that Rosalita air-freighted from Bogotá. The plus of this was that you could bring in much higher volume. The minus was that crates from Colombia were routinely searched before clearing customs, mainly because freight traffic was the main smuggling mode for marijuana. It was just too risky, they decided. Then the *ruana*-man in Bogotá came up with a bright idea. Impregnating the *ruanas* with a solution of cocaine. When the solution dried, the cocaine deposit nestled invisibly in the deep woolen pile of the *ruanas*. At the other end the *ruanas* were soaked once more and the cocaine recovered in solution.

But before they could put this into effect, Rosalita had her first near miss. She had the cocaine in the false-bottomed case, and she got a real going-over at customs. "They didn't bust me, but they sure scared the shit out of me. You know, running drugs is all up here in your head, it's all attitude. You convince yourself, you're three-quarters there to convincing the customs man. I was good, there's no doubt. I knew the ropes, I'd brought in legitimate imports for years. I felt right. When I started wearing glasses I felt even better. Not too smart, not too ragged. Just be what I am. That's the secret of smuggling—one big lie with lots of little truths around it.

"But once you see the other side—once you think: They've got my number—then you're into all sorts of problems in your head. It's all a question of what you see when you look in the mirror. Do you see a young business woman importing goods for a Sausalito boutique, or do you see a cocaine mule pissing in her pants with fright?

"I swore off it right there and then. Chick tried to persuade me. Chick was always very cool. He spread everything around: different bank accounts, a couple of apartments, different phony company names when he sent the money drafts down to Bogotá. Always have a back door open, that was Chick's motto. I said, 'That's fine when you're dealing the stuff. But when you're running it, there aren't any back doors. You just got to keep on going forward: one way out, no way back. I've had enough.'"

Chick and Rosalita lay low for a while. But smuggling is like a drug itself, it gets in your blood, and after a while they were craving for action. Rosalita didn't want to do the Bogotá run anymore. "It's just statistics," she said. "No matter how good your cover, you can't keep coming in from Colombia without the customs turning you over once in a while." Why not get someone else to ferry the merchandise from Bogotá to Guatemala City? she suggested. She could then relay it on from there into the States. A Guatemalan stamp in your passport was perfectly cool. There wasn't much worth smuggling out of Guatemala, nothing you could carry on your person anyway. This time it was Chick who demurred. It meant cutting someone else in, relying on someone else's cool. It was against their hitherto so successful creed—Small Is Beautiful.

Then, in the summer of '75, they found their new move. It answered both their objections: Rosalita didn't have to fly in with Colombian stamps in her passport, and Chick didn't have to lose sleep over the risks of additional mules. They called it the Magic Eraser move.

One day Chick brought a stranger back to their Sausalito apartment. He was an Englishman. He had blond hair scraped back and tied in a bunch, and little wire-rim spectacles. He wore an expensive suit. "He was something like a smart hippie, something like a professor. Chick introduces him. 'This is Dr. Richard,' he says. 'Dr. Richard's in plastics. He's got something to show you, Rosalita.'

"So the guy opens up his briefcase. He takes out a piece of paper, a rubber stamp and two aerosol cans. The cans were unmarked: one plain black, one plain white. He took the black one and sprayed something over the paper. It smelled like new car seats. After a few seconds it dried, and the paper looked just the same as before, except if you picked it up it was stiffer, perhaps heavier. Then he inked his stamp and stamped the paper. It said, Downstream Enterprises. That was Dr. Richard's company. Chick kept pacing around and grabbing me, and saying: 'Baby, isn't it beautiful, you ain't seen nothing yet.' Then Dr. Richard took the other can and sprayed that over the paper. A different smell, bleachy. In a moment all the surface of the paper went a white color, sort of frosted, like a smashed windshield. He shook the stuff in shreds off the paper, and with a little knife he very carefully scraped the rest. When he had finished, the paper was blank. No stuff on it, and no stamp on it.

"Dr. Richard explained. It's simply a very thin, transparent film of plastic. He'd been doing research for years. Breaking the micron barrier, he called it. He was offering Chick the spray cans at $5,000 apiece. I hadn't really caught on. Then Chick said, 'Baby, think about it. Think what you could do with that stuff sprayed on your passport!'"

Chick and Rosalita took a long weekend and made a trial run. They motored down to Mexico with the magic eraser sprayed on the pages of their passports. They got stamped at the border, going in and coming back out. The customs also turned them over on the way out, looking for grass or heroin. They were clean, of course. This pleased Chick enormously. They were even more pleased when, in a motel outside El Paso, they sprayed the white can of solvent on their passports. The plastic skin frosted up into view, they scraped it off, and—eureka!—there was no visible record left of their visit to Mexico.

This was the basic premise of the Magic Eraser runs. Rosalita was able to move in and out of Colombia without any record remaining in her passport. Passport stamps aren't everything, but a Colombian stamp undoubtedly multiplies the likelihood of getting pulled. She would fly to Guatemala City, in the course of her legitimate business. There she would buy a round-trip ticket to Bogotá and back. She sprayed on the magic eraser before she left Guatemala City, peeled it off when she got back with the cocaine, supplied as usual by the *ruana*-man. There was never any problem getting through customs when coming back into Guatemala. When she flew back into the States there was no evidence she'd been anywhere near Colombia. She had a bigger suitcase now: it carried 10 pounds. They were making $50-60,000 a run.

The Magic Eraser worked like a dream for half a dozen runs. But Dr. Richard's invisible laminate had one major flaw: it was susceptible to heat. He had told them to keep the passports clear of any heat source. One day in Bogotá, Rosalita made one of her rare mistakes. She had to leave her room in the Tequendama Hotel in a hurry—there'd been a change of rendezvous with the *ruana*-man—and she left the passport on a windowsill. It was unseasonably hot, the window faced south, and when she returned, the passport was well and truly baked. The pages looked like eggs beginning to fry.

She had to ditch the passport, go to the Spanish embassy—she still traveled under a Spanish passport—and get a temporary replacement. She flew back to San Francisco empty-handed, and they laid the Magic Eraser move to rest.

Chick went downhill. She said this in a matter-of-fact way, as if everyone naturally did. They drifted apart. She left Cousin Bartolomeo's employ and moved to Los Angeles. But she didn't stay away from smuggling long. In L.A., living in Laurel Canyon, she met two people who between them offered a new mule trail. The first was a Swiss girl called Ilse, who had done some dope smuggling, and was up for anything. She was wild and bitter. For Ilse, said Rosalita, running stuff through customs was like saying, "Fuck you!" to all the men who'd done her wrong. The other person who offered his services was someone with a ready supply of false passports.

Ilse and Rosalita ran the classic two-suitcase move. All you need for this move is two identical suitcases and a lot of nerve. Rosalita flew down to Bogotá. Ilse flew on a different flight to someplace en route between Bogotá and whichever American city they had chosen to come in at. The return trip was prearranged between them before they left. Rosalita boarded at Bogotá, checked her case stuffed full of coke. Ilse boarded at one of the flight's stopover points: Panama, Costa Rica, wherever. Her case, containing nothing but legitimate female hand baggage, joined Rosalita's somewhere in the hold of the aircraft. They didn't acknowledge each other during the flight, of course. When they got to the States, Rosalita picked up Ilse's case off the baggage carousel, and took it through customs. If her Colombian stamps caused her to get pulled, she was entirely clean. Blouses, skirts, panties and beauty kit. The danger was that an officer might notice that her baggage identification tag didn't match the one on her ticket, but this was unlikely. A little while later Ilse came through, carrying the coke. If all went well, she breezed through: no Colombian stamps, of course. If she did get pulled over, and cocaine under the false bottom was discovered, she went into a screaming fit: "Oh my God, this is a frame-up, I've never seen these things before in my life. Look, look the baggage identification number is different. Look, it's come from Bogotá, and I've only been in San José—this is *someone else's* merchandise." It could be nasty, but in the end they would have nothing to pin on her. Checks would be run on the bag, but all that would come up would be the false name that Rosalita was traveling under.

Another time Rosalita worked for a Colombian called Juancho Leone—
Johnny the Lion. Leone claimed to be bringing in $10 million worth of
perico a year. He had a very elaborate front: the Santa Teresa Pan-
American Bible Mission, employing scores of people, stocking thousands
of bibles in indigenous Indian dialects, and entirely devoted with crusad-
ing zeal to the importation of cocaine and marijuana. There were Santa
Teresa missions in Colombia, Ecuador, Peru, Bolivia. Rosalita, alias Sister Dominica, carried the cocaine sewn into long thin pockets inside her
voluminous black habit.

Another of Leone's moves used tropical birds—all properly docu-
mented and above board, some of the birds unfortunately dead on arrival
in the United States. In fact the birds had been dead when they were loaded
in Colombia—dead and stuffed with cocaine.

So why no more? Why not make run number forty-four if all the others
had worked so well? It was a question of love and the mule again. She had
got into smuggling for love of Chick. Now she was married to a Colombian lawyer—"The first straight person I'd met in ten years, and I had to
go and marry him." He made her swear off smuggling. They were going
to have a child. Then a year ago she discovered—at the same time that Colombian fiscal investigators discovered—he was involved in a big fraud and
money-laundering racket centered in Medellín. He was now serving a three-
year sentence in Ladera prison. She was through with it all now. "Everyone's living a lie," she said. "You too, no?"

She was tired. The edge was fading from her voice. Her nose was runny
from too many lines. She wrapped her cardigan around her and went to
get a box of Kleenex.

"What happened to Chick, Rosalita?"

Back over her shoulder, so quiet that I wouldn't have heard it if I hadn't
half-expected it, she said, "Chick's dead."

The last time she'd seen him was in Miami in 1980. "He was in a bad
way. He was on the spike, he was snowballing, he was free-basing." These
are the three hard-line cocaine habits: intravenous injection, combining
cocaine with heroin or morphine and inhaling volatile vapors from heated
cocaine—all of them shortcuts to the cemetery.

"On top of this Chick was doing the most damn fool kind of smuggling
there is. He was body-packing. When I used to work with him he tried to
make me do it. He'd say, 'Baby, it's foolproof, you carry it in your stomach, it's the one place they can't shine their flashlights.' I never did it,
though. That's what Chick was in to. He was carrying in a pound at a time,
a hundred *uvas*—"

"Grapes?"

"That's what you call the capsules. Four or five grams of *perico* wrapped
up in a rubber, or a bit of surgical glove."

There are two types of danger for the body-packer. First, the *uvas* can be detected by X-ray, and most of the major airports now use X-rays routinely on suspicious-looking Colombians. "If you don't confess," Rosalita said, "they put you on the pot and wait for the evidence." The other danger is mortal. That is when one of the capsules punctures inside you. This can happen at any time after ingesting it, but the most common thing is for a capsule to get lodged in the caecum, or blind gut, the first part of the large intestine. If this happens the packer knows he's living on borrowed time. No amount of laxatives or enemas is going to shake that obstruction free. The gastric juices work on, and wham—five grams of undiluted cocaine instantaneously absorbed through the lining of the gut, hitting the central nervous system like a force-ten gale. This is called the White Death. Heart on overdrive, temperature like a tropical fever, hemorrhage, pulmonary edema, convulsions, respiratory arrest. All this to cope with while your brain's gunning up through the gears toward the state known as acute toxic psychosis.

Nine times out of 10 a ruptured cocaine package is fatal. If the packer gets himself to a hospital in time, and if he is treated right—oxygen and the maintenance of airways to keep him breathing, heavy shots of short-acting barbiturates to counter convulsions, a course of psychiatric sedatives and blockers—these might just bring him through.

Like many others, Chick never made it to the hospital. Rosalita showed me the clipping from the *Miami Herald*. It was a single paragraph news item:

Nine Mile Island Suicide Was Narcotics Suspect
A man who shot himself in public yesterday has been identified as Ernesto Diaz Marcoletta, a Colombian national. Shoppers scattered as Diaz, 35, appeared in a tenth floor window of a Nine Mile Island apartment block, brandishing a shotgun and screaming. He shot himself in the stomach and fell to his death, witnesses said. According to police, Diaz was suspected of trafficking and other narcotics offenses, and had been under surveillance.

So there it was. Chick's epitaph: two column inches for the narcotics suspect. I copied it solemnly into my notebook.

"But don't you see?" said Rosalita. "Even then they couldn't touch him. He blew himself out through the stomach, so they couldn't find the *perico* inside him. That was Chick all over."

When I left she was sitting, turned away toward the single-element heater, clenching a Kleenex in her fist. I thanked her once more, but she didn't answer. I said, "I'm sorry." She said, "Sure."

CHAPTER NINE

The Best Cook on Caracas Avenue

Julio Cesar was soccer crazy. One evening we went together to a game at El Campín stadium. He had got us the best seats my money could buy—Occidental Numerada, precisely aligned on the halfway line. The vendors threaded, selling bags of *chicharrones*—giant pork scratchings—and glasses of fizzy *gaseosa*, piped through a rubber tube from a tank strapped on the back. The smoke and dust of the crowd hung in a silvery mist over the floodlit arena. The grass shone like an emerald.

Just as the two teams ran on to the field, the floodlights flickered and crackled, and the stadium was plunged into darkness. There was a momentary silence, then an ironic cheer. A pair of Radio Caracol Land-Rovers on the sideline switched on their headlights. The one in front—orange and white, "EL PERIODISMO ELECTRONÍCO"—revved up, crunched gears, and promptly reversed into the one behind, knocking out its headlights. Another cheer. Eventually the game got underway. The visiting team won by a single goal, scored early in the second half. The home team missed a late penalty. Beer cans sailed on to the field.

Out of the crowd a man hailed Julio Cesar. He was called Jairo. He nuzzled conspiratorially up to Julio Cesar and said, "You got anything?" Of course, said Julio Cesar, but not on him. "I've got a car," said Jairo. They pushed off through the crowd. I tagged along, vaguely hopeful of a few more pickings for the Great Cocaine Story.

We drove to El Gose Pagano, on Caracas and 78th, the same club where Julio Cesar had scored the coke I took to Rosalita. El Gose Pagano—the name roughly means "Pagan Good-times"—is a *salsateca*, a discotheque devoted to salsa music. An old town house was still discernible in the warren of small, dark rooms, some bare, some with tables and chairs and candles stuck in bottles. Downstairs was a bar, upstairs the dance floor. The dance floor was empty. It was about nine-thirty. The place would be jumping in a couple of hours, Julio Cesar said. Undeterred, the black disc jockey was crouched in an alcove, playing records so loud that even the scratches jarred your skull. Salsa is spiky, up-tempo Afro-Spanish music, full of complex syncopations and multilayered percussion tracks, with much Hispanic chanting and whooping over the top.

We bought high-priced beer, the only form of entrance fee. Julio Cesar processed rapidly through the nooks and crannies of the place, sometimes stopping to shake a hand and pass a few words, sometimes waving a brief forefinger of salutation across a room. Whoever he was looking for wasn't here. He installed Jairo and me at a table and said he would be back *ahorita*. I had the feeling that Julio Cesar regarded Jairo more as business than pleasure. Jairo was a rich boy. He lived with his family in an exclusive Santa Marta suburb. His father was a chemical engineer with one of the big breweries. Jairo was about to—his sort often seems to be "about to"—study architecture. The natural *alegría* of the Caribbean Colombians had become in him a slightly jumpy, false bonhomie. He smiled like an Arab dealer concluding a deal, and his eyes roved around the room while we talked. Nevertheless, I was glad to talk with him about Santa Marta. He assured me the smuggling and dealing were still very active up there. Most useful of all, he gave me the name of a Santa Marta dealer, Waldino. "He's got a black beard, and he'll fix you up with anything you need," said Jairo. *"Anything!"*

Julio Cesar returned with a *muestra*. We trooped off in turn to the john. Lavatory clogged with newspaper, spots of blood in the washbasin. Two quick scoops on the knife blade, and out again. All night long there would be people coming out of that john, with a motorized zip in their steps, a sparkle in their eye, and a lopsided leer on their face, which they imagined to be a smile.

We had more beers. The floor began to fill up. The music was racked up another decibel, ultraviolet lights went on, eyes and teeth flashed, tail feathers were shaken. Then, suddenly and unaccountably, we were leaving. The music was too loud to find out why. Julio Cesar shouted something about going down *el camino viejo*. The old way? What was it and where did it lead? El Camino Viejo turned out to be a restaurant a few blocks away, and we were going there to meet a man called Mario, who was bringing the deal for Jairo. "You'll like Mario," Julio Cesar told me. *"Es un perro viejo"*—he's an old dog. Upstairs in the restaurant a band was playing. None of us wanted to eat, so we ordered a bottle of aguardiente. Already, it appeared, I was the only one with any spending money left. Jairo was saving his wad for the *perico* he was buying; Julio Cesar's pockets opened strictly one way. In a last stab of lucidity, as the second bottle was ordered, I transferred 11 pesos to another pocket—enough for a bus ride back downtown—and offered up the rest to the gods of the night.

Later there were no diners left in the restaurant, only drinkers, and the tables had imperceptibly melted into one long straggling party. The musicians were relaxing, arms around available girls. Everyone was talking. People sat down opposite me, beside me. Suddenly one of them was Mario, the man we'd come here to meet.

He was very tall, with a streaked beard, black and gray. He was slow, somber and precise, and brought a breath of chill night air into the booze-heated room. His voice was deep and sonorous. He was a Southerner, from Tulua, a small pleasant town set among the cane fields and bamboo groves of the Cauca valley. I judged he was in his late forties. The wrinkles on his forehead gathered like a force field around a frown of concentration. His eyes were blue and hard. One knew right away that he was not a man to be trifled with.

He hadn't brought the *perico* that Jairo was buying, but he had brought a couple of *sucitos*—basuko reefers. Jairo wanted to light up straight-away—he had a nervous greedy look in his eyes, like a kid worrying about chocolate cake. Mario said the restaurant had been in trouble with the po-lice over drugs: Jairo would have to smoke it outside if he wanted some. I had almost forgotten that all this druggery is illegal in Bogotá. One is always being told that the last thing to worry about in Colombia is the po-lice. They are overstretched and underpaid, and you have to be very un-lucky to find one who hasn't got a price.

As Jairo left clutching the *sucito*, Julio Cesar said to me, "You go on. I'll come in a minute." He was talking earnestly with Mario as we left. He didn't look drunk at all: a touch disheveled perhaps, a faint sheen of sweat on the brow, but otherwise a man in control of his destiny.

He joined us on the sidewalk. The street was quiet. We smoked the *su-cito* in a phone booth, two keeping watch while the third toked behind the mouthpiece.

While Jairo smoked, Julio Cesar said to me, "You like Mario, no?"

"Of course I do."

"He's a very interesting man. Like I say, *un perro viejo*. He knows a few tricks." The smoke rolled through me, mists of basuko over seas of aguardiente, a strange inner hush through which I heard and recognized a distinct tightening in Julio Cesar's voice. Business was afoot. "He used to be what we call a *mano verde*, you know?"

"A green hand?"

"*Un cocinero, hombre*. A cook. A cocaine processor. They get green hands from treating the coca leaf. Look, I've told him you might be...interested. He can tell you the tricks, how it's done. I promise you, Mario was the best cook in Colombia!"

I snorted skeptically. Even at this gone stage there were vestiges of per-spective to protect. "OK," he said, with a light laugh. "He's the best cook on Caracas Avenue tonight. He's here, and he'll talk with you for 5,000 pesos."

I didn't want to do it. I was in no fit state to do it. But 5,000 was about what I had in my top pocket, and as Gus had pointed out, these stories don't grow on trees. Summoning reserves of fortitude from my swaying, jelly-fish frame I said, "After we talk, I pay, OK?"

Julio Cesar considered. His pencil mustache disappeared behind a broad, gold-capped smile. "In that case, Señor Charlie, you pay me 1,000 now, and Don Mario 4,000 later."

What the hell. It was company money, publisher's peanuts. I spat co-caine mucus on to the sidewalk, hating Malcolm, hating myself, his dis-honest broker. Julio Cesar pocketed the bill like a cardsharp.

● ● ●

There were delays and detours, mainly connected with the cocaine that the wretched Jairo was trying to buy. There seemed to be some hitch. Mario had to confer with someone: it turned out to be a girl behind the counter at a Rapido-Burger joint on 10th Avenue. Then we had to return to El Gose Pagano, and wait some more, and drink some more, Jairo petulant, Julio Cesar slick and reassuring, Mario grimly courteous, the boss-cat of the group. Julio Cesar slipped off to make regular phone calls. No one answered and no one came. We waited, strung out between cup and lip, until finally the place was empty but for us, and the barman told us that even the salsa had to stop sometime, be sure and come back tomorrow.

Outside, damp gusts of rain, the moon balanced on a tree in a vacant lot. A few taxis cruised, always with someone riding shotgun in the passenger seat. We were going to Mario's lodgings a few blocks east of Caracas, to continue the assault course of drink and drugs. At some time I was going to get an interview: the great secrets of cocaine-making. Please God let me not pass out first.

Mario lived in a single, ground-floor room, just large enough for a double bed and a couple of chairs. He didn't seem to own much: a few clothes, a mirror, a couple of books by his bed: Castañeda, García-Márquez. The walls shrank in, encrusted with magazine photos. Heavy drapes hung over the window. Another shuttered room in Bogotá, another night in the half-lit burrows of the cocaine world.

At some point Mario mentioned something about going to a Turkish bath. This seemed an unlikely idea, but the time for likelihood was past. Julio Cesar put on the radio. Mario emerged from the bathroom. The *baño turco* was ready, he announced. He had a do-it-yourself steamer going, behind the shower curtain in the bathroom. He handed me and Jairo a pair of swimming trunks each. With as much dignity as possible in a cramped smoky room, with a pair of Bogotá street dealers lounging on the bed opposite, I removed my clothes and donned the trunks. They were too big for me, a faded pastel pattern of swirls on them. I took my turn after Jairo. It was impossibly hot inside the cocoon of the shower curtain, but the length of time one endured it seemed to be a point of honor, and Julio Cesar kept forcing me back in for more. A wad of eucalyptus leaves had been placed over the steamer. The raw, minty steam scoured my lungs. The sweat poured out of me. Why was I here?

Later there came a knock at the door, and a soft voice said, "It's Ana." She was a tall girl in tight jeans. She sat next to Mario on the bed. He held a *sucito* sacramentally for her to smoke. Jairo simpered at her, and at one point made some remark to her about how basuko made you feel sexy. Mario did not like this. He began to shout at Jairo. "You are my *guest* here, I treat you as a *friend*, but I do *not* give you the *right* to *talk* to her like that!" He lumbered up off the bed, thin and slow, the frown branded between his eyebrows. Jairo sat in his swimming trunks, quivering with fear, saying "Yes" and "No" like a scolded schoolboy. Julio Cesar said, "*Tranquilo!* Don Mario!" Ana studied her fingernails. I slipped away for another session in the Turkish bath.

When I came out, a miffed Jairo was just leaving, tucking his shirt in as he fumbled with the door handle. Mario ignored him imperiously. The door closed. A faint puff of fog licked my sweating skin. Mario said to me, "We can talk now." I wrapped a blanket around my shoulders, gathered some scraps of paper from my jacket, and settled down opposite him.

"I learned to cook cocaine in Cali, '68, '69. My first kitchen I built myself, up in the hills above the Rio Cauca, near a village called Las Animas—the Spirits. This is in the country of the Gumbianos. These are Indians that chew the coca leaf—well, a lot of them get drunk on *chicha*, but some still use the leaf. The Gumbianos are good, strong people. Few words, much patience. They prune the coca bush small, about a meter high. They call their bushes *ilyimera*, which in their language means 'little birds.'

"I was the first *blanco* to set up a cocaine kitchen in this area. At first they thought I was crazy. A Gumbiano who chews the leaf perhaps uses half a pound a week. I was going into markets and buying four *arrobas*— 100 pounds—of leaves at a time. In those days you could buy an *arroba* of coca for 50 pesos. With good leaves and good chemistry, 100 pounds of leaves will give you one pound of cocaine."

Mario spoke with slow, gruff precision. The voice was untroubled, but there was always a challenge in his eye. His beard jutted. He sent out jets of smoke through his nostrils like a cartoon bull.

There are, he explained, essentially two stages in the "cooking" of cocaine. *"De coca a pasta, y de pasta a perico."* From coca leaf to cocaine paste or base, and from cocaine paste to crystalline cocaine. The first is a simple process of extraction, which draws out vegetable alkaloids from the leaf. "The cocaine is hiding inside the leaf," said Mario.

There are many alkaloids in the coca leaf, but only one of them is the psychoactive substance benzoyl-methyl-ecgonine, known to the world as cocaine. The second, more complex stage of the cooking is designed to separate the cocaine from the other alkaloids, and to crystallize it into a salt.

"To make the *pasta* out of coca leaves is simple. You need kerosene, a quantity of sulphuric acid, and an alkali. For alkali you can use lime or sodium carbonate. I used the simplest of all: *potasa*." *Potasa*, or potash, is a crude form of potassium carbonate derived from vegetable ash. "Most of all, you need patience," he added.

"The first part of the operation is what we call *la salada*, the salting. Here you sprinkle and mix the potash into the leaves. If you are treating a big volume of leaves, you can do this in a pit lined with plastic sheeting. Otherwise you do it in an oil drum or plastic bucket. When you have salted the leaves you let them stand for a few hours. The potash makes them sweat. It starts to melt the alkaloids in the leaf.

"The second part is *la mojadura*, the soaking. This is when we pour the kerosene on the leaves, drown the coca. After soaking you must leave everything to steep for at least a day, better for thirty-six hours. While you wait, the potash is drawing out the alkaloids from the leaf. They float free in the kerosene.

"By the end of the second day you are ready to begin *la prensa*, the pressing. If you don't have a press, you use your feet. The purpose of *la prensa* is to get as much kerosene out of the leaves as possible. The kerosene is rich with the alkaloids. The leaves are dead now, black and rotten. You siphon off the kerosene into drums and throw away the leaves.

"The fourth stage is very delicate. This is when we take the alkaloids out of the kerosene and put them in water. This is done by pouring in water and sulphuric acid. Again you leave it, absolutely still, for a day. The acid takes the alkaloids out of the kerosene and dissolves them in the water. We call this part of the process *la guarapería*. At the end you have the kerosene on the top, the alkaloids underneath.

"Into the alkaloids you pour more potash. This makes them go milky-white. This is the first time the cocaine becomes visible.

"Now you are ready for the last part of the operation: *la secadería*, the drying. You can use a sheet, and dry it in the sun or under lightbulbs. You dry it until it is like moist clay. And so you have it: *la pasta de cocaína!*"

So far, so good. You have your cocaine paste, the greenish-gray sludge that is the building block of the whole cocaine racket. But what about the other half of the operation, the turning of *pasta* into pure cocaine, snorter's snow? This is where the real money lies. Here, however, I was to be disappointed. Perhaps Mario did not consider me worthy to enter this secret inner sanctum of cocaine chemistry. Perhaps I hadn't paid enough.

I tried to wheedle the process out of him, but he was tired of my questions. I decided I'd had my money's worth.

The moment I decided this I began to feel ill. A desperate, last-ditch concentration had held me together while Mario was discoursing. But all the while Julio Cesar had been quietly circulating *sucitos*, and shimmering around with the aguardiente like a butler. As I sat back I felt the blood drain from my face, and the low flame of liquor burning up and down my gullet.

Ana was curled up asleep on the bed. Mario woke her and told her to go and make some *tinto*. As she clambered off the bed she brushed against the heavy gray drape that hung over the window. A momentary stab of light passed through the room. My God, I thought, it's daylight out there. I've got to get out of this place. I got to my feet and began to totter back into my clothes.

It took me ages to extricate myself. First there was a scene about money. I gave Mario the agreed 4,000 for his information. He also wanted money for all the basuko we had plowed through. I had vaguely imagined this was on the house. But no, the account was totted up, a great reckoning in a little room. He would settle for another 2,000. I had nothing left in my pocket save the 11 pesos for the bus ride back to my hotel. Julio Cesar interposed. "Señor Charlie can give me the money later. Tonight, tomorrow, no problem."

Still Mario wouldn't let me go. He became aggressively solicitous. "You must take another *sucito*. You are my honored guest." His thin, powerful hand gripped my arm. I said how much I would like to stay, how interesting it had all been, but now I was tired and ill. "I really *must* be going," I said, absurdly plucking at my sleeve to look at the watch that wasn't there because you don't wear a watch when you're walking around Bogotá.

I stumbled out, the day glaring, the unremarkable street getting on with its morning chores. Three men tinkered beneath the hood of a pickup truck. I slunk furtively past them. A cat rooted in a trash can, arse-up, tail high, its big pink eye staring accusingly at me. My head throbbed wildly. I put my hand over my right eye, where the pain was worse. A wall which should have been three feet away came and hit me on the shoulder. I reeled back and trod in a dog turd. On Caracas Avenue, the cars moved with a jagged, deadly rhythm. Each of them seemed specially targeted on my brain. I got myself across, and boarded a southbound bus. Almost immediately I knew I was going to be sick. I lurched down the aisle, knocking an old man's newspaper out of his hands, and pushed back through the turnstile. The driver put me down, grumbling about people too lazy to walk 100 meters. I dodged up a side street. The patron saint of losers had put a vacant lot halfway down the street. Rubble, grass, litter. I went to the farthest corner of it and lay down. Now began the purgatorial period: what went down must come up. I vomited, I sweated, I vomited some more. I moaned and cursed. I promised the good Lord I'd give up everything—booze, cigarettes, drugs, damn fool cocaine stories—if only He'd let me sleep. Finally came the blessed fitful sleep, curled among the litter. A mazy fever dream in which I fell, spiraled, disappeared, like a drowning spider down a drain hole.

It was late afternoon when I got back to the hotel. The *portero* popped out from his diminutive office. His hair cream stirred unhappy memories of nausea in my stomach. "A message for you, *señor*," he cried, flourishing a scrap of paper.

I read the note with difficulty, partly because of the handwriting, partly because my eyes were not properly working yet. It read, *"Lola ha llegado y le pide telefonear."*

News of another world! A friend from London, Lola Aronson, an achingly beautiful Colombian girl married to an American. We had arranged to meet when she came with her children on her annual visit to see her family. I had left the number of my hotel with them when I arrived in Bogotá, and now she was here. I phoned her. "We're going to drive up and see my grandmother tomorrow," she said. "She lives in a little village—" she pronounced it "bee-lidge" "—in Boyacá. You'll love it, Charlie. Come to stay tonight. We set off tomorrow."

Slumped in a taxi I ran a jaundiced eye over the events of the last week. Gus, Julio Cesar, Rosalita, Mario. I had drunk, smoked and snorted myself into a state of near collapse, and for what? An earful of paranoid fantasies, a few old smuggling yarns, some half-baked cocaine recipes. Was this the Great Cocaine Story in the making?

In a pleasant, modern house in the shrubbed streets of the northern suburbs, I met the Cuadros family. They were courteous, gentle, normal. It was like coming up for air.

"Christ, Charlie, you look terrible," said Lola.

"A touch of fever," I said. "I'll be fine in the morning."

Her mother fussed around me with *manzanilla* tea and aspirins. I was tucked in bed. In the next room the family sat watching a quiz program called *Cabeza y Cola*. It was time to take a holiday.

CHAPTER TEN

Tensa Valley

Tio Juan drove the family Renault. His big hands rested, almost seeming to doze, on the steering wheel. A few miles out of Bogotá, the Autopista del Norte—the country's main arterial road, and the only overland route between its two largest cities—narrows into a pitted two-lane blacktop, choked with trucks belching up black smoke from their stovepipe exhausts. Tio Juan settled the car at a comfortable speed, around forty, and held it there against all comers.

There were eight of us in the Renault. Taking Lola as the family reference point, there were her uncle Juan, her mother Ana, and her nephew Andrecito, a dark, quiet boy of eight, in the front. Her niece Nydia, eleven, her son Sam, five, and her eleven-month-old baby Marco were with us in the back. We were off to see Abuelita, Lola's granny, Juan and Ana's mother: eighty-three years old next week, still living in the village of Tensa where they were born, in the hills of rural Boyacá, *el jardín de Colombia*.

For a while the sprawling, scabby outskirts of Bogotá clung to the highway, a ribbon of shacks and small factories, flower stalls and *fritanga* stalls. Lola pointed out Altogrande, the president's edge-of-town weekend retreat, a glimpse of white walls and red tiles surrounded by eucalyptus. A single sentry was on guard at the gate. Sam knelt up on the seat to get a better look at his machine gun. Soon the countryside widened around us. Here the big landowners had their dairy herds, stud farms and *haciendas*. Black and white Holsteins grazed on the brilliant green savanna. On either side of the flat valley floor rose bottle-green, black-ridged mountains. Clouds were banking over the range to our left, but when we came to a fork in the road—left to Zipaquira, right to Tunja—we took the right. Both these towns were once seats of the Chibcha kings, or *zipas*, who ruled these high tablelands before the Spaniards came. The Chibchas were farmers, traders and sun-worshipers. They traded with lowland and coastal Indians: salt, emeralds and woven blankets in exchange for gold, cotton, parrots and seashells. They were puzzled by the Spaniards' obsession with crosses: to them, two crossed sticks signified the grave of someone who had died from snakebite.

We climbed in brilliant sunshine. The air grew thinner and chiller. This was highland Colombia now. Huge flanks of hillside studded with willow and eucalyptus. Tall *cajicá* grass, black rocks, fast rivers, and the big Andean sky. Down behind us the vast Guatavita reservoir basked in the sunlight. Beneath it lies the drowned village of Guatavita, sacrificed a few years ago in the interests of hydroelectric power. The authorities built a replacement village, Nueva Guatavita, a few miles away, an impressive mix of traditional colonial and modernistic styles, but most of the evacuees from the old village refused to live there, and the place is mostly a showpiece and souvenir-market for weekending Bogotanos.

There is also an "old" Guatavita lake, a much smaller body of water a few miles east, in a dramatic Andean stronghold. It is the Laguna de Guatavita, also known as the Lago de Amor, a lagoon half a mile in diameter, set in an almost perfectly circular crater in the mountains, as still and symmetrical as a giant bowl of green-gray milk. Beneath its waters lies the treasure of Eldorado.

Though the legend of Eldorado tells of a fabulous city of gold, Eldorado was not originally a place, but a person—*el dorado*, the gilded man. He was the central figure in a rite performed by the Chibchas here at this sacred lake, a kind of coronation ceremony, performed at the appointment of a new *cacique*, or chieftain. At the shores of the lagoon he was stripped naked, anointed with sticky resin, and sprayed with gold dust. A raft of reeds was prepared, with braziers of *moque* incense and piles of gold and jewels on it. The gilded chieftain lay on the raft; with four other principal *caciques*, he floated out to the center of the lagoon, to the accompaniment of flutes and drums. When the raft reached the center, the chieftain dove into the lake, washing off the gold, and all the offerings of gold and jewels were thrown into the water.

As soon as the Spaniards learned of the rites of the gilded man, they reasoned that there must be a fantastic store of gold and precious objects beneath the lagoon. The first of many attempts to drain the lake was made about 1545, by Hernán Pérez de Quesada, brother of Jiminez de Quesada, the co-founder of Bogotá. Using a bucket brigade of Indian laborers with gourd jars, he succeeded in lowering the level of the water by some ten feet, enough to recover about 3,000 *pesos* of gold. Forty years later a more ambitious project was set in motion by a rich Bogotano merchant, Antonio de Sepulveda. With a workforce of 8,000 Indians, he carved a great notch in the rim of the lake to channel the water away. He got the level down by 60 feet, recovering many golden ornaments and gems, including an emerald "the size of a hen's egg." One day, however, the walls of the cut subsided, killing many workers, and Sepulveda's scheme was abandoned.

It was not until the early years of this century that the lake was completely drained, but even then the Guatavita jinx struck. In 1899 a British joint-stock company, Contractors Ltd., drilled a tunnel under the lake and up into the center, and the water was sluiced away down this giant drain hole, with mercury screens to trap any precious objects. But the exposed lake bed was covered with several feet of soft mud and slime, and was impossible to walk on. The following day the sun baked the mud to concrete. Drilling equipment was hauled up from Bogotá, but to no avail. The mud had clogged the sluices and sealed up the tunnel, and slowly but surely the lagoon filled up again with water. Twenty years ago the Colombian government passed laws to protect the lagoon. The central area remains untouched to this day, and how much of Eldorado's treasure it contains is anyone's guess.

We came down out of the wind, into the hotter, dustier slopes of western Boyacá. Little pink-washed *fincas* huddled in the lee of the hill, shaded by dark mango, smothered with bright bougainvillea. As the road wound down there was always something just below us, a rooftop, a farmyard, the shiny green canopy of a banana grove. We wound the windows down for the heat, then up again for the dust. A pair of grubby little boys ran out as the car approached. One of them aimed a stone as we passed, but Tio Juan jammed on the brakes and swung around to fix the boy with such a fierce, bullish stare that he froze in mid-aim.

This is the subtropical *tierra templada*, the fortunate zone of the Andes, halfway between the bleaker highlands of the *tierra fría* and the humid swamps and jungles of the *tierra cálida*. Here it is hot, fresh and fertile, near enough to the equator to keep the air sweet and warm even up to 7,000 or 8,000 feet. There are only two seasons, a nine- to ten-month dry season and a two- to three-month rainy season. In Boyacá the rains come around May. It was February now, the end of the dry season, but it all looked lush to me, with many fast rivers. Some of the trees in the valley had lost their leaves, so the woods below us had a grayish look, with rivers glinting through a haze of tangled scrub, but always there was some tree in flower, scarlet *ceiba* or the brilliant yellow, daffodil-like *araguaney*. In these semi-tropical woodlands something is always growing while something else is dying.

We stopped to rest at Guateque. The air was brilliant in the central square with its wedding-cake church in pink and white. In a little shop we drank *tintos* and ate slabs of white Boyacense cheese, not unlike mozzarella, wrapped around plugs of guava jelly, *bocadillo*, a great Colombian favorite. Outside in the neat gardens of the square, men in trilbies and checkered wool *ruanas* strolled among the pollarded trees. Bogotá was rinsed away in these splashes of light. "This is the real Colombia," said Lola. Sam sat on a sack of flour drinking fizzy red *gaseosa*. Tio Juan bought me a bottle of beer. I tried to pay, but he physically restrained me. "This is my land," he said. "You're our guest here." I said I would do the same for him in England, and we laughed because we knew it would never be so.

Finally we arrived at Tensa, a small, self-contained village, a deep-rooted grid of dusty whitewashed houses and precipitous streets. Abuelita's house was at the lower end of the village, a couple of blocks from the market, a couple of blocks from the square, a couple of blocks from just about everything. She came to the door, raising her hands as if in surprise, though she had been waiting all morning for us. She was short and slightly crooked, but looked very strong. She greeted everyone in a slow motion of delight, her children, grandchildren and great-grandchildren, shaking Marco's sleepy fingers with her big, spatulate hands. She had a thick growth of slate-gray hair tied back in a bunch, a brown dress with a brooch at the bosom, gold earrings and a flash of gold in her smile. She would be eighty-three next week: *"nacida con el siglo,"* born with the century.

The sun bounced off the pale streets. Three men stood outside the *tienda* at the corner, drinking beer from the bottle. Three saddled horses were parked in a row beside them. We went in through her front door, dark green paint bleached and flaked by the sun, and down a shady passageway into a small sloping patio filled with pots of busy lizzie and morning glory. A stone walkway ran around the patio. At the upper end it was about three feet up off the yard, so designed for provendering your horse, having ridden it in through the passageway, which used to be higher to allow for this. There was a bench on this high part, looking down over the yard and the roofs below, over the papaya and orange trees in the neighbor's garden, out across to the broad tawny slopes on the other side of the valley. "It is very primitive," said Lola's mama, not unkindly, simply stating the fact, and Abuelita laughed, smiling at her brood. *"Sí, aquí ya estamos como siempre,"* she said. We're the same as always here.

Over the next hour I seemed to meet that half of Tensa village that was actually related to Abuelita, and several other, unrelated villagers who just happened to be dropping by. Someone brought in a crate of beer, which

Tio Juan dispensed. Mama introduced me to her plump, jolly sister, Tia Cecilia; to cousins Miguel and Maurizio, both in jeans; to Señora Fadul, whoever exactly she was. *"Ay! Rosalbita! Mi chiquitica!"* cried Mama, sweeping a little girl in pigtails into her arms. I shook hard hands and soft hands and little hands that bobbed and curtsied.

Later the crowd thinned, and cooking smells came from the kitchen. The men and boys ate first, the table being only big enough for four: chicken with *ají*—a piquant sauce of chili and coriander—and potatoes.

In the afternoon Lola and I strolled around the market. She gaily bargained over pomegranates, mangoes, honey-berries. All the delights of the tropical orchard were there, in a hubbub of stalls under a high, echoing tin roof. I was amazed by the variety of potatoes—*papas de primera, tocanas, tuquerreñas*, a whole range from giant boulder-shaped tubers down to the tiny sweetish potatoes, as yellow as a yolk inside, called *papas criollas*. We jostled through, trailing kids laden with more and more fruit. Outside, the stalls straggled on around a small dusty arena, the village bullring. *Fritangas* were being served at low trestles: sausages, pork-scratchings, black pudding. Fires hissed under haunches of beef. Amid the smoke and noise and general milling there were little islands of stillness—a brightly dressed Indian *campesina* sitting motionless beside a tall rickety tower of baskets, a baby asleep on her back, a bored parrot hunched on its perch at the bird-catcher's stall. Though the place was still busy, all the important transactions, the big sales of wheat and potatoes, had been done in the early morning. There was still some business going on, out where the slatted flatbed trucks were being loaded. A farmer and a wholesaler were arguing loudly about the weight of some sacks of barley. The *romanador* was called for, the official weighmaster of the municipality. He was dressed much like the other *campesinos*, but after he had set up his ancient scales, he donned a pair of wire-rimmed spectacles as a kind of badge of office. The bushels were weighed and pronounced a fair weight, and they all repaired for *tronches*, the traditional exchange of drinks to finalize a deal.

Later we took the kids for a swim. A long, steep, cobbled pathway ran from the village to the river, canopied by an avenue of high *palo verde* trees. From the other side of the valley it looked like a long green tail hanging from the body of the village. It had rough stone steps, with a wider dirt track beside it for horses and mules. At the bottom were small well-to-do summer houses, with the feathered straw thatch of the region hanging over the gables like a sheep dog's shaggy fringe. An orange path threaded through the greenery to a cove, where a pair of big rocks formed a pool. Three girls were washing there. There were squawks and giggles and hasty buttonings as I hove into view. The girls were shampooing their hair, like teenagers across the civilized world, ready for Saturday night. I said I hoped I wasn't disturbing them, *"Espero que no les moleste,"* and there was more laughter and some cheeky byplay on the word *molestar*. One of the girls was unbelievably pretty. She was squeezing the suds out of her hair. I headed swiftly into the deepest and coolest reach of the pool, and there was Lola glistening like a river goddess, laughing that wide, breathless swimmer's laugh. Later we basked up on one of the rocks. The three nymphs had gone, draped in towels. Sam was organizing a game of pirates on a half-submerged tree trunk, with Andrecito and Rosalbita playing along in a confused way. I found myself leaning on an elbow, looking down into Lola's face. She must have seen the danger signals. She gave a sweet smile, rolled away onto her tummy, and said how much she wished Luke was here—her husband—he did so love river-swimming.

The days slid by, bright days and steamy days, picnics beside big rivers, oranges fresh from the tree, morning mists and evening promenades, and even a horse ride or two. There were trips. To Garagoa, where I purchased a black Boyacense trilby in the market. To La Capilla with Tia Cecilia, to get her false tooth fitted: this had taken so long to happen that "Aunt Cecilia's false tooth" had become a family catch-phrase for the slow expectancies of country life. A day at a cousin's farm the other side of the valley, the sunned village neat below us, roofs and gardens, lanes and squares, and the dusty cemetery off to one side, patiently waiting.

By night I slept at the Casa de Campesinos on the edge of the village, a hostel administered by the church, 100 pesos a night for an impeccable little whitewashed cell, eight by six, one small hard bed, one small table, four pegs on the wall to hang your clothes on, and a cross painted in pale blue on the stucco wall. There were a score of these rooms running around three sides of the courtyard. All the ones I peeked into were exactly the same as mine, except that in each the cross was painted in a different way. Mine was in the form of saucers, each made of three concentric circles: five saucers for the horizontal line, seven for the vertical.

It had to end. On the morning we were to leave I awoke to the sound of a radio very loud below my window. The music was something marvelous, dueling up-tempo guitars under a racing vocal line full of long-held shouts. This wild melody was cowboy music, *música llanera*, from the great grass plains which cover the east of Colombia.

There were scores of goodbyes. Abuelita graciously assured me that her house would always be my *ranchito*. "You are a Boyacense now," she said, glancing mischievously at my dusty black hat. A titter ran around, broadening into a communal guffaw. The Englishman in the hat had earned his small place in the family mythology.

We arrived in Bogotá late in the afternoon. There was a jam coming off the *autopista*, apoplectic traffic policemen blowing whistles, the dull shimmer of monoxide. Back in Toothgrind City. A week's stubble, a funny black hat and a heartful of cowboy music were all that remained of Tensa valley.

CHAPTER ELEVEN

Rikki Sings

With deep reluctance I took stock once more of the Great Cocaine Story. According to my original plans I should have been up on the Caribbean coast by now, where the smugglers were: Santa Marta, Cartagena, the hidden coves and airstrips of the Guajira. It was time to forget those bleak, basuko-crazed nights in Bogotá, file them away under the generous heading of "background research." Lola's husband Luke would be flying into Colombia in a few days' time; her brother Alberto was in bad need of a holiday. Why didn't we all drive up to the coast together? It was a soft option, a few more days of company and security, and I was all in favor.

In the meantime I had one more lead to chase up in Bogotá. I hadn't seen Gus since the night he had told me about Snow White. It was quite likely that Julio Cesar was right—that Gus's story about the Snow White syndicate was just another of his paranoid ravings. But what if it wasn't? I owed it to myself—and, yes, to Gus—to check it out. Only this time, I promised myself, I would keep my nose clean, my motives ulterior, and learn what I could by stealth. In this world, as Rosalita had observed, everyone is living a lie.

Dan Kreitman—the American who, according to Gus, had a cocaine source connected with Snow White—had his gold and precious stone store, Galería Pecadillo, up in Chapinero, a pleasant mid-town district full of clothes shops and town houses. I found the place in a basement off 13th Avenue, unobtrusive to the point of exclusiveness. The door was opened by a small, pretty girl. Inside it was hushed, cool and softly lit, and crammed to the brim with pre-Columbian artifacts and jewelry. A long-nosed American in glasses was inspecting some gold work which a fat Colombian woman was showing him. "Be with you in a minute," he said. "My assistant will show you around." She showed me golden pendants and pectorals, nose rings and lip plugs, strange little stone whistles shaped like birds' heads, priapic figurines and many beautiful necklaces and bracelets of Tairona stone: agate, jasper, jadite, quartz, coral, turquoise. I liked her cool, precise movements, her soft voice. Everything was done in whispers here. She told me she had been in England a year ago. She didn't look Colombian at all. She wore a chic blouson, had carefully ruffled mouse-brown hair. Her name was Daniela.

The man in the glasses, who was Dan Kreitman, was writing out a check in an enormous checkbook. The fat lady watched him intently, hand cupped around her chin, a long red fingernail nervously flicking at the flab under her eye. She was selling reproduction gold—three washes over a copper base—to hang on the Tairona stone necklaces. After she had left

I chatted with Kreitman about his jewelry, and about the book I was writing "about Colombia." He was voluble. He had lived in Colombia for fifteen years and knew every corner of the country. "I've eaten anteater stew in Amazonas, iguana stew on the coast, guinea pig stew in Bucaramanga, and I've lived to tell the tale," he said jovially. He talked out of the side of his mouth, his eyes narrow behind the wire-rim specs, more a knowing glint than a twinkle. The red telephone on his desk rang. He spoke a few words in Spanish—fluently but with a New Jersey accent. Then, in English, "Ambassador? How are you today, sir?"

While he was on the phone the door-buzzer went. Daniela unlocked the bolts and catches that kept Bogotá at bay. A pair of American women came in, one blond, pale and pregnant, with her sunglasses up on her head, the other sharp, sexy and anorexic. They were diplomats' wives. Colombia is a "hardship placement," they told me—more money, shorter stay, fortified apartments. They browsed among the artifacts with knowing, delicate fingers. The anorexic one tried on a $500 necklace in coral and quartz. "I must bring Bill in here," she murmured, striking poses in the mirror. From somewhere out back a Colombian woman appeared. This was Kreitman's wife Claudia, a tall, raven-haired beauty from Palmira. She had a big, toothy, cocaine user's smile, and great tangles of jewelry around her neck and wrists. The anorexic lady admired her mauve dress, "But I think the color mauve means you're insecure."

I sat back, enjoying the plush feel of the armchair, the gentle hush of money all around me. The diplomatic ladies prattled on. One had found a new masseuse, "very reasonable." The water had been cut off for the second time this week. They called the national airline "Avi-nunca" instead of Avianca—*nunca* meaning never. I watched Daniela threading agates on a wire: red cornelian, orange sard, apple-green chrysoprase. She smiled at me, made a conspiratorial face behind their backs. The pregnant one bought a Tumaco figure, a Valentine present for her husband.

It transpired that I was out of luck as far as Kreitman was concerned. He was busy that day, and the following morning he and his wife were flying to Miami on business. There was no chance at all to wheedle myself into any information about his cocaine source. But I did ask Daniela if she would come for a drink with me. Not this evening, she said, but tomorrow. There was a play she wanted to see at the Teatro Nacional. Perhaps we could go together.

Daniela Duarte—she shared the maiden name of Eva Perón—lived with her family in a smart white apartment block with tinted windows, up the plush end of 15th Avenue, near Unicentro. I was met by a young, mustachioed smoothie—Daniela's brother, Ricardo. "My friends call me Rikki." He wore jeans and an American bowling shirt, standard issue for the young bourgeois of Bogotá, even down to the pack of Marlboros in the breast pocket. Daniela was still getting ready, he said, flicking his eyes to the ceiling as if to say, "These women!"

We perched uncomfortably on a white sofa. Everything was very polished and just-so, ashtrays too smart for ash, cushions too neat for bottoms. Rikki was soon to leave Bogotá, he told me. He was going to San Andrés, Colombia's island resort off the Caribbean coast. He had landed a job as regional manager for an American company importing air compressors and conditioners. He would have a house by the sea, lots of sun, money, women. His real ambition was to be a pilot. "All my friends are pilots," he said.

Daniela and I took a bus south, and drank some brandy in a café. The Teatro Nacional was not at all the venerable, neo-Classical institution that the name somehow suggested, but small and modern. It smelled of paint and new wood. The play was *The Hostage* by Brendan Behan, a Colombian production of an Irish play with a redheaded Argentinian actress, Fanny Mikey, giving a spirited performance as Meg. In the intermission we met a friend of Daniela's, a painter called Garzón, and afterward we went back to his apartment, met his wife and various friends, and drank a great deal of Chivas Regal whiskey, at $50 a bottle, something of a status symbol. Garzón was an artist with a capital *A*, very melodramatic. His paintings were big, overblown canvases, with grotesque figures in attitudes of pain, madness and beggary. He forgave me for being a gringo because I was a writer, a fellow Artist.

We took a taxi back to Daniela's apartment on 15th. She snuggled up to me in the back seat, whiskey on her breath, scented hair. An unmarried twenty-one-year-old, middle-class girl is one of two things in Catholic Colombia—a virgin or a whore. It would be a kiss and a cuddle, and thank you, goodnight. Vaguely hoping otherwise, I accepted her invitation for a cup of coffee. Daniela put music on the cassette, very low for fear of waking mama and papa down the hall. We were on the white sofa together when we heard the faint thud of the elevator doors in the corridor. A key turned in the lock, and in swayed Rikki.

He looked pretty drunk, and from the way he was grinding his teeth he had probably been on the snort as well. "How'd the party go?" asked Daniela. Rikki shrugged. He poured himself a large Scotch from a cabinet of cut-glass decanters.

"I didn't go to the party," he said. He sat down on the sofa between us, drained his glass and bounced straight up again. Pouring the second shot clumsily, he chipped the top of the decanter.

"Rikki!" breathed Daniela in a tired, admonitory whisper. She was three years younger and 10 inches shorter, but there was no doubt who was the stronger of the two. "Take it easy," she soothed. "What's up with you?"

He cradled the glass nervously in his hands. "You know," he said evasively.

"Orlando?"

Rikki nodded. "He needs the money real bad, Dani. He needs it yesterday." He checked himself. The facile charm clicked back into place for a moment. "Sorry, Charlie. Money problems. It's the same in England, no?"

I assured him it was.

Rikki went off down the corridor to take a pee. I asked Daniela what the problem was. She shook her head ruefully. "It's nothing, really. A bad debt. He wants me to borrow the money off our father. Papa won't give Rikki any more money."

"He told me he'd gotten a job up in San Andrés. Can't he pay it off then?"

"It's a bad business. You know, drugs. Rikki's been dealing on credit. He was getting stuff from an old friend. Small stuff, but it mounts up. Now his friend's got to collect. I'm worried, Charlie. Rikki..."

She trailed off. Rikki was returning. But it was only to say goodnight. "I'll talk to Papa tomorrow," she said to him. "We'll work something out." He plodded off down the corridor.

Daniela stood up. "It's late. Thank you for a lovely evening, and now I must go to bed." She was fussing around with the ashtrays and glasses. I put my coat on. Then I had a sudden thought.

"It's cocaine, is it?"

"What? Oh, Rikki. Yes, he was selling cocaine."

"Did he sell it to Dan Kreitman?"

She gave a half-laugh, a little snort of surprise. She couldn't think why I was asking, but she answered just the same. "Sure. Dan bought coke from Rikki a few times. But..."

"It's nothing. Forget it. Yes, it's been a lovely evening. I'll call you." We kissed in the doorway, a lingering teenage kiss. But as the steel doors of the elevator puffed shut, it was Rikki, not Daniela, I was thinking of. Was he the Snow White connection?

The following day, around five in the afternoon, I called up the Duarte apartment from a phone booth on 15th Avenue. As I had hoped, Rikki answered. "Is Daniela there?" I asked, knowing full well that she didn't knock off at Kreitman's *galería* till five. "Pity," I said, when he told me she wasn't. "I'm in the area, thought I might... Do you fancy a drink or something?"

"Sure, why not?" said Rikki. He asked me where I was.

"Fifteenth and 102nd," I told him. A couple of blocks north, he said, I would see a cocktail bar called The Place on the left-hand side. He'd meet me there in ten minutes.

The Place was Rikki all over. Chrome-flashed American-style bar, pricey tariff on little laminated cards on the table, tabletop computer games in one corner, loud, vapid Californian rock Muzak. Rikki strolled in, neat and coiffed, and joined me at a corner table. He had the look of a man who had risen late and dressed at leisure. There was a fresh red shaving nick on his dimpled chin.

We drank Jim Beam bourbon. He chatted about his new job in San Andrés, his plans to learn flying, his many girlfriends. He liked to talk, to image himself: smooth, man of the world Rikki. I let him talk. The looser the better. Underneath the patter I could see the worries of the previous night simmering. His bitten-nailed fingers fidgeted with the swizzle stick, the lacy paper coaster, the ashtray. I ordered more drinks. While he was at the bar buying cigarettes, I tipped most of my drink into his glass. A girl opposite saw me do this. She was wearing sunglasses, but I saw her eyebrows raise. We exchanged half-smiles, and she touched the side of her nose: if I wanted to spike my friend's drink it was none of *her* business. *Así es en Bogotá*. Her sunglasses and long hair made me think for a moment of Nancy, back at the Fruit Palace. This time around it was me playing the false cards.

When I saw the red spots on Rikki's cheekbones, and heard for the third time his opinion that Brazilian girls were the hottest in bed, I decided it was time. A convenient lull came. I said, "Sorted out your money problems, have you?"

His mouth twisted ruefully. "Not really. It's a bitch. I tell you, Charlie. Never do business with a friend. I'm sorry about last night—it got on top of me."

"Can't you borrow the money?"

He shook his head. "The only person I can borrow from is my father, and the bastard won't give me a *centavo*!"

"I might be able to help you."

He was lighting a cigarette. His blue eyes, faintly reddened by bourbon, bulged up at me through the smoke. "Help me?"

"How much do you owe?"

"Two thousand U.S."

I tried to look like this was a mere bauble, a drop in my financial ocean. Deep preconceptions ran in my favor: in Colombia all gringos are assumed to be loaded unless proved otherwise. "Two thousand," I murmured. I jotted a calculation on a paper napkin, playing it slow. I looked him in the face. "And . . . your job. When do you start, did you say?" Next month, he said. "And you could repay me . . . ?"

"Right away," he said, with a magnanimous spread of his palms. "No problem, Charlie. I get three months' salary in advance." I guessed he was lying, but that was the least of my worries.

The girl in the sunglasses was leaving: I wasn't quite sure, but I think she winked at me. I said, with a sigh of decision, "I'll lend you the money, Rikki. For a friend. Of course you'll want cash. It'll have to be tomorrow.

There's a man I know behind the Tequendama: he'll cash me in dollars. You'll have the bills by midday!''

Rikki closed his eyes, clenched his fist till the knuckles ran white. He gripped my arm, awash in sentiment. "Man," he said. "I can't believe it. You're so... Charlie, you're like a brother to me!" His face clouded for a moment. The unanswered question bobbed back into view. "You'll want interest of course?" he said. "What sort of percentage are you...?"

I shook my head, smiling. "I don't need interest, Rikki. Like I said, you're a friend. No, all I want is... to talk."

"Talk?" He laughed nervously. "Sure, Charlie. We'll talk."

He was really beginning to think he'd landed a prize one: a gringo throwing dollars around in exchange for *company*! He put his hand on my shoulder, shaking his head in amiable disbelief. "I *love* to talk," he cried.

The time was now. "Good," I said. "Well, let's begin by talking about Snow White."

His eyes flickered, a wince of unexpected pain. He shook his head, marshaled an effortful, empty smile. "You're shitting me, Charlie. I don't know what you mean. No, *hombre*. Hey..." He trailed off, pale and reproachful. I knew I was right, and Gus was right. Snow White *wasn't* just a figment.

"Snow White cocaine," I said quietly. "Your friend Orlando works for the syndicate they call Snow White. He's been giving you bits to sell on credit. Now they're calling in the checks. That's about it, isn't it?"

"Shit!" said Rikki, too loud. A couple of waiters looked over from the shiny chrome bar. "*Hijo de puta!* You some fucking narc?" He stood up, tipping his chair to the floor, took a last startled, angry look at me, and began to walk out. I skipped after him. A waiter from the bar and the big man who ruled the cash register moved too, anxious to remind us that we owed for six large bourbons. We all met in a huddle by the door. People were looking up from the tables. I grabbed Rikki's denim shirt. "You want the money, Rikki, or you want to walk out? It's up to you." He jerked his arm away angrily, but the big man was blocking the door and he hadn't anywhere to go. "It's all right, Rikki," I soothed. "Come and sit down. I'll explain."

We trooped back to our table; the big man returned to the till; the waiter brought us two more bourbons, and pointedly slapped the bill down on the table. I lit a cigarette and saw that my hand was trembling.

"I'm not a narc, Rikki," I explained gently. "I'm just an ordinary, nosy journalist. I know something about Snow White, and I want to know more. It's only a story, that's all."

Rikki shook his head. "You'll get us both killed. You don't know *nothing* about this!" He gulped at the bourbon. A little amber rivulet leaked down his clean-shaven chin.

"No one will know," I urged. "Just a few simple questions. Two thousand dollars, Rikki."

He sagged. He was beaten. I felt a surge of remorse. Buying someone's blood and running off without paying: how low could I get? The answer, had I but known it, was plenty lower.

"What do you want to know?" he asked sulkily, stabbing his swizzle stick into our overflowing ashtray.

"The who, the how and the why," I said. "Let's start with who. Who the hell *is* Snow White? Who's Mr. Big?"

It was a bad question to begin with, because it was the one he was least likely to be able to answer. He arranged himself into the full-dress Colombian shrug. "*Hombre*. How do I know? Look, you got me wrong. OK, I laid off an ounce here and there for Orlando. It was the best merchandise in town. But who's *running* this show? Look, Charlie, the big people, the *capos*—they don't have names, they don't have faces. And if they do, you forget them pretty damn quick. You remember that, *escritorzuelo*!"

"All right. We'll do an easier one. How do they operate? How does the pipeline work?" He was shaking his head, ready to play his dumb card again. But I had a better card. "Look, Rikki. You told Dan Kreitman they were bringing 100 kilos a week into Bogotá, regular as clockwork. So I know you know about it."

This knocked Rikki back a bit. I could see his mind clicking: he must be thinking that Kreitman himself had marked my card. *"Carne,"* he said in a tired, flat voice.

"Meat? What do you mean, meat?"

"That's the cover, Charlie, all down the line." He lit a cigarette and leaned closer across the table. At last we were getting somewhere. "They've got a big, big cattle ranch. Hacienda Alaska. Thousands of hectares, down in the *llanos*, Meta department. The *pasta* comes in by riverboat somewhere near Leticia. The *pasta* is the very best, made from Bolivian leaves, Huanaco coca from the Yungas. Then it's flown up to Hacienda Alaska. That's where the processing is done. The chief cook is a German, a brilliant chemist. Snow White stuff is the best, Charlie. They bring it up to Bogotá in cattle trucks. There's cattle coming up from the *llanos* all the time. They've got a fleet of a dozen trucks: thirty, forty head of cattle in each, and a couple of sacks of Snow White cocaine."

There was a break in the Muzak. Rikki stopped, looked around nervously. A new record was put on: daddy-cool disco music this time.

"So where does it come in?" I asked, anxious to keep him flowing.

"Matadero San Felipe. It's a slaughterhouse in the north of the city. That's the drop."

"Then what happens?"

"It's very neat. The stuff comes in with the cows and it goes out with the meat. Refrigerated trucks, frozen beef, lot of legal snow and ice to hide it in. I don't exactly know how it's done, but that's the general idea."

"So that's how they export it, hidden in with frozen meat?"

"I think so. Look, Charlie, I'm just going on things Orlando told me. Jesus, if he ever knows about this, I'll..."

"Don't worry, Rikki. I've told you: no one's going to know anything."

How did they organize the distribution in Bogotá itself, I asked. He shook his head. "*Quién sabe?* I think they've got some meat-wholesaling scam. That's just a guess. Christ, Charlie: you need a goddamn crystal ball, you do."

That really was it. I tried to get some names out of him, but if he knew he wasn't saying. I had scraped the bottom of his barrel. All this lying for a few jottings on a paper napkin....

I wouldn't be writing this now if I hadn't had a bit of luck every now and then. That night I was lucky because I wouldn't have learned a thing about Snow White if I'd waited even ten more minutes before stinging Rikki. We were having a last, consoling drink before parting. I had given Rikki the $100 bill I usually carried, separate from my pesos, for emergencies. I was renewing my empty promises to pay him the rest the next morning. The muffled cries of my conscience, gagged and bound in some cerebral cupboard, grew louder. Then I saw two men out on the sidewalk, now dark, looking in through the plate-glass frontage of the bar. They were staring straight at Rikki and me.

Rikki followed my gaze. He stumbled to his feet, muttering half to himself, half to the face in the window, "Orlando!" They were coming through the door now. Rikki twisted back at me fiercely. "You keep your fucking mouth shut!" he hissed. And then he was going toward them, hand out, "Orlando, *qué tal, amigo*!" I quickly slipped the paper napkin in my pocket.

Orlando was sleek and smooth. He wore a camel-hair overcoat over his shoulders, an open-neck white shirt gleaming beneath it. He had tight ringlets of black hair, coffee-colored skin, Gucci shoes and a gold bangle on his wrist. He looked like a million dollars, every one of them blue. Here at last was the cocaine racket in its finery: up to now, I realized, I had seen only the victims. The man with him was more sinister: fat, shiny, slant-eyed, a Guajiro perhaps. He wore a sky-blue linen suit, expensive too, but creased at the crotch and grubbied at the pockets. His black spiky hair was cut short.

On the surface things seemed amicable enough. Rikki introduced me as "a friend of Dani's." Orlando flashed a smooth smile as we shook hands. Rikki didn't seem to know the other one, and Orlando didn't introduce us. I made to shake hands, but he just nodded. I felt the hooded inscrutable eyes case me for a moment. He looked like Oddjob, the Oriental heavy in the James Bond story, *Goldfinger*. He looked like he could damage people in quiet, special ways. I thought of Gus up a dead-end alley in Perseverancia. My mind raced. Could they know? Did it somehow show? Would

Rikki tell them? I slid my hand into my jacket pocket and balled the napkin tight in my fist.

"We'd like a word, Rikki," said Orlando, smiling again. That smile was like a part of his wardrobe.

"I was just going," I said, getting to my feet too fast, clicking my fingers for the waiter, fumbling for pesos to pay the bill. Orlando laid a hand lightly on my shoulder: a whiff of cologne, a thousand-dollar emerald on his ring finger.

"*Tranquilo, señor.* Finish your drink. Rikki's coming with us." The smile widened. "We're going to a party. Isn't that right, Rikki?" Rikki nodded. Oddjob looked on silently, with an eye trained to spot trouble before it starts to get troublesome.

Rikki obediently gathered his cigarettes and prepared to leave. He said to me—casually, but with a meaningful glance—"We'll meet here at midday tomorrow, then?" I nodded dumbly. The Confucian eye of Oddjob seemed to know all my secrets. Goodbyes were said, Orlando's with practiced charm, Rikki's with another warning glance, Oddjob's with the merest nod, a momentary rearrangement of eyebrows and chins.

I let myself sit absolutely still for a moment, then I paid the bill and walked to the door. I could see them across the street, climbing into a white Mercedes. Oddjob eased the car off the curb and into the fast-moving southbound traffic.

I was still standing there a couple of minutes later, feeling the cool air on my face, when Daniela came up. She was breathless from running. "Charlie!" she said in surprise. Then: "Is Rikki here with you? The maid said he left to meet a friend here. I thought it was Orlando." I told her Rikki had just gone, with Orlando and his ape. "Shit!" said Daniela.

"He's going to be all right, isn't he? I didn't like the look of Orlando's friend much."

"I hope so. I mean, Orlando's an old friend, but . . . That's it, you see. I wanted to tell them. I've persuaded Papa—it took some doing. He's going to bail Rikki out one last time. You know, that money business?"

I stared at her. So Rikki the weasel was going to get his money after all. "I'm so happy," I said in relief.

She laughed, her faced cocked prettily. "You're a funny guy," she said. "I really didn't think you liked Rikki much last night."

CHAPTER TWELVE

One Arroba over the Top

Gus McGregor was on the mend. His leg was still heavily bandaged but he was moving around more freely. He seemed calmer, too. He had even ventured down the street a couple of times to make phone calls at the bar on the corner. He was just about ready, as he put it, to come out of quarantine.

I told him about Rikki and what he'd told me: the processing plant at Hacienda Alaska, the drop at the San Felipe slaughterhouse, the frozen-meat export cover. He listened intently. "Meat," he said steelily. "I was right. It *was* a bloody butcher's knife that bastard tried to rearrange me with."

Gus was pleased but he was also frustrated. "So what's our next move?" he asked quietly.

I felt it was time to tell him. "Look, sorry, Gus. I came to tell you this, but also I came to say goodbye. I'm driving up to the coast in a couple of days' time with some friends."

He looked aghast. "You're not walking out on this story *now*, are you? Look, we're three-quarters of the way there, but three-quarters of a story makes sweet fuck all. Nothing will come of nothing. Think again, Charlie, old cock."

"Well, I'm not quite sure what ... I'm certain Rikki's told me everything. What do you suggest?"

"It's obvious, isn't it? You get your arse up to the Matadero San Felipe, and do some sniffing around!"

"But I told you," I protested, "I'm leaving for the coast."

"When are you going?"

"Friday."

"So? It's only—well, what day is it today, in fact?"

"Tuesday," I admitted.

"Exactly," he said, triumphantly. He was delving through the "Who's Who" now, clawing up heaps of dog-eared paper. I stood watching in dismay. An aircraft droned overhead.

"Christ, Gus. It's a slaughterhouse. What could I possibly find there?"

He wasn't listening. "Gotcha!" he said, drawing out a sheaf of pale, low-grade photocopies. They were pages from some kind of trade directory. He ran a black-nailed finger down the list. "Here we go. This should about do it. FCPC. Colombian Meat Producers' Federation." He circled the address and phone number and handed me the page.

"I really don't think so, Gus. I *really*, really don't think so."

• • •

The San Felipe slaughterhouse lay behind a supermarket in the nebulous northern outskirts of Bogotá. I presented myself at the gates and said I wished to see Señor Santander Gomez Cuartas, junior vice-superintendent.

Getting this far had been easy enough. A visit to the offices of the Colombian Meat Producers' Federation had secured, along with reams of information and statistics about the meat trade, the name of Señor Gomez. As *Jefe de Relaciones Públicas* at the slaughterhouse, he was the official unfortunate delegated to deal with occasional visiting nuisances like myself. I flourished my business card at the security man. This describes me as a "consultant researcher," with a Mickey Mouse company address and Telex number underneath, a useful tool in the nose-poking trade. Judging from the security man's blank gaze it might just as well have described me as an Egyptian rope dancer, but the general effect was enough. He telephoned Gomez and told him he had a visitor at the front gate.

Presently Gomez appeared, a small, worried man with a goatee beard. He wore a white coat with splashes of blood on it, and carried another over his arm. Oozing plausibility, I explained my mission. I was compiling a "business opportunities" report on Colombia, and was very interested in the meat business, had your name from Señor So-and-so at the Federación, and would be most grateful—esteemed *señor*—to be shown around this major meat-processing plant of yours. He gave me the white coat to put on, and I was in. If Rikki was right, this was where the Snow White pipeline disgorged 100 kilos of cocaine a week. I didn't quite know what I was looking for, but surely something must show.

The job in hand, however, was my guided tour of the slaughterhouse. I wasn't looking forward to this. We watched the cattle being herded into the corrals. Most of them were *cebú* oxen—big, placid, humped, white beasts, South American versions of the Brahmin ox, though unfortunately for them not sharing their Hindu cousins' immunity from slaughter. Gomez rubbed his hands and said that a stout *cebú* bullock was worth up to 30,000 pesos. Meat is measured in the traditional unit of *arrobas*—12.5 kilos— and a good animal is always said to yield *una arroba más*, one *arroba* more than half its body weight.

As we walked around the back of the corrals, Gomez stopped. Gesturing me to follow him, he walked over to a group of three men standing around a station wagon. A fourth was sitting in the opened back, pulling on a pair of rubber boots. Gomez introduced me to a tall, lugubrious man, the *matadero*'s senior vice-superintendent, and to the young, bearded manager of the Cafam supermarket. Small talk was exchanged. Sixty million kilos of beef left the slaughterhouse every year, I learned.

The small, elderly man in the back of the station wagon was discussing something with a white-coated official—instructing him, it seemed, for now the official said, "Yes, *señor*, right away," and hurried off, checking his watch like the White Rabbit. Gomez promptly launched into obsequious greetings. "What a pleasure it is to see you, Don Rafael," he cried, ducking and bobbing like a courtier. He plucked fussily at my sleeve. "May I present to you Señor Rafael Vallejo Aragon? He is one of our most distinguished and successful figures in the meat business."

The small man took this heralding as no more than his due. He wore a smart tweedy suit, check shirt, woolen tie. His rubber boots were brand-new: blue with bright yellow soles. The whole gave a careful effect of well-dressed country gent. He stood to shake hands. The palm was hard and callused. He hadn't been born distinguished, I guessed.

I fired in a couple of polite questions about his meat interests. His answers were vague and grand. He soon turned to the others to discuss beef matters. Gomez hung in for a bit, larded Vallejo with more compliments, then said, "We must leave you, Don Rafael, you are a busy man." Vallejo said to me, with mechanical largess, "You must come to my stud farm in Cundinamarca one day, *señor*. I will tell you *everything* about the meat business in Colombia." He laughed a gravelly laugh. "The meat business is very good. We are a nation of carnivores!" He made a grimace, gnashed his teeth comically. "In England you have these—" he searched for the word, and spoke it with distaste "—*vegetarianos*. Not in Colombia. It is not natural. For rabbits, maybe." There was a sudden bullying note in his voice. He covered it with a loud, false laugh, echoed by the entourage. Gomez writhed with delight, but I saw his eyes flick over to me to see how I was taking this slur on my homeland. I thought of making some smart-ass riposte, but the odds were against me. For a moment, though, I found myself staring straight into the little man's hard gray eyes.

"He's an important man, then?" I said to Gomez as we walked on.

"*Millonario!*" whispered Gomez, pouting with pleasure at the thought.

From a raised walkway we could view the entire corral. In the corner was a pen with a few steers lying awkwardly, some moving and struggling. These animals, immobilized by sickness or injury, would be dispatched *in situ*. All the other animals were progressing, hour by hour, pen by pen, toward the *corriente*, the narrow black-railed ramp that led up into the slaughter-house. There a man in white overalls and a safety helmet prodded them up, in single file, with an electric goad wired up to a live overhead cable. The ramp led to an opening, with steel half-doors, like saloon doors in a Western. The patient oxen plodded up. The leading one glimpsed the scene inside, beyond the steel doors. If there is a bovine notion of hell, this was surely it. It skidded back, but the animals behind blocked its retreat, and the prod goaded it on.

Without really meaning to, I said, "He doesn't want to go in."

Gomez laughed, as if I had made some polite little joke. "It is sad, isn't it?" he said, unconvincingly. We walked on into the *matadero*, the killing place.

Just inside those swinging doors, the steer came into a square well, about 20 feet long. A man stood high above it, wielding a long steel pole with a sharp spike at the end. As the animal was released into the well, the man brought the pic down with a swift, hard jab into the steer's neck, just behind the horns. The animal fell, stunned and helpless, eyes lolling, legs cavorting crazily. Another worker jumped down into the well and slipped a heavy chain loop around its left hindleg. This was a deft operation, with half a ton of flesh and bones thrashing about on the floor. A third man, up on a level with the *picador*, pressed a button. The hoist clanked into action, winching the beast up, upside down. It hung swaying from the overhead rail. This rail ran on circuitously, like a ghost train, through the various sections of the slaughterhouse. With a brisk, practiced slash the man next to the *picador* cut the upended animal's throat. Blood poured out like water from a pail, thick crimson blood, splashing and steaming on the wet concrete floor. The next man sliced off the head and feet, a surprisingly easy operation with those big, scoured knives. The whole process, from living creature to headless carcass, took no more than half a minute. At the San Felipe slaughterhouse 800 to 1,000 cattle are dispatched every day. When the darkness comes they switch on floodlights over the corrals, and the sacrifice continues.

When Gomez judged I had seen enough, he took me to his office. When he closed the door I realized what a huge din had filled the slaughterhouse. The whole gory business had made such an impact on my eyes that I had hardly noticed the noise. I felt sick and tired. I saw my knuckles whiten as I leaned on the metal desk.

Looking out of the barred window on to a small, enclosed yard outside, I saw two men talking. One was the little meat baron, Rafael Vallejo. He had his back to me, but the tweed jacket and the white hair were unmistakable. The other was the white-coated minion he had been talking to when I first saw him. I watched with idle curiosity. Gomez was hunting out some statistics for me, tetchily complaining of the lack of a secretary to keep his papers in order. I heard a door opening into the yard. Vallejo turned. Another white-coated figure came into view. There was something vaguely troubling about his back view. The broad, slightly hunched shoulders, the square head of spiky black hair. I had seen it before. With a jolt, I realized I had seen it walking out of The Place a couple of nights earlier. It was Oddjob.

Rikki was right, Snow White was real, and I was right slap in the middle of it. Under no circumstances must Oddjob see me here. He did not look like a man who had much time for funny coincidences. I shrank back, grateful for the grimy film over the window.

Gomez had found the figures, the annual tonnages and percentage breakdowns so vital for my study of the meat business. He began to drone out the data. I mechanically wrote as he spoke, all the while keeping an eye on the trio in the yard. Vallejo was talking, with jabbed gestures of emphasis. Oddjob was listening, head still, occasional sulky monosyllables of agreement. The more I watched, the cosier it looked. Could it be possible? Had I stumbled right up the ladder all at once? If that was cocaine talk going on, then the distinguished millionaire and carnivore Don Rafael was something pretty big. The sun glinted on his white hair. Was he the *capo*? Was he Snow White himself?

In a pause between statistics, trying to sound casual, I said, "Look, there's Señor Vallejo again. He does a lot of business here, does he?"

"Oh yes. He has many cattle ranches in the *llanos*. We handle all his stock."

"And the meat itself? He has distribution networks, that sort of thing?"

"Of course. Transcarne. One of the biggest meat transportation companies in Colombia."

It was all falling into place. Out in the yard there was just Vallejo and Oddjob now. The third man had left. Oddjob's sleazy, slant-eyed, tomcat's face was half-turned toward me. He was talking, with choppy, robotic gestures from his big paws. "Who's that Vallejo's talking to?" I asked.

Gomez had his glasses off for reading the figures and now had to fumble them out of his white coat. "That? Oh, that's one of our packing managers."

Somewhere a siren shrilled. Gomez looked at his watch, closed his folders. "Midday," he announced. "The end of the morning shift. You would like a beer?"

As in all the comedies, the booze was in the first-aid cabinet. He took out two bottles and two glasses. Vallejo and Oddjob were still conferring, but with a hasty, last-minute air now. Gomez was washing the glasses in a basin. No: the glasses were on the desk—Gomez was washing two *more* glasses. He was walking to the door that led out into the yard. It opened with a squawk of metal on the stone floor. The two men outside wheeled around. Gomez bobbed in the doorway. "Don Rafael! Rodolfo! You will take a beer with us?" A curt wave from Vallejo. "How kind, Señor Gomez." A nod of assent from Oddjob, a.k.a. Rodolfo. Gomez fussed happily back into the room, polishing a glass on his coattail. "We will have a party," he chirped.

Fear is blank. Brain dazzled, body frozen, a rabbit caught in the headlights. I heard the fizz of beer, the thin clatter of bottle tops on the metal desk. Vallejo was walking slowly toward us, still talking. Oddjob glided resentfully beside him. In a few seconds he would be here. He would recognize me, he would start asking questions, he would go on asking till he didn't need any more answers. Then he would probably hook me up on the overhead rail and loosen my guts.

There was only one way out: back into the slaughterhouse. I hunched up, hand to my mouth, and blurted, *"Estoy enfermo! Voy a vomitar!"*

Vallejo had just stepped in through the door as I rushed out of the office. The last thing I saw was Gomez's startled face, and the beer spilling past the glass as he looked up from pouring.

I sprinted down the steps, back into the mayhem of the killing floor, slowing to a trot, trying not to attract attention. I kept my hand over my mouth, so everyone would think the gringo *maricón* couldn't handle all the blood and death. I heard Gomez's voice behind me. "Señor Nee-col, this way! Not there, *señor*!" I dodged down a corridor, passed through an empty room with a long line of severed calves' feet dangling from chains, crossed a yard, and came into what was evidently the pig section of the *matadero*. There were squeals without, but in this room all was quiet. A man in a rubber apron was thoughtfully prodding a few dead porkers in a vat of hot water. I slowed to a walk. White coat on, notebook in hand, just an official on his way from this door to that.

I came out into another yard. Pigs milling in slatted stalls, but no one around that I could see. There was a sort of fenced runway through which the pigs were herded into the stalls. Beyond it I saw trucks and cars parked: the back of the *matadero*, I reckoned, the opposite side from the one I'd come in at. If I could just get myself out through some back gate. I edged along the side of the stalls and was just about to break cover when I heard footsteps and voices. I shrank back, but I was still in full view if they came into the yard. The stall nearest me was empty. I clambered over the side and dropped silently into a rich mulch of straw and pig shit. A few inches from my face, in the neighboring stall, a dozen fear-crazed pigs bumped and snuffled against the slats. I crouched shivering while the voices passed.

Skulking at the edge of the truck park I saw that there was indeed a rear gate. A few yards away a man was closing up the back of an old flatbed truck. He wore blue overalls and a battered straw hat: a pig-man, I supposed. He climbed into the cab and started the engine. He'll do, I thought. I stripped off my dung-smeared white coat, dumped it in a corner and trotted briskly up to the truck. "Excuse me, *señor*. Are you going? Can you give me a lift?"

The pig-man surveyed me, chewing on a toothpick. I was breathing heavily: fear at high altitude. There was muck on my hands, my tie, my notebook. He ran a hand over his gray stubble, amiable and puzzled. I tensed with impatience. Then he nodded slowly, and said something in a rich *campesino* brogue. It sounded like "I'm going to Zoggo."

"That'll do nicely," I said, and climbed into the cab. He smiled a broad, toothless smile, fished out a crumpled pack of Pielroja, and offered me a cigarette. I fumbled for matches, trying to speed everything up. Any moment now Gomez and Oddjob were going to come around the corner and start the hue and cry. "My car won't start," I said. "I'm terribly late." He shook his head philosophically and said something else I couldn't understand. Lateness was not a concept that meant much to him. At last, clamping the cigarette in his mouth, he eased the pickup into gear. The truck chugged off lazily down along the red-brick back of the *matadero*. Optimum speed was reached at 5 miles an hour. The pig-man slumped comfortably in his seat, elbow resting on the window. Jesus, I thought, jiggling futilely, I've picked a real winner here.

I regretted my move even more when we reached the roadway, and instead of turning toward the rear gate he swung the truck right, heading for the front of the *matadero*. This brought us right into the central thoroughfare: offices, canteen, lunch-hour crowds of white-coats, slaughterers, truckers. Almost immediately I spotted Gomez, talking to a security-looking man in a peaked cap. He was tugging at his little beard, puzzling at the mystery of the vanishing journalist. Then, off to one side, I saw Oddjob, his fat brown face ranging slowly around like a radar dish. From where he stood he could see both exits from the *matadero*. He was waiting for me to break cover. He was bound to see me as we passed.

We chugged serenely to my doom. I squeezed my hands in mute supplication. In doing so I felt the box of matches still cradled in my sweating palm. With a swift, purposeful movement I spilled the contents on to the rusty floor at my feet. "*Maldita sea,*" I cursed, "how clumsy," and bent myself double to retrieve them. In this position, I fervently hoped, I was just out of view. "It's all right, *señor*, I have matches," said the pig-man. "No, no," I called up from my jackknife position, "I'll get them." He shrugged. The truck hiccupped on toward the gate. I scrabbled in the dust for the little waxy white matches. With this meager camouflage I passed beneath and beyond the gaze of Oddjob.

When the truck stopped I straightened up, thinking we were at the gates. But we were still a good 20 yards short of them. The pig-man had stopped to talk to someone, another *campesino*, another crumpled hat. It was going to be one of those slow, mulled conversations full of pauses.

Craning around, I saw Gomez and the peaked-cap fellow walking purposefully up the roadway toward us. Clearly they were coming up to the gate. They were going to warn the security guard: a mad Englishman on the loose. The pig-man was talking about the price of pork, warming to his theme. I heard again the butcher's phrase Gomez had used, "*una arroba más.*"

Oh yes, we're all after that little bit extra, that one *arroba* over the top. Only sometimes it costs us more than we can pay.

It was now or never. "Thanks for the ride," I said, and jumped out of the cab. The truck shielded me from Gomez. Those 20 yards to the gate were a fast walk through eternity. I waited for the shout behind me but none came. As I passed through the gate the security man waved. I saw him jot something down on a clipboard. One consultant researcher, business done, leaves the slaughterhouse. He must be a busy man. Look how he's running....

CHAPTER THIRTEEN

Into the Chocó

Back at the Cuadros's house, sipping tea, courting forgetfulness. Everything was set for our departure for the coast the following morning. Lola's husband—mustachioed, practical, New England-born Luke—had slept off his jet lag. Her brother Alberto was winding up his business affairs. I was feeling better already.

The phone rang. Lola said, "It's for you, Charlie." I guessed it was Gus: I had given him the number. I took the phone into another room.

"Mate?" said the familiar voice at the other end.

"OK, Gus, listen. There's a meat magnate by the name of Rafael Vall—"

"Forget it. We've got problems."

"Problems? Damn right. I nearly got my balls chopped off up at the *matadero*."

"I'm at the airport." The idea of Gus being anywhere but in his moth-eaten old armchair at the crow's nest was startling. What had happened? I asked. "They've got to Julio Cesar," he said. "I knew it. They don't give up, they just wait till your sweat starts to cool. He managed to flannel them, said he thought I'd run off back to Europe, but it's only a question of time before they come knocking on the door."

"So where are you going?"

"That's just it, mate. I'm not going anywhere at present."

"No money," I said dully.

"Can you meet me? I'll be in the cafeteria. Green carnation in my buttonhole." He hung up.

Another taxi, through the darkening streets to Eldorado airport. Gus was there, in a creased navy blue suit shiny with use. His only luggage was the box containing the "Who's Who." He was looking very jumpy, an alien figure among the black plastic and potted palms. "Thank Christ," he said. "Look, a flight leaves for Medellín in an hour. Can you stand me the ticket money?"

"Why Medellín?"

"I've got friends there," he said. "Also, I need to see a doctor, get some penicillin up my bum. My leg's got worse again, some infection I think. Just can't do it here in Bogotá. Bad climate, if you know what I mean." He broke off to survey a couple of new arrivals in the cafeteria. "There's someone else I want to see there too," he continued. "I'll tell you about him. But first, get me that ticket, will you?"

As I went off to the Avianca counter, he called me back. "Not McGregor, of course. Don't get the ticket in my name."

I got it in the name of Malcolm Goodman. He stuffed it into his jacket pocket. "Now, tell me what you learned today." I told him about Vallejo, the big wheel with the cattle ranches, the man seen chatting cozily with Oddjob. "It all fits, Gus. I reckon he's our man, Mr. Snow White."

"Could be, chum, could be. You did well. There's some people call themselves journalists who couldn't write 'Fuck' on a dusty window." I glowed under the praise of Ace McGregor. He may have been crazy, but he was still the old pro. "On the other hand," he ruminated, "it could be nothing at all. I mean, Vallejo could have been there for totally legit reasons. We need evidence, mate. That's where this bloke in Medellín comes in. He's a bit of a dodgy customer, but we go back a long way." His eyes clouded with some reminiscence, but he shook it off. "The thing about him is, he knows everything there is to know about cocaine *money*. You say to him: Vallejo. You say to him: Transcarne. He'll tell you all their nasty little secrets."

Gus's flight was announced. I got up, but he held my arm. "You really ought to meet this bloke, mate. In fact, come to think of it, for this book of yours you can't afford *not* to."

"Yes. Well, give me his name and number."

Gus screwed up his ginger-pale face. "Don't think he'd be too keen on that. I mean, a girl like Rosalita's one thing. This guy's in another league. No, I've got a better idea. Why don't we meet up in Medellín?"

"For God's sake, Gus, I told you. I'm leaving for the coast tomorrow with my friends."

"Course you are. So you'll be coming through Medellín anyway. No problem." He fished out a scrap of paper from his jacket, and scribbled something on it. He handed it to me: it said "El Ave Perdida," with a street number. "Look. I'll be there at...shall we say midday on Saturday? You'll probably be in Medellín by tomorrow night, but we'll say Saturday. Let you get your beauty sleep. Your friends can drop you in Medellín, we'll go and have a chat with Eduardo, and then you can take a plane or bus on up, and meet your friends on the coast."

"I don't know, Gus. It got pretty heavy at the slaughterhouse today. I feel like a change of scene."

"Medellín," he cried. "City of Eternal Spring. Orchids in the back garden. What could be better?" Another announcement for the flight. We got up. "It's up to you, Charlie. I'll be there. You've put in some legwork on this one. You've had the luck. Ride with it, old cock, ride with it!"

And so it was that I said goodbye to Lola and her family at Medellín with arrangements to meet in Cartagena in a couple of days' time. One last bit of business with Gus and I would be up on the coast. Or so I thought.

Of Medellín I remember little, except an absurd impression that the city was full of one-legged men. Patient monoped street vendors stood on corners. Beggars loped through the streets on crutches, some carrying those officially stamped accounts which explain how their disability was incurred in a bona fide industrial accident, or while serving in the armed forces of the republic. In reality, Medellín is a brash, uncomplicated city, its origins—an early seventeenth-century settlement of refugee Spanish Jews—lost among office blocks, modern churches, parks and cafeterias. It is Colombia's industrial second city, the Birmingham or Chicago of the Andes. It produces three-quarters of the country's textiles; has steel mills, chemical plants, cement works, machine shops; glass, paint, food, cigarette and liquor factories. All this, grafted on to deep-rooted coffee, cattle and land wealth, has made it a banking and financial center—and a laundering center for narco-dollars.

I liked the feel of the place: it had none of the somber quality of Bogotá. People are often nicest in these ordinary, unlovely cities. They do not expect you to be here, it seems, and so they are pleased that you are.

I took a room in a tall tenement hotel near the bus terminals, and at quarter to midday I was sitting over a glass of brown Medellín rum, in the bar curiously named El Ave Perdida, the Lost Bird, waiting for Gus.

He arrived on the dot of midday. The moment I saw him I knew there was something wrong. He brought trouble into the bar like a smell. He was breathing fast and his limp seemed to be worse. He carried the "Who's Who" in one hand, and a blue plastic sports bag in the other. When he saw me he threaded through the bar in a hunched, low-profile way, as inconspicuous as a six-foot, ginger-haired gringo could get.

"Knew you'd be here," he gasped. He slumped into the chair next to me, stretching his damaged leg out straight, wincing. I saw a darker stain on the dark blue trouser leg. I raised my hand to call the waiter—a drink first, then the questions—but he grabbed my wrist back down to the table. "No time," he said. He looked under the table. "Where are your things?" I told him. "Let's go," he said.

"Where are we going? Are we going to meet Eduardo?"

"Tell you about it back at the hotel."

Outside the sun had broken through. The air was balmy. Gus hobbled along, a trainee in Medellín one-leggedness. I carried the blue sports bag for him. It felt light, almost empty, but I could feel something sliding around in the bottom. I offered to carry the much heavier cardboard box. "No, no," he insisted, "you take the bag."

At the hotel the *señora* said, "No guests." I was even more surprised than she was when Gus pulled out a wedge of 1,000-peso bills. He slapped one down on the counter. She tried to pick it up, but his grubby fingers pressed it flat on the surface. *"Nunca me viste,"* he said softly. You never even saw me. The *señora* smiled reassuringly. *"Nunca, señor,"* she said. "There are no gringos here," she added, glancing significantly at me, in the hope that I too was buying anonymity.

My room was on the second floor. A small barred window stared out at a blank gray wall opposite. Gus seemed to approve. He threw his carton down with a thud and sank gingerly on to the bed.

"OK, Gus," I said wearily. "What's the story this time?" He was rolling up his trouser leg. I winced as I saw the blood-soaked bandage. "For God's sake, what happened?"

"I fell," he said.

"Oh, sure."

"It's true," he cried. "Cub's honor." He stretched the leg out on the bed, smearing blood on the rough white ticking. Propped up against the wall, he began to rummage in his pockets, piling the contents onto the bed between his legs. My eyes widened as he brought out handfuls of crumpled paper money: pesos, dollars, even Venezuelan bolivars. They were all high denomination bills. I began to feel very nervous, and a little angry. "What the hell is going on, Gus?"

"Bit of a sorry story, mate, but needs must. I went to see friend Eduardo this morning, at his apartment, very swish, up near the Union Club. And, well, to cut a long story short, there it was. All this loot, bloody oodles of it, stacked up in his office. I saw it through the door when I first walked in. So we're out on his balcony, taking *tinto*, having a chat. The phone rings. While he's on the phone, I say: 'Excuse me, Eduardo, where's the *baño*?' I popped into his office, grabbed as much as I could get in my pockets, and split. It was Saturday morning, see. No one else around. I was going like a bitch down the stairs—he was up on the fifth floor—and I fell."

I stared at him. "This guy Eduardo," I said, trying to keep my voice calm, "he's a . . . cocaine financier, money launderer?"

"Well, sort of. He's into all sorts of dodges."

"But this could well be mafia money you've got here?"

"I told you, mate. There was enough money to buy an oil field in there. This was just a skimming."

"How much have you got?"

"Don't know," he said, riffling the bills with his fingers. "Haven't had a chance to count it yet." His face split into a grin, a naughty boy's apple-stealing grin. Only it wasn't an irate farmer we were dealing with here. There was a silence. I was pacing up and down the room: it only took five paces each way. Then Gus said, in a low, confessional voice, "It wasn't *just* the money, either."

"What?"

He gestured at the sports bag on the floor. I guessed right away, but I unzipped it all the same. A small, squat package wrapped in newspaper. "Peach?" He nodded. "How much?" He shrugged: half a kilo, a pound, he wasn't sure. It had been sitting on the desk in the office. It had practically got up on its hind legs and begged him to take it. "You stupid bloody fool," I said, though whether it was Gus or myself I was addressing I wasn't quite sure. I could have been halfway to the coast by now, cruising through the green hills of Antioquia with Lola and company. Instead, here I was in an airless room, with a pile of hot money on the bed, a pound of stolen cocaine in the bag, and a half-crippled lunatic sitting opposite me saying, "I've got it all worked out, mate, there's no way they're going to find us."

The stuffy room was making him sleepy. He had had a hard morning. He pushed his ill-gotten gains to one side, and settled more comfortably on the bed. In what way, I asked, had he got it "all worked out"? Out of another pocket in the unpleasant blue suit came a couple of slips of white paper. Bus tickets: Medellín to Quibdó.

"Quibdó?" I said. "But that's somewhere in the jungle, for Christ's sake."

"That's right. Slap-dab in the middle of the Chocó."

"But no one goes to the Chocó, Gus. It's a sweat hole."

"Exactly right, mate. It's the last place anyone would think of looking."

"And you want me to come with you?"

"Just as far as Quibdó," he implored. "I can't make it alone, not with my leg like this. I'll make it worth your while. Money, peach, whatever. I'll *give* you the 'Who's Who': what more can I say? Just one last ride, mate. You know what they say—two hearts are better than one...."

"And after Quibdó?"

"I'm going down to Buenaventura. It's goodbye, Colombia, out the back door. I can sell the peach there. With that and the loot I'll have more than enough for boat passage out of Buenaventura." He stretched luxuriously. "Ship up to Panama...Mexico, maybe.... Who knows, perhaps I'll go to Canada. Plenty of McGregors up there!"

I got out my road map of Colombia. The Chocó was a long swath of emptiness between the brown swirls of the mountains and the blue of the Pacific Ocean. "For Christ's sake, Gus. Buenaventura's right down the other end of the Chocó. There aren't any roads. Look."

I pushed the map at him. He was settling down to sleep now. He didn't bother to look at it. "Blue ones," he yawned.

"What do you mean, blue ones?"

"The roads through the Chocó. They're blue." He cocked open an eye. "Rivers, matey, rivers."

I stared at the map. It was more or less true. The one and only road through the Chocó petered out at a small jungle town called Itsmina, but the blue line of the San Juan ran clear on down to the Pacific, debouching just a couple of map inches above Buenaventura.

"But I don't want to go to the Chocó," I whined. "I want to go to the coast."

No answer came. Gus was asleep.

The bus left at six in the morning. We stumbled through the dawn streets, heads full of snow. The bus was already full of chattering black Chocuano faces. Apart from a few vestigial Indian tribes, the inhabitants of the Chocó are almost exclusively Negro, descendants of the slaves who worked the Spanish sugar plantations. The Chocó Indians still refer to the Negroes as *los libres*, the freed slaves. To most Colombians the Chocó is synonymous with disease, poverty and underdevelopment, 30,000 square miles of jungle shading down to the mangrove swamps of the Pacific littoral. Its one redeeming feature is the presence of gold and platinum in the river gravels, though little comes out of there now.

We found seats, a few rows apart. I sat next to a ragged old black in a rummage-sale jacket. He was clasping the seat in front of him before the bus even moved, thin black sticks of wrist with little white hairs on them. With much revving and trumpeting, and shouts of "Quibdó, Quibdó, *directo* Quibdó!" we set off. It was one of those classic Colombian buses, a patchwork of beaten tin built around a snub-nosed Ford 600 engine, "Flota El Progreso de Chocó" painted in curly, festive fairground lettering on the side. Religious trinkets danced above the windshield. Gray tongues of smoke licked up through the floor.

I could see Gus's greasy ginger head over the seat tops. We had been up all night, sampling the ripped-off *perico*, and counting the money: something over $2,500. I was seriously worried about his health, and supposed that was why I was here, bound for the sweatlands, the green machine, the land of night-biting *zancudos*.

We came out through the posh southern suburbs of Medellín, switchbacked down to the Cauca River, and began to climb the sparsely populated Western Cordillera. This was coffee country: precipitous plantations, beans drying on sacks by the roadside. Four hours out, still in the hills, we crossed the state line into the department of Chocó. We rattled on through the dusty outskirts of El Cármen, children running alongside. A last glimpse of the mountains, and then we saw the expanse of the Chocó, laid out below us like a hazy green sea.

With every minute of our descent the heat grew stronger, the air sat on us. The old man beside me was wilting. His mouth fell open, his eye glazed over. He had a wedge of *arepa* bread wrapped in tin foil. He picked at it listlessly, little chunks of damp dough, sparrow's mouthfuls. He had no teeth. Pieces fell on his lap, and mine. I gave him an orange, an *empanada*, some water. I smelled his stale, brackish sweat, a sickbed smell, *la catinga Chocuana*. I would smell it many times in these low, swampy regions.

We were down on the flat now. Little wood and thatch settlements punctuated the monotonous green scrub, the hacked-back hedge of forest. I saw children's white eyes in the dark doorways.

Quibdó announced itself with a brief discord of tin roofs and overhead wires. We were quickly in the center. There were a few picturesque streets of wood, old two-story trading houses with teetering balconies, but most of the town was concrete, drab and smudged, looking like it was built in a hurry. Fruit and vegetable debris sat in the streets, a dank, mildewy smell, sharpened here and there by the piquancies of rotting fish. The mud of the jungle town, that charmless gray river mud that looks like the deposits around a blocked-up drain, lay everywhere.

The bus finally came to a halt on the waterfront: the Atrato River, as wide as a lake. I woke Gus up. He had slept through the entire journey. He stared at me blankly for a moment. "We're here," I said. I could feel the heat coming off him. He was sickening: the excitement of the last few days, the strain of the last few weeks, the excesses of the last few years: bad leg, bad diet, bad nerves: the list could go on. He had a whole lot of bodily debts to pay, and the Chocó was just the kind of place where your credit ran out.

The bus was empty now. The driver was waiting for us to leave. "We're here, Gus," I said again. "Quibdó."

"Quibdó," he faltered. "Keep dough. Keep dough safe." He twisted around to check his sports bag up on the luggage rack. He moved his lips trying to moisten his mouth. He made to settle back down in the seat. I put a hand under his arm to help him up. His armpit was burning with fever.

As we climbed off the bus, a little black boy in baggy shorts danced up, crying, "Hotel? Hotel?" He took my bag and the "Who's Who," and put them in a makeshift wooden barrow. He tried to take the sports bag off Gus. Gus, gaunt, confused and quavery, held on. An absurd tug of war ensued between these ill-matched opponents. I gently released Gus's grip. "He's taking us to a hotel, Gus," I explained in nurse-like tones.

A hundred yards down the waterfront, a small, rickety hotel—Residencias San Francisco—lurked in the shadow of the ugly gray Palacio Episcopal. In the lobby three black boys lounged in front of a large black-and-white TV. A church service through a haze of static. The rooms were little more than hutches, but they had a balcony of sorts, and a view over the river, and electric fans. The air was hot and wet. Gus flopped onto the bed. "Give me whiskey," he rasped. The best I could do was a bottle of beer from the lobby.

Another passenger from the bus had wound up at the Residencias San Francisco, a strange, pallid young man with lank, swept-back hair. As I walked down the corridor, leaving Gus asleep, he was sitting bare-chested on his bed a few doors down. *"Pues, paisa, qué tal?"* he called, in a rich Antioqueño accent—the rough equivalent of "Wotcha, mate!"—and gestured me to join him. He was rolling a joint of dark *mango viche* grass.

His name was Alonso and his primary purpose in Quibdó was to sell lottery tickets. He had stacks of them laid out on the bed. The lottery is a daily institution in Colombia, about the only reliable form of national taxation.

Alonso asked what brought me to Quibdó. I explained vaguely that my friend was sick, and that I was seeing him off on his way to Buenaventura. "He will go down the San Juan, then?" I nodded. "And you?" I said I was going back to Medellín, and then on up to Cartagena. "But you do not need to go back," said Alonso. "You can get a boat here, down the Atrato. It will take you to Cartagena." He gestured down along the waterfront. A group of scruffy cargo boats rocked gently in the pink water. This sounded like very good news. I have a deep dislike of retracing my steps: tramp-steamer passage down the Atrato river was much more like it. Perhaps, after all, I would get something out of this journey to the Chocó.

After dark, Alonso left to tout his lottery tickets around the bars of Quibdó. I went to lie down on my bed, thinking to take a rest before getting some supper. I promptly fell into a deep sleep. I dreamed I was sleeping beside a rushing white-water river, but when I woke it was only the dull roar of the electric fan. I watched the dawn come up, diaphanous drapes of gray-green mist rising off the waters.

I found Gus somewhat restored by his long sleep. His hair was matted, his face looked drained, but it was clear he had sweated out the worst of it. I told him he must stay in bed for the day, and went to get him some bread and fruit. The heat was already massing. After five minutes' walking I was so covered in that shrink-wrapping of sweat that comes in air so humid that your sweat can't evaporate. After breakfasting on eggs *pericos*—scrambled with tomato and onion—I strolled along the waterfront to check out the possibilities of a boat ride downriver.

The boats floated gently on the rubbish-strewn water near the riverside market. They were single-mast, shallow vessels, with a slight upward curve. The largest, about 100 feet, was called *La Gaviota*, the sea gull. A group of blacks were lounging in the shade of the awning that covered the stern half of the boat. I walked up the gangplank. A big Negro in a vest, middle-aged, crew-cut hair the color of gun metal, rose from the group. He was the captain. I asked if he was bound for Cartagena. He was. I asked how long the trip was. Inside a week, he said: three days. I asked if he would take me. With pleasure, 3,500 pesos for everything: hammock, meals and passage. I saw the crew tucking into a mushy brew in tin dishes. The skipper moved to block my view. "To you 3,000," he said.

So far, so good. Then I asked when they were leaving. His big head wavered noncommittally. *"Depende,"* he said. Depends on what? He rubbed his big hand over the back of his head: I heard the rasp of his crew cut. *"Pues . . . depende de Dios,"* he said. Well, of course. All things, no doubt including the departure of the tramp-steamers down the Atrato River, depended on God. One of the crew, a tall, shifty-looking *mestizo*, strolled over. He sliced an orange in two with a Swiss Army knife, and handed me half. It depends, the skipper continued, on the rains. He looked philosophically at the sky. The rains were late, he said. The river was very low, down to 10 feet in some places, too shallow for the boat. They had been waiting for five days already. He gestured out at the middle of the river. Long mud-banks were visible. "How long must we wait?" I asked futilely. He shrugged. A day, a week, a month, *quién sabe?* I felt the sweat trickling down my chest. The *mestizo* held out his sucked-dry orange peel, stuck a splinter of wood in it, and said with a laugh, "You'll have to sail to Cartagena in this!"

CHAPTER FOURTEEN

The Shit Creek Special

The following morning—sky brilliant blue, same boats moored on the waterfront, no sign of any rains—I decided it was time to cut my losses and backtrack by bus to Medellín. Gus was leaving that morning, south to Istmina where the road ran out, there to try his luck for a boat down the San Juan to Buenaventura. The San Juan was going to be low too, of course, but it was a much shorter distance from Istmina to the Pacific than it was from Quibdó to the Caribbean, and with luck he would be able to make the trip on some smaller boat, a fisherman's *luncha* or *panga*.

Gus felt honor-bound to offer me the "Who's Who," as he had promised in Medellín, payment for whatever obscure moral support I had provided on his fugitive trail. But I could see the idea of parting with it was painful to him, and some residual goodness in my heart—"hack's honor," he would have called it—made me refuse. "You might need it," I said.

"Inside the Cocaine Underworld, eh?" he laughed. "Well, you never know, do you?"

We said goodbye on the waterfront, where the truck left each morning for Istmina. I wished him luck. "Don't worry about me, mate," he said. "I'll get through. It's the first law of jungle travel—where there's a Shit Creek, there's someone who'll sell you a paddle."

An hour or so later I strolled up to the row of sheds that served as the Quibdó bus depot, to buy my ticket for the midday bus to Medellín. The man behind the grille shook his head. *"No hay."*

No tickets for Medellín? The depot was nearly empty, the bus was standing in the street. How could this be?

"We have tickets, *señor*," he explained wearily, "but no buses are going to Medellín."

"Why the hell not?"

"Derrumbe." The word that all South American travelers learn to fear. Landslide. "It happened last night," he continued. "Near El Cármen. There is a bridge down too." My heart sank. In these remote regions, the blocking of roads and the breaking of bridges can mean days of delay.

There seemed no alternative but to fly. There was an airfield of sorts north of the town: perhaps I could get a flight direct to Cartagena. At the small Coturismo office downtown the news was bad. There was no flight to Cartagena, only to Medellín. I had missed one flight this morning: the next was not until Friday night.

I sat on a bench, hot, dejected and hung over. Stuck in Mosquito City. One river to the coast, no boats. One road to Medellín, no buses. One flight out, three days and eight hours away. I had just two options left: sweat it out in Quibdó, or join up with Gus for a river ride to Buenaventura. It took me just a few seconds to decide. When in doubt, *move*, even if it's in the wrong direction.

The next morning found me on the waterfront, piling into the truck to Istmina, which turned out to be two wooden streets and assorted alleys on a bluff overlooking the San Juan River. There was one crumbling old hotel, hopefully named Hotel Turístico, run by a crumbling old *mestizo*. His skin was grayish and flecked with yellow liver spots. I expected to find Gus bivouacked here, but the old *dueño*, whose name was Lopez, had seen nothing of him.

Down at the waterfront the following morning there was no news of any boats going anywhere much. Nor was there any news of Gus. I found a couple of houses that called themselves hotels, but they didn't harbor a tall gringo either. It was a mystery: he had done a complete vanishing trick somewhere between Quibdó and here.

In Istmina I sat and sweated and puzzled and waited. My pen left furry blotches on my notebook. My cigarettes drooped. The small store of cocaine Gus had given me grew smaller and sludgier. Then one morning I couldn't even sit up. This wasn't cocaine, this was fever. A hot ague had me by the back. My head ebbed and ached, my stomach turned to water: the Chocó Choo-choo. Strange scenarios flew me away, brought me back. Six months in the hole . . . a gen'lman o' fortune, sir . . . crash on the levee, no boats gonna row.

Old Lopez was standing at my door. "You are sick, *señor*?" I requested mineral water: he brought Coca-Cola. Another time his wife was there, with a huge slab of papaya in her hand. She told me to eat the seeds, a sovereign remedy against fevers. The seeds were black and intensely bitter, almost impossible to swallow. It was like an expiation, a myrrh. I crushed them with the bottle and washed them down with Coca-Cola.

Another time, nighttime, I was terrorized by a giant black flying beetle. It crashed in angrily through the torn netting at the window. I swatted at it with my notebook, missed. It traced a few circles in the air, gathered its wits, and came hurtling down at my pillow in a low, deadly arc. A dreadful, chivalric struggle ensued, which I finally won by slamming the door on it. Its carcass stuck in the door jamb, orange slime oozing from its shattered carapace. Should I drink this too, sovereign remedy against all fears?

The second day of the fever I heard it drumming on the tin roof over the balcony. Rain. I stumbled out on to the balcony. I could feel it on my face and my chest, tiny drops, specks of coolness, like stars coming out all over my skin.

In the morning I rose from my sweat bed, showered down with pails. Señora Lopez was cooking *arepas* on a charcoal griddle on top of an oil drum. The air was clearer after the rain. It couldn't have made much difference to the height of the river, but it seemed like a good omen. And sure enough, while I was breakfasting, in walked a tubby, cheerful man in a small, peaked yachting cap. With him was a mulatto boy, about ten. The man's name was Manuel, the boy was his son Henry, and they were going down the San Juan River, as far as Capoma. I hardly dared ask any more. Some catch, surely: they were going in April, they were *walking* there. But no. They were going in a fishing boat, piloted by a Negro from the coast called Mico, and provided Mico hadn't drunk himself to death last night the boat would be leaving around midday.

It was not the ragged, picturesque old riverboat I had envisaged. It was a low fiberglass *lancha*, 20 feet long, white with orange fittings, and a Yamaha 40 motor. It didn't even have a name. For 2,000 pesos Mico would take me all the way to the Pacific Ocean in it. He was a tough, simian man, about thirty I guessed, quick to anger and quick to laugh. I could tell his price was high by the way Manuel suddenly started looking at the ceiling and whistling carelessly when the figure was mentioned. But Mico had seen the fear in my eye. He knew I'd pay twice that, so all in all it seemed fair. The Shit Creek Special was sailing at last.

It was afternoon before we finally set off, and then we stopped at Andagoya, just ten minutes downriver, where we were joined by a jovial Negress, the district nurse. This brought our complement to nine: Mico the pilot, and his copilot, Federico, a ferrety *mestizo* in a baseball cap; a vivacious Chocuana woman named Tabatha and her two little daughters, prim in lacy bonnets; chubby Manuel and his son Harry, the mulatto boy; the district nurse; and the gringo. And so the little fiberglass Ship of Fools set off for the Pacific Ocean.

Progress was slow because of the river's lowness. Often the propeller hit bottom, the boat shuddered, Mico cut the engine, and we floated amid the whoops and screeches and comic arpeggios of jungle birds. At a sharp elbow of river, overhung with predatory vegetation, the channel was so narrow that we had to disembark entirely, and carry boat, motor, baggage and children across to where the stream broadened again. Later there was another rainstorm. Mico handed out plastic sheets, but we were all soaked by the time we had rigged them up—all except for the district nurse, who had a black umbrella. Tilting it at her feet, and crouching behind it, she was the only one of us who stayed dry.

We plowed on west. Everything turned scarlet and orange and then it was dark. The immense, comfortless trill of frogs and insects settled in behind the whine of our motor.

Two hours after dark, cold and wet, we came to a scattering of wooden shacks. The village of Capoma was a little way inland, I learned. This was Manuel's destination. The new house by the riverside was a schoolhouse, convenient for pupils commuting by canoe. The district nurse knew the schoolmistress well, and it was decreed that we could shelter the night here. We scrambled up the steep muddy bank.

The schoolmistress greeted us warmly. Here, at last, I got news of Gus. "You're the second gringo we've seen here in a week," she told me. Tall? Redheaded? *Poco loco?* She nodded. He was traveling with a couple of desperate characters, *mestizos*. She thought they were gold prospectors. She didn't know where they'd come from or where they were going. To Buenaventura perhaps? She shook her head. "They were traveling *upriver*," she said.

Inside the schoolhouse, the pungent, turpentinish smell of freshly sized wood made me think of a gazebo in an English garden: another place, another life. Soon we were tucking into fried mortadella and plantains, ranged improbably around the little school desks. I handed around a half bottle of rum. We nested down on benches or the floor. I was too tired to ponder long on Gus's whereabouts. I drifted off to the sound of the three women out back, talking and laughing late into the night.

By midday it was just Mico and me. We had dropped off the others, one by one, at huts or villages that meant much to them and nothing to me. There had been other stops, to deliver letters and to buy provisions—rice, salt, *panela*, toothpaste and gas—from an Indian trader. Now the river widened, and the tall trees gave way to stunted deltas of mangrove, and I tasted the salt on my lips.

Mico's family house stood in a cove out near Charambira Point. We were still in the maze of inlets around the San Juan estuary, out of the Chocó, but not quite at the Pacific. The family were all there, easy and distant, potentially fierce people. Mico's father whittled wood for a machete handle, a sister rocked in a net hammock, brothers ranged from approximate ages eight to thirty-five. I was treated to fish soup and *agua de panela*, plied with questions about England, and good-humoredly grilled to ensure that

I thought the Chocó the most beautiful part of Colombia. "It is tranquil here," said the elder brother, a smaller, more philosophical edition of Mico. "The sea, the forest, the fish, the birds, the animals, the Indians and...us." He was listing these out, counting them off on his hand. When the list stopped, he looked at his fingers, half surprised. "That's all there is here," he laughed. "Seven things!"

I made the final leg to Buenaventura in another fishing boat, belonging to a neighbor of Mico's. It was late afternoon when we rounded the last point and glimpsed the tiny gray mass of Buenaventura. Few people speak well of this city—hot, dirty and expensive—but right then it meant a bed and a meal. I had been on the water, face into the wind, motor gunning, for twelve hours.

Whatever happened to Gus McGregor—last seen heading up the San Juan River in dubious company—remains a mystery. Maybe he's swinging in a hammock somewhere in the Chocó. Maybe he's up in Canada, hob-nobbing with the other McGregors. Maybe his luck, the *buenaventura* he stretched for so long, finally ran out. If you ever see his by-line, pay your penny and read his story.

Surfacing in Buenaventura I discovered that time had marched on to the beginning of Semana Santa, the Holy Week leading up to Easter. In the mountains some three hours inland from Buenaventura, connected by good roads, lay the town of Popayán. Popayán is *the* classic place to spend Semana Santa in Colombia. The nightly candlelit processions of holy images are famous throughout the Catholic world, and the town is briefly inundated with pilgrims, tourists, Páez Indians and pickpockets. Prescribing myself a short dose of innocent tourism, I set off.

They call Popayán *la joya blanca*, the white jewel of Colombia. It is—or was—one of the loveliest towns in all Latin America. Founded in 1536 by Sebastian de Belalcazar, one of Pizarro's henchmen, on his trek north from Peru in search of Eldorado, it stands in a temperate mountain valley, altitude a little over 5,000 feet. Below are the cane fields of the hot Cauca valley, above are the rugged green Andean highlands. I remember my first impression of it twelve years ago—the rinsed mountain air, the cobbled streets, the rococo colonial buildings, the seventeenth-century university, the chic restaurants, the leather shops, all bright white against the surrounding green hills.

It was late on Wednesday night when I arrived on the bus from Buenaventura. I had missed the first part of the festival, including the Palm Sunday procession when they bring down the images—Christ the Master, Our Lady of the Sorrows, Death—from the hilltop chapel of Belén, but I was still in time for the climactic Easter processions. The hotels were full, but I found a room at the Residencias Viajero, a nondescript hotel in a workaday part of town. I sluiced away the last grime of the Chocó, and sat up late planning elegant historical itineraries for the morrow.

I should have been reading my Bible: "Boast not thyself of tomorrow, for thou knowest not what a day may bring forth." The following morning, Jueves Santo, the last day of March 1983, at a time later fixed by the newspapers as 8:17 a.m., I was dozing in my bed at the Hotel Viajero, when I heard a soft, deep rumble. I thought at first it was thunder, and then, because I could feel the vibrations of it running up through the metal-frame bed, I sleepily reasoned that it must be some enormous truck gunning its motor below my window. The noise stopped. I nuzzled back into the pillow. But there was no mistaking the second one. It started loud and it got louder, an evil grumbling that swiftly became a roar. The walls, windows, door shuddered around me. The light bulb swayed sluggishly. It was as if some giant pair of hands had grabbed the room by the lapels and was shaking it back and forth. Still in bed, half up, I was thinking: It's going to stop now, because if it doesn't stop something big is going to break and fall on top of me. Cracks sprouted up the wall. A fine meal of plaster floated down on my head. I leaped out of bed. The room pitched angrily. The floor was swampy with movement. I threw myself beneath the bed and lay there with my arms over my head, sneezing amid the fluff and butt ends.

I know the facts now. It was an earthquake that lasted eighteen seconds, measured 5.5 on the Richter scale, and had its epicenter near the village of El Tambo, some 15 kilometers west of Popayán. Right then, as I levered myself out from under the bed, all I knew and cared about was that it had stopped. The first thing to break the chilly silence was the sound of a door slamming and a woman laughing. I went out into the corridor. A young couple were down the far end, heading out. "What the hell was *that*?" I called. *"Un temblor, hombre! Un temblor!"* I felt let down—the man's shrug, the woman's laugh. He called it a *temblor*, a tremor, not a full-blown, earth-moving *terremoto*. I returned to my room feeling foolish. Had I really hurled myself under the bed? How silly. It was only a *temblor*. They probably have to sweep this plaster dust up every day.

I dressed quickly. Out in the street there was rubble and broken tiles on the sidewalk, but you could find that any morning of the week on any Colombian street. It wasn't until I turned the corner, heading toward the old part of town, that I began to see the real signs: whole roofs caved in, shattered shop windows, broken gutters swaying in the breeze. The nearer I got to the center, the worse it became. Now I realized my luck—partly because I was staying in a newish part of town, and partly through geological factors unknown, I had weathered the quake in one of the few parts of town scarcely affected by it.

The old colonial heart of Popayán looked like a bomb site. The churches, the cloistered university, the Hotel Monasterio were all in ruins. By the time I got there they had cordoned off the center, with soldiers at every corner a block away from the cathedral square, Parque Caldas. I talked my way in past a wide-eyed young conscript. In human terms, the epicenter of the disaster was the cathedral. The entire roof, the famous domed cupola, had caved in on a churchful of people celebrating morning mass. They had been pulling the dead out for an hour now. A long line of soldiers and *campesinos* ferried stones out of the shattered building. They wore bandannas over their faces, bandit-style, against the fog of dust. I saw a dead body brought out on a stretcher, head covered with a blanket. A pair of white ankle socks and sandals stuck out—a little girl in her church best, with a few grazes on her skin that her mother could have medicated in a moment.

They were also bringing the holy images out of the cathedral: amputated, lopsided, dust-covered figures, yet paradoxically more human than ever, as if they too had been walking and talking until the clock reached 8:17 a.m. They carried away the Christ down the smoky street, borne high on a running, straggling crowd. Perhaps this was nearer to Calvary than the regular pomps of Holy Week ever got.

The TV cameras had arrived from Cali. A man in jeans was poking a microphone at an army officer, but a surge of people bearing another stretcher out of the cathedral knocked him to the ground. There was an old man on the stretcher. He was looking around him, head cocking up out of the blanket with busy, birdlike movements. Someone ran after, carrying a trilby, and plonked it on the old man's head. He said something— I couldn't hear it—and there was a moment of brusque laughter. There is so much laughter in Colombia, so much grace under pressure, so much marvelous, rickety improvisation—all of it never more tested than today.

The rumors flared and multiplied: thirty dead, fifty dead, a hundred dead. There were radios everywhere. People cupped them anxiously to their ears, huddled around them in groups, listened in at open car doors. The commentators brayed and babbled. They knew no more than anyone else. By the afternoon the death toll was said to have reached 200. But this was well short of the final count: 490 lives were lost on Holy Thursday, and some 35,000 people were left homeless. Outside Popayán, whole villages—El Tambo, Cajibio, Piendamó—had been virtually flattened.

All day I wandered the broken city, with that hollow feeling inside that is really fear, but that feels like a sadness. By late afternoon, like an exhausted body, the town seemed to sway through a sudden oscillation of mood. There was a defiant surge of adrenaline in the air. The street vendors and roadside cooks had sprouted like irrepressible weeds. Later, this fragile mood faded and there was just exhaustion. And with it came the worst realization of all. This wasn't just a dreadful day, a nightmare from which they would awake next morning. The *terremoto* was here to stay. Tomorrow their houses would still be in pieces, their livelihoods buried. Tomorrow, next month, next year, they would still be putting the broken city together again.

That night everyone slept in the street for fear of another tremor. All night, fires burned at the street corners and trucks rolled through the dark town. There was a general curfew: any attempt to move more than a block encountered tired, suspicious soldiers who sent you back. It was like a city under siege. The air was filled with the smoke of the bonfires, and the smothering taste of masonry dust as the fall-out continued.

On Good Friday morning I joined the thin stream of refugees heading for the new bus station on the edge of town. There I found more scenes of chaos, and a degree of urgency owing to the rumor that all the gas stations in town would soon be out of fuel, and then no more buses would be going. A bus was leaving for Cali as I got there, but it was already jam-packed, and the driver was turning people away. Another bus came, but it was for Pasto, due south. I was buying some provisions in the depot store when another Cali bus came in, and I was again too late to squeeze in. I was beginning to feel the panic of being stuck, Chocó despairs revisited, and when a fourth bus rolled in, dusty and dilapidated, I piled in hastily with the first surge of people, and was well ensconced in the aisle at the back before I'd even learned where the bus was bound. For La Vega and Valencia, I was told. Where were they, I asked, wedged in too tight to consult my road map. In the mountains, *señor*. As the bus headed out, I began to wonder if I was being wise. There wasn't a single tourist aboard. There must have been eighty people in that rattletrap old bus, and it looked like every one of them was going into the mountains because they *lived* there.

During a hot, honking, two-hour wait for gas, I had ample time to reconsider.

I was about to cut my losses and head back into town, when a young man, bright-eyed and earnest, said to me, "Up around Valencia it is very beautiful."

"I'm sure it is," I said, "but there's no way on. I must get north." The time for sightseeing was over.

"But you can," he cried. "The road runs out at Valencia, but there is a trail that goes down into Huila department. It is the old pilgrim way, the *camino real*, between San Agustín and Popayán. From Valencia it is three days by foot to San Agustín, or perhaps you will be able to get a mule to ride. From San Agustín, of course, there are buses."

When the bus finally set off, I was still on it.

Valencia was a straggling, one-street village, subsisting on cold-climate crops and the sale of milk to the dairies that supply Popayán. The air at dusk was chill and rare. Fifty pesos bought a musty bed for the night in a house that served as the village inn.

In the morning the sky was gray. There were horsemen in the street, wood smoke in the air, milk churns waiting to be trucked down the mountain. I learned that I could hire a mule at the house of Gustavo Papamija. This was easy to find, I was told. It was *la última casa*. So out of the village I went, walking east, up to the last house. It was an hour's easy going on a trail bordered by stubby trees and green meadows. On the way I met an old, pixielike Páez man in a woolly hat. He insisted I rest and eat with him in his hut beside the trail. It was dark and smoky inside. Old clothes and horse tack hung from the mud walls. A watery gray broth simmered on the *candela*, the low wood fire that is never allowed to go out. The soup—maize and cabbage, both growing in the plot outside the door—tasted thin, stalky and saltless. I brought out white cheese, bread and aguardiente. We ate out of black pots, mostly in silence. It was a gentle, tonic silence, full of birdsong. It is *sano* here, he said—a word often used by the country folk of Colombia—sane and healthy, not like the other Colombia of *mala fama*, bad name. I reflected guiltily that it was precisely the country's *mala fama* that had brought me here in the first place.

Gustavo Papamija's house was low, white and tin-roofed, huddled in the lee of the hill. Gustavo was not at home, but his wife was—a small, tubby Indian, wearing trousers under her dress—and his two big sons, and a black-haired, beautiful girl, about twenty, called Anilia, and assorted kids, dogs, chickens and a goat. A mule was available, but it would have to be fetched from another farm. We agreed on a price: room and board for the night, and the hire of the mule to a village called Puerto Quinchana, all for 2,000 pesos. At Quinchana I could catch a truck to San Agustín.

Around nine o'clock on the morning of Easter Sunday, I breasted the Páramo de las Papas—the bleak heaths of the Andean highlands—aboard the wide, sure, slow back of Michaka the mule. She was fourteen years old, chestnut brown with a black streak down her rump. I was assured she was *muy mancita*, gentle and tractable. I had directions to leave her with a Señora Paz in Quinchana, a day and a half's ride from Papamija's house.

The *páramo* was a blanket of swirling cloud and driving horizontal rain. It was only an hour's ride across it, I was told, but it was going to be a cold, wet hour. To my left I saw the Laguna de Magdalena, a small lake glinting through the mist like tarnished pewter. This was the source of the Magdalena River. I persuaded a reluctant Michaka off down a side path toward it, and found the stream issuing from the lake. There was nothing much to see, a thin black trickle through yellow tussocks, but it was something to know that this same water was going to run right up through Colombia, fatten into a wide river, and flow into the Caribbean Sea 1,000 miles away. In fact I suddenly found this very encouraging. "Coastbound!" I shouted into the rain. "From now on, coastbound," I said more gently to Michaka. She looked unimpressed, and turned back up toward the trail.

Once the sun had dried me, I decided that there could be few pleasanter ways of spending Easter Sunday than coming down through the stupendous forested gorges of the Huila highlands on the back of a mule. The local populace seemed to have other ideas, for I didn't see a soul on the trail all day. I learned the ways of Michaka the mule—very set ways, as she knew the trail intimately. She knew where a certain broad-leaved plant grew, and no amount of shouting and cuffing could dissuade her from stopping for a few mouthfuls. She knew where the track ran too steep and stony, and refused to budge until I dismounted. When *I* wanted to dismount for some reason, however, she knew it was unnecessary, and ambled implacably on while I tugged at the reins. I talked to her about this and that. She signaled mysteriously with her ears. I quickly developed a deep respect for her, but was never quite sure if the feeling was mutual.

Toward evening we came to a cluster of farms in a green valley, with the stubble of recent clearance on the slopes. At one of these I found a bed for the night, and grazing for Michaka. The next day we made it to the dusty, one-horse village of Puerto Quinchana around two o'clock. I found Señora Paz, said goodbye to Michaka, and a couple of hours later I was rolling out to San Agustín in an open-sided bus.

I lingered a day and two nights in San Agustín, famous for its extraordinary collection of pre-Columbian statuary, strange brooding figures scattered among the woods and hills around the village like petrified extraterrestrials. From San Agustín, I got a bus to Neiva, a hot, unremarkable town in the lowlands, and from there I flew to Bogotá. The whole crazy tangent became a circle, and I was back where I'd started three weeks ago. I didn't leave Eldorado airport this time. I sat tight and waited for the next flight to the coast. It left at dawn, for Santa Marta. By breakfast time I was on the coast at last. *La costa del caribe!*

CHAPTER FIFTEEN

Chilean Packages

Back in Santa Marta, "the pearl of the Americas," everything was in place. The same scruffy waterfront, with its promenade of coconut palms. The same banana boats lying off on the glazed sea. The same seafront cafés doing their slow morning business. I had a *tinto* at the Pan-American for old times' sake. The waiter said no, they didn't have bands on Saturday nights.

I cut up across the Parque Bolívar, away from the sea, and into the grid of hot side streets that ran up toward the *mercado popular*. The scrubby, sandy foothills beyond the town looked parched. The streets were pale, bleached with sun, sliced with shadows, the low houses predominantly

whitewashed, but here and there daubed with pastels, faded Mediterranean tones of pink, blue and pistachio-green.

I turned into 10th Street. Looking at where the whitewashed frontage
and grilled windows of the Fruit Palace should be, I realized I had come
on to the street too high. I walked back down a couple of blocks, toward
the thin band of sea. I was on the right part of the street now, but I still
couldn't see the Fruit Palace, and it took me a moment to shake off my
expectations, and see that the house was still there, much the same as before, only the signboard had been taken down, and instead there was
painted boldly on the wall, "Restaurante y Mercados EL PROGRESO."

Inside, the counter was in a different place, and the burly man behind
it was definitely not Julio. Otherwise everything was much the same, only
the range of *jugos* was not as it had been in Julio's day. The place was
empty, as ever.

I ordered a sapodilla juice. We traded a few pleasantries. He was surly
but not unresponsive. The sun streamed in from the yard where I had lived.
Behind a line of washing was the henhouse where poor old Harvey had
ended up on that night of fiasco all those years ago.

"This place was once called the Fruit Palace, wasn't it?"

The man looked up from the blender with a squint of suspicion. He admitted that it was.

"I stayed here for a while, a few years ago, in the little room out back.
I was hoping to find the man who used to run the place, Julio. He was a
friend."

He shook his head. No, he didn't know anything about Julio. He had
bought the Fruit Palace from someone called Luis, four or five years ago.

I drank my *jugo*. The radio played an unexpectedly sad ballad. There
were two caged birds above the door—yellow and black *toque*, scarlet
sangre de toros—and a guinea pig running loose, fattening up on café dust
before going into the pot. It was so quiet in the Progress Restaurant and
Stores that I could hear the dry, scaly rattle in the corner, as the guinea pig
snuffled at the corpse of a cockroach.

At the Hotel Corona—a converted monastery on 12th Street, very run-
down, recommended by the man at El Progreso—I took an upstairs room,
300 pesos a night, no meals. It was scruffy but clean: a flagged floor, a low
bed, a ceiling fan, a cubicle with a shower—or at least an overhead tap—
and a bathroom. The long shuttered window opened onto the hotel courtyard, but the fruit trees in the patio were bushy enough to keep the room
private. The desk boy, Omar, was a friendly, handsome Creole, about
eighteen. Other people involved in the running of the hotel—vague *ad-
ministradores*, porters, maids—were sometimes there, but Omar was always there, lounging at the desk, puttering in the courtyard, or lying on
his bed in the back room ready to poke his head out. He listened all day

long to *vallenatos* on the radio—Radio Galeón—and read his way slowly through a huge pile of Venezuelan trash mags. These cartoon penny-dreadfuls—*un cine en su bolsillo*, a movie in your pocket—are staple reading for Colombians of all ages.

Also staying at the Corona, just down the balcony from me, was a traveling couple, Renate and Renaldo. She was a languid, blousy, *jolie laide* Swiss; he was a Titianesque Venetian with a fierce black mustache and long black hair, out of which a small plaited pigtail emerged piratically. Neither of them spoke English, so we talked in Spanish. Renate droned through travelers' yarns; Renaldo was quieter, more mercurial. They had been traveling around South America for five years, and while they hadn't been in Santa Marta long, they had slid with ease into its nonchalant rhythms. Santa Marta pampers your vices so attentively they begin to feel like virtues. Renate slept late in the mornings, but Renaldo was always up around six-thirty, while the sky was still pink, to head down to the town beach. He would jog along the crescent-shaped bay, a good fifteen minutes' trot there and back, do some exercises, swim and return, purchasing the morning paper on the way back. After a shower he was ready for his Santa Marta breakfast, the *blanco y negro*, two generous rails of cocaine and two stiff cups of *tinto*. The *tintos* were brought by Omar, over whom he held a mysterious sway. Thus torqued up, he would attend to the day's small businesses—purchases, money-changing, and so on. Then it was back to the Corona, where Renate was raising a sleepy head, or reading in bed. They would share a joint of Punto Rojo, and then take a long, leisurely breakfast proper at one of the seafront cafés—eggs *pericos*, perhaps a shrimp *ceviche*, bread and guava jelly, coffee, *jugos*. Breakfast would slide effortlessly into lunchtime, a couple of beers here, a chat and a deal there: lottery-sellers, street vendors, gringos, Samarios, they seemed to know them all. After this came the siesta, ritually observed, then around four o'clock the day's second segment would begin, another period of activity, often their time for receiving people in their room. They had a profitable little sideline in drugs, selling discreet batches of slightly overpriced *perico* to gringos who didn't want the hassle of scoring off the street. Around 5:30, just as the sun was beginning to cool, they took another swim at the town beach, and returned to the Corona to prepare for the evening's festivities.

The pace of life was slow, not dull but slow, a lazy adagio punctuated by sudden scherzos of small-town drama, and by the insistent undertone of villainy that ran through the place. Nothing happened, nothing was done, but always in the most entertaining way. Pleasant though it was to let the clock run slow, and sit in the sun, and have time bring you scenes as a breeze brings scents, I had a job to do. I was here to write a story, and I knew that Santa Marta, if anywhere, was the place to do it. I was going to forget all about Bogotá, Gus, basuko addicts, slaughterhouses and earthquakes. This was Santa Marta, *la costa*. I was back in the smugglers' den, the good-time town, the rock 'n' roll South America. At last I was going to get this story off the ground.

I had a plan of sorts. Part of the problem in Bogotá had been my own approach. It was no use expecting to bustle in with my pen and notebook, and put it together from a few secondhand stories. As Gus had pointed out, the people that matter in the drug racket like to keep everything off the record. I had been two months in Colombia, spent most of my money, been jacked full of cocaine and basuko, and had still yet to meet anyone that mattered. I had *possibly* shaken hands with a cocaine baron—Don Rafael Vallejo at the San Felipe slaughterhouse, who *may* have been Gus's mysterious Snow White—but that could hardly count as the scoop of the decade. It was time to tuck my notebook under my pillow and enter Phase Two. Surely Gus was right when he said one night in his crow's nest: "The only way to get into this story is to become a part of it."

My plan was, in a nutshell, to pose as a would-be buyer of a consignment of cocaine. Ten kilos seemed a nice round number: a middle-sized amount, serious enough to require proper smuggling rather than a simple mule run through customs, but without getting up into the industrial volumes being moved by the big mafia syndicates.

One problem about posing as a buyer was cash, or the lack of it. Here in Santa Marta a kilo of cocaine cost around $15,000, a little more than in Bogotá or Cali, because it was closer to the retail market. There tends to be little bulk discounting in big drug purchases, so 10 kilos was going to carry a price tag of something like $150,000. I didn't actually need the money, as I wasn't actually going to buy any cocaine. All I needed was the appearance of having—or of being able to get hold of—the money. I needed, in short, collateral.

Accordingly, soon after arriving in Santa Marta, I telephoned Malcolm in London. A secretary, a tinkling double-barreled voice from another planet, told me to hold on a minute. The minute ticked away expensively. "Sorry, he seems to have just popped out." More minutes. Then at last the distant, flushed voice of Malcolm. "Charles! Super! How's it going?" I assured him it was all going wonderfully, piping hot stories at every turn, practically writing itself, and so on.

"Listen, Malcolm, I'm calling because I think I'm going to need a bit of backup."

Over all those miles of cable I heard him wince. "Pretty difficult, Charles," he brayed. "End of the tax year. They're pretty sticky up in Accounts at the moment."

"I don't mean money, though Christ knows, I could use some. I want collateral."

"Could you be more specific?"

"In a few days' time I'm probably going to send you a cable. I'm not sure what it'll say, but when you get it I want you to cable straight back to me. What you'll say is: 'Price is good, but check all transport before proceeding.' That's all. Have you got that?''

"Yes, I've got that."

"Good. Send it to me at the Corona Hotel, Santa Marta."

"Yes, all right. But, you know, what's all this in aid of?"

"Call it a sprat to catch a smuggler. Look, I must go." I ran through it one last time. "Oh, and Malcolm, don't sign it, will you? No names. What? Yes, of course it's all above board. Yes, totally kosher. Bye now!"

The next stage was to find someone with 10 kilos to sell. I did not anticipate many problems here. The coke runneth over in Santa Marta. I decided to try Waldino, the black-bearded Mr. Fixit so warmly praised by Jairo, the Samario I had met with Julio Cesar that night on Caracas Avenue.

It didn't take long to find Waldino. Availability was his *métier*. The desk boy at the Corona, Omar, knew him by sight. He suggested I ask for him at La Casona, a bar near the waterfront. There I was directed to a stationery shop off 5th Avenue, the town's main shopping and business street. In the cluttered, slightly funereal shop, a black-bearded man was helping a pair of schoolgirls with exercise books and pencils. It seemed an unlikely venue for starting up a cocaine deal, but when the girls left, I walked nervously up to the counter, clutching a roll of tape, and asked if he was Waldino.

He wasn't, but he could find him. Waldino was one of his partners. He handed me a pen, and a promotional notepad, and said to write my name and where I could be contacted. The pen had a picture of Spiderman on it.

"OK, mister," the man said briskly. "Waldino will find you."

It all seemed unbelievably slick and easy. But a few hours later, toward the end of siesta-time, slight complications began to creep in. There was a soft knock at my door, Omar's voice saying, "You have a visitor downstairs." It was the man from the stationery shop.

"I have spoken with Waldino, *señor*. Unfortunately he is detained for a few days in Cartagena. He says if your business is urgent you must meet him there."

Anxious to get things moving, I said, yes, I would meet him in Cartagena. The man said I should be outside the Paragua café at three o'clock tomorrow. This was down in Bocagrande, the beach resort part of Cartagena. Once again he assured me, "Waldino will find you."

I told the man I would fly to Cartagena, to give a businesslike impression, but my resources were getting low, and it was in fact Flota la Velocidad—the Velocity Bus Company—that took me to Cartagena the next morning. It was a hot, cloudless day. We trailed dust and *vallenato* accordions out of Santa Marta, south to Ciénaga, and across the narrow causeway between the Caribbean and the swampy lagoons of the Ciénaga Grande, dotted with floating villages of mangrove wood. Not long after midday we were nosing through the dusty white outskirts of Cartagena. On a wall a graffito read, "TU ESQUELETO ES VIVO"—your skeleton is alive. Of that I was certain, if of little else.

The bus disembarked us near the San Felipe fortress. I took a town bus down to Bocagrande. This is Colombia's most fashionable beach resort, a long, thin isthmus jutting out south from the old walled town, fringed with beaches and gridded with hotels, boutiques and sidewalk cafés. At the far end, a late addition to the city's many fortresses, stands the Cartagena Hilton. Locals call the area "Miami Chiquita"—Little Miami—and that about sums it up.

In the lobby of the Hotel Succar, where I went to buy a street map, a bespectacled American, sweating profusely, was carefully consigning his money, passport, air tickets and watch to the hotel safe. The *portero*'s eyes glinted as the money was counted out—$2,500 in American Express checks and a few hundred more in bills. I grinned at the American. He scowled back. "If I wasn't such a trusting guy, I'd put my goddamn shirt in there as well!" It transpired that he had arrived that morning from Panama City, tried to change some dollars where he shouldn't have, and ended up with that local speciality, *el paquete chileno*. A "Chilean package"—for reasons obscure—signifies any raw deal, any crockful of short change: a bagful of oregano instead of grass, a gram of borax instead of coke, or in this man's case, an envelope containing a neat wad tied up in a rubber band, with a 1,000-peso bill uppermost and every other sheet blank paper. He had that hot, haunted look, a big man running his hand through his hair. I thought of Harvey, hopelessly outpointed by events that night at the Fruit Palace. There's something about this place: the heat, the ceiling fans, the smilers with knives. Beware the Chilean package! *La costa* means the cost as well as the coast.

At three o'clock, as arranged, I was waiting outside the Paragua, a big pavement café on a corner of 2nd Avenue. It was quiet, siesta-time. A few people moved slowly on the shady side of the street. It occurred to me that Waldino knew nothing of what I wanted—not a word had been mentioned about cocaine. For all I knew he might be hoping to sell me a gross of Spiderman pens.

3:15, 3:20, no one came. A waiter cleaning tables near me started to chat. Then I saw someone strolling purposefully across the street toward us, a small man in a floppy yellow T-shirt. I had seen him over on the other side, in the Presto fast-food joint, drinking something out of a paper cup. Now he joined me on the sidewalk, hand stretched out. "Hey, my friend. Where you from? You been in Cartagena before? You gonna be glad you come. *Con mucho gusto!*" We shook hands. "Luis," he said, then repeated it for my benefit in the form of "Louey." He cocked his head to one side like a parrot, waiting for my name in return. *"Perfecto!"* he cried, "I have a real good friend called Charlie. From Estados Unidos. Man, you'd like that guy!" He spoke fast, slurring, half in the gabble of *costeño* Spanish, half in grating greengo-Eenglish. He was small, grubby and unshaven, and looked like he had shrunk inside his clothes. As he spoke he was leading me gently toward the street, drawing me away from the chatty waiter. The waiter shrugged and shook his head philosophically. He'd seen it all before. Just another Bocagrande street boy fastening on to another dollar-rich gringo. I was beginning to think exactly the same.

"No," I said, pulling away from his grip. "I don't want anything. I'm waiting for a friend." We were out of the waiter's earshot now.

"Claro, hombre," said Louey. "Your friend Waldino, my friend Waldino. He sent me to get you. We go just a couple of blocks, this way."

The couple of blocks turned out to be more like twenty. We hopped aboard a bus that took us out of Bocagrande and up to the walls of the old town. Louey didn't pay, just gave the driver a curt wave of greeting and pushed us both through the turnstile. "Everyone in Cartagena knows Louey," he explained, and settled his scrawny frame in the seat, very casual, legs loosely crossed, ankle on knee. He spent the journey looking out the window, dreamily fingering his stubble.

He was watching me, I thought. All the while I was waiting he was there, checking my credentials, seeing if I had anyone with me, sniffing my scent. I was in at the business end at last. I'd need more than a street map if I lost my way now.

Inside the old walled town everything is very tall, narrow and close. It is beautiful, but somber and inquisitorial: dirty white walls, deep eaves, cobbled streets, huge wooden doors studded with iron nails. Sultry eyes watch from grilled windows and luxuriant balconies. The touristic parts of the old town, El Centro and San Diego, are where the governors, priests and merchants lived, but there is another, rougher quarter called Getsemani, a warren of white one-story houses, *casas bajas*, once inhabited by artisans and soldiers and street traders, the flotsam of the *conquista*. Into this we now plunged. Louey led the way with a long, jaunty stride, calling out greetings every few yards. I followed behind like his pet dog. The streets were steep, some just wide enough for a car, some so narrow you could touch both walls as you passed. We turned this way and that. I had no idea where I was or where I was going.

Louey dipped into a narrow, tiled café, La Reina Victoria, and asked the boy behind the counter for two cold beers. Down the far end of the bar stood a short, wide, stocky man, a *mestizo* in his sallow coloring, a Negro in the bones of his face and the wide, flattened nose. His beard was, as promised, black and profuse. His eyebrows and hair wiry.

Louey walked up to him, said something I didn't hear, scraped a chair around and settled himself astride it. The man put out his hand. *"Señor, qué tal?"* he said pleasantly. "I am Waldino." The boy brought the beers and a *tinto* for Waldino.

"Who gave you my name?" asked Waldino.

"A Samario called Jairo. I met him in Bogotá."

His small eyes flickered, looking for the face to fit the name. He found it. "Ah! Jairo." Rich, feckless Jairo. Not an impeccable reference, I guessed from his face, but at least genuine.

There was a short spell of aimless pleasantries. Waldino was a Guajiro, I learned, from San Juan del Cesar, a small town halfway between the Sierra Nevada mountains and the Venezuelan border, doubtless a good breeding ground for *contrabandistas*. Eventually a silence fell, and there was nowhere else to go but down to business. I looked around. A couple more people had come into the café. "Can we talk here?" I said.

"Perhaps you would like to go out back," said Waldino. "I'll show you the view."

We walked out through a storeroom, Louey following, and into a little backyard. Waldino had an oddly dainty way of moving, considering his swarthy looks. Short, busy steps, pointed black leather shoes. I wondered vaguely if he was gay. The view was stupendous—a tumbling scree of tiled roofs, the blue sea stretching off into the haze. The yard was a mess. An outbuilding had recently been demolished, but there was a straggling catalpa tree giving shade, and a chair, an upturned crate and a pile of rubble provided us with seats. We arranged ourselves hierarchically: Waldino, me and Louey. Louey unzipped his jeans and drew out a twist of brown paper from a pocket sewn inside the waistband. He began to roll a joint, and I began to make my pitch.

"Jairo tells me you're a good person to do business with, Waldino."

He received the compliment graciously, but somehow at arm's length.

"What kind of business are we talking about?"

I dabbed the side of my nose with my forefinger.

"Ah! Negocios blancos, no?"

"Yes, white business."

"And are we talking here about little business or big business?"

"If the price is right and the quality is good, we're talking about 10 kilos. Is that little business or big business?"

His eyes narrowed. He scratched his beard watchfully, his eyes penetrating me with the crystal-ball gaze of the Colombian dealer, whose livelihood—perhaps his life—depends on the swift sizing up of potential customers. "Ten kilos," he said, with a modest shrug. "This is no problem. I can get it." He knitted his pudgy fingers, rested them on his thigh, and staring at them intently he said, "You got money?"

I took a deep breath. "At this precise moment ... No." He was still looking down at his hands, but a single shaggy eyebrow cocked up challengingly. "Let me explain, Waldino. I am here, essentially, as a *representante*." He opened his eyes wide for a moment, gave a little wary sigh, "Ah!" This description of myself seemed to have explained the situation a little without in any way improving it. I hastened on. "I am here on behalf of certain... friends, in London. They wish me to establish a connection, work out the arrangements. Once everything is worked out—good *perico*, good price, good setup—I will cable them in London. They will have the money transferred to me."

He pursed his lips. "You going to carry the *mercancía* out yourself?"

"Of course not," I said. "That will have to be worked out between us. I'm sure you must have—"

"Sí, sí, hombre," he said, waving aside any doubts. "Transportation no problem." He stood up, hands in pockets, looking out to sea. The sounds of the city floated up on the sullen air. The sun was sneaking around the edge of the catalpa tree, melting the shade on me. Louey handed me the joint. I smelled the fresh, resinous smoke, like minty hay smoldering on a summer's day. The smoke licked around my skull, the sun toasted my face. I handed the reefer to Waldino but he shook his head, and I instantly regretted having taken some. This silence was too long. I must fill it.

"My friends in London," I volunteered. "They are very keen to make a connection here. They have dealt mainly in hashish from the Middle East. If you can provide the right service, they will want to place regular orders, big volumes. I think we could both do very well out of this."

He looked impressed; he was still demurring, still worrying at my weak points. "You don't even have a little money to put up front?" he said. "Not even a *poquito*?" His finger and thumb measured out the thinnest wedge of bills that a self-respecting *contrabandista* could imagine.

I shook my head. "It's up to you, Waldino. I assure you the money is no problem, but only when I know exactly what's happening. Of course," I added, "I could front you 1,000 pesos for a little *muestra*, but I'm sure you don't need me to do that. We're talking about a serious deal here. My friends in London are... well, they're big *capos*."

As I said this I had a brief, unsettling vision of Malcolm, ruddy and bespectacled, the phantom Mr. Big in a Bloomsbury bow tie.

Waldino looked at his watch. "OK," he said. "I have to make a phone call. You wait here." He tripped back into the café.

I paced around the little yard, smoking a cigarette. Who was Waldino phoning? What did he think of me? I sat back down. In a corner a lizard moved across hot masonry, yellow and black, darting and waiting.

Waldino returned. "I think I can help you with this," he said. "I shall be back in Santa Marta on Friday, two days. You are at the Corona, no? I will find you there. We will talk about this *very* carefully."

The interview was over. The hook seemed to have caught. Louey guided me back through the labyrinth, back to where there were crowds and buses and reality. Surely it had all been a dream. I hadn't really just opened up negotiations for a 10-kilo move. I hadn't really just sold them my very own little Chilean package.

CHAPTER SIXTEEN

Waldino Can Get It

I returned to Santa Marta. I swam, I wrote, I waited for Waldino. On Saturday afternoon, three days after our meeting in Getsemani, he came. I walked out of the shower in my room at the Corona to find him standing in the open doorway. He murmured an apology as I fumbled a towel around my waist.

"I have brought it, Charlie," he said. He was carrying two large plastic bags. I felt a stab of panic. Sweet Jesus, I thought, he's bringing me the deal *now*. The fool's got it all wrong.

"Brought it?" I said. I stared at the bulging carrier bags.

He bustled in and laid them on the bed. "I think you will like it. I know you will like it. You want to try some now?" I stammered without meaning. "Señor Charlie," he said, with a broad, reproachful grin. "This is primo grade merchandise. What I tell you? Waldino can get it, no problem. *Max*-imum quality. *Muy puro.*" He spat out the phrases with relish.

"But, Waldino, I don't want the stuff now!"

He stared at me, nonplussed. The gap between his eyebrows and his beard momentarily widened, like a trapdoor long covered with undergrowth, then it clamped shut again into a petulant, bullish frown which I didn't like one little bit. He said quietly, "You do not want to try the *muestra* I have brought for you?"

"Muestra?"

The bags had nothing to do with it. He had only brought me a sample. Watching me closely he reached into his shirt pocket, and drew out the familiar little rectangle of paper. "It is only a little, of course. I can get more, plenty more, but . . ."

"Yes. No, that's fine, Waldino. Thank you." I cursed my stupid, clumsy paranoia. Jumping to the wrong conclusion could be fatal. There wouldn't always be a chance to jump back again.

I took the proffered *muestra* and tried to settle into the cool professionalism that I felt the situation demanded. I poked and sifted the white crystal. Waldino fidgeted around the room, anxiously muttering his adman's phrases. I peered and dabbed and tasted, pulled a face or two, demurred like a wine-buff. *"Reluce demasiado, no?"* I said. Too much glitter in it.

"Amigo," he came back earnestly. "That is good. The snow is sparkling. You try it and see."

I laid out a rail on my shaving mirror and took it up through a 100-peso note. It was good. *Muestras* usually are, I thought, remembering the Harvey fiasco. Waldino hovered by. I complimented him on his powder. There was no doubt about it. It was cool as a mountain stream. I offered him some, but he declined. "It's for you, Charlie." I took another snort up the other nostril. My brain put on its sailing shoes.

"You can get this stuff in quantity?"

"Of course."

"And the price?"

He scratched his head and seemed to wrestle with complex currency calculations. "Twenty thousand U.S. a kilo," he said. I knew this was high, so we haggled a bit. It was all absurdly genial. I might have been shaving a few pesos off a bunch of fruit at the market. We eventually agreed on $17,000 per kilo. That this was not an especially good price didn't much matter to me. I wanted only to keep the ball rolling.

I then broached the all-important question of trasportation. Who was going to do the smuggling, and how?

There were two options open, said Waldino. The first was to use his connections inside the Santa Marta docks, and get the merchandise on board a ship bound for Europe. The second—and the one he recommended—was to use a *barco privado*, a small private boat. He knew a *trasportista* who offered a tidy, all-in service, running dope and cocaine to the Dutch Antilles, about 400 kilometers northeast of Santa Marta. There it was transferred to a cargo ship bound for the Netherlands. It could be picked up at Rotterdam or Amsterdam. This pipeline worked like a dream, he said. It was run by a "very special friend." The cost of this service was $30,000, non-negotiable, bringing the total money required up-front, for 10 kilos of pure cocaine delivered in Amsterdam, to $200,000.

I said I thought the price would be acceptable. "Of course," I added—now I came to the linchpin of the whole scam—"I will have to check all this out, Waldino. I will need to meet your *trasportistas*, discuss everything with them."

Waldino looked pained. "Charlie. This is difficult. These people are professionals. I work with them many times. They trust me. You must trust me, Charlie. I told you, Waldino takes care of everything."

"Of course I trust you, Waldino. But you must understand, this is my job here. I too work for professionals. They want me to know exactly what's happening before they put any money in."

Waldino continued to stall. Naturally I had anticipated this. As the middleman, he had considerable vested interest in keeping the links in the pipeline separate. He existed in the space between me and the others. This was the whole point of my arrangement with Malcolm. His cable was going to force Waldino to take me to them.

As we talked there came a knock at the door. Before I was even on my feet Waldino had scooped up the *muestra* off the mirror, and was ready to toss it out the window. I heard a familiar voice call my name. *"Tranquilo,"* I said, staying his arm. "She's a friend."

I opened the door, and there stood Renate. "Hello," she said, languid against the door jamb, sunglasses and thin white blouse. Waldino's manner shifted abruptly. *"Buenas tardes, señorita,"* he said, smirking like a tango-singer. Renate eyed him coldly. *"Señora,"* she corrected, untruthfully, a reflex action after five years on the road with every small-town stud in South America bidding to get into her knickers. She was not beautiful, but she had one of those ripe, pale, faintly corrupt bodies—a touch of Rubens—that seem to fill the swarthy Latin with anticipations of sexual *delicias*.

I introduced them. She said, "We thought you'd like to come over for a drink, Charlie." Then to Waldino, "You want a drink too? You can meet my husband."

Waldino thanked her. "Another time perhaps." We had a quick conference out on the balcony. We arranged to meet the next morning at the Telecom. I would cable my "friends" in London, telling them of the price, and we would await their reply. He was just about to go when he remembered his carrier bags, still sitting on the bed.

"By the way," I said, recalling my earlier mistake. "What *is* in your bags?"

"Bollos," he said. "Here, have a couple." *Bollos* are small puddings, made of maize and milk, wrapped in plantain leaves. "They're for my little daughter," he explained. "She loves them."

"You have a daughter?"

"No, *hombre*," he laughed. "I have three, and a son also." He gave a silky little bow to Renate—*"Hasta luego, señora"*—and tripped off along the balcony. So Waldino was a family man. I found this vaguely unsettling.

The next morning I met Waldino outside the Telecom on 5th Avenue. I made great play of the cable. It must be sent in code, of course, Waldino. Our code is real estate. (I had cooked this up in bed last night.) The telegram read: "TEN HECTARES IN EXCELLENT POSITION STOP TWO HUNDRED THOUSAND DOLLARS ALL SERVICES INCLUDED STOP AWAIT INSTRUCTION." I explained it all carefully to Waldino, and translated it into Spanish for him. I even showed him the words in my little pocket dictionary. What was it Rosalita had said? One big lie with lots of little truths around it. He was definitely impressed. He didn't even mind when I had to borrow a few pesos off him to pay for the telegram.

I sweated the next thirty-six hours, fretting over the endless possibilities of a screw up at Malcolm's end. Then the answer arrived, bristling with authentic London digits, and bearing the prearranged message: "PRICE IS GOOD BUT CHECK ALL TRANSPORT BEFORE PROCEEDING." Malcolm had got it right. The hook was baited.

"You see, Waldino? I told you. I have to check it all out, the whole move, before they come up with the dollars." I tried to sound resigned rather than triumphant.

He took it well, stubby hands raised in mock submission. "OK, OK, OK. I will talk with the *trasportistas*. They will show you everything, explain everything. Then we get this thing moving, OK?" Off he went, tubby figure squeezed into a shiny, palm tree-print beach shirt, an almost palpable little cloud of worry over his head. All these big numbers floating around, all these little problems in the way.

Two, three, five days went by, and nothing happened. I met Waldino a few times, but he seemed evasive and tetchy. A few twinges of doubt began to steal in. Was Waldino faking too? Were his cocaine runners as chimerical as my big London *capos*? The rhythms of Santa Marta grew daily more torpid, and I grew daily more certain that nothing at all was going to happen, that the Great Cocaine Story was finally going to sink, like the sieve of empty promises it had always been.

I spent a lot of time with Renate and Renaldo, sliding gracefully downhill. It was the *blanco y negro* for breakfast, Punto Rojo for lunch, *ron coco* for tea. Of these *ron coco* is not the least. This simple, sweet and deadly drink is prepared as follows: Take a ripe brown coconut, slice off the top, drain some of the milk, pour in a generous slug of rum, white or brown to taste, replace the top, and leave it to steep for a day or so. Cocktail books would doubtless recommend it served with crushed ice, but there was no ice at the Corona, and anyway the best way to take *ron coco* is straight out of the shell, passed around like a pipe of peace, with reinforcements of rum to top it up with compound interest. In Santa Marta they call this way of drinking rum *chupando el mono*, sucking the monkey.

Then one morning I returned to the Corona from breakfast at the seafront to find Waldino leaning at the desk. He greeted me warmly and asked if I had anything planned for the day.

"Nothing special."

"OK then, let's go!" He steered me back out of the door, into the street.

"Where are we going?"

"To see a man about a boat."

Outside, parked up on the curb of the narrow street, was a brand new maroon Sierra station wagon, glinting in the sun. A couple of *gamines* were peering into it. Waldino shooed them away officiously. They had shaven heads, which meant they had been pulled into the police station once too often. With a jocular bow, Waldino opened the passenger door and ushered me in.

"Very impressive, Waldino," I said. The new seats, baked in the morning sun, gave off a pungent plastic aroma. "Is this yours?"

"It belongs to one of my partners," he said. With a crunch of gears we bounced off the curb and down toward 5th Avenue. He drove slowly down the avenue, a hirsute arm resting casually on the open window. He called out and waved at friends. He looked very pleased with life, eyes twinkling amid the black undergrowth. In the kudos language of Santa Marta, a brand-new station wagon spoke loud and clear.

We were going to Taganga, he explained, a small fishing village just around the headland from Santa Marta. We were going to meet a man called Agatón. I asked if this Agatón was the *trasportista*, but he only said, "not exactly," and when I started asking something else he growled amiably, "No more questions. I'll take you there, I'll do the talking. You sit back and enjoy the ride."

We headed out past the market, through the rind of wooden shacks at the edge of town, and up into the scrub hills. Santa Marta lay below us, the streets trapped in a hot, chalky haze. Twenty minutes later we were in Taganga. There was not a lot to the place: a few sand streets that gridded up from the sea, a few boats bobbing in the bay, a few fishermen at their chores. We stopped the car in shade and strolled around the shore for a bit. We drank a beer at one of the stalls by the beach. Waldino began checking his watch. It was getting near lunchtime. He went to talk with a fisherman mending a net strung between almond trees. He came bustling back. His shirt had half untucked itself from his waistband. He looked scruffy, hot and a little worried.

"Let's go," he said.

"Where?"

"To Negangue."

"But isn't Agatón going to meet us here?"

"I don't think so."

We climbed back into the car. The seat burned my back. "Look, Waldino," I said. "Does Agatón know we're coming today?" He gave that wavering *"Sí-i-i-i"* that most often means "No."

"For Christ's sake, does he know we're coming or not?"

"No. I know *he* is coming." I stared at him. Even Waldino had to admit he owed me an explanation. "I know Agatón's bringing the boat in today. He's meeting someone. Sometimes he comes in at Taganga, sometimes Negangue. They're hard to get hold of, *hombre*. You have to *find* them, and the best time is when they come in."

"Come in from where?"

"From their place, Charlie. Their *ranchito*. They don't often use the road. It's quicker and quieter by boat. OK, enough questions. We go to Negangue."

Negangue was a few inlets farther east. We had to drive up to the main road, the Troncal de Caribe, which runs all along the coast from Cartagena to Riohacha, and then back down a winding track through dry, buff-colored hills dotted with *mesquite* and fuzzy black thorn scrub. At the bottom lay a deserted crescent bay and a single dilapidated wooden farmstead. There an old man was sitting, shaving bits of kindling for the range. Four freshly caught iguanas lay outside. They had their front legs tied behind their backs, the claws knotted with wire. Waldino asked if Agatón had been seen here today. No he hadn't. He asked if there was any chance of some lunch—most houses will sell you fried fish and *patacones* for a couple of hundred pesos. But not today. The boys weren't back with the catch yet. The beach was hot, the sand grayish. We sat on rocks beneath a stand of almond trees at the eastern end of the bay, and we waited, smoking cigarettes and getting hungrier.

Around three o'clock I was surprised to see a taxi skidding down the track to the bay. It drove right down onto the sand, and kept on going as far as it could, which was to the rocks where we were sitting. A woman got out, a big handsome woman in a cotton dress with a bold black-and-white pattern. She took out some large parcels, wrapped in plastic and newspaper. The taxi went off back up the track, streaming a plume of dust behind it. She joined us in our patch of shade.

"What you got there?" asked Waldino pleasantly.

"Ice."

"You've come to cool us down then?"

"I've come to meet my husband, *tonto*. He'll cool you down if you like." Poor old Waldino. Every time he looked at a woman she started talking about her husband.

At last we heard the sound we'd been waiting for. At first it was just a faint counterpoint to the gentle whisper of the waves. Then it was definitely the chug and whine of an outboard engine. There were two men in the boat, one black, one *mestizo*.

"There's Agatón," cried Waldino.

"There's my husband," said the woman.

Agatón was a big, flat-faced Negro who looked like Sonny Liston in a bad humor, though differing in one essential respect—he only had one hand. His right arm ended up in a gnarled stump, mauvish in color. He had blown his hand off with dynamite, I later learned, part of the fisherman's lot. He could stun a 100-pound tuna with one blow from this natural club.

He waded ashore, greeted Waldino with a gruff grunt and a cuff on the shoulder. The woman kissed him on the cheek. His hand briefly cupped her rump. He nodded at me. The boat was hauled a little way onto the sand. The woman nuzzled up to the *mestizo*, who wore a baseball cap. I wondered which of them was her husband.

Agatón tramped up the sand, sat down in the shade and lit a cigarette. Waldino skipped along in his wake. They conversed, Waldino voluble, Agatón implacable and ursine, blowing great spouts of tobacco smoke out of his nostrils. Waldino was explaining me, I realized: Agatón didn't know the first thing about me. I could tell from the way Waldino's hands were working. Agatón kept glancing over at me. I kicked around at the water's edge, hoping he was gaining a good impression of me. The woman was loading her cargo of ice on to the boat, helped by the little *mestizo*. He was wiry and unshaven, wearing a vest and long, frayed denim shorts. His cap bore the words "Pittsburgh Pirates."

Now Waldino and Agatón were walking toward me. Waldino hardly came up to his shoulders. Waldino said, "This is Charlie." Agatón held out his good hand. This being his left, I took it in my left. This unfamiliar motion, in my nervousness, became a clumsy and elaborate clasp.

"Waldino tells me you need help with some cargo?"

I nodded, uncertain exactly what Waldino had told him, anxious not to get any wires crossed at this delicate stage.

"It can be arranged," he continued. His deep, smooth voice was almost hypnotic. His face was inscrutable, but there was a glint in it—not quite friendliness, perhaps, but yes, a glint of amusement. "We have good contacts with Europe," he said. He looked off into the distance, as though Europe might actually be glimpsed on the horizon.

"And this is the boat?" I asked, for something to say. He shook his head. The boat was called *El Problema*.

"We have another," he said. "In this one we fish. In the other we handle exports."

He turned away. The interview seemed to be over. He had a few more words with Waldino, then they walked off toward the farmstead. They conferred with the old man. Waldino went and climbed into the station wagon. For a moment I thought he was going, leaving me here at the end of the line with this dubious trio, but he was only moving it to park it up close to the palm-thatch shelter that served as the farmhouse kitchen.

"What's happening, Waldino?" I asked.

"We're going to go for a ride in the boat."

"Where to?"

"To see the boss, of course." He was jaunty again now. "Hey, *amigo*, don't look so worried. You are among friends. This is Waldino!" He thumbed at his chest. "Any friend of Waldino's is welcome with these people."

He strolled over to talk to the *mestizo* and the woman. He did not seem to know them, but soon they were joking together. Waldino motioned me over and introduced us. The *mestizo* was called Miguelito, the woman Rita. Miguelito shook my hand, quickly, wordlessly. He leaped up into the boat, moving like a monkey, and began to tinker with the engine. Rita leaned against the side, running her eyes up and down me. She had a way of chewing her lower lip, and a half smile that seemed to be a suppressed giggle. Her hair, coarse and glossy, jet-black, was piled untidily on her head. The skin on her face was bad: pockmarked and oily, with a perceptible shadow of mustache, but it was a strong, animated face. I couldn't quite place her: part *costeña*, certainly, but with something else mingled in, something which made her taller, more aquiline, more mongrel. "So," she said, smiling at me, "you are coming with us to Finca las Brisas."

I looked at Waldino. He nodded his head encouragingly. "I believe I am," I said, and she laughed her big, throaty, slightly cruel laugh.

We pushed the boat back down into the shallows. *El Problema* was a 12-foot *pesquero*, a dusty, muted blue on the outside, the traditional fisherman's orange on the inside. We arranged ourselves on the plank seats: Agatón at the bow, Waldino and me in the middle, Rita behind us, with Miguelito standing beside her, working the tiller. The sun was just beginning to lose its bite. Its softening light gave the headland waters a rich, creamy appearance. Miguelito started the engine first pull. We were off to Finca las Brisas, Sea Breeze Farm, to meet "the Boss."

No one spoke much during the trip. We scudded along, always within sight of the shore.

After about three-quarters of an hour Miguelito began to guide the boat inshore. I couldn't see anything except a wild-looking headland, with huge white boulders packed in earth. As wc cut close to this promontory pelicans flew up above us. Then I saw the bay, and the ragged settlement of wood and palm-thatch buildings, huddled between the sand and the steep rise of forest behind it. Gangling coconut palms swayed like feather dusters high above the roofs. It looked like the classic tropical hideaway. If Gauguin had stopped off here he would never have made it to Tahiti.

Coasting in there was a small incident. Waldino had spent the voyage in an apparent trance of content, trailing his hand through the water. Now he suddenly leaped up, shouted, "Ay! *Mierda!* Stop, stop!" and started lurching back to the stern of the boat, seeming to catch at something in the water. He tumbled into a tangle with Rita, who squawked and cried, "Help! He's after me!" But he wasn't trying to ravish Rita, or to catch a fish with his bare hands. It was his watch. In the choppy water around the headland, it had worked off his wrist into the slipstream. With a quick, practiced twirl of the rudder, Miguelito brought the boat around. We bobbed idling in the golden water. Waldino moaned and groaned about how much it had cost him; it was quartz, it was digital, it was Japanese. We edged back to roughly where the watch had sunk, and peered rather hopelessly over the edge. Agatón rubbed the back of his head. His stony face split into a droll, red-eyed grin. "We can't leave it there," he said. "The fish will know what time it is, and then we'll never catch them!"

Miguelito told Agatón to take the tiller. Agatón moved past us, swift and limber for a big man with one hand. Miguelito crouched down, bony hands gripping the white gunnel. He took off his baseball cap, threw away his cigarette butt, dropped off the boat in a crouch, and dived down. He went up and down four or five times. He could touch bottom but he couldn't see the watch. He climbed back in, water streaming off his skinny body. "No luck," he said. "You'll have to buy another one."

We headed into the bay, Agatón at the tiller. Waldino hunched in disgruntlement. A flashy Japanese watch is an essential item in the Colombian hustler's wardrobe. As we neared the shore I heard dogs barking. Miguelito hopped out into the shallows, hauled on the rope. Agatón cut the engine. *El Problema* bumped and scraped ashore. "Welcome to Finca las Brisas," said Rita, and laid her hand on my shoulder to steady herself as she climbed out of the boat.

An old black woman, a patterned scarf around her head, a tin dish in her hand, came out of an open-sided building. Agatón went up to meet her, leaving giant footprints in the wet sand. I heard him call her "Mama." An old brown dog fussed around Rita, who was clearly his favorite. Back through the buildings, where the farmyard petered out among the palms, I saw two knotty, bare-chested *costeños* on either side of a giant pile of coconuts, machetes in their hands.

I helped Miguelito unload the stores from the boat. The sun set. I wondered when we were going to meet "the Boss" and where he was. I asked Waldino.

"He's not here just now. He's in Riohacha. Agatón says he will be back tomorrow. He will discuss everything with you."

"Who is he, Waldino?"

"He's called Ariel"—pronounced Arry-el. "He's one of the best, Charlie, top drawer *contrabandista*."

After a while we were summoned to the kitchen. Kerosene lamps hung from the palm-wood rafters. Waldino and I were given chairs at the little table, places of honor. Agatón perched on an oil drum, Miguelito sat on the stoop, and Rita, not eating until after the men, leaned in the doorway smoking. Mama served up huge bowls of *mondongo*—a murky broth of odds and ends, with a dish of coconut rice on the side. The talk was desultory, through mouthfuls, mostly about the fishing. They were taking *El Problema* out the next day, for snapper, swordfish and fat-eye. They would be gone two days, selling their catch in Santa Marta at dawn. There was talk too of a *cosecha de marimba*—literally a harvest, but in this case a consignment, of marijuana—which was due in soon. There was no effort to hide anything from me. Their life of fishing, farming and smuggling seemed as elemental as the breeze and the breakers outside, and the immense monotone of frogs and cicadas that sang me to sleep.

• • •

The following day Agatón and Miguelito—the *muchachos*, as Mama called them—had left before I woke. I breakfasted on eggs, rice and greasy *tinto*. Waldino snored late in a mangy hammock. Rita was nowhere to be seen. There were many dogs, of which the nicest was the aged brown fellow who had greeted Rita. He was called Leoncito, the little lion. He was lean and warty and silver-whiskered, and his eyes shone with the deep animal savvy of an old dog who has lived on his wits. He took a shine to the soft-hearted Englishman, and padded along after me as I strolled around.

The two workers I had seen when we landed lived in a little shack the other side of the banana grove. They were called Flaco and Crespo—Slim and Curly. They harvested the coconuts, bananas and avocado, and looked after the animals. Flaco was thin, slow and sunny. Crespo was malevolent and knotty, with bulging eyes. He kept his machete polished and keen, and always looked ready to start slicing something or someone into pieces. I soon realized that he didn't bear a special grudge against me, or even gringos. It was just people he didn't like.

Crespo apart, I felt blissfully at ease. I had brought nothing with me from the hotel, no clothes, no notebook, not even a toothbrush. I almost felt I had left my lies behind as well.

Rita was up when I got back, pouring a large mug of *tinto*. "You sleep OK?" She yawned. "Bugs didn't bite you?"

We sat outside the kitchen smoking cigarettes. She spilled some coffee on her dress. *"Porca madonna!"* The phrase sounded familiar but odd—it took me a moment to realize it was Italian. I asked her where she was from. "From around here." But you speak Italian? "Hey," she smiled, "the gringo's clever. My father was Italian, from Genoa."

The sun was still soft enough to sit in. Mist rose off a little stillwater lagoon at the end of the bay. Leoncito basked in the dust at our feet. Rita seemed disposed to tell her story.

I was right when I'd thought she had a mongrel look. Her father was in fact half Italian, half Turkish. Her mother was Colombian, from here on the coast.

"So you're half *costeña* then?"

Rita shrugged. *"Quién sabe?* Papa said she was a *gitana"*—a gypsy. "I never knew her."

Her father came to Colombia in 1944, settled in Barranquilla. "He was a *fascista*," she explained. "When things got bad in Italy he got out, like the other fascist rats, South America or bust. He always called himself an exile. He had his flags and emblems, his little picture of Mussolini.

"He had a business in Barranquilla, import-export. No *narcotráfico* in those days, mostly what we call *café calientito*—you know, contraband coffee. I was a little girl, six or seven, when *La Violencia* came. Papa got mixed up, we had to move out, in exile again. We lived in a lot of places, me and Papa and a great big suitcase.

Papa died of a stroke in Asunción, Paraguay. It was the night General Somosa, the exiled Nicaraguan despot, was assassinated in Asunción. There was a curfew, Rita braved it to get a doctor, she was picked up by the police. She got back the next morning and he was dead. "So you see, the bullet that killed the fascist Somosa had Papa's name on it too."

She had drifted back up to the Caribbean, the only home she'd known, picked up with some old childhood friends, who were now running dope out of Barranquilla. "And that was how I met Ariel." The way she said it answered at least one of my questions. Neither Agatón nor Miguelito was her husband, probably no one was, but Ariel was undoubtedly her man.

"Tell me about Ariel."

She laughed. "Ariel will tell you about Ariel. It's like there's lots of Ariels: he'll be someone different for you. He's hard to find, hard to catch. Like we say, *nació de pie*—he was born on his feet."

She spoke lightly, not a trace of menace intended, but I felt the knot tighten again. Which Ariel would he be for me? The one who could smell a rat at a hundred paces?

The sun was hot now. We walked down to the seashore, strolling through the shallows, toward the headland we had rounded last evening. Diamond Point, they called it, huge white boulders packed together with a rough green and brown grouting of vegetation. Pelicans flew in chevrons, slow, graceful and prehistoric, peeling off for their lethal, vertical dives.

"I've been living here two years," she said, "off and on. Every day it looks more beautiful."

"So this is Ariel's place?"

"No, it is Agatón's. He's lived here all his life. His father drowned a few years ago. There's brothers and sisters: they come back sometimes, but they live in Santa Marta or Riohacha now. There's really only Agatón and his mama. For years they've worked with a *marimbero* up in the Sierra. They bring the dope down on mules, load it into the boat, take it out to meet a yacht somewhere out there." She gestured off into the Spanish Main, where the pirate ships still await the cargoes of gold.

"So Ariel . . . ?"

"Ariel's the boss now. He handles all the business: a bit of *marimba* still, but mainly the big one, *el perico*. That's Ariel's specialty. Well, you know that. That's why you're here, no? You want to move some *perico* out."

"Yes, of course."

Enough questions, I thought. We walked on in silence, nearing the headland. A strange marine corpse lay on the wet sand. I bent to examine it. Rita strolled on. Hardly checking her pace, she pulled her dress up over her head, dropped it in the sand and walked into the sea wearing nothing but pale blue panties.

Life may have left a few scorch marks on her face, but her body was in its prime. She struck off strongly toward the headland, and I followed.

The sea slapped heavily against most of the promontory, but there was a little inlet where the water was green and calm. Rita had swum in there. She floated propped between two rocks, half in the water, breasts lolling, basking like a voluptuous mermaid.

I had felt the currents tugging as I swam. "You don't want to go too far out," she said. I had seen a gringo nearly drown once, up the coast at Cañaveral. He swam out through the breakers and couldn't get back. He was only a few meters from the shore, but he was on the wrong side of the current. The waves shut like a door behind him. The fishermen have a rope they throw out, with coconut shells to make it float. He was lucky: he got hold of it in time. When he came out he was gray all over, naked and gray.

After we had rested a bit, Rita said, "I'll show you the boat, the one that takes the *perico*."

"Ariel's boat?"

She nodded. "Speedboat. He bought it last year, for the longer runs. You know Agatón's fishing boat, it's called *El Problema*. So Ariel calls his speedboat *La Solución*! Come on. We can climb over the headland further down. They keep it in the cove on the other side."

She swam off back toward the bay, pale blue rump bobbing above deep blue water. As she waded the last few yards up on the rocks, I saw her stumble and pitch into the water. A faint yelp of pain carried back over the wide roar of the breakers. Then she was up again, hobbling out, falling heavily onto the sand.

I called, "What's happened?"

"Erizo! Hijo de puta erizo! Mierda! Que pica!"

I had no idea what *erizo* meant, but as I came out of the water I saw her craning her foot around to look at the sole, and I saw the long black quills embedded there, and I realized that *erizo* meant sea urchin, and that Rita had stepped on one.

The only thing to do with urchin's spines is to pull them out one by one. They're strong and slightly barbed, and it's a painful business. She leaned back on her elbows in the sand. I cradled her callused foot and began to work. She bit her lip with the pain. The grimace turned to a wicked laugh, then back again as another purple-tipped quill came out. The sun beat down. The waves roared. Another wince of pain, eyes holding mine, limbs pressing. Coarse sand was smeared over her breasts. Her big thighs twitched, widened. Wet blue cotton, shadowed and fringed with crow-black hairs. A man could disappear in there and never be seen again. Inside the cocaine underworld! No one would know, just the *gitana* and me, and the incurious pelicans.

Wrong again. Straightening for a moment to wipe the sweat from my eyes, a flash of brightness turned my head. The sun dazzled off a polished blade. On the headland above us, staring intently down at us, stood the misshapen figure of Crespo.

Rita followed my gaze. *"Testa di cazzo,"* she swore in her Genoese fascist Italian. "That creep never leaves me alone." She was pulling away, disentangling herself, leaving me like this. She shouted up at him, *"Zapatero, a tus zapatos!"*—cobbler to your shoes: in other words, mind your own business—but he made no sign of hearing her. She pulled out the last few spines herself and started hobbling back up the bay to where her fallen dress lay like an old memory. When I looked up to Diamond Point again, Crespo had vanished. I crawled off into the sea and cooled myself down for a while.

This might be difficult, I thought, following the distant, hopping figure of Rita back to the *finca*. This could be taken very amiss. Oh yes, Don Ariel, I saw them with my own pop-eyes, the gringo playing peek-a-boo with your woman on the sand.

In fact Ariel did not arrive that day. No one seemed surprised, least of all me. In Colombia patience is not so much a virtue as a survival instinct.

CHAPTER SEVENTEEN

A Friend in Riohacha

The next day, around midday, Agatón and Miguelito returned, having sold their catch at dawn in Santa Marta. We lunched on swordfish fried in coconut oil. Two or three hours later, in the laziest part of the lazy day, a barrage of barking from the farm dogs announced two visitors. They came down the forest trail behind the *finca*, two men, one elderly and light-footed, with long, lank gray hair under a dirty Panama, the other young, stocky, curly-headed.

The older man was greeted warmly by everyone there. Waldino knew him as well, and he introduced me. "This is Garman. He's a very good friend of Ariel's, isn't that right, *viejo*?"

Garman said to me, "The gringos call me Herman." He had a faraway smile, full of big, broken teeth. There was something sharp and mischievous in his eyes. I liked him immediately.

Of the younger man I felt less sure. His eyes were the unexpected blue one sometimes meets here. They were not mischievous, but stoned and wild, with a porcelain shine in the iris. His name was Juancho.

Waldino was not pleased with the news they brought. Herman had seen Ariel in Riohacha, and Ariel had said that he would not be back down at Finca las Brisas for another two or three days. "This is very bad, Charlie," Waldino whined. "We *must* see Ariel, talk this through."

I was relieved. Ariel sounded sharp, too sharp for my shoddy scams. "Oh well," I said philosophically. "I'm pretty happy, Waldino. I've seen the setup, met the people. It all seems very tight to me. Perhaps we could discuss a few points with Agatón. I think that'll be enough."

"No, Charlie. That's not right. Ariel's the boss. And I tell you this—if Ariel finds out you've been here *without* meeting him, he'll be pretty sore."

Leaving me to ponder this new and cheerless perspective, he went off to talk with Herman and Agatón. A few minutes later he returned. "It's OK, Charlie. It's all fixed. We go tomorrow morning, with Garman. He'll take us to Ariel in Riohacha."

We set off early the next morning—Herman, Waldino, Juancho and me—through the diaphanous shade of the palm grove. The trail was clear but narrow. Herman took the lead, looking fresh and easy. He seemed to have a whole repertoire of gaits to choose from. We climbed steeply and soon we could look back over the bay, and the treetops, and the huddle of thatched roofs beneath the palms, all tricked up in the morning sun like a snapshot of paradise. We stopped in a clearing to rest and take water, a glade of tropical trees, immensely tall, groping for the light: cottonwoods, *anattos*, the delicate spreading tree called Mulatto's Ear. A strange, deep gurgling sound, like some crazy underwater siren, whirled through the forest. Herman and Juancho knew it so well they didn't even look up. Howler monkeys, I learned. Little red fellows with beards. Juancho uttered the longest sentence I had heard from him: "Best way to get coconuts down: throw rocks up at the monkeys, they throw coconuts down at you."

After another hour we came quite suddenly out of the trees and found ourselves on the dusty verge of the Troncal de Caribe, running east to Riohacha, west to Santa Marta. Here Herman had a pickup parked. We said goodbye to Juancho, who would go on to Palomino, then up into the Sierra by foot. As we drove off toward Riohacha, I looked out of the window at the place where the trail had come out on to the road. It was hardly there at all, a momentary gap in the trees, unmarked and, unless you knew exactly where to look, invisible. The way back to Sea Breeze Farm was as secret as the way back to yesterday.

We crossed a steel section-bridge over Quebrada las Lágrimas, the Brook of Tears. A sign announced we were entering a Yellow Fever Zone. The truck chugged along, warm wind blowing through the open windows. The landscape grew harsher, drier, paler, and then we were over the state line and into the Guajira.

There are few reasons for going to the Guajira, and I was going for the most common one: to do business with a smuggler. When the word "cocaine" first trembled on Malcolm's lips, he was all but handing me a ticket to the Guajira.

The Guajira peninsula juts like a snout into the Caribbean, 150 miles long and no more than 30 miles wide at its narrowest point. Apart from a few minor hillocks toward the tip, it is as flat as a runway, a hot, arid spit of rock, sparsely dusted with scrub and thorn. There are just two towns of note, Riohacha—the department's capital—and Maicao. The rest of the peninsula is populated by semi-nomadic, goat-herding Indians, by vast flocks of flamingos, and by a shifting army of *contrabandistas*, who use its inhospitable spaces for their airstrips and its deserted shorelines for their boats. The Guajira is one big hideaway, an old-style badlands.

On the outskirts of Riohacha, Herman pulled up beside a big concrete building, baking under a cloudless blue sky. It was the new bus terminal. Waldino said, "You get out here, Charlie." For one blank moment I thought they were putting me on a bus back to Santa Marta. But he continued, hairy arm pointing across me, "You go on down that road there. It takes you downtown. You can take a look around Riohacha, get some lunch. We'll come and find you later."

They hadn't said anything about this arrangement. He must have worked it out with Herman. I was suddenly piqued. "For Christ's sake, Waldino, is this guy the Pope, or what?"

"It is better this way," he said silkily. "I can explain about you, get the little problems out of the way. Then you can discuss things with Ariel, nice and simple. It's the way we do things, that's all."

Herman smiled, taking no part, always quiet and vigilant. I shrugged. After all these weeks I could wait a few more hours. "Where and when?" I sighed.

"There's a bar on the waterfront called Los Cocos. You be there at—" His naked wrist was uninformative: he tutted petulantly. "Be there at sundown, Charlie. Around six. Someone will come."

I walked down a wide, littered, tumbledown street—wood walls, tin roofs, lopsided telegraph poles—and through a warren of market stalls. Downtown the streets were narrow and silent. They seemed to lead nowhere in particular: a hot town square where no one walked, a scalded seafront without a beach. A few skyscrapers—banks, apartments: monuments to drug money—protruded above the low white houses. A long wooden jetty snaked out, a fisherman or two, a gang of workmen repairing a winch. In a stand of palm trees were three big, open-sided bars, more or less the town's social center. One of these was the meeting-point, Los Cocos.

I took a drink at the bar next to it. The waiter was drunk. He wore a yachting cap too small for him. I asked for a Cuba Libre: he brought me a whiskey. There was no rum, he said. I asked him what kind of whiskey it was. As I suspected from the bouquet, it was one of the bootleg brands—raw corn-liquor, flavored with essence of cough lozenge, packaged with a marvelously off-target sense of Scottishness. I told him I didn't want it. He replaced it with aguardiente.

"Why you here anyway?" he slurred suspiciously.

I trotted out the touristic formulae. Doing a quick *vuelta* of the Guajira. *Para conocer la región.*

"There's nothing to see here," he said, sitting down beside me. "We are underdeveloped. Once we were rich with pearls. Now we've only got two things."

"And what are they?"

"La droga y la muerte!"

Drugs and death.

It was Herman who came for me at Los Cocos. We drove through the dusk to a house on the outskirts of Riohacha. A featureless, vaguely suburban street: low houses among shrubs, expensive American cars, tall TV aerials pointing inland. Here, unlike in the center of town, I got the whiff of big money behind the bland façades. There were lights in some of the houses, but none where we pulled up. The house was shabby, with a small withered garden in front, and peeling shutters. Around the back was a veranda. I saw coils of rope, a couple of broken chairs, a hanging bowl with cactus in it. This was no one's home. People came here for a while, then went away again, leaving the shutters to creak in the breeze.

We went in through a screen door. In the passageway I saw two lit rooms. The one to the left was obviously a kitchen: I could hear the clatter of plates, water being poured. Herman led me toward the other. I heard low voices, two men, but as Herman pushed open the door and ushered me through, the voices stopped and I entered in silence.

The room was lit by two kerosene lamps, which threw big, expressive shadows on the walls. It was hardly furnished at all: a few hard chairs looking like they'd been lifted from a café, a table, venetian blinds. Everything else—and there was a lot—lay stacked around, very new looking. I saw a TV, ghetto-blaster stereos, electric fans, crates of drink, shiny boat-tackle, and some kind of harpoon gun for big-game fishing. It looked like someone had been out that morning with the express purpose of spending $10,000 as quickly as possible. Leaning against the wall, pinned to hard-board, I saw a navigational map of the Caribbean. This was well-thumbed and annotated, not new at all.

The man sitting behind the table was lean and good-looking. I guessed his age at about thirty-five. The remains of a meal—fish, rice, Aguila beer—lay beside him. A cigarette burned in the ashtray. His arms rested loosely on the tabletop. He batted a small tin of toothpicks idly from hand to hand and he watched me with what seemed, for the moment, friendly curiosity.

The other man was Waldino, sitting in one of the chairs, little legs neatly crossed. "Charlie," he said, "I want you to meet Ariel. Ariel, this is the *Inglés*, Charlie."

Ariel rose to shake hands, rangy and confident. His palm was callused. Not a trace of dampness, though the air inside the room was still. He had a healthy sheen of sun on his face, a sailor's tan, sea-wrinkles around the eyes. He had a couple of days' stubble. He was clearly tired, but he looked like someone who fed on tiredness. He wore a loose, short-sleeved shirt, blue jeans and beach shoes. He looked good. If he wasn't a smuggler he might have been a seafront gigolo, or a gambler looking for a game.

Herman brought three beers in, then left us. "I'm sorry," said Ariel. "We have no electricity tonight. The beer is warm."

I was seated, my cigarette was lit, and not a word of small talk could be found in my head. Ariel sat back, waiting. I shot a glance at Waldino, but he seemed to have nestled down into his beard. He wouldn't look at me, and I knew it was up to me to call the first shot.

"Waldino has..." I began. Because the room was still, because my throat was dry, it came out in a cracked whisper, and I had to cough and start again. "Waldino has told you about me?"

"Of course. He has told me all about you, *Inglés*."

"Excellent." There was another pause. "So, as you know, I—"

He cut in suavely. "You're asking him for 10 kilos, but you haven't got the money yet."

It seemed a bald summary of all I'd labored over, but I couldn't dispute it. The voice, though brisk, still seemed friendly enough. I said, "The money is agreed, of course. Two hundred thousand including transportation. Waldino has shown you the telegram?"

"Ah yes. The telegram."

He was watching me. The telegram didn't count for much. If my pitch was genuine, the cable was genuine. If I was lying, the cable was a lie. Circular evidence in a very linear game.

It was all I had. I blundered on. "My associates in London need to know everything about the move before they arrange for the money to be sent."

"OK," he said, the soul of reasonableness. "You've seen my *finca* by the sea. You've seen my men. Agatón: a very strong man, my boatman. You've seen..." There was a chilly humor in his eye. I thought he was going to say "my woman," but he let it trail off. "You've seen enough, no?"

"Yes, I think I've seen enough. There's just a few points of information, a few details to clear up, and then..."

He came back quickly. "You're right, *Inglés*. You're right." He lit a cigarette, took a drag, then let it stand in the ashtray. The smoke threaded up, gray and blue. I was just about to start in with some questions, when he said: "First thing to clear up, *Inglés*, is this. How do we know you're not a UC?"

I didn't understand at first, but I knew the tone had subtly changed. Waldino couldn't ignore my startled face this time. He looked pained, as if he had to remedy some social gaffe I'd unwittingly committed. "UC, Charlie," he said softly. "*Agente narcótico*."

A high, mirthless laugh broke from me. "Jesus! Do I look like a policeman?"

Waldino shook his head, furtively reassuring me, but Ariel said, in a bored voice, "A lot of policemen don't look like policemen, *Inglés*. That's their job."

"So how do I know that *you're* not a narc?" I said.

"You don't. You have to trust me. Trust all the way: that's the bottom line when you're smuggling. You know that."

"I trust you, Ariel, of course."

"Sure you do." His voice had hardly changed throughout this little crisis. It was still friendly, coaxing, feline. He wore his hair swept back, but it flopped forward over his forehead, and when he pushed it back he looked haggard for a moment. Then he smiled and said, "OK, *Inglés*, I'll tell you how it all works." Waldino, signaling the release of tension, got up and stretched, and paced the room a bit.

"Our move is up to Aruba," said Ariel, easing into a familiar routine. This is the westernmost of the islands of the Dutch Antilles, Aruba, Bonaire and Curaçao—the ABCs, as they're called. "The island is 400 kilometers from Finca las Brisas, four days in the speedboat, open sea all the way. I have my partner in Aruba, my cousin. He's a very big wheel in Oranjestad. My cousin's got a big agave plantation. He supplies agave oil to big cosmetics companies in the Netherlands. They use agave oil to make suntan lotion, to make all you *blanquitos* nice and brown like us, OK? That's how the *coco* goes over. It goes with the agave oil."

He got up and walked over to the corner, picked up an untidy pile of paper, riffled the pages. "I got documents here: shipping lines, freight bills, everything. My cousin sends the agave shipment out every six weeks, a regular order. Just as soon as you put your money on the table we can map the whole thing for you. Precise dates, times of shipment. We can tell you the merchandise will be at this hotel, on this street in Amsterdam, at this hour precisely. *Inglés*, we'll even tell you what the weather will be. It'll be raining. It always rains in Europe, no?"

"Never stops, Ariel, except when it snows."

"We'll make it snow all night! So—you go back to Santa Marta and cable your friends. Tell them everything is A-OK on the move. We've done this run twenty times, smooth as stone. Different volumes, different clients. It's worked every time."

He dumped the pile of shipping papers back on the floor. As they landed they nudged another pile of odds and ends, and off the top of this something small but heavy, wrapped in a cloth, fell to the floor. The cloth parted, and out poked what was unmistakably the black snout of a handgun.

Ariel saw my eyes flinch. He laughed. "Don't worry, *Inglés*. It's not pointing at you tonight!" He picked it up, cradled it affectionately in his hand for a moment. "Everyone carries a friend in Riohacha, *Inglés*. We say: *Gata con guantes no caza ratones.*"

He wrapped the gun back up and replaced it. A cat with gloves on doesn't catch any rats. Thus far and no farther, I thought. Time to start talking myself out. Ariel's claws would be long and sharp.

"There's one other thing, Charlie," said Waldino, studying the bubbles in his beer bottle. "Ariel and I have talked this over, and—"

Ariel cut in, born on his feet and still running. "We've decided that I will *supply* the merchandise as well. Waldino had made other arrangements, but this is better, no?" He cocked an eye at Waldino, who nodded vigorously. How easily he had slipped into the henchman's role, I thought.

"I have a very good source," Ariel continued, "just come onstream. *Perico de primera calidad*. It comes up from Bogotá. We pick it up in Barranquilla. They call this Snow White cocaine."

"Jesus."

Two pairs of eyes narrowed. "You know something about this, *Inglés*?"

"Know it? Jesus. It's only the best damn cocaine I've ever tasted. Someone gave me a *muestra* in Bogotá."

Ariel gave a thin smile. "You get around, *Inglés*, no?" He had noted it down, everything was filed away. "So," he said, concluding the business. "Once we get the dollars we're there. Am I right?"

"We're there, Ariel, we're there."

It all linked up. My confused stumblings had actually unearthed a whole pipeline. I could trace my phantom 10 kilos of cocaine all the way—Huanaco leaves from the Yungas of Bolivia, mulched with kerosene and acid into cocaine paste, smuggled up through the jungles of Peru to the Colombian border near Leticia, flown up to the Hacienda Alaska in the southern *llanos*, elaborated by a German cook into prime cocaine hydrochloride, trucked up in cattle wagons to the San Felipe slaughterhouse in Bogotá, distributed through Rafael Vallejo's Transcarne meat network, offloaded in Barranquilla, driven down the Troncal de Caribe, carried down the trail to Sea Breeze Farm, loaded into a speedboat called *La Solución*, ferried by Agatón and Miguelito to the island of Aruba, delivered to a businessman in Oranjestad, packaged up in a cargo of agave essence, nursed across the Atlantic on a Dutch cargo ship, picked up in a hotel room in Amsterdam, spirited to London via any number of mule-runs, wholesaled, brokered, buffed, diluted, thirty thousand grams of one-in-three, sixty thousand hungry nostrils twitching, a hundred thousand toots at the parties that really matter, the suave new *soirées* where as likely as not you'll see Malcolm himself, jawing with some beautiful literary agent from New York, who's wishing he'd shut up about this super book on the cocaine trade, and let her get her nose down into that sweet white candy.

CHAPTER EIGHTEEN

Bad Moves

Two days later I was sitting in the Bar Mamatoca in San Martín, the dockside *barrio* of Santa Marta. It was the twilight hour, the bar was half-empty, the music turned up too loud. I had got a message from Waldino to meet him here. When I got here there was only Ariel, whom I had not expected to see at all. It was getting pretty close to the day of my sudden disappearance from Santa Marta. I had sent off another cable to Malcolm, just to keep Waldino happy. "ALL SYSTEMS CHECKED PROCEED IMMEDIATELY." I had a few days' grace—"These big financial moves take time, Waldino"—before it started to become apparent that there was no 10-kilo order, no big London *capo*, no 200,000 U.S., no reason at all why I should have been poking my pink gringo nose into their private business. By that time I would be miles away, perhaps even sitting on a plane bound for London. According to my plans, in fact, this was going to be my last night in Santa Marta, and I felt a stab of nerves when I saw that it was Ariel I was going to spend it with.

We sat drinking *tintos*. The *tinto* keeps you sharp, Ariel said. He was looking smarter than when I'd seen him before: loose white jacket, open shirt, pointed black slip-on shoes. There was a pallor of tension under his weathered skin. The *contrabandista* had business tonight, and he wanted some help with it.

We were waiting for Waldino and Rita, he explained. With them, he hoped, would be a Swedish seaman—his name was actually Sven, but he spoke of him simply as *Sueco*, the Swede, just as I was always *Inglés*, the Englishman. The Swede's ship, the *Nordic Star*, had docked in Santa Marta that afternoon. The Swede did not speak Spanish, but he did speak passable English, and this was where I came in. "You must help us talk to him," Ariel said. "We have a proposition for him."

While we waited Ariel spelled out the situation. The container ship *Nordic Star* called in at Santa Marta once every two or three months, homeward bound for Göteborg, having already visited Houston and Panama. On its last few voyages home it had unwittingly carried back five-kilo consignments of cocaine supplied by Ariel. The coke was eventually bound for Hamburg. That was where the order originated. Ariel had nothing but praise for the efficiency of *Los Tedescos*, the Germans, who had set the business up. They had their man—the Swede—aboard the ship. They paid good prices and they paid up-front: the Swede handed over dollars, in exchange for the package of coke. The linchpin of Ariel's side of the operation was a *winchero* who worked at the docks. He ferried the *perico* into the restricted port area in a compartment under the seat of his motorbike. Once inside it was a piece of cake for the *winchero*, in the course of his legitimate work, to meet up with the Swede and exchange the packages of drugs and dollars. So slickly had this run in the past that Ariel had not even met the Swede. He knew him by sight, because it was part of the arrangement that the Swede should come onshore, on the night the *Nordic Star* docked, and take a turn or two, natural enough, along the waterfront bars. If he was wearing a red bandanna around his neck that meant everything was cool—he had the money, and would await the drop at the prearranged time. The time was always 11:30 a.m.—half an hour before the end of the morning shift—on the day after the ship docked. On every occasion, the Swede had been wearing his neckerchief, and the meet had been made, smooth as clockwork.

The previous night, however, disaster had struck. The *winchero* had got involved in a fight over a bargirl. A man had been knifed to death, and the *winchero* was languishing in the town jail. Ariel had considered going straight down to the Comisario to try and bail him out, but he had decided this would be costly—backhanders all around—and could well lead to awkward questions. The best course of action, he concluded, would be to target on the Swede. The Swede must be persuaded that he himself must carry the *mercancía* onto the boat.

To this end Waldino and Rita were out on the beach drag, trawling for the Swede. They would bring him here, and we would explain to him, nice and easy, that there'd been a little change in the plans.

So we waited.

I've been through this movie before, I thought. Just a few blocks away, just a few years away, talking someone through a cocaine deal, and here I am again, torqued up on *tinto*, dust in my throat, and a dim foreboding in my gut that if history really does repeat itself, this time around it's tragedy's turn.

The Swede was not what you would call classic mule material. Mules tend to be neat and inconspicuous, like Rosalita in her specs. The Swede was about as inconspicuous as a bear at a tea party. He may not quite have stood six foot six and weighed two forty-five, but he was generally built along the lines of Big Bad John. A blond curly beard half-covered his face, and more hair came sprouting up like reinforcements out of the neck of his denim work shirt. Lurking amid this undergrowth was the red neckerchief that signaled "All Clear."

Waldino chivied him respectfully toward a seat. I could tell he was completely fazed by the man's size. He came about up to the Swede's breast pocket, out of which a pouch of Dutch black-shag tobacco poked. Rita too kept darting glances at him, biting her lip, with that droll, intrigued look of hers. In fact everyone at the bar was staring at him. If it wasn't for the music, a silence would have fallen, like in Westerns when the baddie shoulders through the swing doors into the saloon.

It was clear that the Swede was not at all pleased. He looked as if he felt like uprooting a few pine trees. Installing him at our table, on a chair not intended for a man of his size, Waldino hurried off to the bar to order beers. He glanced at Ariel as he passed, and shot his black, piggy eyes heavenward.

Ariel played it very cool. He let the Swede simmer down a bit and get his bearings, and then he rose slightly to shake hands. The Swede's big, gnarled paw, with engine oil worked deep into the grain of the skin, completely engulfed Ariel's hand. Ariel introduced himself as Manuel. The Swede scrutinized him solemnly and answered with a deep, sonorous grunt, which I realized was the name Sven. When it was my turn to introduce myself I called myself Frank. I don't know why.

Ariel motioned me to begin. The Swede's cold blue eyes peeked out at me from his sailor's wrinkles. "You speak English, Sven?" I asked.

"Yaw. I am speaking English OK."

"Good. Our friends here have a problem. The man who brings in the merchandise is out of action."

"So." He nodded slowly.

"So they..."

"So they must find another man focking quick."

I had already suggested this to Ariel. It was not possible, he said. "I don't think they can do that, Sven. These things take time to set up, even here in Santa Marta. There must be complete trust, as I'm sure you..."

"So."

"So...they are hoping you will carry the merchandise aboard yourself."

He banged his bottle down on the table—it was already empty—and shook his grizzled head. "No deal. You tell these focking people it's no deal. The gear comes onto the boat, I'll be there with the dollars. But I don't do no focking carrying."

The interview continued much in this fashion for a while. The Swede was implacable. The grunt of "So" rolled down like a boulder to block every avenue that Ariel could suggest.

The Swede's argument, reasonable enough, was that he kept himself strictly offshore. His role in the operation began and ended in Europe. He wanted as little as possible to do with the Colombian end. He didn't like Santa Marta, any more than he liked any other South American port. They were all the same, gutters of sweat and treachery, filled with con-artists. He had the pay-offs clearly balanced in his mind. If he got busted aboard the *Nordic Star*, or in Göteborg, OK, it was trouble, but it was trouble he could live with. No previous record, wife and two kids. He'd be going on conditional discharge, or at worst a few months in an open prison, all very cozy, free association and smorgasbord every Sunday.

It was clear the Swede wasn't going to deviate one inch from the prescribed routine. Ariel had just one crumb of comfort. The *Nordic Star* would be undergoing a few minor repairs tomorrow, and wouldn't be leaving port until Thursday evening, nearly forty-eight hours from now. Ariel had until Thursday morning to find someone to ferry the *perico* aboard the *Nordic Star*. The Swede would be waiting, at the usual place, at 11:30 on Thursday. No merchandise, no money.

The following day—so close to the end, just about to pull up the ladder and disappear forever—I made the slip I had feared all along. It was a hot, still day with many flies. The rains were not far off, the air drooped over the roofs. Ariel and Waldino, philosophical about the stubbornness of the Swede, had gone off to Barranquilla to pick up the five kilos of Snow White. They seemed confident they would find a way of getting the merchandise on board the *Nordic Star*.

I was planning to leave Santa Marta at six that evening: I had already bought a bus ticket. They would not be back in town till midnight, they said. It seemed ideal. When they came by the Corona that morning—Waldino had a little *muestra* of basuko to give me, in the hopes of further interesting my "associates"—I secretly knew I was saying goodbye for the last time.

I felt bad about it, I had to admit. I was leaving town with a story of sorts in my bag, but with a very nasty taste in my mouth. I had come to respect these people in their way—Ariel the boss, Waldino the pirate, Rita the gypsy, Agatón the pilot. As the song says, "To live outside the law you must be honest." I was the dishonest law-abider. These are your cocaine smugglers, Malcolm. Public Enemy No. 1, traders in misery and corruption. You wanted the truth and all I've done is tell them lies.

I spent most of the day writing at my table at the Corona, pausing from time to time for the refreshments so vital for serious work in the tropics— fruit, bread, beer and basuko. The afternoon wore on. The door and the long, shuttered window stood open on to the balcony. No breeze stirred the sapodilla trees. I was just thinking about starting to get my bag packed up, when out of the stillness came a voice at my window. A familiar voice: "Charlie. *Qué tal?*"

I started like a guilty thing. "Waldino! Ariel! *Qué tal?*" I hadn't heard them coming, and—more to the point—they weren't supposed to *be* here. But here they were, Waldino leaning at the window, Ariel sauntering in through the door, hands in pockets, eyebrows genially raised over cold blue eyes, and here was I, with papers, notebooks and news clippings strewn around the table, the incriminating tools of the trade, the snoop at work on his gleanings.

"I thought you were in Barranquilla," I laughed, hastily rising from the desk.

"We made the pickup sooner than expected," said Waldino, scratching his beard. "We got back quickly. We're going to have another go at the Swede tonight. We want you to come."

Ariel strolled around, idly appraising the room and its contents. He was at his most dangerous when he was slow and easy like this. He could spring out of this mood like a jack from a box. His gaze fell on the cluttered writing table.

"You're working, *Inglés*? We're disturbing you?" Ariel's voice was colorless. He used the formal, third person "you."

"No, no." I moved between him and the desk. "Will you have a beer, Ariel?"

"But you are writing, I think?"

"No, well—yes. Just a couple of letters." I waved an airmail envelope at him.

"Letters, *Inglés*?" The voice had hardened. Waldino had begun some inconsequential chat, but he stopped in mid-flow to look at Ariel. Ariel, dispensing now with any social niceties, riffled through the scattered papers on my desk. He squinted at my notebook. He couldn't understand the words but I could see he was beginning to understand the general drift.

"So who you writing to, *Inglés*?"

"That's my business."

He looked me in the eye for the first time, and said softly, "No, *Inglés*. It's our business. We're partners, remember?" Waldino was standing at his shoulders now, the henchman's position. His brows were knitted in puzzlement. He spotted the publisher's Letter of Introduction, peeping out of a pile of papers under the ashtray, his magpie eye alighting on the glimpse of tasteful green letterhead. He extricated it with his stubby fingers, holding it up by the corner, as if it were valuable and fragile. *"A Quién se Interese."* To whom it concerns . . .

They both read the letter, with its ornate courtesies and cringing subjunctives.

"El autor británico . . ." said Ariel thoughtfully.

"I can explain," I said.

"You should have told us, *hombre*," said Waldino. He shook his head at me reproachfully, almost pityingly, as if I had spoiled everything with a fatal blunder. "We're your friends, Charlie. You should have told us."

Ariel shot an angry glance at Waldino—Waldino whose job it was to check my credentials, Waldino who had introduced me to Ariel's setup, Waldino on whose back I had ridden into Sea Breeze Farm. "Hey, stupid," he said to him. "You brought in a flea in your beard, and now we're all going to itch." He turned back to me. "So you are writing a story about us? You are going to tell the world about Finca las Brisas, about the *Nordic Star*. We're going to be *estrellas*, Waldino. Big stars. I'm not sure we like this."

"I can explain," I said again. My mind raced and got nowhere.

"No need," said Ariel sharply. He let the letter fall from his fingers. The ceiling fan caught it. It floated off the table and landed on the floor at my feet. This was a very bad moment. They were entitled to take it badly. Somewhere in my life someone had said, "It's one thing to lose, it's another thing to cheat and lose." That was about the size of it: I had cheated and lost.

Then Ariel laughed. *"Carajo! Eres un zorro, no?"* Waldino looked at him in surprise. Yes, Ariel was definitely smiling, calling me a crafty fox, shaking his head in disbelief. Ariel put his hand to his forehead and massaged along the wrinkles as if so much disbelief had given him a headache. He said *"Carajo!"* again, called me some more names, and said wearily, "I want to discuss this with my *compañero* here."

He jabbed Waldino on the shoulder, motioning him back out on to the balcony. They closed the door, pushed shut the shutters on the window. I stood in the empty, half-darkened room.

They came back in. Waldino looked chastened. He closed the door behind him and leaned against it. Ariel advanced. Everything felt suddenly close and claustrophobic. I was trying to read the look on his face. "You know what a lot of my friends would say about this business?" I shook my head. "They'd say it was time to check your oil, *Inglés*." I stared at him uncomprehendingly. He made a graphic gesture, and I quickly understood that *mediendo el aceite* meant sticking a knife into someone's belly, like a dipstick into the oilpan. He let this possibility hang in the air for a moment. Somewhere below I heard Omar discussing a soccer match with one of the *porteros*. Ariel continued: "But we've got a better idea, no?" He cocked his head at Waldino, who hastened to agree. "Oh yes, Don Ariel, we've got a wonderful idea." I looked from one to the other. The bastards are enjoying this, I thought.

"This problem of ours, Charlie," said Waldino. "As you know, we—"

Ariel cut in. "You will take our *perico* onto the *Nordic Star* tomorrow," he said.

I sat down heavily on the bed. They weren't going to kill me, they were going to co-opt me.

The fateful morning dawned pink and gray. Ariel was at the door, unshaven, bringing an all-night smell of stale tobacco and beer into the room. The *perico* was in place, he said. He had thrown it over the perimeter fence a couple of hours earlier. "She's ready and waiting for you, *Inglés*. Legs wide open." He dumped a large carrier bag on the bed. In it was a brand-new "executive" briefcase, purchased that morning from Waldino's stationery store off 5th Avenue. Black imitation leather, gold-plate fittings, combination locks, made in Taiwan.

We ran through the layout one last time. The map Ariel had drawn the previous night was already grubby with handling. The harbor was roughly triangular. When I came in through the checkpoint, the two main covered *bodegas* would be on my left, the grain silo on my right. Up in the apex of the triangle was Wharf Three. Off to the side of Wharf Three, over the rail track, was a generating plant. This was the Spot Marked X: between the back of the *generador* and the perimeter fence lay five kilos of pure Snow White cocaine, "ready and waiting." How I got myself to the generator, and how I got myself and the cocaine onto the *Nordic Star*, were my problem. We ran through the directions for once I was on board the boat: up the gangway, right down the passage, through the swing doors, second door on the left. That was where the Swede would be waiting, in the john. He would be there with the money at 11:30 precisely. He would wait ten minutes, no more. The timing was critical.

Into the briefcase I piled notebooks, business cards, calculator, passport and the wretched Letter of Introduction. A whole lot of little truths around one big lie. . . .

Under a beating sun, in a newly laundered white shirt, I sallied forth from the Corona, a man about his business. I went up to the stationer's and bought a clipboard to complete my business researcher's kit. I cut back across the cathedral square, light bouncing off the white walls. In the shade of a mango tree an old man sat on a fruit crate. He chewed reflectively on a slice of sugar cane. How I envied him his ease.

I walked down 10th Street. There was the ex-Fruit Palace, El Progreso. I had a bit of time to spare. I stopped to take a *jugo* there, but checked myself at the doorway. Today of all days, let the shade of Harvey rest. Let me not end up in the henhouse today.

The first stage was easy enough. At the Harbor Police Station I presented my letter of introduction and my business card to an acned young cadet at the desk. As instructed by Ariel, I asked him to present these to the *Commandante*, who would issue me with a pass to enter the docks. A few minutes later, I was duly ushered down a corridor, to a door which read "Vice-Commandante Policía Portuaria, Departmento de Seguridad," with a name below it that was almost as long. A tall man in naval uniform was writing at the desk, a cigarette holder between his teeth. My card and letter lay on the neat, polished desk. He rose courteously, and we shook hands. His arms were thin, brown and hairless.

"*Entonces, señor.* You are writing a book about our country."

"Yes, Vice-Commandante."

"And you wish to visit the port area. For what purpose exactly?"

He held his cigarette holder in his delicate fingers and scrutinized me. I trotted out my spiel: *informe económico*, foreign trade statistics, port expansion program. I larded in a few oblique compliments about the vital significance of this thriving port to Colombia's national development. The word *desarrollo*—development—has an almost mystic ring here. I threw in a couple of polite questions about the Harbor Police. He told me he was in charge of some 150 officers and marines. "We keep a very tight control here. Perhaps you are aware, there are many...bad elements in Santa Marta. Much contraband, *narcotráfico*."

Sweat pricked my back. My throat was dry. I nodded gravely.

"You will wish to see Señor Bustamente," he said, jotting the name down on his notepad. "He is Director of Operations. He will have the details you need." He explained how I might find him. He reached into a shallow wooden tray on his desk and drew out a small, mimeographed docket. He wrote on it my passport number and name. He stamped it and handed it to me. He clicked his heels as we shook hands. "I hope your visit will be of benefit to you," he said.

Two minutes later I was at the checkpoint. I presented my pass, a *permiso provisional*. The guard frisked me cursorily. He gave the contents of my briefcase a quick once-over and waved me through. It was 10:15 a.m. and I was inside the docks.

I saw the *Nordic Star* straight away and strolled over to join a knot of people watching the loading. They were trucking containers of coffee into the loading bay. I wandered around, clutching my clipboard, looking vaguely official. I had no idea how I was going to get myself onto the ship itself, but that was for later. Right now the important thing seemed to be to get myself noticed, to *establish* myself—a vague but thoroughly legitimate presence, jotting notes on his clipboard from time to time. The first duty of shoplifters, snoops and smugglers: to become a part of the landscape.

I found Señor Bustamente in one of the big covered warehouses—Bodega No. 2, according to Ariel's map. He was, as his name somehow foretold, a large, fat, expansive man. He said he would be delighted to answer a few questions. After he had finished his business we walked back through the *bodega*. Thousands of sacks of pale, unroasted coffee were piled everywhere. We went up some concrete steps into a cluttered little office. A secretary in a tartan skirt brought us *tintos*. I plied him with questions. We discussed the containerization program. We flourished our calculators to convert deadweight tons into ordinary tons. He regaled me on the subject of *diversificación económica*, as instanced by the declining proportion of bananas in the exports from the port. Twenty years ago, 98 percent of products exported from Santa Marta were bananas; last year it was only 16 percent.

Every interview reaches a natural plateau, after which one can either coast down through the formalities and take one's leave, or overstay one's welcome with more questions. Just as we were reaching this point, I introduced the subject of the *Nordic Star*.

"Just to get the feel of a typical day here, Señor Bustamente. Perhaps you could tell me a bit about the ships in dock today. The biggest would be..."

"The *Nordic Star*. Swedish container ship. Three thousand six hundred tons, unloaded the day before yesterday: paper, industrial machinery, chemical products. Today we are loading. Coffee, bananas, melons, textiles."

"How long will that take?"

"We shall be finished this afternoon. We are operating, as I said, our new roll-on roll-off system."

"Ah yes, the roll-on roll-off system. This is most interesting for my study. I wonder, would it be possible to observe this in action?"

Of course, he said, glad of a chance of shaking me off.

We strolled down together. As we watched the loading I racked my brains for questions, last-minute points, nebulous patter—anything to keep him there at my side, so everyone could see me enjoying an amiable but businesslike chat with El Jefe Director. Finally I could cloy him with small talk no longer. We shook hands and he returned to the *bodega*.

I checked my watch. It was time to move on to my next "appointment," the pickup at Wharf Three. I set off purposefully: always look like you're going somewhere, Ariel had said. I passed the harbor rail depot. Men were unloading sacks of grain on to an overhead track. The sun was like a weight on the top of my head. My heart beat wildly. I could still turn back. The moment of reckoning could be delayed. Which was worse—the Harbor Police fingering my collar for drug-running, or Ariel checking my oil in some dark, piss-ridden alley in San Martín? It was not a question I could answer. The only thing to do was to keep on walking.

I was at Wharf Three, in the northern corner of the harbor, by 11:00. The layout was just as Ariel had described it. Looking away from the waterfront, across a wide open patio with parked cars and containers in it, I could see the narrow-gauge track that ran all the way around from the far side of the harbor. My eye followed the curve of the track to the point where it reached nearest to the perimeter fence, and there it was—the generating plant, a couple of low breeze-block buildings and a cat's cradle of high-voltage transformers. Behind it the ground rose steeply: a couple of chalky-colored mounds, with a rough sand track running between them. From there, at about four o'clock this morning, Ariel had slithered down to the perimeter fence and tossed over the cocaine, wrapped in an old sack. Unless it had been spotted by an unusually vigilant guard, it should still be there, just another bit of rubbish in another cranny, with the single vital difference that, once reclaimed and transported to its destination, this particular bit of rubbish would be worth a quarter of a million dollars.

I now had to leave the busy thoroughfare of the wharfs and warehouses, where my presence was unremarkable, and head into the no-man's-land of the open patio. With every step I took, my cover became more and more meaningless. I was heading toward the edge of the dock area. There would be no one to interview there, no possible reason for a researcher to be bending his busy steps that way. I had got to the edge of the patio when a group of workmen suddenly appeared from among the freight trucks and started walking toward me. After a moment of frozen panic I did the only thing I could think of, which was to stand myself up against a pile of planking and pretend I was taking a pee. They passed quite close by me, but didn't make any comment. As I made the last 50 yards between the rail track and the generator, there was nothing in my mind except the rushing of my blood and the pumping of my heart.

I spotted the sack immediately, lying among a thin scattering of other detritus. I knelt down beside it and pulled out the plastic package inside. It was at this point that the first major hitch occurred. The sack had landed on a nest of broken *gaseosa* bottles. Five kilos, thrown up and over a 12-foot fence, lands with quite a bump, and by sheer bad luck a shard of glass on a standing bottle had pierced straight through the burlap sacking and—as I discovered when I took the package out—straight through the plastic as well. Cocaine poured out of the rent like salt. I struggled to fit the package into my briefcase. I was clumsy, and the package sagged. The tear in the plastic lengthened. Several hundred dollars' worth of *perico* wafted off on the breeze. Cursing, I manhandled the drugs into the case. It was a tight fit—Bustamente had given me a few brochures and photocopies, and I had to jettison a couple to get the stuff in. The white dust was everywhere, sticking to my sweat-drenched shirt and arms, and to the fake velour inside the case. It was a horrible mess. As I forced the case shut, one of the hinges at the back snapped. When it was at last shut, it had a lopsided, suspiciously full look. It would have to do. I dusted off the coating of cocaine from the case and from my clothes. My hands had gotten grimy with something oily among the rubbish, and in dusting myself off I smeared the oil on my white shirt.

I straightened up and leaned against the wall, panting with heat and fear.

It was 11:25 by the time I was back at the *Nordic Star*. I had just a few minutes, fifteen at the most, to get myself inside the belly of the boat for my rendezvous with the Swede. This was the last and possibly the stickiest part of the whole operation. I was carrying now, staring at ten years without option in the delightful purlieus of the town jail. I slid back into the knot of people. It is a sociological law in Colombia: wherever there are people working there are always at least as many standing around watching. They were loading *cajas* of bananas now, 20-kilo wooden crates, green bananas that would ripen on the voyage. I glanced around furtively. No one seemed to have noticed my presence or my absence. I let myself cool down a bit.

I steadied myself to make my move. Nonchalantly up the gangplank, clipboard in hand, prayer on my lips that no one would challenge me. Then

I saw, to my dismay, the bulky figure of Señor Bustamente bearing down on me. With him was a small, saturnine man sporting a florid tie. I stood my ground—I had nowhere else to go.

It seemed to be all right. Bustamente was beaming cordially, the little man he was introducing to me was the Port Systems Manager. "I was just telling Señor Lino about you," said Bustamente. "I think he can fill you in on some of those details about the port expansion program." I shook hands with Señor Lino. A twinge of distaste crossed his face as he felt my damp, dirty palm.

I was well and truly trapped. Little Señor Lino waxed lyrical about the *desarrollo portuario*, from its widest ramification to its smallest detail. I dutifully jotted notes on my clipboard. I looked at my watch: 11:35. The Swede would be waiting already. I had five minutes at the most. I couldn't just say, "Excuse me, thank you very much," and walk up the gangplank onto the boat. The only thing to do was to try and ease the conversation to a full stop, and hope they would leave me. At a suitable lull, therefore, I slipped the clipboard under my arm, put my pen back in my breast pocket, picked up my briefcase, and assumed that sullen, introverted politeness with which the Englishman signals his withdrawal from company. I hovered in vain. Another Englishman would have taken the hint but Colombians are made of sterner stuff. It was ironic really—I had sweated small talk to detain Bustamente here half an hour ago, and now that I was praying he would leave me alone, he stuck to me like a burr.

Then I noticed something that made my blood run cold. Out of a corner of my briefcase, where the lid sagged away slightly around the broken hinge, a thin stream of cocaine was leaking out. A little conical pile had formed on the ground already. I moved to cover it with my foot. The powder continued to pour, implacably, like flour from a punctured sack. Anyone watching us could have seen it: Bustamente or Lino might see it any minute.

Still talking, on automatic pilot, I shifted the briefcase under my arm, and with a swift, uncomfortable maneuver, cupped my hand under the leaking corner. I felt the cocaine pour into my palm. My hosts droned on, I hopped from foot to foot in agony.

Philosophers say that life begins beyond despair. I was about to break down completely, sob out my confession, the whole sorry story from the Fruit Palace till now, when someone called to Bustamente from inside the loading area of the ship. One of the banana crates had been damaged. Bustamente walked up the gangplank, into the ship's belly. Lino followed. There was nothing more natural than for me to follow also, firmly cradling the case under my arm. Inside, the ship hummed dully.

11:38, two minutes to go. Only a few yards separated me from the Swede, from my burning desire to get rid of the illicit chemical. I had a brainwave. I broke in urgently on their conversation. "Excuse me, *señor*. Is there a bathroom I could use?"

"Of course," said Bustamente. He started directing me back out of the ship, around the back of the coffee warehouse.

"No, no," I cried. He stopped, looking puzzled. I made a grimace of apology, fidgeted unhappily, and said, "It is very urgent. *Malo del estómago.*"

A man in overalls laughed. He called out to one of the loaders.

"Show the gentleman up to the *baño*, quickly," he said. I heard them tittering sympathetically behind me, as I trotted up the stairs behind my escort. We followed the route Ariel had explained. The swing doors closed behind us, softening the noise of the loading bay to a hush. I thanked the man, and lurched into the john at 11:40 precisely.

I thought the place was empty at first. I thought I'd missed the rendezvous. Then I saw that one of the cubicles, the farthest from the door, was occupied. I sidled up to the washbasin opposite it. I wanted to knock on the door, or call out for the Swede, but if it wasn't him I'd look pretty silly. I ran some water, made noises with the liquid soap dispenser. As I splashed my hands, I gradually crouched down farther and farther, till I could see the feet of the man in the stall. They were certainly big enough to be the Swede's: heavy-duty black boots. Now I saw the boots shifting. I straightened up sharply, and just as I did so, the broad blond brow of the Swede peeped cautiously over the door of the cubicle. Our eyes met.

"It's you," he growled. He straightened to his full height. His beard jutted over the top of the door. "You're late," he added.

"For Christ's sake hurry up," I hissed. "I've got people waiting downstairs."

"What focking people?"

"What people? Never mind what people. Let's do it, for God's sake."

"Pass the case in. Keep washing your hands."

I handed it over the door. "Be very careful," I said. "The *perico* is coming out. The plastic got torn."

"So." There was silence for a moment. "It don't open," said the face over the door.

"Shit! I forgot—the combination. Six-six-six."

There was another agonizing silence from inside the cubicle, as the Swede's ursine paws fumbled with the wheels of the combination locks. He seemed to take ages. Someone was drilling metal deep in the bowels of the ship. It jarred my head. I heard one catch spring, then the other, and even as I was saying again, "Be careful," I heard him curse and I saw the fine white powder floating down in spots on his black boots.

"I can't take this focking gear, man," he said in an angry half-whisper. "This right up the focking spout. I can't pay you for this. I don't know how much is here."

He was shutting the case up again. "Oh God!" I cried. "Look—give me less money. Give me half. Surely you can give me half."

"No focking deal. I am not permitted to open the envelope. It's all or nothing. This is damaged cargo. You must take it back."

"Back? Back where?" He pushed the case over the door. I tried to shove it back at him. He raised a huge fist, swore evilly at me. I staggered back, clutching the case. Cocaine was smeared all over the shiny black plastic. I had to get back down below. Bustamente would be wondering where I was. I thought of just jettisoning the case there and then, but of course I couldn't. It had all my papers in it, for a start. And I couldn't leave the cocaine either. What was my friend Ariel going to say if I turned up without the drugs *or* the money? Checking the oil wouldn't be in it. He would roast me alive.

Frantically I started rubbing and sweeping at the cocaine dust on the case. Without thinking, I did what everyone does when they have cocaine dust on their fingers. I kept putting my hands to my nose and snuffling up the dust. I did this half a dozen times. The case was clean, but as I lurched back out into the corridor, I realized I had made yet another false move. This was pure Snow White, remember. Not a trace of cut, not a footstep in the snow. As I pushed back through the swing doors, I was ten feet tall with a face made of ice. Coming down the steps I couldn't even feel my feet. I was dancing on air, and I still had a briefcase crammed full of the stuff.

"Better?" asked Bustamente with a broad grin. I nodded and leered. The noise was appalling. The three men were still talking, just as before. They didn't seem to have noticed anything amiss. They laughed knowing masculine laughs about the gastric perils of Santa Marta. The conversation continued. Perpendicular forces seemed to be straining forth from my skull. Yet, incredibly, I could hear the talk being punctuated by a familiar, stilted gringo accent, which was saying *"Sí"* and *"No"* and even *"Claro, hombre"* at all the right moments.

I failed to understand the noise at first. Was someone screaming in my car? No, it was the lunchtime siren cranking up for its wail. There was a general bustle out of the boat. Trucks were parked, gloves were peeled off. Bustamente's hand was on my shoulder, gently steering me down on to the wharf, talking all the while with Lino. I let myself be led. One survival instinct throbbed inside the mêlée. Stick with El Jefe Director—don't let him out of your sight. We joined the stream of loaders and *wincheros*, sailors and secretaries, making their way out through the checkpoint. This is it, go with the crowd. Everyone was showing passes as they left. Thankfully I still had my pass ready, fastened under the clipboard. In a moment of inspiration I asked Bustamente his thoughts about Sunday's soccer game. He was wonderfully opinionated on the subject, and we were chattering away as I passed through the checkpoint.

I stepped out on the other side like a drowning man touching *terra firma*. It was then that I felt the hand on my shoulder.

I wheeled around, took in the soldierly uniform, the rifle strapped on the shoulder. The phantom of liberty dispersed in the hot sea winds. The guard was holding out his hand. Of course, he wanted the case. I was just about to hand it over, but all he said was, "Your pass, *señor*. You must hand in your pass. It is only a *permiso provisional*."

"Of course, of course." My hands shook as I took the pass out from under the clip. The guard said, "Excuse me," with a little bow, more to Bustamente than me. I saw his eyes flicker down over the briefcase, but he didn't ask to look into it. No one would be crazy enough to smuggle cocaine *into* Colombia.

Waldino was waiting at the corner, with a clear view of the checkpoint. He skulked there while I said goodbye to Bustamente and Lino, then he motioned me over and bustled around me with questions. "You got the money, Charlie? Who were those people you were talking to? What happened, Charlie?"

I couldn't say anything. Strange pharmaceutical juices clogged my throat. I opened and shut my mouth like a goldfish.

He peered into my crazed eyes. "What's happening, *hermano*?" He was beginning to sound worried. I started walking toward the beach drag. He pulled at my arm. "Hey, no, Charlie. We must go to the Mamatoca. Ariel is waiting."

I shook my head. "Corona," I croaked. I walked on. Waldino skipped around me, so confused by my behavior that he didn't try to persuade me. We turned into 10th Street.

A voice from a doorway hailed us. *"Señor, qué tal, pues?"* Waldino hadn't answered. It must have been me he was addressing. I focused on a vaguely familiar face. It was the owner of the Restaurante El Progreso, the Fruit Palace as it was. We were standing outside the familiar cedarwood door. "Did you find your friend Julio?" the man asked.

I was coming around now. Things were beginning to resume their rightful position. "I need a drink," I said. The man stepped out of the doorway to let us enter.

The quiet, midday calm of the Fruit Palace soothed me, and two straight rums put back a little of what the morning had taken out. There were just two other people in the café. The *señora*, wearing the same turquoise dress as before, served them with huge platters of steak and kidney beans. By the third rum I felt ready to tell my story. But now it was Waldino's turn to demur. He put his finger to his lips, and jerked his head at the diners. *"Wincheros,"* he mouthed. "Don't say anything."

He called for music, and under the cover of Juancho Rois singing "La Gordita" I told him the whole sorry story. At each revelation he sank into deeper gloom. When I had finished he slumped back in the chair and spat out the word *"Coño!"*

"Christ, Waldino, I don't see what I could—"

"Hey, *hermano*. I don't mean you. I mean that *hijo de puta* Swede."

We left the Progreso, ditched the briefcase back at the Corona, and went off to find Ariel at the Mamatoca. His reaction was much the same as Waldino's. I had done my best. These things happen in the uncertain world of contraband. It was the Swede's fault: he should have been prepared to haggle a bit. The main point was that I'd saved the whole thing from disaster by bringing the *perico* out more or less intact. OK, they'd lost a few grams, perhaps even a kilo, but this was Snow White—dynamite *perico*. They came back with me to the hotel and took the stuff away.

I lay on my bed for a while, watching the ceiling fan. Then I packed my bags, paid off my bill and walked off through the siesta-heavy streets to the bus station.

CHAPTER NINETEEN

Indian Country

I had one more trip to make on this half-cocked odyssey. I thought of it as a way of forgetting, of washing all the drugs and lies away. It was a trip I'd wanted to make when I was first in Colombia, and never had, and I was determined to do it this time before my money ran out and my batteries went dead. I was going up into the mountain Indian territories of the Sierra Nevada.

The Sierra Nevada de Santa Marta is the highest coastal range of mountains in the world. On a clear day you can see the snow peaks while paddling in the Caribbean. At the shortest point the mountains rise from sea level to over 19,000 feet in 28 miles, a gradient surpassed only by the Himalayas. The best way to get up into the Sierra, I was told, was from the southeast, where the slopes rise more gently. The Indians of this corner of the Sierra are the Arhuaco, the most numerous of the mountain tribes and marginally more acclimatized to the white man than the fiercely isolationist Kogui who live on the northern slopes.

Both tribes are the remnants of the Tairona culture which flourished for perhaps 1,000 years on the Caribbean coastlands before the Spaniards arrived in the early sixteenth century. The Tairona were primarily farmers. They cultivated maize, beans, yucca and other staples on irrigated fields and terraces that one of the Spanish *cronistas* compared to those of Lombardy and Etruria. They fished the Caribbean for tuna, snapper and *ojo gordo*. They wore cotton, kept bees, drank *chicha* and chewed coca leaves. Their ceramics and stonework were decorated with elaborate figures—

warriors in feathered headdresses, monstrous fanged humanoids, jaguars, snakes, bats, foxes, birds, turtles and crocodiles.

Of greatest interest to the colonizing Spaniards, the Tairona were the master goldsmiths. The Spaniards bartered—axes, tools, knives, combs, beads, shirts, colored hats, wine and gunpowder, in return for gold. But the Tairona were fierce, proud and cunning, and through the sixteenth century the coastal foothills of the Sierra were the scene of bitter skirmish warfare. In 1599 the governor of Santa Marta, Juan Guiral Velon, led a final campaign of attrition. The chiefs were hanged and burned, and the great Tairona townships—Taironaca, Posigueca, Betoma—were put to the torch. The last remnants of the tribe—those not killed, or rounded up for baptism and slave labor in the Spanish *encomiendas*—retreated to the higher slopes of the Sierra, to valleys too distant and inaccessible for the Spaniards to follow. The jungle reclaimed the abandoned terraces and temples, and covered the intricate pathways that connected the villages, and guarded the Tairona gold even more jealously than the Indians themselves had.

To the average *mestizo*, the Indians represent poverty and underdevelopment and not much else. They are *gente baja*, low people. The Indians respond to this with their ancient, disconcerting, stone-like gaze, and their inner conviction that apart from the minor inconvenience of colonization, the continent still entirely belongs to them.

The way into the Arhuaco domain is from Valledupar, a cowboy town in the Cesar valley, five hours by bus from Santa Marta. At the bus station off 22nd Street I put coins into the blind man's cup. He grinned like a monkey and turned his moon-glasses up at me. *"Que vaya usted con Dios."* I took a last look at the lazy, rakish streets of Santa Marta. Goodbye to the fruit palaces, the smugglers' lore, the gold-toothed piratical smiles.

Valledupar was full of jeeps, and cowboys with big straw hats and shiny wristwatches. The Hotel Comercio—*"ambiente distinguido y familiar"*— was two rows of small blue rooms looking on to a thin strip of courtyard. The ceiling fan worked, the bed was comfortable, and there was running water at the end of the yard. The place was more or less par for the course for $2 a night, and I liked it a lot better than some I have stayed in for 200.

In the morning I set off to obtain my permits. One has to get permission from the local office of the DAS—Departamento Administrativo de Seguridad—before traveling into the Sierra. It is a "controlled" area, and anyone found there without authorization is liable to be suspected of marijuana or guerrilla connections. In an old side street off the main plaza, peeping out among the piles of identity cards and forms, a neat small man wrote down my particulars in a neat small hand. Next I toiled out to the Casa Indígena, the government office that administers Indian affairs, on the edge of town. Without a letter of introduction from them, I was assured, I would be refused entry into Arhuaco territory. A letter was typed up, outdoing Malcolm's in its baroque lardings and formalities. It was addressed to the Arhuaco chief in person, Don Luis Napoléon Torres.

I was at last prepared, administratively if not spiritually, to journey up into the Sierra. From Valledupar there were trucks or jeeps to Pueblo Bello, the last *mestizo* village, 3,600 feet up, and from there a road of sorts led on to the chief village of the Arhuacos. This is known on the maps as San Sebastián de Rábago, but to the Arhuacos themselves, it is Nebusimague.

Pueblo Bello was not well-named. I stood in the dust by the roadside, surveying the thin line of habitation down the village's one and only street. I found a *tienda* and had a couple of beers. The owner was slumped in a seat, radiating a profound boredom. A boy served me. He asked me about England. How much would his *moto*—a Yamaha 175, parked outside the store—have cost in England?

I had missed the daily jeep up to San Sebastián, so I asked the boy if he thought there might be any trucks going up there. He didn't like to say "No," so he said, "Yes, tomorrow morning." I asked him if he knew anyone who hired out mules or horses. He didn't. He praised the village hotel, El Hogar de Mamá. I bought a can of sardines and a half of aguardiente, and set off down the street. I had no intention of staying at Mamá's Place, or anywhere else in this glum little one-horse town. If no one would take me to San Sebastián I would walk there. It was about 15 miles, I reckoned. I asked the way at the village police station. Two young soldiers were sitting on the veranda, their heavy black boots on the railing. They couldn't believe I was going to walk there. "Eight hours at least," they told me. If I didn't pick up a truck, I would have to camp on the way and then pick up the jeep the next morning.

I set off. The road snaked into the distance, a sand-colored scrawl slowly winding upward through tough, rocky terrain. The mountains were hard and pale, with a patchy down of esparto grass, but the watercourses that ran down the folds of the hill were braided with tropical greenery.

I soon passed beneath a large sign, strung between two concrete posts. "RESERVA TERRITORIAL INDÍGENA," it announced. From here on out it was Indian country, where even the Colombians are foreigners.

An hour later I was squatting exhausted on a clump of cootch-grass. The sun was still high overhead. I was drenched in sweat, my mouth caked with dust. Everywhere I looked the ground was hard and dry, and the only places where there was any shelter were the steep, boulder-strewn streams. It was not a hospitable sight. Then down on the trail below, I saw a woman riding a mule uphill toward me. When the figure came into view around the final bend, I saw that it was not a woman at all, but a handsome young Indian with long black hair. He wore the traditional Arhuaco dress—a white woolen *manta*, or blanket, turned back at the shoulders so it fell in one fold, front and back, like a tunic, held at the waist by a belt of *fique* fiber. He wore trousers of the same coarse wool, and leather sandals. On his head, instead of the traditional *tutosome*—a woolen hat like an elongated fez—he wore a black cowboy hat.

He stopped to talk. "You are going to Nebusimague?" he asked. I said I was. He looked up at the sun and said it was too far to walk before dark.

"I'm going to sleep in the *monte*," I said. He looked at me disbelievingly. I asked if there was water up ahead—I didn't want to get caught in a dry stretch when it got dark. He said there were some rivers, though it was very dry for a while. He said he was thirsty himself, and I got my water bottle. As he drank I saw him wince with displeasure—it was river water, and I had added some sterilizing tablets. The taste was obviously very strong to him, though he was too polite to say anything. He spoke in a pleasant, lilting voice. His Spanish was fluent, but had a formality, a carefulness in placing the words, that showed it was not his first language. I had not yet heard the strange, susurrating tones of Iki, the Arhuaco language.

After a bit he asked, in his polite, precise way, *"Quiere usted montar?"*

"But the mule can't take both of us," I said, making a show of reluctance, though there was nothing I would have liked better.

He laughed. "No. You ride," he said, and climbed off the mule.

This is the genius of Colombia. One moment you're sitting in the dust, red-faced and gasping. The next you're up on a high-pommeled saddle, feeling the powerful grace of the mule beneath you, as he pulls steadily up the steep, rutted track.

The young Arhuaco's name was Victor—they all use Castilian names— and he was eighteen years old. He had been down in Pueblo Bello, selling maize and buying provisions. He jogged alongside the mule, not at all out of breath despite the steepness. I thought it must be chewing coca that gave him such sprightliness. I asked him. He said, "No, I am not married."

I assumed he had misunderstood my question, so I asked again. He explained that it was forbidden for an Arhuaco to use coca until he was married. "Only men may take coca," he said. "Not boys, not women, not girls. Only men."

We climbed and climbed. The mule's name was Rosario. Sweat-suds flecked his brown neck. For long stretches we traveled in silence, with only the measured fall of Rosario's hooves, the creaking of the saddle and a low undertone of grunts and whistles from Victor to keep the mule going. There was no sight of Pueblo Bello when I looked back. The mountains seemed to close like a door behind us. We breasted the Alguacil Plateau, at nearly 9,500 feet the highest point on the journey to Nebusimague. A kind of swallow with an immensely long tail flitted past us. I asked Victor what it was called. He deliberated carefully. *"Turi,"* he said. I later learned this was simply the Iki word for "bird." We came down from the plateau through the shady gorge of high trees and stopped to rest in a clearing. A few round, grass-thatched huts were scattered in a valley below. I reached into my bag for bread and *paso de bananos*. I handed them to Victor, meaning for him to tear a bit off each. He gave a radiant "Thank you!" stuffed the loaf into his bag and ate his way through the entire *paso*. I hadn't the gall to stop him, after his kindness to me. He presumably thought it was some kind of payment. "Delicious," he said, tossing away the empty bark wrapping.

We took a precipitous shortcut, which sliced off a wide elbow of the road. Rosario slithered on the stones. Twice my *campesino* hat came off, to Victor's amusement. The sky flushed pink. The evening star—*Virakoku* in Iki—appeared. Victor produced a flashlight from his bag.

We must have gone on about two more hours in the dark, taking turns on the mule, stumbling on the rocks. My feet hurt. I felt like giving up, but Victor kept saying we were *al llegar*, almost there. Then I heard the sound of dogs on the breeze, there were plots of maize and cane by the roadside, and now Victor quietly said, "We're here." In the darkness I could just make out a stone wall that encircled the village. Low thatched roofs huddled within it, humped like sleeping animals in a pen.

"We must go around to the other gate," said Victor. "You are a stranger," he added.

A knot of young Arhuaco men were hanging around the main gate—the eastern end of the village. Victor spoke with them in Iki, and then one of them said to me, "Please enter." The gate was barred shut. It had a little thatch roof like a churchyard lych-gate. The way in was by a smooth, notched log leaning against the wall. I followed Victor up this gangplank, over the wall and into Nebusimague.

Once inside the village I could see firelight in some doorways, and knots of people standing around. Everyone seemed to be whispering, rustling. There were no hard sounds. No metal, no traffic, no music. I saw the moon, big and low over a black flank of mountain. The smell of wood-smoke filled the air. The strange lunar village twittered and rustled about me.

After a bit I was beckoned over to meet a small, weasel-faced man. A thick wad of coca distended his cheek. He shone his flashlight in my face. He was polite but brusque. He was not Chief Napoleón, I learned, but one of the village administrators. He demanded my letter and read it aloud by torchlight. Don Napoleón was not available at present, he said. I must present myself to him tomorrow morning. He gave me to understand that upright, honest people didn't come skulking into the village after dark like this.

I was, I realized, a bit of a nuisance. I had not expected to find a hotel in Nebusimague, but had imagined there would be some kind of village hostel for *viajeros*. There was none. Where was I going to sleep? I said vaguely, *"En el monte,"* gesturing out to the countryside beyond. There was a twitter of mirth as this was relayed to the crowd by the weasel-faced man. There was a brief conference. I was to be allotted a small empty house about ten minutes' walk back down the valley. The weasel shook my hand and told me to present myself at the *casa de convención* tomorrow morning. I was escorted down to the house by four young Arhuacos.

The grass outside the house was already wet with dew. I ate a moonlit supper of iguana eggs, *ersatz* sardines and aguardiente, and fell into a dreamless sleep.

The following day I met Chief Napoleón. There was nothing much to mark him out as the *cacique*, only that his clothes were bright white, rather than the muted cream wool worn by everyone else. He was rather a disappointment: small, fussy and saturnine. He did not look at me while the weasel explained about me. For the time being I was no more than an administrative problem, an item on the parish agenda for the morning.

The *casa de convención* was a long rectangular building in the center of the village. It was dark inside. There were benches along the wall and rails of knotty wood. Chief Napoleón's desk stood in the corner, before the only window. He put on a pair of horn-rimmed glasses. They gave him a comic schoolmaster look, with the fez-like *tutosome* instead of a mortarboard. An absurd pun on "Arhuaco" and "Whacko" flitted through my confused mind. The weasel gave him the letter from the Casa Indígena. He read through it, breathily mumbling the words to himself, squinting through his specs, holding the paper up to the light of the window. In that bright little rectangle there were children's faces, and a brilliant blue sky and buff-colored adobe walls. The meetinghouse was quite full now. The men greeted one another, each doling out a little helping of coca leaves into the other's *mochila* bag. All the men carried their coca kit: a *mochila* full of the crisp, dried leaves, and an hourglass gourd, called a *popóro*, which contains the powdered lime necessary to activate the stimulant principles of the coca leaf.

Having read my letter, Chief Napoleón made what sounded like a well-rehearsed speech on the evils of visitors and tourists. "We see a lot of requests like this," he said, jabbing a stubby finger at the letter. "Tourists come to look at us. Doctors and students make reports on us. People photograph us." He spoke the word "photograph" as if it were some social disease. "We see no benefit," he continued. "We, *el pueblo indígeno*, receive nothing. They come, they take, they go."

I stood there with my hands behind my back, like a scolded schoolboy, saying, "I understand, *señor*, I understand," radiating useless waves of liberal sentiment. I heard the words, "tariff," "contribution to the community...exploitation...inconvenience...we charge 500 pesos *por cabeza.*"

Under the watchful eye of the assembly, I paid over a 500-peso bill to Napoleón. He briskly sorted it away in an old ledger, where I saw one or two other bills. The mood now perceptibly softened. Napoleón conferred gruffly with the weasel, and then he announced in a loud, orotund voice that I was to be granted the freedom of Nebusimague for eight days. After certain formalities I would be free to walk around, and...he couldn't apparently think of anything else I might want to do, so he just added "and so on," and spat a gob of green coca-cud on to the dirt floor.

The weasel was dispatched to relay the chief's ruling to the Inspector of Indigenous Police. Now that I was legitimized he was quite friendly. He had been *cacique* of the Arhaucos for seven years, I learned. The position is not hereditary: the chief is elected by the tribal council of *cabildos*. Nebusimague is the tribal capital and administrative center, with a permanent population of about 200. The majority of the Arhuacos, some 15,000 in all, live scattered through the territories in small villages in the high valleys on the southern and eastern flanks of the Sierra. The weasel returned bearing a sheet of paper, with the words "Confederacíon Indígena Tayrona" styled in red and black. "Now you are free," he said. "But you must be sure to obey our laws, or we will put you in a hut with no food or water." My stomach gurgled nervously. "Are you strong?" he asked, and gripped my arm to feel the muscle, and again there was a discreet mumble of laughter around the dark room.

As I left, I turned to say *"Hasta luego"* to Chief Napoleón and the weasel, and back came a ringing chorus of *"Hasta luego"* from everyone in the building. It came quite unexpectedly, out of the gloom, like the sudden chime of a big deep bell. It wiped away all the hassles of the morning. I stepped into the clean mountain air, with the sun bouncing off the stone walls, and I reflected that it had taken a while to obtain my passport into Arhuaco lands, because it was a kind of passport into another time.

From the back of my house, which looked south across a marshy stretch to wooded slopes, I could see a cluster of huts. The smoke seeped out of the thatched roofs, so they seemed to be steaming in the morning sun. In one of these lived Valentín, an Arhuaco of about thirty years old, short, flat-faced, with long black glossy hair. He was a sunny character and liked to talk, unlike most of these passive, introspective people. His face would split into a wide grin, showing discolored teeth. As is common with the Arhuaco, Valentín and his family had three homes, each with its own little plot of a hectare or two. One was higher up, near the *páramo* north of Nebusimague. There he cultivated cold-climate crops: potato, manioc, beans. At the lower *finca* he had cane, bananas, maize and coca.

From Valentín I learned a little about the use of coca among the Arhuaco. They do not actually call it "coca," which is a Spanish derivation from the Quechua work *kuka*. They call it *hayu*. As I had learned from Victor, only married men are permitted to use the leaf. When a young Arhuaco is to be married, he undergoes a period of instruction and initiation under the tutelage of a *mame*, an Arhuaco priest. Valentín would tell me little of this, but I gathered that the strength and endurance afforded by chewing coca leaves were linked with the manliness and virility of the adult male.

The Arhuaco chews his coca leaves throughout the day. The leaf suppresses hunger and relieves tiredness. As Valentín simply put it, the coca *"cuida del cuerpo"*—it takes care of his body. It is a kind of freedom from the prickings of the flesh.

I asked Valentín if he would sell me some leaves. This was such bad form that he pretended he hadn't heard. One evening, however, he gave me some. He apologized that they were not the best. The finest leaves are olive-green, smooth, almost glossy, with a soft, slightly spongy texture. These were paler and drier, but they smelled good—a slightly metallic odor, but soft and aromatic, like a form of tea.

CHAPTER TWENTY

Sierra Medicine

There were two ways of getting myself back down to Valledupar. The first and simplest was to return the way I had come, through Pueblo Bello. The other way was to strike out through the mountains to another *mestizo* village, Chemesquemena, about 25 miles northeast of Nebusimague. The trail to Chemesquemena, I was reliably informed, was clear to follow and very beautiful. All you had to do was keep with the rivers—follow the San Sebastián River upstream, cross the watershed, pick up the Los Mangos River, follow it east until it joins the Guatapuri River, then turn north and follow the Guatapuri as far as Chemesquemena. What could be simpler?

Late one afternoon I suddenly decided to go. I said goodbye to Valentín, who assured me I would be in Chemesquemena in two days' time. That night I slept beneath a giant caracoli tree beside the San Sebastián River. The river was swollen and blackened after the previous day's rains. I slept fitfully and dreamed of familiar faces. Waking to the spiky, unfamiliar skyline, the rushing of the river, the moving moon, it seemed impossible to believe that this was the reality, and the people I knew so well were the dream. At sunrise I breakfasted on bread and *panela*, and after an hour of quite steep walking I stood high up on the watershed, looking down on the breathtaking panorama of the canyon below, dense cloud forest in its hollows, pale brown *ico* grass on the upper ridges. Occasional tiny grass-roofed huts clung to the skirts of the slopes, and all along the south side of the valley I could see the trail running off eastward, mile upon mile into the morning haze.

The path came out of the forest canopy and wound along the slope. The river roared below. This was a hot, rocky stretch, and I was glad when the path finally dipped back down into the shade of the greenery. I swam, ate some lunch and crossed the Los Mangos River over a wood and concrete bridge. The builder's signature—Jorge Los Rios, George of the River—was etched in the concrete. I picked windfall mangoes and set off for the afternoon's trek.

During the afternoon the character of the day began to change. The first thing I noticed was that the trail, though fairly level, seemed to be getting harder and harder. I found myself panting and drooping. I stopped frequently for water and fruit. I was also confused about the trail. When I crossed the Rio Los Mangos, I had thought I would pick up the Guatapuri River and head northward, but consulting my compass I found I was still going east.

I soon realized why I was feeling so feeble. The air over the buff-colored peaks was massing, gray and charged. There was no doubt about it: a storm was gathering. I heard the thunder ricochet up along the ridges. The first fat drops spat onto the dusty track, and within seconds it had turned into a downpour. I was on a high, bare stretch of trail. There was nowhere to shelter, I had no waterproof gear to put on, and by the time I reached some trees I was drenched. I huddled for a few minutes under some bushes, but the rain was too strong and pounded through unabated. There was no point in sitting there, so on I went. The path had turned into a rivulet of mud and leaves. The feeder streams that had purled down the rocks a few moments earlier were now running faster and louder. Water poured off the brim of my hat. I cursed my unpreparedness.

Suddenly, in front of me, I saw a little dog scampering along the trail, and when it cut off left, down a wooded slope, I followed it, thinking it must be leading me somewhere. Then just as suddenly as it appeared the dog vanished, and I found myself teetering at the edge of a gorge, staring down at the boiling waters of Los Mangos 50 feet below. I hacked back up the slope, slithering in the mud, and rejoined the trail. The only thing was to keep on going, but after a while even this option was closed off. The trail wound down into tall woodland, and disappeared entirely beneath the swollen waters of a feeding river. I stood there, uncertain. I knew there must be stepping stones under the water: all the feeder rivers I had crossed had had some kind of ford. I felt gingerly for the first stone, the rush of the water grabbed my foot, and I fell. For a moment I thought I was going to be swept away, thrown like a soft tomato against one of those big boulders, but I managed to fall slightly backward and get a grip on some rocks. I crawled out and lay on the bank, shivering. The trail was blocked, the light was fading fast, and the storm showed no sign of letting up.

Then I spotted, down in a hollow of the woods, what I'd been looking for all along: a cave. When I got to it I saw it was not really a cave, just an arrangement of rocks, but it was space enough for a half-drowned rat to crawl into. I pulled off my wet clothes and wormed into my sleeping bag. The light had gone completely now. I took a few slugs of aguardiente. It looked like it was going to be a long hard night.

I don't know how long I sat there—probably not much more than an hour. I listened to the roar of the river. Then I began to notice a subtle addition to the noise. The raging of water outside the cave was now counterpointed by another, softer, liquid sound. Swiveling around I found water pouring steadily through the back of the rock. It had been coming in for a while before I had heard it. The cave was awash. Unknown to me, my sleeping bag had been quietly soaking up water. The cave was too small to stand up in. I had to drag myself out in my sleeping bag, floundering like some preposterous mermaid. There was a big humped rock a few yards from the cave: I must make for that, higher ground. I scrabbled some belongings together from the cave and set off for the rock. I promptly sank up to my thighs in a morass of mud and leaves. My boots were unlaced, and I walked clean out of one of them as I forded this mulch.

After three journeys I was up on the rock with my things scattered around me. Thankfully my flashlight still worked. Everything else was in a pitiful condition. My world seemed to have shrunk to tiny, primitive proportions—the cave, the morass, the rock.

Water was still dripping off the trees, but I was aware that the rain had stopped. I considered my options. I couldn't stay here, wet and shivering on the rock. I couldn't go on across the swollen river. The only thing to do was turn back. I squeezed everything into my bag with difficulty. It seemed to weigh twice as much as before.

Back on the trail I was amazed at how quickly the storm-waters had been soaked up. The land had drunk up the water, and now the trail was mostly as dry and firm as it had been that afternoon. The storm had come and gone, and I alone on that hillside was unable to cope with it.

After about half an hour I recognized the stretch of woodland where I had followed the little dog off the trail. Maybe there *was* a house around somewhere. I took the same side-path I had slid down before, and found a fork in it I had not seen previously. In a few minutes I came out into a small grassy clearing. There, sitting in the moonlight, was a small farmyard, and the round thatched hump of an Arhuaco house.

I stood irresolutely at the gate. All was silent, except the distant river in the gorge below. A dead hog's plum tree stood in the farmyard. I saw what looked like a mound of old blankets lying in the yard, a few feet from the entrance to the hut. As I got nearer I saw there were two figures asleep beneath the blankets, children I supposed from the size of them. The moon was bright, the dusty yard as mysteriously dry as the trail. I went up and tapped one of them on the shoulder. The figure started up. It was not a child, but a small, squat, very ugly man with matted black hair, who might have been anything between forty and four hundred years old.

I stuttered forth my supplication. I was caught in the storm, I needed shelter, I would gladly pay.

"You are wet," he said in gruff Spanish. He woke the woman beside him, spoke to her in Iki. She climbed out of the blankets, without much obvious enthusiasm, and shuffled off inside. "You may sleep here," said the little man. He told me to hang my wet things on the rails of the corral that ran down one side of the farmyard. A pair of small white *cebú* cows stared at me. In another part of the corral I saw a mule and a horse. Chickens, small pigs and a dog or two were loose in the farmyard. I asked the old man if he had any matches. He said he had the *candela* going inside the hut. He went in and lit me a cigarette. I lit another off it, for him to smoke. He took it out of politeness, but coughed and spat when he smoked it, and threw it away.

I asked him if it would rain again.

He shook his head. "The rains have gone on," he said, gesturing east. We stood in silence for a while. There were rustlings in the farmyard, a night bird calling. "The rains come at the full moon."

I looked up, ashamed that I hadn't noticed. Full moon in the Sierra. If you were after purification, this was surely it.

I slept naked in the farmyard, among pigs and toads, with a cowhide mat beneath me and a woolen blanket on top. The ridges of the mat bit my back, and the fleas bit everywhere else, but I have never felt so snug in my life. I was touched with gratitude to the little farmer—who, like some good dwarf in a Grimm fairy tale—had offered his humble hospitality to a stranger lost in the storm.

At dawn a cock crowed, old and wheezy, like a rusty door being forced open. In the east the sun was glinting pink on the mountaintops, in the west the moon was still precise and bright. Dew sparkled on my mangy belongings hanging on the corral. The little farmer appeared up the path, leading a mule carrying two *cestas* of maize. He was traveling up to Nebusimague today. He beckoned me into his dark, smoky hut. His wife fanned the *candela*. A blackened pot sat on the glowing wood. A mess of grayish pottage bubbled sluggishly. I breakfasted on a bowlful of gruel, which seemed to taste of little else than the layers of black wood-carbon on the bowl. It was doubtless maize.

Their children stared at me, their dogs growled at me. The little man and his wife bent over their wood dishes, ladling the gruel in with their hands. Nothing was said.

I loaded my damp gear into my bag. The old Arhuaco stood watching me. He explained carefully how I should recognize the point where I must ford the Los Mangos, in order to pick up the northbound trail along the Guatapuri. As I was sorting my bedraggled clothes, I came upon the bag of coca leaves given me by Valentín. They were a sorry sight, blackened and mulched against the side of the bag.

"You need coca," said the farmer. He got me to hold out my towel. He dipped his hand in his *mochila* and deposited fresh green leaves on the towel. "You have a journey. You need medicine for your journey."

I thanked him profusely. He laughed and said something unintelligible in Iki. I said, "I do not understand Iki."

He translated into his rough Spanish, "Do not thank me, thank God. God gives it."

I offered him money, making clear it was not for the coca, but for his hospitality. He refused. I pressed him, saying he had been my "hotel" for the night. He didn't seem to understand the word. I walked with him back up the trail. We shook hands. He was going west. I was going east. I thanked him all over again. He said, "The white man will do the same for me if I am lost."

"I hope so."

I set off down the trail, one boot flapping open like a vaudeville tramp's. I walked for a day and a half, living on Spam and windfall mangoes, chewing the old man's coca. I swam in the big rivers, and slept beneath a giant carocoli, and in the morning woke to find a blue hummingbird hovering near my head like the spirit of a departed ancestor.

On my third day out of Nebusimague, at midday, I made one last ascent on a rocky stretch and found myself on a real dirt road, with real tire marks leading down to a bridge. On the other side, sun bouncing off the tin roofs, stood Chemesquemena.

There followed the truck ride down to Valledupar, the long, hot bus-haul to Bogotá. I was tired and careless; the old farmer's coca leaves did not travel well. They sweated in the hotlands, and when I unpacked them in Bogotá they smelled like compost, and the first specks of mildew could be seen on them. *Coca caspada*. It was as if they were sickening for the Sierra. I could believe it. I could believe anything by now.

I nearly chucked them away, but I didn't. They were a gift, a memento, evidence that I hadn't been dreaming. Now they're sitting on the customs man's desk. They're what this story, this whole business, is about. Behind all the greed and the violence, the need to make laws and the itch to break them, there is just this handful of leaves, medicine for the journey.

ANDREW H. MALCOLM

FINAL HARVEST

ANDREW H. MALCOLM

FINAL HARVEST

On the drizzly cold morning of September 29, 1983, the small town of Ruthton, Minnesota, was stunned by a double murder: two of its most prominent citizens had been ambushed and gunned down in cold blood.

An intensive manhunt followed. So too did a sudden focus of media attention, for these apparently remote murders were quickly seen to have a wider significance. They were symptoms of painful and little-understood changes creeping across the vast plains of the troubled Midwest, destroying a unique and valued way of life that has contributed so much to America's national strength and character.

No one could be better qualified to handle this story than Andrew Malcolm, a native Midwesterner and the grandson of two farmers. As Chicago bureau chief of The New York Times he has covered the developing farm crisis and has a profound understanding of the region and its people. Writing with compelling detail he recreates the lives of the tragedy's main characters and retraces the course of events that led inexorably to that fatal encounter in the weed-strewn yard of an abandoned farmhouse.

Storm Watch

It was such a happy time.

On September 28, 1983, Susan Blythe returned from a long trip to Texas with a car and a trailer full of her family's furniture and clothing. To her waiting husband, Rudy, it seemed she was finally accepting their move away from their friends in the fine homes of north Dallas back to their modest home in rural southwestern Minnesota. He knew how Susan felt about their small-town life, and how he felt about it. Ever since they had moved to the Midwest from Philadelphia, Rudy had wanted to own a small country bank. It was a dream that had dominated his thoughts, his savings, even his weekends, when he would bundle his wife and son into the car and cruise the streets of the rural Midwest looking for likely bank candidates to buy. The attraction was the lack of bureaucracy. Being his own boss. The sense of community. The intimacy with clients. And, not least, the intoxicating sense of being needed that would surely earn him wide acceptance among the men he always sought out. It all appealed to him so much that after the final papers were signed on Thanksgiving in 1977, he had marched Susan and little Rolph outside in the snow and had his father take a picture of the three of them by the bank's brick walls beneath the stylish sign, Buffalo Ridge State Bank. Finally, it was his.

The two males—big, tall, heavyset Rudy, a good bit overweight for his forty-two years from his nervous eating of the last few months, and short, stocky Rolph, an instant guard on any football team of eleven-year-olds—had organized a family party for Susan's thirty-ninth birthday that homecoming night, complete with a store-bought cake that said, "Happy Birthday, Susan." Cake was not on Rudy's diet, but this was a special night, much more than a normal birthday. These months of trouble at the bank, with Susan still in Texas, were about to end. The dream was back on track.

He and Rolph were waiting at home as Susan drove slowly through the darkened, leaf-strewn streets of the little town of Ruthton, some five hundred miles northwest of Chicago, that Wednesday night. She knew the community well from the four years she had spent in its confines before the move to Texas. Word spreads quickly about everything in a small town, especially when it concerns someone as important as The Banker. All 332 residents knew Susan Blythe was coming back.

Shortly after 10:00 P.M. she turned off the main highway onto Leo Street and pulled up in front of her house. As she did so, she saw movement in the front window. Rolph's chubby face ducked behind the lighted curtains. When the front door opened, there was an explosion of hugs and kisses as the pent-up homemade warmth swept into the cool autumn night. Presents were piled by the hearth, including a matching skirt, sweater, and blazer from Susan's parents back in New York. Rudy gave his wife a sweater and skirt and a nightgown. Rolph handed her a box containing a new pair of slippers.

The big man and the little man sang "Happy Birthday" then. And they lit a few candles on the cake; they were men, but when it came to Mom, they knew better than to light all thirty-nine. The cake was cut, the rainbow sherbet dished out, and they all sat down at the table.

It had taken Susan two days to make the trip from Texas. After her safe arrival at home for the birthday party, it seemed that everything was moving so rapidly, like a sled rushing downhill toward the woods. There was audible joy to this high-speed homecoming celebration, and Susan wanted to slow it down to savor more.

The sherbet was melting, and it was past Rolph's bedtime. But everybody that night wanted to talk at once: Sue about Texas and their friends there; Rolph about school and football; and Rudy about the bank. He had a list of things he urgently wanted to tell her, and every time the subject turned away from the bank, he would remember some other financial news. "Oh, Dad," Rolph said at one point, "all you ever talk about is the bank."

"He's right," said Susan. "Can't this wait until later?"

"Oh," her husband continued, pretending to almost forget the big news, "the DeRuyter loan was paid off." Susan did listen to that—ninety thousand dollars was no small sum. As a bank board member, she knew about that loan. It was one of those that had been bothering Rudy, considering the continuing agricultural recession and the declining value of farmland and collateral. But her husband patted the pocket of his blue oxford shirt. He pulled out a pink deposit slip. And he smiled.

Then Rolph was tucked into bed. No time for Dad to read to him tonight. That was okay. Everybody was back together again, and not just for a short visit. Susan and Rudy strolled outside into the chilly, wet September night. Lyle Landgren, the deputy sheriff, cruised by on his nightly rounds and waved. The thought of unpacking everything that night in the light rain was too much for the Blythes. "Leave it," said Rudy, "and I'll help you tomorrow after closing."

"Okay," said Susan. She pulled the car into the garage, and they went indoors.

"Oh, I forgot to tell you," Rudy said later as his mind continued down the mental list of news items, "I have an appointment tomorrow to show the old Jenkins farm." Susan needed no reminding about that place. For four years they had owned that farm, ever since that son of a bitch sold his mortgaged cattle, declared bankruptcy, and stuck them with a thirty-thousand-dollar loss.

"Who wants to buy it?" Susan said through the bathroom door as she finished her shower.

Her husband replied. But the water was running. It sounded like one of those Scandinavian names.

"Who?" said Susan, happy that they might finally be unloading the farm with the haunted house just north of town but too tired then to really care. She opened the bathroom door, the steam billowing into the cooler bedroom. Her husband was in mid-sentence.

" . . . don't know him. No one seems to. He's from up north somewhere. I tried to check. But he phoned and I'll meet him out at the farm tomorrow morning."

"Well, will you meet him before nine?" asked Susan. " 'Cause I could take Rolph to school in the bank car and get it back in time for your appointment." She knew how strongly Rudy felt against using the company car for personal business, but the windshield wipers didn't work on their own car. It was eighteen miles to the Pipestone school, and just three blocks to the bank.

When they crawled into bed, it was eleven-thirty. The clock radio was on softly. The last thing they heard as they drifted off to sleep, together again, was the weather forecast for Thursday. Storms were coming.

The morning dawned cold and drizzly and foggy. The family was running late. Susan quickly whipped up some toast, poured the juice for Rolph, and dumped some hot water in a cup with some instant coffee.

"How long do you have to be married," Rudy said as he took a sip and made a face, "to get a real cup of coffee in the morning?"

"You know how to make it yourself," she said. "Get off your keister and do it. I've got to get going." It was an eminently forgettable remark, the kind of crack, when said with a smile, that seems to require no apology. Within hours, those nineteen words would sound harsher in Susan's mind than she ever intended.

Susan was still in the bedroom when Rudy got up from the breakfast table, hugged his son, and donned his bright yellow rain slicker. "Will you be back by nine with the car?" he called. And Susan said yes, but she didn't hear him leave for the bank downtown. He was in such a hurry, in fact, that he did not kiss his wife good-bye. So when she emerged from the bedroom dressed in her exercise clothes and talking to her husband, Rudy was gone. She didn't think much about it then, for she was in her own hurry.

At the bank that morning there was a minor legal problem. Deems "Toby" Thulin, Rudy's new loan officer, was a little embarrassed. He had been out driving the previous night in a pickup truck the bank had recently repossessed, and was stopped by the state highway patrol. The truck's license plate sticker had expired, and the officer issued Toby a ticket. No problem, said Rudy. In a few minutes they'd drive the six miles up County

Road 7 to the Tyler Town Hall. They'd get the new registration in the works, get Toby back to work reviewing the bank's problem loans, and Rudy could make his ten o'clock appointment out at the Jenkins place.

Rudy liked Toby, who was even newer in Ruthton than his boss. Toby was thirty-seven, wiry, athletic, a Vietnam veteran who liked a cold beer with the guys on a hot Sunday after a couple of softball games. He had bumped around the Midwest for a number of years working for banks and loan companies and doing some odd construction work. But things had not really been expanding in his world, especially for someone without a college education. Toby was not succeeding financially. He had tried to hide it all; men are supposed to in the country. But his wife, Lynnette, saw the impact in the longer, quieter periods: his quicker temper, his frequent absences, sometimes even a wavering of his religious faith. She got part-time work and made and sold crafts from their basement to bring in a few extra dollars for them and their three little girls. Lynnette had even put out a feeler for her husband with an executive search company. There had been nothing for months, and then along came a real possibility—a job with a little bank in Ruthton, Minnesota. The opening with the Blythes looked good, although soon after Toby began work, the strains of their situation had prompted the Thulins into a trial separation. They had a marriage counseling session set for the next weekend.

Getting the truck registration papers didn't take long. Rudy, who rarely carried any cash, simply wrote out a check to the state for $37.68. Then the two bankers went to have a coffee in the café in Tyler. It was hunting season, and there was nothing Toby liked more than hunting or fishing, or talking about hunting or fishing. He was a good shot, and among friends he might make some quiet reference to all the shooting he'd seen and done over in Vietnam. Rudy liked hunting and fishing, too, or rather he liked the fraternity; the guys out in the boat, the late dinner, telling stories around the fire. It was soon nearly nine o'clock and time for Rudy to take Toby back to the bank in Ruthton and then go out to the Jenkins place for the appointment at ten.

In the closing days of September the fields along County Road 7, like those along thousands of miles of prairie roads from Ohio to Colorado and from Minnesota south to Texas, are lined with dead or dying things. Green grasses turning yellow. Leaves scuttling back and forth. Tumbleweeds piled against fences. Some of the corn has been picked by then. Much has not, and in the winds, the crisp, crumpled cornstalks rub against one another across the empty fields in a strange kind of dry death rattle.

On the drive past these fields back to Ruthton, Rudy decided to stop by the abandoned Jenkins farm just to check so that everything would go smoothly with the potential buyer an hour later. Rudy did not believe in locking up the empty houses and barns he was selling. He figured if anybody was going to break into an isolated farmhouse, a locked door would not stop him. Anyway, there wasn't anything to take out of the old house. When Jenkins had left four years ago, he'd even torn out the bathtub.

It was raining again as Rudy approached the Jenkins farm. The station wagon's windows were closed, so Rudy and Toby didn't hear their slowing tires swishing on the wet pavement. But other men did. When the car turned into the gravel driveway, these other men also heard the crunching of stones. They ran and hid.

In Texas at that hour Charles Snow was in his tiny office with battle prints on the wall. After thirty-one years of military service, the blunt, tough-talking maintenance supervisor had retired from uniform but retained the taut mind and manner of the top sergeant he had been for so long. It was just another day at work for Snow, who could live on his army pension but liked the camaraderie of men. He hoped to get away a little early that day for some work out on his small country ranch. He likes the open air, the immense country sky free of wires and walls, printed rules and confining clocks, and he is drawn to those who feel the same.

Rudolph H. Blythe, Sr., had gone to the country club not far from the retirement home he and his wife, Dorothy, had in Gainesville, Florida. He spent the morning talking with friends in his investment club. His wife stayed at home with the cleaning woman; Dot's legs, stricken with polio, were bothering her again and walking had become difficult. To pick up her spirits, perhaps they'd call their son Rudy tonight and see if Susan got home all right from Texas.

Bill Slater should have retired too, but the old railroad man couldn't keep away from the trains. He was out that morning helping crews survey the repair work on a crumbling old rail line near Utica, New York. His wife, Alice, was at home watching TV.

Robert Berg, an agent for the Bureau of Criminal Apprehension, Minnesota's state detective force, was enjoying a slow morning in his office in Worthington, Minnesota, near the Iowa border. He had just finished up a homicide. Someone had beaten a two-year-old girl to death, and Berg had spent the better part of three months investigating the case.

Tom Fabel, the tall, eloquent deputy attorney general of Minnesota, was in his St. Paul office. He'd come downtown early to do as much legal work as possible before the phones started ringing. He hoped to get away by midmorning for an extended weekend in the woods.

Mike O'Gorman, another BCA agent, was a hundred miles south of St. Paul investigating a "house shooting." An angry husband, seeking reconciliation with his estranged wife, had stormed out of his farmhouse and then apparently shot a .22-caliber bullet through the residence, narrowly missing the woman. Guns are common in the countryside. In fact, many rural homes have more guns than people. Investigating this near murder

would consume O'Gorman's day and keep him away from a radio and the
news that would take control of his life for many months.

Judge Walter H. Mann was in his chambers doing paperwork. Karen
Rider was at home humming in the shower. Lynnette Thulin was in Professor Hilton's classroom, when she felt slightly nauseous. She looked at
the clock—9:10. At that moment Abe Thompson, sheriff of Lincoln
County in southwestern Minnesota, glanced at his watch. Suddenly both
his phone lines lit up simultaneously.

That was strange.

CHAPTER TWO

Paradise Lost

On the surface, Ruthton, Minnesota, looks like any of a thousand other
midwestern towns, an aging collection of small houses scattered on straight
streets around a downtown one or two blocks long.

It is a quiet place and folks pretty much like it that way. Besides Jensen's
Food Market, there is a run-down laundromat, an American Legion office, Duane DeBettignies's Buffalo Ridge Printing and Gazette Shop, a
New-Used Furniture and Upholstery store that looks mainly used, and a
tavern with a Schlitz beer light but no name sign because everyone knows
it is the Polar Bar. The row of storefronts includes a Senior Citizens Center, where no one ever bothers to change the "Open" sign even after midnight, a "Plbg and Htg" office, a tiny library, a few abandoned buildings,
a Tom Sawyer-style whitewashed fence on one vacant lot. Next to Alene's
restaurant and bowling alley sits a small park with fading framed tributes
to high school sports achievements. These naturally include the 1981 basketball team, whose 17-0 record and state tournament appearance got
Ruthton and Rudy Blythe so excited that practically the entire town traveled to the final game and the bank's fancy hospitality suite. The nicest
building, of course, is the bank, whose big windows shine across the street
from the restaurant. Most of the town's homes along the curbless streets
are aging, with a little garage out back, its white paint peeling in spots.
Some corners have lone streetlights that shine down on the little Girl Scouts
and Cub Scouts en route home by six. By 9:00 P.M. the streetlights are the
brightest things visible, save for the café's red Coca-Cola machine, whose
familiar *ker-thumk* dispensing sound is sometimes the only sign of late-
night life.

The fields are never far from towns such as Ruthton. They sit there like
time itself, silent and dark and taken for granted. In winter the fields are

sleeping. In spring they are wet and foul. By fall they are dried and tired. But come summer the fields are alive with lush green growth that is lovingly tended by men in dusty baseball caps who swarm about with implements that put finishing touches on the soil as a sculptor might before his clay dries.

Each morning a thin band of pink light eases gently into the eastern sky over the tasseled tops of the mile-long cornfields. As if on a signal, the crickets' chirping gives way to the birds' singing. The stars start to fade. And soon the sun is back out, baking the corn and the soybeans and anyone or anything not in the shade. It is a wonderful time of year—life unfolding as it should, rich in its promise of harvests to come, rewarding of its bounty for long labors lavished, reassuring in its regularity.

The work is hard in the spring: plowing the fields, planting them, feeding them, and waiting patiently for the sun and soil, the rain and God to work their magic. In the barn they invest the same care in the hogs, the milk cows and the cattle. Set the alarm for three each spring morning to check the cows for birthing problems. Be alert for those little mood swings, droopy ears or tail, dull eyes, that presage disease. Help the neighbors 'cause, sure as shootin', they'll help you someday. Soon those little hogs are big hogs. The cattle are filling out nicely. And those little green shoots of corn, 20,000 or more to the acre, will start reaching for the sun. If everything goes right, in 126 days those 20,000 little shoots should become 14,000,000 kernels, bulging yellow nuggets of nutrition that should pay for all the seeds and chemicals of spring plus perhaps a little for the labor too.

There will be some rough times, for sure. I remember back in the 1930s, everyone's father would start out. It might be the sawdust story, how that useless substance sold for more than wheat. Or the one about grandpa having to sell off all the animals or the bank taking them for some reason. Or the tale about the grasshoppers that came hopping in from somewhere by the millions to consume everything of value before them.

But the story endings were always the same. Hard work will cure anything. Hard, honest work, the father would say, slowing for emphasis. And . . . don't . . . you . . . forget . . . it, . . . son.

Because there was so much to do, there was an organization to daily life, a semiassigned list of chores, except in the kitchen, where Mom ruled. Up around dawn, two hours' work outdoors, a hearty breakfast, more long hours outdoors, a hearty dinner with everyone appearing from different fields promptly at noon. More long hours outdoors, a lighter supper after five, when rural roads suddenly became deserted, some more work outdoors. Then, by nine or ten, the sheds were shut, the doors were closed, and the lights were extinguished. Around the clock, around the years, through the generations.

It went on like that across the entire midsection of the United States, which became not just one region among many, but more of a national reservoir of values and scenes insulated by the coasts. The area came to be called the nation's Heartland.

Life there bred a boldness, or bluntness. It was a physical, common-sense challenge, a life where things get done by doing, plain and simple, with as much applied force as necessary. The Midwest, home to nearly half the gross national product, was a land where old values like hard work, patriotism, and neighborliness hung on long after they had been discarded as unfashionable most everywhere else.

The region also bred caution; this morning's sunshine could lead to this afternoon's thunder, or worse. Each year's school schedule contained a batch of "snow days" for the blizzards that closed the roads for a while. Sell some of the corn, okay, but hold some back, just in case, right? Keep some money in the cookie jar for a rainy day; sure this year's crop is okay, but next spring could be different. Still, midwestern farmers devised strains of grains and methods of producing them that were so efficient they now feed several lands, and through their export earnings quietly finance much of the country's manufactured imports.

Sudden violence doesn't seem to fit the peaceful countryside, but in the Midwest there is always the threat that what seems normal, calm and peaceful—a little cloud, for instance, or a refreshing breeze or a light rain shower—can suddenly turn lethal. Within the cloud, perhaps, are ice balls that can in an instant smash windows, kill livestock, and turn to pulp the crops lavished with so much attention and money. The breeze can suddenly build speed, knocking down trees, ripping off doors, or, worse yet, flattening the frail green stalks that stood six inches apart as far as the eye could see. The shower can expand into a full-blown thunderstorm fifteen miles tall, a moving mountain of black air unleashing the same energy as a twenty-kiloton nuclear bomb.

Nature isn't the only thing that hides its feelings in the Midwest. New-comers or casual travelers just passing through a café conversation could very easily think the region has no politics, no prejudices, no alcoholism, no nagging wives, no brutish husbands, no racism, no financial instabil-ities, no anger, no suicides, nothing at all wrong really, except the weather and crop prices.

Public displays of emotion run against the grain of independence and self-support that stiffened the backbone of so many midwestern immi-grant groups. There's some yelling at home, to be sure, but more often than not midwesterners, mainly the rural men, keep their troubles inside like a brewing rainstorm. The surface looks calm, until one day, seemingly with-out immediate cause, there is an explosion, a violent storm of emotion. It is lethal lightning that usually nails not someone or something who "de-serves" it but someone or something who happens to be unlucky enough to be around.

When a string of massive thunderstorms rumbles across the land and a single whirling cloud dips down from the taller blackness as if pointing, it is terrifying. The storm is coming. And if it's coming for you, there is nothing to stop it. But there is a rhythm and a balance to the storms, to their death-dealing destruction and to their life-giving moisture. If the storms fail to come, according to an even broader rhythm of years, then life becomes unbalanced, the crops fail, the nation's balance of payments suffers, and food prices rise. Midwestern life begins in the overcast spring. It has boundless optimism in the summer sun. And life ends in the foggy fall.

Yet these large unchanging rhythms mask gradual changes. The Midwest may have a reputation for resistance to change, but few parts of the United States have shown more dramatic changes over time and none has been able to adapt better than the agricultural middle, where every state save a handful has seen industry come to dominate or rival agriculture in its economy. Once there was no world market, no grain embargoes, no OPEC, no inflation, no floating interest rate, no rising expectations, no cynicism about government, no need for much money or college, no nothing that a good strong back, a long day's work, a few sturdy sons, an understanding wife, a fear of God, and a few good neighbors couldn't handle. Once rural America was insulated from a meaner outside world by distance—self-contained, self-satisfied, self-supportive.

But across the region dramatic changes were afoot. Industries such as steel, cars, rubber, banking, chemicals, manufacturing, and farming were being crushed by forces far beyond their comprehension. The ore and coal mines of Minnesota, Kentucky, and Illinois were troubled because the area's aging steel mills were being outstripped by advancing young competitors. The steel mills were troubled because their buyers, the auto makers who created one out of every six manufacturing jobs in the country, were being challenged, also by energetic competitors, also from abroad, who knew the American customer better than the local firm did. The American farmers' exports, a national economic mainstay, were being hurt by the strong U.S. dollar and cheaper competition from developing countries forced to export their agricultural products to finance their huge international debts. New financial and physical realities were overwhelming the established ways.

During World War II and after, the Midwest's booming factories from Youngstown to Wichita drew millions of workers who got rising wages and overtime guaranteed, and, of course, a better life for the next generation, guaranteed. Many of these new workers were drawn from the farm by the security of a weekly wage impervious to the ravages of weather and shifting government policies. In 1950, twenty-three million Americans lived on farms. Thirty years later nearly four out of five had left the land.

They moved into the cities, the Minneapolises and Chicagos, the Akrons and Omahas, discarding the smaller towns like Ruthton. The rural reward for producing much of the country's self-reliance and spawning an agricultural revolution that tripled production in a competitive new world was that thousands of midwesterners became economically redundant, no longer able to afford to work on a farm.

While the isolated farm certainly remained, its ties to distant places became crucial. The price for its increased production was greater specialization and a dependence on others—and their prices. Where once a farmer could grow his own "tractor" (a horse), its "fuel" (oats and hay), and his food, now he needed a powerful machine from Moline. It needed fuel from Saudi Arabia. And he had no time to fool with a few hogs, a few cattle, and a few chickens for himself; cheaper to concentrate on his speciality—corn and soybeans or wheat or cattle or hogs. In 1974, when soybeans were bringing the farmer nearly $10 a bushel, a new tractor cost $14,360, twelve times its 1950 price. Today the price of soybeans has fallen to around $6 a bushel, while the price of the same tractor has nearly quadrupled to $55,000.

While farmers benefited briefly from inflation, which pushed up the value of land and other assets used for collateral, they found themselves in the mid-1980s on the cutting edge of deflation as their interest rates stayed high while their land prices plummeted and their crop prices stagnated. A record number of foreclosures, forced farm sales, and voluntary liquidations spread as local bankers, frightened for their institution's own future, squeezed the local farmers, who didn't see how they could work any harder or get any more efficient. For every seven farmers who went under, one local business folded too. Opportunity was shrinking in the land of opportunity, fraying established values and relationships. It built severe tensions within communities as bank vice-presidents foreclosed on high school classmates, who were doing everything their fathers said would guarantee success.

There was less trust in communities once held together by nods and handshakes. Now store owners, longtime friends, asked for payment up front or a letter from the bank guaranteeing payment come harvest. The bank, which was struggling through its own confusing world of deregulation, was leery of many new commitments. In many cases it had been purchased by a larger regional bank that sent in a cost-cutting team from the city to straighten things out, oblivious to the local social bonds. They sent out computer-printed warnings to folks who'd never missed a payment, and were proud of it, just to be sure they wouldn't think of such a thing now. They printed out letters to the grain elevator and the livestock sales barn telling their owners to put the bank's name, too, on any checks for the farmer. The unprinted message in all this was unmistakable: suspicion and fear were being unleashed.

Some families, known locally to be in financial distress, became too embarrassed to attend church. Others dissolved into sleeplessness, bickering, or worse. Bankers stopped dropping by the bar for an after-work drink with the boys; the boys would move away from the table as they sat down, and after a few more beers someone might get to talking loudly about hogs and bankers and worms, all in the same breath. Some studies predicted three or four out of every ten farmers would be gone in a few years, which prompted some to quit and many to work even harder. Many small towns became largely collections of the elderly. Mental health centers were busy. So were liquor stores. And the rural suicide rate far exceeded its urban counterpart.

Federal agencies, established as agricultural lenders of last resort, were closing down farm operations that had the same land and the same assets as when the same loan officer first approved the borrowing. The farmers had gotten so good at their business that in some years the government paid them increasing incentives not to farm; the more they didn't work, the more they would receive. Others were forced to increase their farm's volume to satisfy creditors' demands. This new production added to the surpluses, further depressing crop prices.

Poverty has always dwelt in the countryside, but now there was more, with many farmers needing a full-time wage job to support the full-time farm job. More wives went into town to new jobs. Farm fathers found themselves telling their boys: don't become a farmer, son, it don't pay to work this hard. Some sons listened, some didn't. Giving up and losing out on the land may not have meant much to the world. But it meant the world to them.

Hardship, like midwestern storms, strikes unevenly. But the widespread hollowing out of mid-America, physically and emotionally, left behind decaying towns and neighborhoods packed with thousands of poor who knew firsthand how empty the promise of prosperity was. It left behind Merle Haggard's song, asking, "Are the Good Times Really Over for Good?" It left a new name for an old area—the Rustbelt.

"A few years ago," said Duane DeBettignies, the editor, publisher, chief reporter, and owner of the Ruthton newspaper, "in the course of four months we lost Red Lauritsen's lumberyard, the Red Owl Grocery, and the Allis-Chalmers dealer, Hildegard Implements. They was all liquidated 'cause there were no buyers. We used to be up and thriving. But now I'm thinking about the paper. I'm fifty-four, I don't know if I wanna be scrambling around like this in a small town like this for another ten years. I just don't know." Time was, in fact, when Ruthton had three farm implement dealers, a drugstore, a movie, two car dealers, a furniture store, three restaurants, a roller-skating rink, a creamery, a doctor, and a dentist.

Now Ruthton's Doc White, the dentist, has moved away to the Twin Cities. Doc Sether, who passed out lollipops to generations of children, died years ago. No one ever took over his clinic, so one day it just closed, and people had to go elsewhere. Not being the county seat, Ruthton, out on the northern edge of Pipestone County, has seen its population nearly cut in half over the years, dwindling closer to 300 now. One in ten of the county's residents moved away in the last decade, leaving behind only 11,690 souls in an area of about four hundred square miles.

In Ruthton, there are no longer school holidays in early May so the boys can help in the fields with the planting and the girls can help in the kitchen. The school bus drivers are women now, some with little preschoolers in tow to save on the baby-sitting; their farm family needs the extra income, and it's one formerly male job the women can do that the men don't seem to mind too much about.

There is today still plenty of simple philosophy about. "We get in trouble with our attitudes and greed," said Mr. DeBettignies one day as he worked on his recalcitrant printing press. "I mean attitudes about each other, different people, and countries. People has gotta stop once in a while and be thankful for what they've got—health, family, a roof, food—instead of always thinking about what they ain't got. You know, you don't have to be wealthy in dollars to be wealthy in life." But there are new currents even in his life. His wife, Marlys, has to work now, or at least she chooses to; she's a registered health service nurse for the government, one of a few sectors actually increasing employment. Of their three children, none settled in Ruthton.

"I was born and raised in a small town," says DeBettignies. "I loved the freedom from the drag of life, all that city traffic and hassle and run, run, run. Ruthton was a good place to raise children. I got no criticism of kids when they leave. Small town or large town, you gotta go where you think you can make it, even if it is a desert."

Not many young folks were sticking around Ruthton. The opportunities there were dwindling. Hope was drying up. And then came the rumor that the bank was being sold.

The speed of a rumor in a small community is proportional to its surprise and perceived import. The rumor flashed around very quickly over coffee cups and phone lines that after all these years of quietly running the only bank in town, Clyde Pedersen, too, was pulling out. He was selling the Buffalo Ridge State Bank. Clyde was a known commodity to everyone, not exciting but not threatening. He hadn't created the bank; he'd inherited it. Now he was selling out to some Easterner, that big tall fellow who was seen striding around town a few times. The new owner was married, they said, to some woman from Philadelphia. He had a kid, a boy, they said, probably spoiled rotten like a lot of those city kids. They must be rich, awful rich, to buy a bank. In some places, even in Ruthton in another era, such fresh blood might not have been threatening, might not have spawned incoherent fears of new financial priorities, different standards, stricter accountings, new ways. It might even have raised fragile hopes. As usual, DeBettignies heard the rumor quickly. His first thought: "What will happen to my loan at the bank?'' His second: ''Why would anyone ever buy in here?''

CHAPTER THREE

The Beginning

Rudolph Hamma Blythe Jr.'s bubbling enthusiasm filled the car as he drove along the open prairie highway with his family. To those who didn't know him well, Rudy's size magnified everything he said and did. Even his friends would wince sometimes at his powerful physical presence. They had since his days on the offensive line of the high school football team when his schoolmates back in Philadelphia voted him the loudest member of the class of '59. When you are six feet four inches tall, have a full tenor's voice, and carry 250 pounds, sometimes more, a whisper from your mouth can be heard as a shout.

Rudy was taking his family to Ruthton, Minnesota, to see the small-town bank he wanted to buy. It had great promise; he just knew it. The town had a lot of potential too; he could tell just from walking around. He'd heard that the bank's present owner hadn't been all that interested in the community, so he wouldn't be a hard act to follow. And the price seemed right. It was a lot of money, but Rudy had managed big sums in his bank investment and trust jobs in Minneapolis and Des Moines, and the interest rates would be going down soon, no doubt. He would get a large loan now with a floating rate and cut his costs with a new loan at a lower percentage when the rate fell in a few months or so. Rudy was very eager to realize these plans because, nearing the age of forty, he had just about had it working for other people.

After eight years of marriage Susan Blythe could tell when her husband was happy and excited. He would talk very rapidly and a little loudly, the words and thoughts pouring out. Although she couldn't always understand the forces behind his happiness, it usually made Susan feel good too.

''It'll be just great!'' Rudy Blythe said as he slowed the car. ''Well, there it is!'' His wife looked all around her.

''There is what?'' she said.

''There's Ruthton,'' her husband replied, pointing ahead. She looked in that direction. There, across some flat muddy fields, stood a large clump of bare trees with some discolored houses in scattered disarray and a rusting water tower standing overhead. Oh, God, she thought.

Rudy Blythe was never a subtle or graceful person. Each morning back in high school in St. Davids, Pennsylvania, along Philadelphia's famous Main

Line, he'd come running over the hill toward the quiet male crowd of serious, suit-clad commuters waiting decorously on the train platform with their morning newspapers carefully folded to the business or sports pages. Young Rudy was often running late in those comfortable days of the mid-1950s, when a grandfather named Ike presided over the prosperous land.

Rudy went to a prestigious private high school, Haverford. He was an average student, hovering around the middle rankings of his class of 150 in a school where going to college was a given. Young Blythe's appearance was forceful, with his broad nose, his big ears and thick lips, his intense eyes, and those big shoulders, seeming even more immense under his football pads.

All the guys had a nickname or two in those days to avoid using the Jr. or the Roman numerals parents tacked on their names. James Ray Shoch III, who played next to Rudy on the line, was Jamie. Young Blythe was Rudes, or, more respectfully, Animal, for his build and strength and ways.

Rudy loved his world of males and male groups. The sense of acceptance, of belonging, of being one of the guys. He was most comfortable if the group revolved around something physical like sports—football, wrestling, swimming. Males have a way of automatically awarding deference to their larger peers. But it need not always be a group based on physical endeavor. Rudy was in the Auto Club and the Glee Club, too, where he would stand out in the ranks of serious singers due to his developing penchant for plaid clothes. He was to seek out such groups throughout his life. Rudy had to be around people. In his groups everybody knew Rudy Blythe. He liked everybody, and everybody seemed to like him.

In his family, too, male companionship was important. On Saturday mornings his father, a leading research pharmacist who revolutionized the drug industry by inventing the time-release capsule, would get up with Rudy. He would make breakfast for his son, and they would play games. That was the special time for them. Teenagers often shun association with anyone as gross as a parent. But Rudy would talk proudly to peers of his father's accomplishments. They would pick up on his serious tone and no one would make the usual mocking quip. Over the years, at home and abroad, Rudy would seek out male associations with the plodding, powerful determination of a defensive tackle. Where the groups existed, Rudy became a member. Where such groups did not exist, he helped create them.

The Blythes were solidly middle class. Coming out of a small New York town, the son of a farmer and a graduate of Columbia University in the midst of the Depression, Rudolph Blythe the father had started the research operations at Smith Kline & French, which he turned into a large success. Although Mr. Blythe only got one dollar from the company for the patent on his time-release capsule—first applied to amphetamines before leading to the invention of Contac—he was paid well and was very prominent in the industry. There was a little family money, too, and over time Mr. Blythe was able to parlay his funds into a profitable stock portfolio, an activity that dominated many family discussions and became a satisfying pastime well after his retirement. Vacations, like most everything in the Blythe family, were usually put to good use. Sometimes they'd visit relatives in rural New York State. Rudy especially liked those small towns with the surrounding livestock and all the pets, where the routine seemed more relaxed than life around Philadelphia. During those visits he first began talking about country life.

Rudy's mother, who was crippled by a childhood bout with polio and channeled much energy into painting, believed strongly that it was good for young men to work. At fourteen Rudy, her younger son, was a busboy in a Philadelphia diner. Later, he would demonstrate toys, sell Fuller brushes, and usher at the movies.

Sometimes Rudy worked as a waiter or a barman at one of the private parties that lit up the large homes along the Main Line. Half the time it seemed Rudy was working at these parties and half the time he was an invited guest. He knew the hosts and guests through his own well-connected parents, although his mother had warned him about acting like a guest when he was really an employee. One night, at the debut of a judge's daughter, the judge asked Rudy, the waiter, to bring him a scotch and soda in the den. When the young man complied, he remarked knowledgeably about the sailboats in the paintings hanging along the well-lit, wood-paneled wall. Impressed, the judge asked the young man some questions. The two got to talking, and the judge, quite naturally, asked the young man to sit down, and they talked for the rest of the evening. That was how Rudy Blythe once got paid by the hour for being a guest. He could do that when he turned on the charm. He could overcome that latent, explosive impatience that lurked so close to the surface.

Rudy wasn't happy in college at first. For one thing, he had to study foreign languages, never his strong point. For another, Rudy always said that Franklin and Marshall was a pseudo-Ivy League school, and one thing people remember about Rudy Blythe was his distaste for pseudo-anything. It had to be genuine. His father had some connections at the University of Iowa, two days' drive away. The school had a good reputation, and Iowa City, a lovely, university town plunked down amid the cornfields of eastern Iowa, was largely free of pretension.

Rudy transferred there for his junior year. His parents were worried about their son's acceptance in a region so far from home. They asked a friend, an academic dean, to check on Rudy occasionally. The first year the dean invited the young man over for an evening to help decorate the family's Christmas tree. Rudy helped decorate the tree, then promptly excused himself. He had a date and a party to attend. The dean sent word back to Rudy's home that the young man had settled in just fine.

Rudy was obviously happier in Iowa City, but he wasn't dedicated to anything. One night his parents received a phone call. It was Rudy, announcing that he had decided to drop out of school and enlist in the army. His parents argued against his move. They were worried that he would not return to college after the army. "Mother," said Rudy with an unaccustomed air of authority, "that's why I'm dropping out now, so I can do better when I do return." After a while both parents gave up on dissuasion. "Well, it's your life," they said.

Rudy had announced to his father that he would be the best damned soldier the army had ever known. He wasn't. But in typical fashion Rudy tried to make the most of a situation. In typical fashion he didn't quite succeed.

"Rudy," one friend recalls, "was always a plunker, never the star."

He originally wanted to join the army's security service. There was an air of eliteness about it. And they liked large men. There was some minor trouble brewing in a place called South Vietnam, and President Kennedy had dispatched a few security advisers to take care of the situation. Electronics was also a possibility, but looking at his school record—and the army being the army—Rudy Blythe was sent instead to foreign language school in California en route to a foreign listening post in Eritrea, Ethiopia. After three unsuccessful months of nonstudy Rudy was transferred into an accounting course. He wouldn't be a listener at the listening post in Eritrea. He would be an accountant.

Rudy loved his time in Ethiopia. In many ways he was his own boss there, running the accounting branch for a base of some thirteen hundred men. And the primitive surrounding country was just about as far away from St. Davids, Pennsylvania, as anyone could imagine. The rural life held an increasing appeal for him. Someone coming into the country from the city would have a built-in advantage, it seemed. A person who wasn't necessarily a star somewhere else could stand out in the rural arena. One time at an African rodeo, Rudy, the large white foreigner, and a game one at that, was invited to ride a bull, just like a real cowboy. When tall Rudy with his tenth-of-a-ton weight climbed on the scrawny creature, the bull fell down. Rudy loved that story. It had everything—being in an exotic land, being invited by the group, being a sport, being big. He told the tale often for years.

After he was discharged from the army in 1965, Rudy remained in Africa. He wanted to see more of that rural, primitive continent. For several months he hiked across parts of it, took trains and planes, hitchhiked, and rode the local buses—jammed with people and animals and boxes of all kinds.

In Kenya he fell in with some Britons who introduced him to rugby. They clamored to have him on their team. Rudy loved it. Like football without pads. Rock-'em-sock-'em, knee-in-the-face, dirty, sweaty fun. And afterward, as a team member, he was included in the parties. The group.

After some months Rudy went back home, through Europe to Philadelphia to Iowa to the university again. Earning money as a bartender, he plowed through the academic work with renewed energy and a new perspective. He drew on his time and interest in Ethiopia, writing his thesis on the economies of undeveloped nations. Rudy had a new interest, of course—rugby. His enthusiasm was so infectious that he founded the University of Iowa Rugby Club, an achievement so satisfying that he listed it on his résumé for years afterward. Two years later came graduation. There was the document to prove it: Bachelor of Arts—Economics. He had done what he promised.

Rudy returned to Philadelphia. A girlfriend had gotten him an interim job at her father's company. Rudy worked on the shipping dock, loading and unloading trucks with the burly crews. Soon he enrolled in Temple University for a master's degree in economics. He led a busy life in those days. Some schoolmates were still in the area, so there was a network of friends. There was a string of young women, too, smaller, dark women attracted to this large, jolly fellow with the lovely voice who liked good times and could use a little feminine guidance on his selection of clothes.

Immediately upon his return, Rudy had found the local rugby club. He played there on the weekends. He was also getting involved in politics, another group to belong to. Both Rudy and his brother George worked in the trenches of political organizing, envelope stuffing, voter phoning, door-to-door pamphlet delivering. Both would run for minor political office. Both would be firm Republicans. Rudy always called himself a fiscal conservative and a social liberal, that is until, years later, he stood in the check-sorting room of his bank's basement and saw where those socially liberal government checks were being cashed. It wasn't at the children's clothing store.

Rudy went to school at night. By day he did his research and homework and, when called, fit in a little substitute teaching to earn some money. One morning Great Valley High School in Malvern, Pennsylvania, called him. He was strolling through the teachers' lounge there during a free period when he noticed a teacher grading papers. She had removed her heavy ball earrings and was idly rolling them in her hand as she waded through a pile of themes.

"You remind me of Captain Queeg," said Rudy, referring to the tyrannical captain in *The Caine Mutiny*.

"Don't you mean Captain Bligh?" said the English teacher, confusing her tyrants. A pleasant conversation ensued until the class bell rang.

The woman was Susan Slater. At twenty-four she was three years younger than Rudy, around eight inches shorter, and at least a hundred pounds lighter. A small-town girl from upstate New York, Susan had been born in Dunkirk, by Lake Erie. Her father, Bill, and mother, Alice, had carved out a comfortable, if at times itinerant, middle-class life for themselves and their children, Susan and Charles. A civil engineer educated in Cleveland, Mr. Slater worked for the Erie Railroad when trains were a part of every traveler's life. Mr. Slater and his family moved along the rails, on their company pass, from modest home to modest home around the East and the Midwest, to whichever small city the company decided needed his talents. It was good, decent, steady work in good, decent, steady places like Dunkirk in New York, Morristown in New Jersey, Niles in Ohio, and Huntington in Indiana, places with fifteen thousand or more good, decent people.

As a youngster Susan was shy and submissive, but one hot day after a hard play at a Niles playground a very thirsty little Susan walked toward the drinking fountain. Other children were in line and when Susan got near the front, still more crowded in. Then others came. And, as her mother watched, Susan stepped back. There seemed to be an inexhaustible supply of other children ready to push their way in. Susan waited patiently for ten minutes or so. And then the little girl had had enough. With a good deal of noise, she muscled her way to the front and drank her fill while everyone else waited. The Slaters told that story often over the years. Mrs. Slater still believes that was the last time Susan, the child or adult, was pushed aside.

She had a determination to be heard too, which perhaps grew from having to stand up for herself in a family with two tall men: a six-foot-three-inch, 240-pound younger brother who was a Little All-American offensive tackle in college, and a six-foot-one-inch father who unconsciously taught his daughter to have the same kind of firm, outspoken opinions that he expressed out on the rails or around the dinner table. Susan was taught to be a little forward about what she wanted in an era when outspoken females were not the norm. Being straightforward, getting things organized, and setting out to do what seemed necessary had its early rewards, too. Once she decided she wanted a beautiful new red bicycle, told her father that she wanted it, and her father got it for her. A lasting lesson. Speak up. All he can say is no. If you don't offer your opinion, how are people going to know it?

Susan was popular in school, an outgoing, easy talker. The first fall after moving to Huntington she was elected class secretary, just like that. She was the girls' tennis champion at school. And in her senior year, when she tried out for the class play, *Riddle Me Riches*, she got the female lead.

Her family was and is close and demonstrative about its closeness. The Slaters did not travel much beyond their moves down the line. So Susan grew up envisioning the world as a tidy series of Nileses and Huntingtons, friendly, comprehensible small towns with similar people, similar interests and values, and a nice country club where familiar families went for golf and big evening dinners on tables with linen tablecloths. The Slaters spent their summers at a modest cottage they rented in northern New York State on Lake Erie.

As expected, after high school Susan went on to college. She chose Allegheny College in Meadville, Pennsylvania, and concentrated on English. She went to the football games and she dated regularly, if not all that seriously. She just didn't see the boys as very capable of intelligent discussion beyond campus gossip. Her dates were always physically modest, athletic young men, slim, well under six feet, not the bulky behemoths who played football in the fall and spring and wrestled in the winter and went to Penn State and thought Hemingway was a running back for Notre Dame. When graduation came, she went into teaching. The only question was where to work. That decision was easily resolved when a fellow she knew and wanted to know better decided to pursue his business studies in Philadelphia.

That was how Susan Slater, three years into her teaching career, nearing the proper middle-class marrying age, and having drifted away from the business student, came to be in the teachers' lounge in Malvern that weekday morning in the fall of 1968. She didn't think much of that encounter with the substitute health and social studies teacher, certainly not enough to cancel her Saturday night study session when he called for a date. Susan had let her studying slide a little for a Monday test on Milton for an extra teaching certificate. She'd planned to devote that entire weekend to review. But when Rudy Blythe called a second time and suggested that she might like to go to an Eagles football game on Sunday afternoon, she hesitated and then accepted for reasons she really could not explain, even a lifetime later. In a way, Blythe reminded Susan of her father. When he entered a room, the room got smaller. He was tall and strong and outspoken, and Susan, outspoken herself, was drawn to that.

The Eagles game that late October Sunday was one of those nondescript matches more memorable for spectators as a social event than an athletic one. Afterward, Susan and Rudy stopped by the house of Rudy's brother George for dinner.

Their second date was a rugby game. Rudy starred. They dated pretty regularly after that, and their companionship grew increasingly intense. They taught during the day. Rudy went to his evening economics classes. From ten o'clock until long into the night, they would sit and talk in Susan's apartment about their lives and their values. The subject of marriage in general came up. Rudy said marriage was something a couple works out over time. It wasn't an idyllic state they fell into upon leaving the altar. You grew into marriage, he said. It was a commitment.

Actually, Susan had already made a commitment. She'd stopped dating other men. By Susan's twenty-fourth birthday her mother had warned her that she was being too picky about her men friends, but Rudy seemed different from the others. Susan could talk more easily with him. He was serious, not self-conscious, more experienced.

Susan, like Rudy, needed to belong to a group. From those groups she would pick out one or two women to become her very close friends. They would have long talks, sometimes daily. The conversations centered not on gossip so much as personal thoughts and events and, sometimes, fears. She could bounce a fear off a female friend and perhaps get a new insight or confirmation that her fears were okay or just feel better from talking to someone she trusted.

One weekend, at Susan's suggestion, she and Rudy drove to her parents' home near Albany as a birthday surprise for her mother. Susan remembers silently anticipating her parents' reaction to Rudy. They knew about him, of course, from late-night phone calls. Susan had always praised the man; she always would.

Mrs. Slater remembers opening her front door and, happily, seeing her daughter. Looming up behind Susan was a very large man carrying a cake box. He must be the new boyfriend, taller than the others. Bigger too. He also had the bluest eyes she had ever seen.

Mr. Slater didn't notice the blue eyes. And being a large person himself, he didn't notice Rudy's size. Not exactly immune to the meaning of a twenty-four-year-old daughter suddenly bringing a young man home to meet her parents, Mr. Slater looked to the young man's mannerisms and how and what he chose to talk about. "And he turned out to be okay. A kind man. You could tell that."

Rudy never formally proposed to Susan. Gradually their talk of marriage just grew more prominent and both agreed, at some unrecorded moment, that it would be fun. So, taking a deep breath, Rudy picked up the phone in Susan's apartment one Sunday afternoon soon after meeting Susan's parents and dialed their home.

"Hello, Mr. Slater," said Rudy, nodding to an anxious Susan sitting nearby. "This is Rudy Blythe. I'm calling to ask permission to marry your daughter."

They had a short, businesslike conversation. Seconds later, Susan's phone rang. It was her father. "Tell me more about this young man Blythe," he demanded. "How can he support you when he's in school?"

Rudy promptly sent him a copy of his personal investment portfolio. Young Rudy hadn't earned it, of course. When his grandmother died, she had left a modest inheritance. Mrs. Blythe divided the funds in half and invested them in stocks for the boys. The holdings had done quite nicely, and the future father-in-law was reassured.

On August 9, 1969, Rudy and Susan became man and wife, a happy event with lots of friends. As a wedding gift, Susan's mother-in-law gave them a week at a resort in the Adirondack Mountains, then they left with the Philadelphia Rugby Club on a two-week trip to England. Rudy played rugby and they both socialized with his friends. They toured the countryside and stayed in cozy little bed-and-breakfasts. In the evening they might visit a neighborhood pub. There, sitting in the corner one night, Rudy confided to his new bride his fondest hope: to take her and return as a businessman to Ethiopia. It was a beautiful place, and the country had good opportunities. In fact, Rudy had already mailed out more than a hundred résumés to companies doing business there.

She was stunned. Ethiopia? Ethiopia was not part of the deal! She thought she had married a proper Philadelphia man and would spend the rest of her life in that bright, big city in the East, with lots of children who would go off to school so she could do Junior League work. Tears began rolling down Susan's cheeks. Sobs seeped out. Rudy tried quietly, and then desperately, to sell the advantages of that African land, the clear air, the fascinating culture, the countryside, the luxurious life of a foreign businessman and his wife, a car and driver and maid, everything. But Susan wasn't sold. Her reply was basic: "Not me, buster."

That was the last time Rudy and Susan ever talked about his Ethiopian hopes. They settled down instead in suburban Philadelphia in half of a duplex. They both commuted to work and school and devoted free hours to redecorating the aging half-a-home. Rudy still mentioned the Ethiopian idea to his friends, but if he ever got any responses to his job applications, he never told anyone. He began drifting from his graduate-degree work, which he never would finish, and directed his job-hunting comparatively closer to home. A friend who had been in their wedding party was working at a big midwestern bank in Minneapolis.

Rudy knew a little about the area from his university days in Iowa. Politically, Minnesota tended to be liberal, with an abiding faith in activist government, contributing one of its sons to the Democratic party ticket in every presidential election but one for two stormy decades. The state's harsh climate attracted hardy Scandinavian types, innovative, independent folk who could work the land or foster a high-tech corporate revolution. Minneapolis was en route to becoming the region's nicest city, an economic and transport center with theaters, urban lakes, and shiny new skyscrapers.

To Susan, Minneapolis certainly was better than Ethiopia, even if it wasn't Philadelphia. She could do some teaching and some of the social volunteer work she found so rewarding. Rudy was happy in his work as an economist. He and his wife could get out into the countryside easily enough, and they quickly started acquiring some small rural tracts near a lake in northern Minnesota where they would go weekends and each summer vacation.

Soon, Rudolph Hamma Blythe III was born. Better known as Rolph, the chubby little fellow was the first of several children Rudy and Susan planned. They were doting parents. Rolph was proof of that love they expected to grow in marriage. Every time Rudy went on a business trip alone, he would be sure to bring a nice gift home for his son, and maybe some little thing for his wife, too.

Rudy became more sedate, more serious. He applied himself at work. One executive was so impressed that he took Rudy from economic forecasting in the bond department and brought him into the trust division, which seemed like a promotion at the time. Privately, Rudy began to register unhappiness there almost immediately. It was a more hierarchical department. Rudy didn't like working directly under someone. He did not like the way some of the bank's trust people advised clients about what could be done with their money, and he didn't like the heavy responsibility of investing other people's hard-earned savings. He began talking about buying a farm. He'd be his own boss there. They'd bc out in the country all the time, all that fresh air and freedom. Or better yet, maybe he'd buy a bank in some small town. He could hire someone to help do the things he couldn't or didn't want to do.

Rudy began to shop around for a little bank, though none of them seemed to be quite right. Meanwhile, his dislike for his work in the bank's trust department increased. He sent out résumés. Then, one day in 1973, he announced to Susan he was off to Des Moines for a job interview. He was hired to help run some bank investments by a statewide chain of banks directed from a Des Moines headquarters.

Susan did the house-hunting in the new location. After a few days, she came up with a list of candidates ranked one through four. Rudy picked the big one, on River Oaks Drive.

The job was definitely a step up for Rudy. An assistant vice-president, he was promoted to vice-president, then to executive vice-president, and was finally made a director of an investment subsidiary. He got a nice salary. The bank paid for his membership at the prestigious Wakonda Country Club. And the Blythes made a lot of friends, "fun people," Susan recalls, "people like us."

Rudy traveled widely around the state, informing local employees of his activities and their responsibilities. Arriving in Iowa's friendly, tidy small towns as the emissary from distant Des Moines, home of the boss, was good for Rudy's ego. The travels were also good for scouting small banks for sale.

Owning a small-town bank had become Rudy's dream. "It would have to be small," he'd say with a laugh. "I'm no millionaire." To be the president. To be making his own decisions. To be building something of his own in a cohesive small town with that warm sense of inclusion. Some of Rudy's friends gently suggested that there were many unseen facets to running one's own business, especially anything as complex as a bank in something as complex as a small town. They noticed that Rudy, who could be gracious and charming one minute, would suddenly become strong-willed and stubborn the next. "When Rudy decided something was right," recalled one Iowa friend who saw him regularly on their gourmet dinner club outings, "it was very right. And when Rudy decided something was wrong, it was very wrong. Nothing and no one would change his mind."

Susan was outspoken, but she didn't criticize Rudy's idea. "Sure, I had misgivings," she remembers. "But he was a banker and an investment person. You can't throw a wet blanket on your husband's dream, and I was willing to try it. I was also naive, very naive.''

Every few weekends the three Blythes would pack up their car and drive into the countryside to look at yet another little bank Rudy had found in a town with fewer people than some high schools Susan had taught in. Then, in the fall of 1977, a friend from Minneapolis phoned Rudy with a rumor that the bank in some place called Ruthton was for sale. Rudy jumped to investigate. This one seemed like a real possibility. The price wasn't too bad—$521,000—and the bank's subsidiary insurance agency, if new blood were pumped into it, might just be able to produce enough in commissions to carry the loan on the bank.

Rudy looked at the bank's books. He checked his own assets. He applied for a loan through his old employer in Minneapolis. If he and Susan sold off their vacation lots and some stocks, they could make a down payment of about 20 percent. They could borrow the rest with a floating interest rate. At one point the accountant told them they wouldn't be in any financial trouble unless interest rates passed 17 percent. They all had a good laugh over that unlikelihood.

One day during the negotiations, which went on all fall, Susan decided to meet Rolph in the car halfway home from his Des Moines kindergarten. Driving along the winding streets of her affluent neighborhood, Susan noticed a pickup truck with a couple of scruffy-looking men in it pulling away from the opposite curb. As it left, she saw in the bushes someone with the same color coat as Rolph. It *was* Rolph! The two men had offered the frightened little boy a chocolate bar and said his mother sent them to get him. As his parents had instructed him long before, Rolph had run and hid. It was the last time he walked home from school alone in the city. And Susan began to think that maybe life in a nice, quiet small town would not be such a bad thing.

Rudy visited Ruthton several times during the slow negotiations. Sometimes it seemed Clyde Pedersen, the bank's owner, wasn't all that interested in selling, and that worried Rudy. Then came the big day, November 15, 1977. Rudy appeared at the bank early. There were last-minute details, interminable signings, and then just as they were about done, the town siren went off. The siren is a noisy symbol of midwestern life. Depending on the hour it sounds, a wailing siren can mean it is quitting time, there is a fire, a tornado is approaching, it is time all teenagers were home, or, on this day, it is twelve o'clock noon, time for lunch. As Rudy watched, Pedersen and all the bank workers got up, donned their coats, and headed for home to eat, politely waiting for their new owner to clear the bank door before locking it. Rudy, who had just spent a half million dollars to become president of a mortgaged dream and to become an integral part of a small town's life, was left standing in the cold on Main Street all by himself. He should have remembered that, but Rudy sometimes missed early danger signals that others saw as obvious. He dismissed the incident as funny, bought his own lunch at Alene's Cafe across the street, and returned to assume ownership promptly at one o'clock.

Rudy's life became hectic. It was fun being so prominent, but being so jolly and friendly all the time could be exhausting—learning everyone's name, reassuring everyone of his good intentions, and, most importantly, maintaining a business-as-usual atmosphere. When he was there, a good number of people seemed to drop by the bank for no apparent reason. Change is usually threatening in places like Ruthton. So Rudy had a lot of learning to do fast—names, procedures, methods, and he was studying for his insurance license, too. A lot had to be done with that insurance agency besides changing the name to Blythe. Its income would support the bank loan, and Clyde Pedersen, who had his license, had agreed to stay on for only a few months.

At the same time, Rudy and Susan agreed, something would have to be done about their house, which had come with the bank. It was nice—a big backyard, close to the office, trees well cared for—but the blue color would have to go. Although it was over twenty years old, the three-bedroom ranch-style house was Ruthton's newest. It was big by modest Ruthton standards, but small by Blythe standards. The dining room, for instance. How could anyone entertain in such a cubbyhole? So, while Susan stayed in Des Moines a couple of extra months to sell the house there, the Blythes hired a builder to knock down some walls into the garage and get in a decent fifteen-by-twenty-foot dining area. Everybody in town saw the carpenter's truck parked in front of the banker's house and the unfamiliar workman grabbing lunch at the café.

Say, what're you doin' up to the Blythes'?

Puttin' in a formal dining room.

A what?

A big dining room.

What for?

The man says it's too small. His wife wants a bigger one.

Ain't that somethin'? They just got here and already everythin' is too small.

Because of the money they control, bankers are always prominent people. They are especially so in small towns where there is only one bank, and when the one banker is over six feet tall; when he has strong, loud opinions; when he wears plaids; when he comes from Philadelphia; when he buys the old rail depot and has it hauled to his house for a storage shed; when he is new.

Thanks to the automobile, rural residents can now easily take their money to financial institutions in other communities. Many people in Ruthton did, especially when Clyde Pedersen refused to pay interest on checking accounts. But the other banks mustn't be too far away. The customer has to visit them regularly to apply for, to maintain, and to pay off the credit that is such an important part of rural life. Most Americans borrow money to buy a house or a car. Farmers borrow money to earn a living. They borrow for new equipment, to be sure, but they also need loans every year to buy that spring's seeds and fertilizer, that summer's herbicide and fuel, that year's cattle or hog feed. The harvest comes but once a year. The bills appear more frequently. A farmer's relationship with the banker determines more than whether he gets a new car; it determines whether he gets to earn a living doing the kind of work he was raised to do.

There have always been times when bankers were resented or envied or feared. Often they eat better than the folks growing the food. Dealing with a banker is also one of the very few times that a farmer, by definition an independent operator, must in effect ask someone else for permission to do what he wants to do on his own land. By and large, farmers can deal with the gamble with nature—the winds, the hail, the drought, the floods. Those events are controlled by forces larger than any individual. You can buy insurance against that kind of calamity. Only a fool would stand outdoors and rage at the weather.

But a banker is different. He's human. He's vulnerable. He is fair game. Not many people in the countryside will stick up for a banker, his wife, or his kid. Bankers are, oh, so friendly when times are good; then they can't pass out the loans fast enough. But didja ever notice, things get tough for everyone and they're a different sort?

Rudy Blythe entered Ruthton with the best of intentions, considerable energy and dedication, and some half-baked plans for improvements. He didn't know what he was getting into, but he was eager to learn and to help. Rudy thought he knew a lot about banking. He was determined to bring some big-city imagination and style to Ruthton. They would see. Everyone would see. Rudy had some big plans to boost profits, to boost local investment, and to help the town with employment. Over time, he had decided, he would have some impact in his little corner of the world.

The plans would jell over the next few years. Rudy would put them in place. They wouldn't work, but Rudy would not realize this at first. Then he would grow frustrated and frightened and impatient. He would try, desperately and sometimes noisily, to force his plans to work. Meanwhile, all around him things were changing drastically, not for the better, for reasons he didn't understand.

For years the Buffalo Ridge State Bank, like many similar institutions across the region, had been run conservatively and safely. A handful of tellers would take in local deposits. The bank would pay the depositors between 4 and 6 percent interest. Clyde would, in effect, rent the deposits to larger, distant financial institutions for their lending purposes, earning 6 to 8 percent for himself. The difference was his income to cover costs and profit. The bank would make very few local personal loans. Clyde Pedersen could have made more money that way, but that method carried more risks, involving keen judgment of each borrower's character and broad financial outlooks. It also required confidence that times were getting better, and that local borrowers would be able to repay local lenders on time throughout their commitment.

Few knew it at the time, but the country's fifteen thousand banks were about to enter a revolutionary new age in the nation's financial life. The Buffalo Ridge State Bank and its city and country cousins were about to encounter deregulation. The government would no longer tell them what they could charge or pay for everything. That would depend on their wits and their expertise in a brave new world of tough competition. Survival would depend on how well the bank could handle an era of startling inflation when the numbers, the customs, and the expectations of past generations would be shattered by baffling new pressures that threatened everything.

Rudy had no choice but to change the bank's fundamental direction. Greater risks or not, he had to earn more money because he had to pay more money for his dream. The interest rates were creeping up. If he was going to have to pay interest on checking accounts, he would have to come up with an extra $30,000 in income to cover it.

Rudy would be at the bank every morning before his employees started arriving at eight-thirty. At around ten he would wander across the street to mingle at the café during the countryside's morning coffee break. This was the part of banking Rudy liked best, socializing. He called it public relations. He felt it gave a friendly personality to a potentially impersonal banking institution, and he was very good at it.

Rudy would tell army stories and address people by their first names and slap folks on the back. He would ask questions of the farmers and the businessmen, and they were pleased with the interest of this big man. Not many people asked for their opinions. Getting to know Mr. Blythe, er, all right, Rudy, could help when they needed a loan. Word was he was making more local loans. And he was receptive.

The coffee drinkers always complained, of course, about the weather and the cost of supplies, and the low price they got for their corn and beans. Rudy said he understood. But if they thought they had it tough, let him tell them about Ethiopia and farmers over there. Now that's tough. Rudy was upbeat, optimistic, sure of the future and himself among the men. After all, things were not exactly bad now. And they were going to get better. They always had, right?

The scene would be repeated at lunch. Afterward Rudy would quietly pay his bill plus those of everyone he had been talking to, some of whom said thanks. Rudy usually carried very little money. Everybody knew that.

He said so. It seemed a point of pride. Rudy either had just enough cash to pay for the lunches or he wrote out a check.

The evenings in those first months in Ruthton were quiet ones for Rudy, who was living alone while Susan and Rolph finished up in Des Moines. Their furniture was there, too. The real estate agent said it would help sell the place, so Rudy lived in Ruthton with a mattress on the floor, a few chairs, and a table. He ate out a lot, so he was putting on more weight. He began to jog. Late at night people would see Rudy jogging around town with his dog, a pink-eyed, short-haired German terrier named Rufus.

One day Rudy heard about some local men who played basketball over at the school on occasional weeknights. It'd be fun, a little workout, meet some people, be part of a group of guys again. After dinner, he ran over to join in. But when Rudy talked with Susan on the phone later that night, he said a funny thing had happened. He'd sat on the seats a while. Then he'd shot some baskets at one end of the gym. He sat around again. Everybody said hello, but no one had asked him to join their team. Rudy was puzzled. But after talking, the husband and wife agreed the men were probably shy.

Susan and Rolph arrived in Ruthton in February 1978. Some friends in Des Moines had warned Susan that small-town life was not for everyone. "You are always on display," they told her. "You won't have any privacy. Everyone knows who you are and what you're doing." Susan would reply that she had lived in small towns before, well, small cities. They're all the same. Besides, Susan would say, she didn't do anything all that exciting or worthy of gossip. "We're just run-of-the-mill people too."

Susan vowed to give Ruthton an all-out Slater try. Like Rudy, she'd get involved in everything. First off, she'd introduce herself and learn everybody's name.

"Hi," she would say time after time as she approached someone in the bank or a store, extending her hand and hoping to learn his or her name in exchange, "I'm Susan Blythe."

"Yes," the Ruthton resident would say, unsure how to reply to anyone as important as a new banker's wife and looking startled at a woman proffering her hand so boldly, "I know."

So much, Susan thought, for the subtle approach.

Within days of her arrival Susan had joined an evening college extension course, a magazine article-writing class whose members, all women, met once a week in Ruthton. When her classmates from around the county identified themselves, they used their husbands' names—not Betty Smith, but Betty, Fred Smith's wife—as if they belonged to their men like possessions. It was a manner of speaking and thinking that Susan found foreign, and it silenced her for a moment. In those few minutes before the teacher entered, the other women chatted around Susan with animation.

A main topic of interest seemed to be the new folks in town and whether or not the banker's wife, what's-her-name from that big eastern place, Philadelphia, was ever going to move to little old Ruthton. Susan was listening idly until, with a start, she realized she was sitting in on a gossip session about herself. She made a mental note: be wary. Confidentiality among friends was crucial to Susan.

Everyone in Ruthton knew what everyone was doing. It was especially easy for a banker's wife who helped sort the canceled checks. Susan knew who paid whom how much for what service. She knew when alimony checks arrived, where people shopped, even how much a new dress cost. Acquaintances expected her to talk about that, but she wouldn't. Her reluctance made Susan seem snobbish. One night a man called Rudy at home about a new car loan. The next day at a women's gathering, Susan, without thinking, addressed his wife, "Oh, tell me about your new..." Then she caught herself and awkwardly changed the subject. That was confidential bank business. Years later, Susan realized that she made a lot of mistakes like that, mistakes that isolated her. "I spent too much of my life at the country club," Susan would say in hindsight. When little first-grader Rolph came home from the Ruthton school the first day, he had a thick sheaf of schoolwork, much of which struck Susan, the former teacher, as busywork. She disagreed with some of the grades. She decided to spend more time at the school and did some substitute teaching, although she was appalled at the cafeteria manners she saw during lunch hour and overheard some teachers correct mistakes with "No, no, stupid, not that way." She found herself trying to teach the students to think for themselves, even to question her statements, but she had little success. The other teachers told the students what to think, and everyone was comfortable with that method.

Rudy, meanwhile, was looking for someone to look after the bank's daily operations, especially loan-making, which he knew nothing about. He hired a man named Jerry Ihnen from southeastern Minnesota.

Susan knew how important Jerry would be to the bank. But she didn't know how Jerry's wife would take to Ruthton. If she was anything like Susan, Rudy might lose his new assistant as soon as he and his wife saw Ruthton's rusty blue water tower. So Susan did what she wished someone had done for her on her arrival: she organized a welcome tea, two teas, in fact, to introduce Glenice Ihnen to the other women of Ruthton. And Susan would meet them too.

Susan sat down with the little Ruthton phone book and began calling everyone. The first half of the book was invited for Thursday, the second half for Friday. By the end of the first page, Susan had not gotten one acceptance. Each woman would have to check her calendar, meaning she would have to check with her friends to see what was going on here. A formal luncheon tea? Invited to the banker's house? Me? Some women said it would certainly be nice to come, but, you know, it depended on whether or not their husbands were home for lunch that day. At one point a frustrated Susan suggested to one woman that she leave her husband's noon dinner in the Crockpot and plug it in. "That's what Crockpots were invented for," she said. The other woman didn't laugh.

Many of the women were secretly thrilled to be included on the list of anything as exclusive as the banker's wife's formal tea. Then, in talking with friends, they discovered that virtually every female in town had been invited. They were a little disappointed.

At the appointed hour, no one arrived on time. Then, suddenly, as if they had been gathering together around the corner, all the ladies arrived at the Blythe home in a single chattering mass. Instead of meeting their new neighbors one by one and having a moment to chat as each arrived, Glenice and Susan were jammed into the living room, meeting one woman after another, two or three seconds apiece. They remembered no one exactly.

Not knowing any rural caterers and wanting things to be perfect, Susan had been up since dawn making masses of finger sandwiches. Thinking she would honor her guests by using her finest tableware, Susan brought out her silver wedding service. Susan was too busy making sure everything was going well to talk much with her guests, but she did overhear comments in the crowd about the lack of chairs. A couple of women remarked on how darling the dinky little sandwiches were, but why didn't Susan use the bigger sliced rolls that most people used around there? They made good hearty sandwiches, not one little bite. The talk about the college graduate's showy silver pots didn't get going until later at their homes on the phones. They laughed then. But Susan didn't know it.

Susan got her party supplies at Jensen's Food Market at the far end of Ruthton's downtown block. The market is a tiny, dark place with creaking wooden floors covered with linoleum squares. A meat counter stands in the back where customers can examine a limited selection of cuts and patiently wait while Marv rings up the bill for other customers in the front at the old cash register. When the Blythes arrived, Marv Jensen was the sole survivor of five Ruthton grocery stores. He had been in the business for thirty-four years, ever since he gave up those long nights as the depot agent for the railroad. Running his own business had been a dream of Marv's back in the late forties. He'd bought the grocery and fed himself and family all these years. But it didn't seem to work anymore. People see things on television and they want them, but you couldn't carry every kind of salad dressing and soap in that little place. So people just drove the eighteen miles down to Pipestone or the twenty-five miles up to Marshall. They probably work there anyway, if they have a job. No work around here. Marv was trying to sell out, but who'd be dumb enough to buy?

Especially when the building was falling apart. The furnace was old. The bathroom kept flooding. One of these days Marv would have to get Jimmy Lee back in here. Now there's another thing. Jimmy Lee Jenkins. He's a small farmer. But you can't make it just as a small farmer no more, either. You gotta pick up odd jobs wherever you can to make ends meet. So Jimmy did some plumbing and general fixing for the folks.

There is one customer door at Jensen's Market. Shoppers come in, angle to the left past the freezer case down one aisle maybe seventy-five feet, turn right at the end, and come back down toward the door past the cash register—a simple U-shaped traffic flow that Ruthton shoppers have been following since Before Marv. Susan wasn't accustomed to such customs. If she picked out her frozen foods first, they'd be partially thawed by the time she checked out. So Susan shopped counterclockwise, coming at everyone else head-on. They had to squeeze past each other in the narrow aisles. A few times people said, politely, "You're going the wrong way." Susan would think to herself, "No, you are," and saw no real need to change. How could anybody seriously care which way people pushed their shopping carts in a little grocery store? It never occurred to the townspeople to change; the flow moved that way because it moved that way. It was a minor but symbolic thing. Whenever Susan thought about shopping at Jensen's, she thought about that stupid way of shopping. And whenever a lot of people thought about Susan Blythe, they thought of a big-city woman who always went against the small-town flow.

Down the street at the bank, things were going pretty well. Interest rates hadn't been going down as Rudy had expected, but with inflation he'd made a fair chunk of money on the sale of his Des Moines house. And Jerry Ihnen seemed to be working out. Rudy liked the small bank staff. They had dubbed him the Cookie Monster, because whenever they bought a bag of cookies to share during coffee breaks, Rudy would mooch most of them. He took each woman to lunch on her birthday and when Valentine's Day rolled around, they each got a red rose.

Rudy had also taken care of Edgar Ronning. He had formally retired but filled in as a part-time teller on busy Fridays. Rudy had been impressed with him from the first day of his bank ownership when Edgar was the only bank employee to walk up and introduce himself. Rudy also paid him to attend local senior citizens meetings and represent the bank.

Rudy plunged into involvement in everything local he could find. He told his mother it was his responsibility as *the* banker. If the banker wasn't energetic, didn't have ideas and confidence, wouldn't work hard and invest locally, then nothing would ever change in Ruthton. It would continue its downhill slide.

Rudy was appointed to a vacancy on the Ruthton town council. Later, he was elected in his own right. He helped finance prizes for the best-decorated bike in the Memorial Day parade, and he made regular bank donations to local clubs. When Ruthton's high school basketball team got into the state tournament, Rudy rented a suite at a Minneapolis hotel and reigned there as host to whip up civic spirit—and a drink or two as well—for any Ruthtonite who stopped by. And when Catherine Ness and Sharon Fadness needed an enticing boost for the Ruthton Girl Scout troop, Rudy quietly put up two hundred dollars to finance a trip to Duluth.

Rudy had other ideas, too. He founded the Lions Club to boost civic spirit. He suggested the town council give a break on the water rates to a local man who might bring his bait business to town. It would mean a couple of jobs and might get a little economic momentum going. Then Rudy started talking about a new investment. If he and a few local men with a little money could get a good piece of land, they could apply for a grant and maybe build a senior citizens home right there in Ruthton. There were more old folks all the time scattered around town. This way they'd get good care and meals. They would stay in town and maybe their kids would, too, and help support local businesses. And Ruthton needed a doctor again, so Rudy negotiated with a doctor from Pipestone. One Saturday, he got Lions Club members to fix up a little office for the physician. The club and the bank underwrote the rent for a while. And a doctor actually started taking appointments in Ruthton again.

In phone conversations with his distant friends, Rudy was ebullient in those first couple of years. When Rudy's father came to visit, his son would take him across the street to the café, and Rudy would hold court with the farmers and they'd talk about crops and the weather and the price of farm equipment. A few days later they'd drop by the bank to see their pal Rudy about a loan. There wouldn't be much of a problem. Times were good. Land was great collateral; its value was rising every day, thanks to inflation.

Some new customers even came from another bank. One, that Jim Jenkins fellow, the handyman who fixed Marv Jensen's plumbing, who lived on the road to Tyler, consolidated a couple of loans on his little ten-acre place and brought the business to Rudy's bank. With the interest rates inching up, people were shopping around more for banking services. Jenkins and the others were making their payments. Things were going swell for Rudy. The guys in the Ruthton Volunteer Fire Department, a major male social institution in most midwestern communities, even invited Rudy to become a full member. Rudy was thrilled.

The Blythes had joined the country club in Pipestone too. Rudy got into a regular foursome of banker golfers. Rudy didn't care if the Mother's Day buffet was served on paper plates, though his wife certainly did. Generally though, Susan seemed satisfied. She was, however, putting on a lot of weight. Rudy noticed on the phone bill that Susan was calling her mother and friends back in Des Moines a lot. She just wouldn't quit smoking. And that was too bad about the Ruthton school board election. A longtime member had announced her retirement from the board, so Susan announced her candidacy. She had only been in Ruthton about a year, but she had some definite ideas for needed reforms. Then it seems there was a meeting between the school board president and the retiring member. Afterward the member said she had changed her mind; she was running for reelection. Despite all her ideas and campaign energy, Susan finished last.

As long as Rudy took his family on regular weekend trips and let Susan make all those phone calls and go back to her parents' cottage on the lake in New York every summer, things seemed to be okay, although there was some concern, and some inconclusive testing, when another baby wouldn't come along as planned.

Rudy, meanwhile, had given birth to a new idea at the bank. He would open a branch office, a sign of growth and new investment. The new branch would be in Holland, eight miles down the road toward Pipestone. It began with a Saturday full of public relations. At noon a stagecoach came down the main street of Holland, Minnesota. And sitting up there next to the driver, waving a big cowboy hat and smiling to beat the band, was, of course, Rudy Blythe. Some "holdup men" with pistols ran out into the street. Rudy tossed "gold" coins into the sparse crowd. The stagecoach stopped by the newest branch of the Buffalo Ridge State Bank, and the president of the bank jumped down to make a few remarks about the future, about Holland, and about a new age of banking service for its 160 residents. Everyone then adjourned to the park where the new Holland Branch of the Buffalo Ridge State Bank provided everyone with free Buffalo Burgers.

Susan was there, too, that day in 1979. She had become bored and frustrated with life in Ruthton and more willing to reveal her feelings to Rudy. The town didn't like any of her ideas. When she suggested building a Ruthton swimming pool, they said a town pool would be too dangerous; someone might drown and their relatives would sue everyone. When Susan suggested a special Friday library night so she could expose the kids to new books while their parents did some banking, they said there weren't enough chairs. Someone even commented on Susan's clothes, so she started wearing less of the bright blues and reds she liked and more navy and brown. She needed new clothes anyway; she was many pounds heavier than two years before.

Susan didn't have a close circle of friends, although Sharon Fadness was nice and gave her some tips, like not to mention her college days quite so much. Susan's mother noticed that their phone conversations were turning more negative.

Eighteen months into his dream, Rudy seemed more preoccupied about money. Everybody was. The Blythes had planned to combine a family vacation with a trip to the bankers' convention in Hawaii, but Rudy had canceled it, saying things were a little tight at the moment. It wasn't like him. Still, he was the same old Rudes in many ways. He went fishing and hunting with some friends, well, with some customers from the bank. Susan had given him a twelve-gauge shotgun, but Rudy wasn't all that keen on the killing part. She asked him once why he went, and he described it as a social occasion, getting up early and traveling with other men and then sitting with them for long hours hidden in camouflaged blinds, talking in whispers, telling stories.

On his return, Rudy would wrestle with Rolph—he called him Tigerboy—and, when it was bedtime, Rudy would tell his son fanciful stories about a knight named Gluckajuck. Afterward, if there wasn't some town meeting to attend, Rudy would sit in his reclining chair while Susan paid bills. And he'd check his stocks in the newspaper or read one of the biographies he liked. Rudy's tastes didn't change much, even when the notices of interest rate increases started coming more frequently from the bank in Minneapolis.

Much of Susan's discontent with the town focused on sports. Everyone took them so seriously, yelling at their own players, sometimes angrily, laughing at opponents' mistakes. She saw an intense basketball coach pound the floor once. A lot of hostility there. There was no effort to let every child play in every game. Some like Rolph practiced every practice but rarely got in a game. That wasn't fair. Someone else might have gone to the coach quietly and offered some suggestions. Susan made the suggestions in a formal letter to the coach and sports authorities.

At school a male teacher might slam a miscreant up against a locker now and then, just to get his attention. And it worked. But that bothered Susan, frightened her, the muzzled violence. Rolph had to survive in that social arena by day and at home had to undergo his mother's questions about school. Sometimes on the way home he would stop by the bank. With his father, and sometimes with Susan, too, he would get a hot chocolate at the café or play a video game. Sometimes he'd go straight home. Sometimes his mother would find him in his closet, thinking. She knew it was the school problem.

The situation didn't improve. One night at dinner Susan corrected Rolph for holding the fork in his fist like a scoop. "You know better than that!" she said. Rolph broke into tears.

"I'm sorry," he cried. "I have to eat one way at school and another way at home and I can't always remember which is which." Like his mother and father, Rolph had few real friends in Ruthton. Everybody knew him, of course; he was the banker's son. When invited, they came to Rolph's birthday parties that Susan organized around some theme, such as "pirates." Everyone would get a pirate's costume, and they would run around the yard looking for buried treasure, chocolate pieces of eight Susan had hidden there that morning. There would be ice cream and cake and, as usual, Dad would take two pieces.

But when the parents weren't around, Rolph had a hard time. His schoolmates say it was because he was so rich and they weren't; Rolph always had a quarter for the video machines. When he got a new bike, no one seemed to notice the shiny new thing; they just made fun of the training wheels. When Grandma Slater sent him a New York Yankee baseball uniform, Rolph went running out to the diamond to show his friends. They laughed. They said everyone in Ruthton cheered for the Minnesota Twins; didn't he know that? Rolph never wore the uniform again outside the house.

Susan felt Rolph's school problems were worsening. She talked to Rudy about them, but he had a growing number of other problems on his mind. The last thing he wanted was a fight with the local school. "I don't hear Rolph complaining," Rudy would say. "You can't protect the boy all his life." Susan was not satisfied. They had Rolph tested psychologically. He was normal. But Susan was taken with his completion of one question: A woman is _____. Rolph's answer: sometimes a mother. Susan decided Rolph should change schools. They could drive him to public school in another town. It cost an extra $1,500 a year, but what's money for? We're talking basic education.

"Can you imagine what everyone will say here?" Rudy said to Susan, his voice rising. "Ruthton is good enough to put its money in the Blythe bank, but the Blythes are too good to put their son in the Ruthton school?"

Eventually Rudy went along with the idea. Maybe Susan had a point, and where Rolph went to class would become the least of Rudy's worries.

One day after that Susan was going down to the bank to see Rudy about something. There are two sets of front doors on the bank, making an enclosed vestibule. Susan had entered the outer door and was reaching for the handle on the inner one when it flew open. The little chamber was suddenly filled with a short dumpy man wearing a dirty jacket, glasses, a stocking cap perched on the back of his head, and a scowl plastered on the front. His face was flushed pink. He stormed by Susan without a greeting or an apology. Inside, Susan asked Rudy who that man was.

"Oh," he said, "that's Jim Jenkins."

It was the end of the beginning.

And the beginning of the end.

CHAPTER FOUR

Across the Tracks

James Lee Jenkins did not normally move quickly. He couldn't, now that he was middle-aged and the tolls of various progressive ailments were starting to add up. Short and stocky, he had a thick body and seemingly strong legs, although they tended to swell up now whenever he overworked them, say, by hefting heavy loads in a wheelbarrow. He was easily winded, too.

He often complained of an upset stomach whenever he ate, which was not all that regularly since Darlene left him. Like many lonely men after a divorce, Jim Jenkins had come to see meals as a simple refueling stop that interrupted work once or twice a day. Jim would find a diner near his work and patronize it for meal after meal, day after day.

At Alene's Cafe in Ruthton, Jim would order the day's hot plate special, whatever it was. Elsewhere, he would order the same hamburger or the same scrambled eggs and toast. He would sit silently at the same table and shovel the stuff into his mouth until the plate was empty. Since restaurants didn't take credit, Jim would have to pay cash for his meal. He never left a tip. But he'd grab a free toothpick and shuffle out the door into the dusk. The last thing anyone would see of Jim Jenkins that day, if anyone thought to watch, was the dirty jacket and trousers going out the door and always, always a heavy stocking cap rolled up tight and pushed way back on his head. Some people said they'd seen a bald spot growing under the hat the few times Jim ever took it off.

Folks didn't see Jim Jenkins around much, though, not after dark anyway. It was his eyes. The eye doctor over in Marshall had told him that he had retinitis pigmentosa, which didn't mean anything to Jim until the doctor said it was incurable and usually resulted in blindness. But Jim didn't listen to everything those college graduates said anyway. Jim never could remember the name, but he knew it was bad, and it seemed to be getting worse. Seeing was like looking down a tunnel. Jim would turn his head this way and that to aim his tunnel vision. At night he could hardly see anything, though he still tried to drive. Several times on the way home in the evening he'd missed his own driveway and ended up in the ditch. His country neighbors would come over with a tractor to pull the pickup back onto the road again. Everybody knew those accidents weren't on account of drinking. Jim never touched the stuff. It was his eyes, Jim said. All part of his diabetes. Well, screw it. Screw the eyes, too. And screw that special diet.

Jim had agreed to try some glasses, but he took the bifocals back right away. They didn't work. He wore the regular glasses pretty much all the

time, except when he was milking cows. You don't need glasses to find a
cow's tits, not when you been doin' it all these years.

Jim was a quiet man, the only son of a modest farmer named Clayton
Jenkins. They were good folks, neighbors say, and neighbors know. Although how Clayton and his wife, Nina, could ever make it financially,
farming only eighty acres, no one could really understand. For longer than
anyone could remember, Jenkins had farmed his place—soybeans and oats
mostly—just outside of Florence, a little town just up the road from Ruthton.

Clayton loved the country and his work. If he worked hard, the bills
would get paid. If things got tight, he would work harder, and if things
got really bad, he would work harder still. The storm would blow over
presently. Until then, they'd get by. They always had.

He and Nina struck friends as good parents. Like many fathers and sons
in the countryside, Clayton and Jim were together many hours every day,
sharing plantings and harvests, repairs and chores. Jim learned a lot from
his father, so much that he decided to quit high school. He wouldn't need
any education since he was going to be a farmer. His father didn't make
much fuss over that decision; it seemed natural enough.

In the 1960s Jim had joined the National Guard more as a means of
earning a little extra money than for any military reason. But Jim still got
the basic soldier's training in marching and sharpshooting, the proper
shooting positions and all. He was in a transportation unit and began hon-
ing the basic mechanical skills he was taught at home. He learned to operate heavy machinery and to fix it when something went wrong. From then
on, whenever he needed some personal satisfaction or praise, he would
plunge into mechanical work. "Jim is a workaholic," his friends would
say, "and he can make anything work."

Whenever they needed mechanical or welding advice, they would ask
Jim. And hours or even days later, when they heard that dead engine suddenly roar to life out back, everyone would rush outside and there would
be Jim, stocking cap perched on the back of his head, standing by the re-
suscitated machine, wiping the oil off his hands and maybe smiling a little
at everyone's wonderment.

There's one thing everyone remembers about Jim Jenkins: he was a hard
worker. By the age of twelve he was out baling hay for the neighbors at a
penny a bale. And in school he was a real loner. You'd never see Jim at a
dance or a party. You wouldn't see Jim shooting baskets after classes either.
When the school day ended, and lots of times even before, he'd just be
gone. He wasn't different strange. He was different familiar. Lots of guys
were quiet; he was more so.

You'd see Jim in town on an errand or out in the fields alone doing work
for hire or emerging from Marv Jensen's bathroom to get a different
wrench. You might see Jim at the town fair, moving around the edge of

the festivities holding a can of pop. He would talk briefly with a few folks. He might even pick up a little repair business that day, although, of course, he would never appear to seek it.

Jim was a regular part of the community. Everyone seemed to recognize him but hardly anyone really knew him. Jim didn't make appointments; he just showed up, quiet-like and unannounced, and then, when his work was done, he was gone. The one time he made an appointment, many years later, Jim used a different name.

Jim may have been on his way to a repair job on that sultry August day in 1960. It may have been due to the tall corn obstructing the view. Or it may have been a bad day for Jim's eyes. But in one instant on a back road, Jim's pickup truck collided with an old lady's car, head-on hard. Just like that she was dead. Jim never saw the crumpled body in the crumpled vehicle because he had hit his head in the crash. Very hard. For a while they were worried about his life. After seventeen days in the hospital, the doctor said he should see a specialist, a trick Jim knew doctors often pull to get more money from patients. Screw the special doctor. Jim didn't need advice.

Jim got married the next year. He was twenty-four, five foot seven, 185 pounds. She was Darlene Abraham from over by Lake Benton, a woman whose face would gradually grow harder and harsher in the coming years as if she were living out a long, sad country music song.

Things went okay for the Jenkins couple at first. Of course, Jim would be a farmer; his father was, so he would be too. Jim wanted to be his own boss, to work hard in the fields and the barn, to rule over the animals and his kids and his wife. Jim's son—of course, they'd have a boy—would look up to him and learn from him, same as Jim did from his dad.

Jim had some problems, one of them money. He couldn't or didn't keep track of money. He was working hard; everyone knew that. He paid most of his bills, and things would take care of themselves whether or not he was able to balance a checkbook or figure out a rate of return on his invested capital to boost his equity while covering interest charges. Jim would just try something. If it works, fine. If it doesn't, try something else. When it breaks again, fix it. He'd spend two days fixing an old part that would cost $5.99 new. Time and time again he'd buy old machinery no one else wanted anymore and stubbornly invest himself in its repair until it worked—for a while anyway.

There might be more efficient ways of doing things. One time when he had a herd of dairy cows and needed cheap feed, Jim would drive forty or fifty miles one-way to a vegetable processing plant that gave pea silage away free just to be rid of it. Jim would drive there every day or two and haul the smelly stuff home to feed his herd because his farm was too small for adequate pasture. Some people admired the stubborn determination of a hardworking man making use of waste products to make ends meet on a ten-acre place that used to be part of a far larger farm. Other farmers would see Jim drive his little truck east and return late in the afternoon with a load of free pea silage. They thought Jim was wasting a lot of money on gas fetching that "free" livestock feed. He could put that money toward buying better food to improve the cows' milk production, bring in a little more income, and still give Jim two or three free afternoons a week to invest in other farm work. That's what they thought anyway. What they said to Jim was nothing. Like as not, midwesterners think free advice is worth exactly what they pay for it. Besides, although he was never prone to accepting advice in the past, Jim now seemed downright opposed to even hearing it. Jim looked fine, but some part of him had leaked out on that dirt road on that sad, sultry day in August 1960.

Friends said that after that day Jim seemed to get more easily angry. He was given to "wild fits of temper," one remembered. You couldn't tell when it was coming, not even his family. One moment Jim was fine. Then along would come some little annoyance, and *boom*, Jim was livid, yelling and swinging. One day Carl Johnson got an urgent phone call for help from Clayton Jenkins. Arriving at the Jenkins farmstead, Johnson said he found shattered glass all over and a Jenkins uncle forcibly holding Jim down after a family fight.

Jim didn't seem bothered much by his economic frustrations, so consumed was he with working hard. Some of his friends from school saw how hard their fathers—mostly farmers—worked for so little income. They scouted for work at the dwindling businesses in the shrinking midwestern towns. Then they thought, for the first time in several generations, about going somewhere else to live.

By the early 1970s a lot of the guys from high school were gone, but Jim was still around. He and Darlene had had a daughter, Michelle, and then along came a boy. They named him Steve. Financially Jim was going from one problem to another. He would start farming somewhere nearby. Things would go along adequately for a while, then there'd be some unpaid bills or bad checks. Maybe a minor court suit. Darlene would try to pay off the bills, and Jim would run up some more. Not on fancy clothes or anything like that. But there was all that gas for the truck Jim drove everywhere. And Jim never had enough money at one time to buy any good, new farm equipment outright. The steady string of repair bills on his old machinery was increasing too. Sometimes Jim's father would have to bail his son out. Once Jim owned so much money that Clayton Jenkins had to put a new mortgage on his own property when he nearly had the old one paid off.

To bring in extra money, Jim did repair work. Or he hired himself out to help on another farm. At one point Jim hooked up with a local entrepreneur named Louis Taveirne. Louis was a strong, heavyset man, hardworking and clever and a little feared for that by some. He always seemed to get what he wanted and to do well at whatever he tried, whether it was owning a country supper club or an isolated dump. For a while Jim ran the dump for Louis, checking what was brought in and covering it with dirt. Then Louis said some state inspectors had complained about inadequate soil covering the refuse. Jim got angry, and Louis had to fire him.

Jim decided to try something new during the day, when the cows were quietly making milk at home. He'd get some heavy machinery and do some of the county's roadwork. Louis had an old grader for sale. Jim saved his money and brought the machine for $1,600. He got it working right and went out to grade roads. But the county had its own machinery or hired contractors who didn't have to build their workday around a bunch of cows. A few weeks after that, Louis spotted his old grader for sale in a machinery lot. The dealer said Jim had sold it to him for $1,000.

Jim just wanted to milk cows anyway. He loved working with those animals. He'd be out in the barn before dawn and still out there after dark, feeding and milking and sometimes talking to the gentle creatures. Jim felt important in the barn. What he said went. The animals did what he wanted, usually when he wanted. If they didn't, he could hit them, and they'd get the message real quick. Simple animals were predictable. They didn't have lawyers. They didn't have a lot of documents. They didn't talk with twisted numbers on paper that showed things were one way when Jim damn well knew they were another.

Jim might grumble in the house about those fancy lawyers and tricky bankers. Everybody would listen. Jim was finding that people tended to listen to him much more when he was angry, so sometimes at home, he'd put on a little anger. And it worked. Sometimes a lot of real anger would come on without trying. That really worked. For a while.

Nobody said much about it at the time. Jim was considered "strong-minded." Later it would come out that Jim was more like a dictator at home with his kids and wife.

With Jim working so hard, Darlene was pretty much responsible for raising Steve and Michelle, or Mickey. After the usual string of high school boyfriends, Mickey would marry at a young age and move away. Steve would hang around with his male buddies, hunting without a license and talking guns or army. Sometimes he and a friend would run around the fields on the edge of town, spying on unsuspecting people and pretending to be junior commandos.

Steve struck some adults as a bit strange. He would smile or laugh when no one had said anything funny, as if he were listening to things other people couldn't hear. He had come to admire his father deeply. There was joking between the men. And there was a male acceptance, not communicated in words. A handing of the wrench, without speaking, during some motor repairs as if the father were sure the boy knew what to do with it. Young men like that, even if they don't always know what to do with the wrench.

Steve wasn't all that intrigued with solving mechanical problems. But he enjoyed being with his father at those times. Jim Jenkins was at his happiest then. So was Steve.

When things seemed to go right for Jim, he thought the hard work might work out after all. Jim had been working a small farm near Arco, Minnesota, about twelve miles north of Ruthton. He discovered in the mid-1970s how much his little piece of land there had increased in value due to something called inflation. So he sold it. He made several hundred dollars more an acre than he had paid. Just like that. Although he didn't understand precisely what he had done so well, this inflation stuff made Jim feel successful. He put the money toward a down payment on a new farm four miles north of Ruthton on the road to Tyler. Sure it was expensive, almost three thousand dollars an acre, its value also having been inflated. It was a smaller place, just ten acres. But the farm by Ruthton was Jim's dream. Big fields surrounding him—not his, but big anyway. Neighbors who needed repairs. Dairy cows, forty to sixty at a time. No one telling him what to do.

Jim got the place in 1977. He dealt with a farm credit organization some miles away. He had a contract for deed, meaning he didn't own the land outright, but would eventually as long as he kept up the payments.

Then this new banker fellow from the East came to Ruthton. He bought the whole damn bank. The guys at the café were saying that this Blythe guy was making loans to local farmers right and left. That meant Pedersen was gone. Good thing, because he'd repossessed a quonset hut that Jim had bought a while back. Blythe wouldn't know about that. So Jim walked into the Buffalo Ridge State Bank and arranged a loan. The bank bought out the contract for deed, and gave Jim a new mortgage on his little farm with more money to expand and improve his herd. It was all Jim's as long as he continued to make the payments to Rudy's bank. So he did. And the two men's country dreams were linked by ledger.

For several years Jim Jenkins and Rudy Blythe traveled in their own orbits four miles and two worlds apart. And then Rudy began to think of leaving the town. Or, rather, Susan suggested it. She obviously wasn't happy in Ruthton. Part of it was her fault, Rudy knew. She was having a lot of confrontations because of her constant attempts to fix things. She was going to fix the Blythe family right out of the small-town banking business if she wasn't careful. At first, Rudy realized, he had excluded Susan from much of the bank's affairs. It was *his* dream. She was along as a member of the cast. Maybe if he involved her more, it would give her an outlet, calm her down.

"You don't know how to handle these people," Rudy said, pleading for a change. "You're making too many waves."

Susan was feeling very frustrated. Nothing worked. She had but one or two local friends to speak of, nothing to do. Just housework and making dinner for Rolph, and Rudy, when he came home for dinner. She was fat. She was not pregnant. Rolph was obviously unhappy too. And all Rudy talked about was the bank, that damn bank. He wanted her down there, helping. Susan began to wonder, out loud, just who or what Rudy Blythe loved more. He was working too hard. They hadn't had—couldn't afford—a proper vacation. All their money was tied up in that bank. Rudy was trying to do things for the town. So was Susan. What were they getting in return? Rejected, that's what. They had gotten so used to being left out that on New Year's Eve Rudy and Susan went to bed well before midnight. One year, they had to greet Sharon and David Fadness in their pajamas when the couple dropped by for a late-night toast.

Tensions were increasing between Rudy and Susan enough so that rumors floated around town of Blythe family frictions. Perhaps the bank's lawyer remembered Rudy's offhand remark about moving out of town with Susan or else she would get out by herself. Or perhaps someone passing by on a nice day with the windows open and the chickadees chirping in the budding willows heard voices yelling within the banker's house, a public display of private frustrations that the participants never knew had seeped out. Rolph and Rufus, the dog, wouldn't know the news was spreading either; they would be hiding in the boy's closet, off in a faraway pretend world.

There was some yelling, too, out north of town on the Tyler road. Hard times had set in for Jim Jenkins and his family there. In the winter it was harder to get about for feed. Jim's cattle were often leading a hoof-to-mouth existence. For Jim's family, it was hand to mouth. Jim had a knack for fixing machines, to be sure, but most other things he touched turned to crap. Time after time, he would get an idea he thought was good and set about working it out in his own way. And, sure as sunset, it would collapse all around him, and on anyone else nearby.

In early 1980 Darlene Jenkins announced that she was leaving. She had had it. As it happened, Darlene would stick around for a few more months. But the die had been cast and shattered at the same time. Not only was Jim's wife leaving him; she was leaving him for another man. He was Louis Taveirne, the broad-handed dump owner, the man who had been paying Jim to stay at the garbage site all day covering up the refuse people brought in. Louis Taveirne.

Darlene's departure was a devastating emotional blow for Jim. Months, even years, later he would talk of it with teeth-clenching bitterness, although by then Jim was blaming someone else. His wife's departure also meant he'd lose his children. Mickey, who was closer to her mother, would go off with Darlene. Steve was torn, but at fifteen he still had to attend school. And what kind of household could a poverty-stricken dairy farmer run for a high school kid?

Steve harbored hopes of somehow reuniting his folks. So, for a while anyway, the youth would tell each adult good things about the other. Their blunt reactions caused him to stop. Steve would choose to spend a lot of time with his Jenkins grandparents. He had a lot of time to kill then; he was going to be like his father, so he dropped out of high school. His grandparents let him ride his bike around the old farm and roam alone in the far woods, where he built dummies of logs with bottles for heads. He dressed these pretend people in spare shirts and slacks. He set them up in the fields and among the trees. And then he shot at them over and over again.

One evening LeRoy Knutson was driving along a back road testing a used car. He spotted something in the ditch. It was Steve Jenkins, unconscious. The boy had fallen on his bicycle and one end of the handlebar had been driven into his body. Knutson took the limp teenager to the Tyler Hospital, where an angry Jim Jenkins soon arrived. To some that day, the father seemed irrational, less concerned about Steve's injury, a ruptured spleen, than about his son being treated by someone from outside the area. A local policeman was summoned. There was a lot of mumbling about outsiders and foreigners. Jim didn't want the doctor on duty to treat Steve. He was adamant about that. The doctor was a Filipino, one of many foreigners working in midwestern country hospitals now that few American doctors accepted such isolated working conditions and low pay. Jim called him "a pineapple." Later, he made an angry visit to Knutson's service station, ostensibly over LeRoy's having taken the boy to Tyler. The whole thing reminded Jim of that goddamned banker in Ruthton, Rudy Blythe. Jim said Blythe had tricked him while signing some documents; the banker had put a second sheet under the original, Jim said, so he had unknowingly signed away his land. None of this made any sense to Knutson. He put it down to a worried parent's concern and promptly forgot it. A lot of farmers have harsh things to say about bankers. Few ever do anything about it.

A lot of bankers have harsh thoughts about farmers too. And a growing number were doing something about it in 1980. Rudy Blythe was among them. He was getting into some severe financial troubles himself, trying to carry the loan for the bank at a floating interest rate that had continued to climb and was nearing twenty percent. Twenty percent! He had to take out another note on the bank. Sometimes Rudy could make only the interest payments to the Minneapolis bank, thirty thousand dollars or so every ninety days. There was nothing left over to go toward the principal. Some days there would be two notices of interest rate increases in the same mail. The Minneapolis bank, which was finding a lot of its borrowers strained, was getting a little worried too. It wanted more security for these loans. As Clayton Jenkins did for his boy Jim, so did Rudy Blythe, Sr., step in to bail out his son. He put up a considerable bloc of his stock as additional collateral.

The pressures were building on Rudy. Then came the Jenkins problem. The guy, it turned out, had a string of bad debts back through the 1970s. Everybody except the new banker seemed to know that. Now, suddenly, Jenkins was walking away from that little farm north of town. Something about his wife leaving him. Big deal, thought Rudy. Wives are leaving husbands all over the country. It's not the bank's fault.

At least the cattle and the land covered Rudy's mortgage. Then someone said Jenkins had been over at the cattle sales barn. He'd sold the mortgaged cattle, or most of them, and for slaughter prices, too, instead of waiting a few days for health tests and getting a much higher price. And he had left a bunch of the animals out at his farm starving. When Rudy went out to the place, he found that someone had ripped out all the plumbing fixtures, sinks, tubs, toilets. Someone quoted Jenkins as saying that if he couldn't have that nice little farm, then nobody would.

Rudy was furious with Jenkins. He would pursue that son of a bitch wherever he went to get his thirty grand back. But the farmer declared bankruptcy and just disappeared.

Rudy went to the Lincoln County prosecutor, Michael Cable. He wanted Cable to file criminal charges against the farmer. Jenkins had stolen the cattle that belonged to the bank and sold them. To Rudy, it was clear as day. To Cable, it was a judgment call. How could he prove that Jenkins knew the sale was illegal? The guy did it locally; he didn't sneak off with the animals to another state. Rudy could always slap Jenkins with a civil suit, though that would be like trying to squeeze blood from a turnip. Cable said he wouldn't prosecute criminally.

Rudy got mad. At work, he began talking tougher to the farmers, any one of whom could be trying to pull another fast one like Jenkins. Many folks remember him dismissing their loan applications with a quick wave of the hand. "That is a very stupid idea," he told one man. "Get the hell out of here and don't come back until you've got a better plan."

There were a few farm sales, too. Rudy wasn't only cracking down on new loans. He and many other bankers were beginning to examine old loans. Some farmers sold out voluntarily or retired early. Interest rates going up while the commodity prices went down. Payments falling behind. Property values plummeting. Better to get out now with a little than hang around trying hard and lose it all.

The Blythes would make a day of it at those farm auctions. Rudy would work the crowd, talking with people, agreeing that it was sad about the sale but noting that some farm operations just wouldn't be able to make it. Susan would work the tally table in a shed, keeping track of who bought what for how much. Even Rolph earned some money, receiving twenty-five or fifty cents for running the sales slips from the auctioneer to Susan.

As time went on, there were some disturbing late-night phone calls. One woman told Susan she hoped Rudy would die. It became a minor family joke. Susan would sometimes tell Rudy as he left for work to be sure and keep his head down low. She had recognized the woman's voice even though the caller had been drunk. Her kid had a loan at the bank, one of those motorcycle loans that was often past due on payments.

There were other anonymous callers. They yelled about the Blythes' dog or promised to shoot him dead. They complained that the Blythes let him run all around town, upsetting garbage cans and threatening children. As it happened, the Blythes, who had always lived in city neighborhoods, never let their dog run loose in town. Many days Susan would take Rufus out to the old Jenkins place and let him run there. The bank owned all ten acres now. The Jenkins place had become a kind of private Blythe park. Rufus would go crazy, dashing off into the woods while Susan strolled along behind or simply sat on the cement steps by the house, soaking up the prairie sun. But Susan didn't go into the house, which she thought was dark and cold and full of anger.

Sometimes Rolph would go out to the farm with her. Rudy went, too, but not often. The Jenkins place seemed to be a symbol of something to him, something that he didn't enjoy revisiting, although he talked about it considerably. A few years later when friends in Texas heard that something had happened at the Jenkins place, they would nod and say, oh, yes, they knew about the Jenkins place. Rudy had told them.

In the next few years other farms were repossessed and put up for sale at a rate that accelerated across the region, pushing down even more the value of the remaining operating farms, which prompted more banks to call in more farm loans and put more farms and machines on the market, pushing down values even further. But for Rudy Blythe, there was only one Jenkins place.

Rudy was feeling very frustrated. He had brought all the pieces of his dream together—the college education with its knowledge and ideas, the wife and son, the life in the country, the bank in the midwestern small town. He had assembled them properly there in Ruthton. And no matter what he tried, the damned thing wouldn't work. His college education was actually a minus in that society; new ideas were threatening to old ways. His wife was miserable. She was still putting on weight and so, come to think of it, was he. His initial investment had been eroded by all the added loan notes; he'd even had to move his bank loan to his old employer in Des Moines. Rudy knew a lot of people, but you couldn't call them friends. The guy he hired to run the bank wasn't exactly setting the world on fire. Then came the election.

Up in the northeast corner of Pipestone County, Ruthton has long felt politically neglected. The town was properly Democratic in an area where Franklin Delano Roosevelt has yet to be displaced in memory as the ideal president. But in 1980 Rudy, long intrigued by politics and active in Republican state conventions in both Iowa and Minnesota, determined to boost Ruthton's role. Having been reelected Ruthton town councilman, Rudy set his sights on county commissioner. There was a need for a public spokesman. He would take little Ruthton's case to the rest of the county, stand up for the town, his town, against an incumbent, some friend of Louis Taveirne's. Rudy was trounced. He couldn't have won even if he'd received every one of Ruthton's votes, which he didn't.

Rudy was crushed by the outcome. There was no moaning or complaining. However, the confident bounce was gone from his step. Suddenly Rudy seemed to agree with Susan; maybe they should leave Ruthton, he said. He could put the bank up for sale. Meanwhile he would look for work around the area to help with the finances. The extra income would ease the financial drain on the bank until times got better. Rudy would still draw his bank executive's salary. Then maybe in a few years, when interest rates would certainly have gone down, they could come back to run the bank in Ruthton or somewhere else, if Susan agreed.

In early 1981 Rudy told Lee Bush, the bank's attorney, to offer the bank for sale. Rudy's asking price of $900,000 seemed good to Susan; you always ask for more than you expect to settle for. But it struck Lee as way out of line. The price was 30 to 35 percent more than a realistic one. No one would want to buy the Buffalo Ridge State Bank at that price. But wait a minute, thought Lee. Maybe that was Rudy's plan.

There was not exactly a line of eager buyers waiting in front of the Buffalo Ridge State Bank each morning. A couple of men did contact Lee and look at the bank's books. But the potential buyers backed off, or Rudy found their final offers too small.

While Susan scanned the want ads in every major midwestern paper she could find, Rudy began sending out his résumé. He started in the adjacent area. Maybe he could find a good financial job in Sioux Falls or teach a little economics over in Brookings, South Dakota. He'd still be close to the bank, just in case it didn't sell.

The weeks passed, and there were no job offers. Rudy's résumé went out to an ever-widening circle of banks and recruiters across the Midwest and then, naturally enough, down into the Sunbelt. Everybody had good things to say about the Sunbelt in those days. There were jobs in the Sunbelt. Times were booming. Nice climate. Rudy flew to New Orleans one late summer weekend in 1981. He didn't take the bank job offered there. But it was heady stuff to be flown into a city, picked up by a friendly executive, interviewed on his ideas, wined and dined, and flown home. After four years with people who never saw the worth of his plans, it was great to be patted on the back again. A real confidence-booster.

So Rudy was primed when the interview and then the job offer came from the big bank in Dallas. They wanted Rudy to help run their trust department, dealing with the investments of corporations. It was familiar turf for Rudy, and a mandate that promised a minimum of management above. They even flew Susan down. She loved Dallas.

Susan went on a house-hunting expedition, making up a list of choices for Rudy to see. His pick had a swimming pool and an assumable mortgage at 13 percent. On October 6, 1981, they signed the purchase agreement. A few weeks later in Ruthton, on a snowy, dark Friday night, the Blythes packed up their station wagon with luggage and Rolph and Rufus, and eased slowly down the slippery road to the Sunbelt. Rudy would return to Ruthton monthly for a few days to oversee things—until the bank sold, that is. He could also check in by phone. Jerry Ihnen seemed adequate for the moment to run the bank. Rudy hadn't announced the new arrangement around town. He feared some kind of panic, the banker leaving because he needed to earn more money to keep the bank. There wasn't any panic at all, just a couple of muttered good riddances.

Susan was thrilled to be living again in a world of clubs, friends, and a brightly lit downtown where people met to talk about something other than corn and the weather. But Rudy's friends back East and elsewhere could tell he was less than enthusiastic about the move to Dallas. His job wasn't too bad. He didn't have quite the leeway he expected or maybe it was harder for a self-employed person to get back in harness on a larger team. But Rudy was getting a good salary, and since no one had bought the Ruthton bank yet, he was in frequent telephone contact with Jerry. Once a month or so, Rudy would drive back to Minnesota by himself. It took two days to get there, but it was a legitimate business trip, so he drove the bank-owned car. That made it basically a free trip, which was good because the Dallas house alone was costing him over fifteen hundred dollars a month to carry. Besides, it was good to be the boss up there, even just now and then.

Somebody else was on the move looking for new work in the prosperous Sunbelt that year. He probably passed within a few blocks of the Blythes' sprawling home on one of his hitchhiking forays between the Midwest and Texas, where the money was.

After he'd lost the farm in Ruthton, Jim Jenkins went into Marshall for a few months to work as a diesel mechanic for a bus company. He lived in a rented house trailer there during the divorce business and through his personal bankruptcy; Darlene wouldn't change her mind. She'd made that clear.

It wasn't long before Jim became frustrated with others telling him what to do. He missed being out on the land and briefly rented a little farm to the north. Maybe he and Steve could get started again milking cows. But the barn burned down. That seemed a bad sign, so Jim drifted down to southern Ohio for a while, loading trucks for some manufacturing company. Steve came, too, shuttling between his father and mother. Then, like most everyone else in difficulty in the Rustbelt of 1981, Jim Jenkins turned to the beckoning Southwest. To Texas, to be precise.

Charles Snow looked the middle-aged man in the eyes, as he always did when considering a new employee. Jim Jenkins responded with a firm gaze and an equally firm handshake. Snow was impressed. The guy was short and dumpy, near as broad as he was tall. He was wearing one of those funny northern stocking caps rolled up tight on the back of his head. Snow noticed the man's arms were thick and strong, his hands rough and blunt, the sign of a hard worker, outdoors a lot, too, and down on his luck as well, by the looks of it. That was good; the guy would appreciate the work more.

"Got a place to live?" asked Snow.

"Nope," said Jim. Snow got to thinking. He ran the maintenance operations for the entire public school district of Brownwood, a conservative town smack in the middle of the Lone Star State. The city has an economy based on nothing in particular and everything in general—a little oil and gas, some cotton and grains, explosives, clothing, pipes, sheep, cattle, and even a little dairying.

One fifth of Brownwood's twenty thousand residents attend public school. Snow and his band of two dozen maintenance misfits must keep up all eleven schools and their grounds, plus a minor fleet of vehicles, from a garage on the southwest edge of town. It's a chickenshit job compared to Snow's previous career, an exciting, thirty-one-year stint in the U.S. Army as a combat engineer building roads and soldiers to protect his country according to its leaders' orders. They were great times. He got into two wars—Korea and Vietnam, in the latter serving three combat tours as a first sergeant, the highest-ranking enlisted man, destined to carry more experience than the privileged officers but never to become one. And determined to make up for that through toughness.

For three decades Snow had worked with men, young and old, watching them, judging them, training them to fear him but not the enemy, teaching them to build things and destroy things, to work together and to kill together. When he retired from the military, he'd gotten a job back in his home state whipping a bunch of losers into a decent civilian platoon of workers.

Snow had been having some trouble with nighttime vandals around his maintenance garage. He had put up some floodlights. He'd topped the tall fence with barbed wire. And now he had a better idea. This guy Jenkins didn't have a place to live or a penny to his name—something about his wife running off with an older man up in Minnesota and the bank foreclosing on his farm. "Everything just closed in on me," Jenkins had said.

Snow made the guy an offer. He'd give him a job, $3.35 an hour to start, eight hours a day, five days a week. In addition, he could live in the maintenance garage for free. He should leave the lights on now and then, play the radio loud, and make himself seen outside the building at all hours. It was a good deal for Jim—no rent and lots of privacy except when the other workers invaded his sanctuary every morning. And it was a good deal for Snow—an end to vandalism losses with nothing for guards coming out of his budget.

Jim worked his ass off in the new job. Snow, a lean, slightly balding man of medium height with a round face and hard, tattooed forearms, knew the appreciation would show in the work. He liked losers. They made good men if you treated them right, trained them right. Some people he had to yell at just to get their attention. Some he had to yell at after he had their attention. Jim Jenkins was one of those Snow told what needed doing and then left pretty much alone. Jim would work along at his steady pace, slower than the younger men but a lot longer. At the end of eight or ten or even twelve hours, the younger guys would be tired and thinking of a little partying. Jim would be tired but still working steadily.

Jim worked better by himself, unless he had to measure things. Then Snow or Jim Perry, his grounds foreman, would send along some kid who was told to double-check Jim's measurements without Jim seeing him, which wasn't all that hard given Jim's eyesight. Usually they could find work for Jim to do alone. First, they tried him on cement. As often as not, Jim would lose control of the heavy, full wheelbarrow and spill the fresh wet goo. Or he'd have to stop every few steps, huffing and puffing, he was in such lousy shape. Within the hour, his legs would start to swell up, but he would plug away.

Then they put Jim on grounds work and mechanical repairs, fixing mowers and trucks. Whenever the other men took breaks, Jim would keep on working or go off by himself to eat and rest. When everyone else went home to shower and play and rest, Jim would stay at work.

For the first few months, while Rudy and Susan Blythe were 160 miles away shopping for their north Dallas home with the swimming pool, Jim Jenkins lived in a small wooden loft above the maintenance garage, up among the light bulbs and air filters and toilet paper cartons. It was hot up there by the roof at the top of the raw wooden steps. Jim slept in his clothes on the floor on a piece of foam rubber he would roll up by day. From there, he could see under the railing down into the machine shop with the broken motors and flat tires and cracked school desks. Outside the rippled steel doors, the lot was strewn with old wheels, sinks, pipes, and other construction refuse.

The garage is in a quiet semi-industrial neighborhood with a bank of small houses and scruffy lawns. Many nights Snow would drive by looking for troublemakers. Instead he'd find Jim under a truck, putting in a few extra hours of work, unpaid, just to have something worthwhile to do. He couldn't just do nothing. "I figured I'd gotten me a treasure in Jim," Snow recalled later.

One day Jim heard that James Lancaster, Brownwood's school superintendent, had an abandoned tractor at his little farm outside town. It was a John Deere machine, a very old model with tires chewed by cows and parts rusted by seven years of disuse. Jim told Mr. Lancaster he thought he could fix it up. The superintendent laughed and said, "Go to it," knowing full well the thing was beyond repair.

One Saturday months later, there was a knock on the front door of James Lancaster's house. It was Jim Jenkins, come to make a point. There, parked by the curb, was the old John Deere tractor, chugging away. Superintendent Lancaster exclaimed at length over the minor mechanical miracle. Jim just smiled.

Snow said he could use the tractor now and then out at his country place, which aroused Jim's interest. Snow had two hundred acres about twenty miles west of town. It was small by Texas standards, just a hobby for an ex-soldier with a penchant for the countryside and a pension from the military to invest. The land was twenty times larger than Jim's last place. It was large enough to graze and grow a fair crop of hay.

That year, right after Snow had cut and baled the hay, he had to undergo a hernia operation. Jim offered to bring the bales in. Snow said, "I can't pay ya."

Jim replied, "I didn't ask."

That weekend Jim showed up and spent two days moving and stacking more than fifteen hundred bales of hay. When Jim finished, Snow felt guilty and stuffed forty dollars in his shirt pocket. Jim gave it back. "I just wanted to get back in the fields," he said.

That was the beginning of a closer relationship between Snow and Jim Jenkins. They both liked being outdoors on the land. They both liked being around animals. Snow kept a few dozen head of cattle to graze on the tough grass that struggled under the Texas sun among the squat, wiry mesquite trees. Jim and Snow and maybe Norm Cox, who helped Snow out too sometimes, would talk while they were working outdoors in the warm Texas evenings or on weekends. Jim would get to grumbling about bankers, especially one prick back home, and Norm, who also grew up on a farm, would agree they were bad folks, leading you on to borrow when you might not want to and then leaning on you to pay when you might not be able to. Jim would go on about his home farm country too, how beautiful Minnesota was, how black and thick the soil was compared to Texas sand. Jim said he liked Texas, especially the mild winters, but he was saving his money to go back up north and farm again someday.

Jim seemed to have a way with animals, so it was logical for Snow to turn to the quiet Yankee for help. Snow had had Jim Perry shop around for a horse for one of his daughters. Everything was going fine until Snow saw the horse lying down in the pasture for the longest time. It was sick and wouldn't, or couldn't, get up. The vet was summoned. He gave the animal a few days to get back on her feet before she would become crippled. "If she doesn't get up soon," he said, "it'd be best to put her to sleep." For the better part of three days Jim Jenkins sat out in the pasture with that horse, talking to her, feeding her, encouraging her to get up. The deadline came. The horse was still down. Perry walked out into the pasture with a .22 pistol. He held it toward Jim.

"No, sir," said the farmer, "no, sir. I can't do it." And he walked away into the mesquite with his fingers in his ears.

One day about six months after Jim's arrival, a kid shows up and starts hanging around Jim all the time. The kid looks different; maybe they dress that way up in Minnesota. His head is shaved. He's always wearing camouflage shirts and pants, sometimes with a big knife strapped to his leg. The kid and Jim live together in a tiny trailer next to the garage. They eat together. They work together, even though the kid isn't on the school district payroll. Everybody figures the kid is Jim's son and he's on leave from the army.

They were half right. He was Jim's boy, Steve, although no introductions were made. But he wasn't in any real army. Steve, now seventeen, had been interested in the military since early childhood; family snapshots show him in a uniform by the fourth grade. Like many country kids, he was around guns at an early age. But his fascination with being a soldier never waned. In fact, it intensified. Whenever Steve had a couple of dollars, he would buy adventure magazines and *Soldier of Fortune*. Steve had set his sights on the marines—the tough guys that got all the respect. After the divorce Steve talked to a marine recruiter. The soldier told the kid to forget it; he wouldn't make it in the marines on account of his missing spleen. If joining the regular army ever occurred to the teenager, he didn't act on it. Instead, he enlisted in his own private army, a one-man battalion with all the gear and weapons he could find and buy. He'd get his training by himself. His father said some guy down in Brownwood knew a lot about military stuff. He'd been a sergeant in Vietnam.

What got Snow's attention was the kid's fascination with the military and soldiering. The kid talked more than his dad and had a chip on his shoulder. He often seemed ready to argue. At times, he was given to frantic outbreaks of activity, like the time Jim and Steve were assigned to help renovate an old building by removing some walls and windows. Steve went wild smashing the windows out and making a mess instead of prying them out one by one and carrying them to the dumpster. One day when Steve appeared at the office to pick up his father's paycheck and Perry wouldn't give it to him, Steve flew off the handle, calling the tall foreman, the man who had introduced his father to Snow, "the son of a bitch of the month." Or the time a female friend of Steve's was complaining about another woman and he offered to build a homemade bomb by hollowing out golf balls and filling them with explosives to drop in the woman's gas tank.

Of course, Snow knew nothing of this. He had seen far worse recruits in his day. They'd come off the bus, those little peckers, trying to look tough but really looking lost, dropping things, forgetting their right from their left, closing their eyes when they pulled the trigger, freezing up when the shells whistled overhead. There was nothing different about this little Jenkins kid except he was a darn good listener. Snow knew his stories were good. But still, it was flattering. And the kid was full of questions that Snow liked to think about. What's it like in battle? Do you actually see the enemy? How's it feel to kill somebody? Were you ever afraid? Sitting in Snow's office, in his pickup truck, or out working at Snow's ranch, Steve Jenkins was always fascinated by Snow's tales, especially about how the former first sergeant tamed his fear.

"Of course you're afraid," Snow would say. "You're shitting lemon juice out there." Then he would add the lesson: "The biggest fear in war is showing you are afraid, especially if you're a leader. But you can't show it. Never!"

Because Steve and Jim didn't get along all that well with other workers, the sergeant assigned them to a major renovation project at a former high school being converted to a citywide sixth grade. None of the workers wanted to fool with tearing out the old furnace and pipes, which were wrapped in dangerous asbestos. But that didn't deter the Jenkins men. They just tied scarves around their mouths and waded into the demolition work.

Snow loved them. He even put Steve on the payroll, part-time, since he was doing so much work. Then, when the builders came in to start fixing up one end of the school while Snow's men were tearing down the other, Jim got a second full-time job, as a night watchman for the builder. Presumably he slept sometime, but no one ever saw him. The way the builder programmed Jim's payroll, he was getting some overtime pretty near every day. But one week, after Jim's job classification had been reduced, the know-it-all machine spit out a paycheck at the old, higher rate. Immediately that morning, Jim appeared in the construction office to inform Norma Jean Parker, the secretary, of the error, and the overpayment was deducted from his next paycheck. Jim said he had to earn a lot of money so's he could go back to Minnesota and buy another farm. But he was going to earn it honest.

Jim had a reputation around the construction site for being mild-mannered and a very hard worker. Quiet but never late, never absent. He always did what he said he'd do. Sometimes he would stop by the office to chat with the secretaries, who found him nice. He'd tell the women he had cancer, took a couple of treatments for it down in Mexico City, he said. He'd also talk about farming and Minnesota and how his wife had run off with another fellow and this big banker had taken away his land even though he'd made the payments. The women would sympathize; those problems were not uncommon in their lives.

Some days Steve would be there trying to turn the conversation to guns. When Norma Jean mentioned once that she had a .38 pistol, Steve thought that was neat. He said he wondered what kind of hole that would make in a body or piece of plywood. The conversation came to an abrupt end. After a few months, Steve left his job; fellow workers said he was too destructive. But Steve continued to hang around anyway, helping his father. They were rarely apart.

One day Jim got in trouble. He had seen a teacher pull a misbehaving student from a classroom over at the junior high school and go to spank him in the hall. A stern Jim stepped in. He said that wasn't necessary, that he had never had to spank his boy. The woman, terrified, notified the principal, who notified Superintendent Lancaster, who summoned Jim immediately. Steve went along.

"What are you doing here?" asked Mr. Lancaster.

"I come to see the fireworks," replied Steve.

"Well, there aren't going to be any fireworks," said the school district chief. "Your father is about to get fired."

As they talked, Jim was not defiant. Mr. Lancaster got to thinking about Jim's good work record and the hard times he knew the man had had and, of course, his incredible persistence with the tractor. So he didn't fire Jim; he just gave him a very stern warning. Jim thanked him.

The Jenkins men ate most of their meals at the Kountry Kitchen. From the three-story brick school under renovation, it was a two-minute walk to the brightly lit little restaurant with the cheerful waitresses, Jackie Foster and Mary Graves. The women took turns opening the place at 6:00 A.M. Minutes later, Jim would shuffle in with that distinctive, rolling, overweight gait of his. He was quiet. He'd always go to the same booth in the back. He'd sometimes have a hamburger, but he seemed to live on scrambled eggs and toast and a glass of milk. He said his stomach was always bothering him, and his teeth, too. Some days he ate all three meals there, all three of them scrambled eggs and toast and a glass of milk. Usually his kid was with him. But if he wasn't and if things were slow, Jackie would sit down at the table with Jim and they'd talk. Jim struck Jackie as a lonely man and she wanted to comfort him. He told her about his love for Minnesota. He said he was going back someday.

During his limited free time Jim was often with Ted Beard, a former farmer who had become the manager of an appliance repair shop. Ted liked Jim Jenkins right off. One day Jim got to talking with Ted's sister-in-law Joyce while waiting for a bus. They got to dating and Joyce brought him over to Ted's house for a family picnic one weekend. Ted liked Jim's soft-spoken plainness so much that he recommended him to Jim Perry, his longtime hunting buddy who was looking for a good worker over at the school maintenance garage. That's how Jim got his job in Brownwood.

He and Joyce eventually stopped seeing each other though. She had a son, Benton, who was Steve's age. The boys hung around together. While

Steve didn't try to smartmouth adults—he was always especially respectful to the ladies—he gave adults an eerie feeling. A kid that age still playing soldier. Benton had started talking more about guns and shooting after he met Steve. Joyce blamed Steve for that, and didn't like him much. Jim got angry with Joyce; Steve was his only son. "Jim thought the world and all of Steve," Beard remembers. "He'd do anything for him. Sometimes it was hard to tell who was the father, Jim was so eager to please the kid."

Jim seemed to fit in with the Beard family. Ted's wife Dorothy made him elk steak once, and Jim exclaimed over that. He'd never had it before, said he'd never liked hunting much and his eyes were bad too. At that dinner Dorothy said something about wanting to get extra stereo speakers for the big radio in the living room and put them all over the house. She thought that would be dandy so you wouldn't have to turn on radios in every room. The next day when Ted got home from work, his wife was all excited. Jim Jenkins had shown up that morning with his boy and they had climbed all over the house stringing stereo speaker wire to nearly every room. Jim had left, said he couldn't hang around for dinner, but now all Ted needed to do was buy the speakers and plug them in.

Ted was impressed. Jim didn't talk much, but he sure let his actions speak for him. Like the time he asked Ted to help him find a used pickup to buy. It had to be white. Then the bank said Jim would need a cosigner on the loan, and Jim asked Ted. Ted said sure. He didn't even ask how much the note was for. If Ted trusted you, Ted trusted you. Sure enough, within a few months Jim Jenkins had the loan paid off. The Jim Jenkins Ted Beard knew always did what he said he'd do.

The Steve Jenkins that Charlie Snow knew always wanted to know more about the military. At one point he prodded Snow about target practice. First, said Snow, beginning the first sergeant's litany so familiar to every former military recruit, you learned how to set your rifle's sights. One notch up, fire a couple, another notch, fire a couple. Check your ammunition. Check the firing range. Now sight on the target. Don't grab the trigger. Spread your legs. See, that gives you stability. Now put your elbow down. Wrap your arm through the strap like this. Holds the piece tight, see? You don't wave a rifle around loose. Now, put the target on top of the sight bar. Fire once. Okay. Were you listening? I said put the target on top of the sight bar, not behind it. Do it again. Not bad. Now stand up and fire. Plant your legs like this. Put the butt up against your shoulder. Wrap your arm in the strap again. Good. Now look down the barrel and squeeze off a round. Did I say jerk? I said squeeze it off. Take a little breath, hold it, now aim, and squeeze the trigger gently. Don't close your eyes. How you gonna sight again if your eyes are closed? Try it again. Little breath. Hold it. Aim. Squeeze. There! See? Bull's-eye! Now do it some more. What? Well, I never shot for the fucker's head. It's too small a target. Aim for the body. At least you'll wound 'em. Then if someone comes to help, you can get him, too.

Snow noticed that Steve had some tattoos. On his right arm Steve chose drawings of a pair of crossed battle-axes, Sylvester the Cat, his first name, and the Special Forces insignia. On the left arm was his Social Security number, which the military now uses for soldiers' ID tags. One payday Steve proudly walked into Snow's office with a rifle. He had bought it with his earnings. Snow recognized the M-1 carbine right off. He took a look at the kid's new toy; it was a reproduction, but lethal enough to put a neat, fatal hole in a target.

Snow invited Steve to his ranch to try out the piece. The seventeen-year-old leftie was a very good shot. He'd rigged a military-type shoulder strap on the carbine just like the real thing and he'd wrap his arm in it like a real soldier to aim tightly. Steve could skip a tin can across a field, *bam, bam, bam*, just like that. And he reveled in Snow's compliments. The rifle had developed a stubborn ejection problem. It would jam now and then, despite several repair attempts. But Steve had worked out his own rapid routine to unjam the shell and start shooting again. Snow told him to come out to the isolated ranch anytime and shoot all the skunks, armadillos, and rabbits he could find. They dug holes that cows could step in, and they ate vegetables.

Lots of times Snow would drive down the dirt road to his place and get out to open the gate, and he'd hear gunfire back in the trees. He'd drive in, and off in the distance, Snow would see Steve in his camouflage clothing, sometimes wearing a full backpack and a steel helmet, running through the grass holding his rifle, throwing himself on the ground, assuming the proper prone position, squeezing off a couple of rounds, rolling over, squeezing off a couple more shots, and then jumping up to run zigzag across the field and fire, standing behind a tree. The kid was in great shape, an eager learner, a super shot.

Late in the spring of 1983 Steve Jenkins disappeared as quietly as he had come. His father said he'd gone back to Minnesota.

Jim kept on working both jobs, night and day. In midsummer he walked into Snow's office and said he was overtired. He was going to quit his maintenance job and just work as a watchman for the construction company. Snow told him to think about it carefully. That guard job was temporary; as soon as the work was done there, Jim would be laid off. Jim said he already had thought about it. He wanted to quit. Snow shrugged his shoulders, and Jim left.

A few days later Jim came back. The work had finished at the construction site, he said, and he'd been laid off his watchman's job. Could he have his old maintenance job back?

"I told you what would happen," said Snow. "Would you hire yourself back after that?"

Jim thought for a moment. "I don't believe so," he said.

For a second, Snow thought of hiring Jim back on the spot, just for the honest answer. But before he could open his mouth, Jim cut in.

"It don't matter anyhow," said Jim. "I'm going back to Minnesota to farm again." He pulled from his back jeans pocket a big zippered wallet connected to his belt by a chain. The wallet was bulging at the seams. Jim said some men dream of having a few hundred dollars in their pocket. Now for once, he said, he had several thousand dollars in his pocket. He was gonna go get him another dairy farm.

Soon after, Jim appeared as usual at the Kountry Kitchen to eat. He told Jackie and Mary that he was leaving Brownwood to go back to farming in Minnesota. They were very pleased for him. He said he was sorry that he had never left them a tip after all those meals; he'd been saving every penny for the farm. Now, Jim said, he wanted to make it up to them. They should pick a time and place, and he would take them both out to dinner. They chose Saturday night and the China Inn, which featured an entire seafood dinner for $8.60. Saturday night right on time, as the women closed the Kountry Kitchen and removed their aprons in an excited hurry, Jim drove up in his pickup truck. The white truck was washed clean. Jim was wearing a new Hawaiian shirt.

The next morning bright and early Jim set out on Route 377 to Dallas and on to Interstate 35 for the long trip home.

At about that same time Rudy Blythe was on the phone from Ruthton to his wife in their Dallas home. There were some serious problems at the bank. He wouldn't be able to sell it for a while. He hoped Susan understood. Could she come home?

Rudy had been spending more and more time back in Minnesota. As a result, Susan had been leading the life of a single parent in Texas. She'd even had to get a job there, helping to manage a savings and loan branch. Rudy said they needed her eighteen-hundred-dollar-a-month salary to help cover the Texas mortgage and living expenses. Rudy was pouring everything else back into payments on their bank just to cover the interest.

Susan had noticed that Rudy was talking louder and quicker lately. When he did snatch a few days to visit her and Rolph in Dallas, he tossed and turned in bed all night. So Susan didn't argue about returning to Ruthton. Maybe it wouldn't be so bad this time, she thought.

CHAPTER FIVE

The Heavens' Artillery

Rudy was worried. He was in deep trouble, and he knew it. His bank might be failing; certainly its capital base was eroding. And there was no one around to help.

Rudy had long known there were problem loans at the Buffalo Ridge State Bank. Every bank has them. When he worked in Dallas and visited Ruthton monthly or chatted on the phone with Jerry Ihnen, Rudy was detached from the problems. During that year he knew about some of them, but they didn't seem so pervasive from a distance. Jerry was hired to run the bank. And he did—except, of course, for those increasingly frequent times when a nervous Rudy overruled him from afar. In the fall of 1982, Jerry made an announcement: he was leaving to start his own insurance agency.

That bombshell was delivered with two weeks' notice. Rudy was angry. More important, he was frightened. Not only was he losing the man who ran the bank, making it impossible for him to stay in Texas, but this man was taking with him intimate knowledge about Rudy's insurance agency, whose steady flow of commissions provided the financial foundation to pay the bank loans.

As a result, Rudy quit his Texas job in October 1982. The Dallas bank said it would hold his position open for six months while Rudy tried to sell the Ruthton operation. Susan would stay in Dallas with Rolph and her volunteer work and her full-time job at the savings and loan. She expected the Minnesota bank to sell any day.

Now, instead of commuting from Texas to Minnesota each month, Rudy was commuting from Minnesota to Texas each month, trying to balance a financially troubled bank and a financially troubled personal life with an expensive house and a family in Texas. Then the Texas bank wanted its bridge loan paid back. It was one thing to give an employee a loan to buy a local house. It was quite another to leave that interest-free money outstanding to a former employee. Once again, Rudy had to turn to his father for financial help.

Going back to work for a while didn't bother Susan. That was part of the bargain in a modern marriage, and it was good to be needed. As soon as Jerry had given notice, Susan had begun looking for a replacement. It was hard to do from Texas, but Rudy was busy running the bank by himself. Susan placed ads in midwestern newspapers and wrote letters to corporate recruiters. She interviewed candidates by phone, and then checked with their last employer. The only serious possibility was a fellow named Deems Adair Thulin, not Too-Lynn but Too-Lean—call me Toby.

He was a Minnesota boy, thirty-seven years old, a Vietnam veteran the application said. He lived with his wife, Lynnette, and their three little girls. He'd worked for over ten years as a bank insurance salesman and loan officer in a couple of little Minnesota cities. Now he was in northwest Iowa, unemployed. It seemed strange for a guy like that, so Susan called his last employer, the Sibley State Bank. The man at Sibley said Toby had worked for them only about a year. There had been a mutual parting of the ways. It was mainly a personality conflict.

Big deal, thought Susan, who'd had ample experience with small-town personality conflicts. So she recommended that Rudy interview Thulin.

Rudy liked Toby right off. They were both tall, over six feet. Toby was also from outside Ruthton. A fellow veteran. He had only one year of college, so he was no intellectual threat to Rudy, who was no intellectual. Like Rudy, Toby liked the outdoors, hunting, small towns, and his children. Rudy hired Toby immediately, and Toby began work in November 1982.

The new man's first assignment was to help Rudy wade through all the bank's loans. A substantial number of borrowers were behind in their payments, men who had guessed wrong on economic conditions and interest rates. Rudy had guessed wrong himself; the institution that loaned him the money to buy the bank had flagged Rudy's loan as a problem and was watching him more closely. Now Rudy had to do the same down the line.

If Rudy's borrowers weren't behind in payments now, they could be soon. Maybe he'd better move to get his money out of these guys before they went under and took his investment with them. Rudy was going to have to get tough. He and Toby would methodically go through the loan files. They would visit these guys on the farms now and then, and ostentatiously inventory the collateral. There were going to be no more Jenkins tricks, selling the stuff themselves and then raising their hands helplessly as they walked into the protection of bankruptcy and left the bank holding an empty mortgage bag. Rudy was still stuck with that Jenkins place. All around him farmers were going under or walking away. For every few farmers gone, another business in some town would collapse too. The more farm machinery and farmland and houses went on the market, the less each was worth.

Rudy and Toby sat down and figured out what that tractor and this land and that corn dryer were really worth if sold today. They discovered, as all the local bankers were discovering, that the declining value of the collateral often was no longer equal to the loan. Something had to give, and this time it wasn't going to be Rudy's dream.

When Dick Ness stopped by the bank to chat with Rudy one day, he thought he'd ask for a little loan. He wanted to trade in some old farm machinery for new stuff, take advantage of the discounts the manufacturers were offering to spur stagnant sales. Ness knew he'd have to pay a higher interest rate, but the rates would probably be going down soon. No, said Rudy, he didn't think they would. The problems were here to stay. He thought a lot of people would fall by the wayside. That disturbed Ness. Jolly Rudy down in the dumps and talking gloom. Maybe this financial situation was more serious than he thought.

Rudy was harsher with other applicants. There were new stories of broken pencils and yelling about stupid ideas. Sometimes it seemed as if Rudy didn't even take time to think about a proposal. Just an abrupt No!

Sometimes, to convince a recalcitrant borrower, Rudy and Toby would resort to what they called the white-hat-black-hat method. One banker would go into a meeting acting like Attila the Hun, talking courts, fore-closures, attorneys. The other would try to calm his partner down, noting the client's presumed intention to repay. But the black-hat banker would remain unconvinced. This guy was four months behind in payments—what was it now, four months behind?—and he was always promising to pay something next month, and then he didn't. Well, they'd been understanding long enough. This wasn't a charity operation. The bank had obligations too.

Then the black-hat man excused himself from the room for a moment. The white hat would apologize for his friend but say he hoped the borrower realized how serious everything had become, and maybe, if this client could come through with a hefty payment right quick, then he could calm his partner down and everything would be okay.

Faced with being closed out in ten minutes or getting to keep his existing note as long as he brought the payments back up to date, the borrower's decision seemed a simple one. He could probably scrounge up some money somewhere and make a big payment, maybe tomorrow, if that would be soon enough. Or maybe the borrower would say that he didn't have to put up with this kind of behavior, that he'd been a regular customer for years, and he might just take his business to another bank. You know, get a loan from a Pipestone bank, and pay off Buffalo Ridge.

The white-hat guy would say, gee, they sure would hate to lose his business, but it was a free country. Either way, something would have to be done about these payments. Nothing personal, you understand. Just business.

Toby was moving through the bank's loan lists alphabetically, examining each, updating values, checking for troubled ratios of debt to equity. He didn't know the personalities involved and didn't like the arm-twisting part of banking. Have you gotten to so-and-so yet? Rudy would demand. No, Toby would say, I'm just up to *H*. Rudy wanted things in order, and quickly, if not to sell the bank, then for his own peace of mind. So he'd have Toby jump ahead in the list to suspected trouble spots.

Toby, a former air force sergeant who used to talk often of his dislike for high-and-mighty officers, would tell his friends that he hated playing the role of enforcer. It reminded him of his days as a prisoner of war in Vietnam undergoing intensive interrogations by Vietcong commanders. Whenever Toby knew he was going out to visit a muddy farm, he'd wear his combat boots. He joked about that but told Lynnette several times he was worried about the mood in the countryside. It was turning ugly. He'd never seen this kind of militance among farmers. But Toby had an array of lingering debts himself. He didn't have much choice about enforcing collections for the Buffalo Ridge State Bank; he needed a salary. He hadn't had any work to speak of for more than a year, a time when his impoverished family sometimes discovered small envelopes of money in their coat pockets after leaving the church cloakroom.

It had been a very trying period for Toby and Lynnette. Lynnette had seen the lack of work and the financial hardship corrode her husband's confidence and their relationship. He was spending more time away from home; he always seemed to have something to do with the volunteer fire department in Sibley or his nearby National Guard unit. He'd mumbled about not even being able to support his family anymore. And he started in again on all that Vietnam stuff, the nightmares about women and children coming at him with knives.

As a young woman, a bank teller from a religious family who lived in a series of little midwestern towns, Lynnette had set her sights on a tall, handsome young man with curly brown hair whom she'd met at summer camp. During the Vietnam War she wrote to Toby every day. He replied, religiously by his standards, every other month. He told her that the fighting in the Special Forces had been so fierce and so isolated that he only got her letters in large bunches upon returning from the long patrols. When she finally wrote and said to forget ever seeing her again because he couldn't even be bothered writing, he telephoned her from the faraway hospital where he said he was recuperating. He proposed to her. Lynnette had said yes, of course she would marry him.

Toby had also spent most of his life in a midwestern small town. He was a child of the post-World War II baby boom, one of seven children born to Larry and Camilla Thulin of Ada, Minnesota. His father was a hardworking contractor who called his son Toby because it was his own navy nickname. Toby's mother, who was a music teacher, chose the name Deems for her son because of her admiration for Deems Taylor, the American writer, painter, and operatic composer. The name Toby stuck, however, and he emerged as his father's favorite child for the love of the outdoors and hunting that they shared.

According to his mother, Toby's childhood was not the most peaceful. There were the deaths of two siblings, one only two years old and a favorite of Toby's. And she said her marriage was disintegrating bitterly, although in those days the only socially acceptable thing to do was persevere until the children were grown, divorces being for Californians and other rich folk. So in the Thulin household there was lots of yelling, and the children had to choose sides.

Toby's mother, who was still teaching as she approached her seventies, believes in studying music as one of life's essential disciplines. So Toby studied music, practicing one full hour every day. He played piano for a few years and then violin with a musical sensitivity that belied his youth. He worked his way up in the high school concert orchestra until he was to become concertmaster. But that year the high school had a German exchange student who happened to play the violin. Out of politeness, he was given the lead chair. Out of disappointment, Toby Thulin gave up music.

He still tried in track and swimming. He would practice and practice, running extra sprints, swimming extra laps. Then when the big race came,

Toby would finish third or fourth. Never the star, no matter how hard he tried.

Toby went to Nazarene College for one year, before dropping out and joining the air force. Finally, it seemed, he found success in the service. His mother remembers his stories about the dangerous foot patrols in the jungles of Southeast Asia and then spending weeks teaching English to village children. His father remembers Toby's tales about being a gunner in the door of one of those C-130s, the fixed-wing planes they called Puff the Magic Dragon because their Gatling guns fired so fast, they seemed to be spitting white-hot lead. What Toby's father would have given for one of those guns when the kamikaze planes came after his fuel ship in 1945! Thank God, Toby had come through all that fighting unscathed.

When Toby came home, he and Lynnette got married right away. After his discharge from the air force in 1969, his father gave him a job with his firm. Toby liked the rough company of workingmen. He spent a lot of time with the National Guard, volunteer fire departments, deputy sheriffs' patrols, scuba diving club, fishing and hunting buddies.

Toby loved hunting—birds, deer, whatever was in season. Nothing can quite prepare anyone for the loud pop of death by gun. One moment there is a living creature, ears perked, eyes alert, heart pumping. Then, in a flash, the hunted thuds down, limp and flaccid on the cold, wet ground, eyes staring blankly, blood seeping slowly in waning spurts. One second, life, hope, and promise. The next second, death.

Toby was a very good shot. You had to be in Vietnam, he'd say; you didn't get a second chance. He went out hunting with the guys so much that he even missed his daughter's appearance in the Miss Osceola County pageant, for "required" National Guard days that Lynnette later learned were really optional.

The Thulins' stay in Sibley, Iowa, started out well. It is a typical northwest Iowa town of three thousand dominated by a water tower, a tornado siren, and friendly pedestrians who greet strangers with a "Howdy." Most residents have lived there for so long that they hardly glance up at the spectacular prairie sunsets.

The modern brick and glass structure of the Sibley State Bank was one of the newest structures in town. The bank originally hired Toby to sell insurance. He spent weeks organizing a massive system of files. Then Toby began disappearing on daylong sales trips that didn't seem to produce much business. He also sought some days off for counseling at a veterans hospital in a nearby city. He said he'd been exposed to Agent Orange and needed help, and his boss said, certainly, do whatever you need to get straightened around, although another bank officer swore he saw Toby going into a local store when he was supposed to be at the counselor's.

After barely two months, Lynnette was seen as something of a complainer. Toby, too, was less polished than anyone had anticipated. Some coworkers thought perhaps he was being pushed to be something that he wasn't, namely a bank executive. At one employee coffee break Toby began describing his favorite position for sexual intercourse. Then there was the question of the checking account. Toby didn't open a free employee's account at Sibley State. He went two blocks away to pay a fee at First National.

Toby did knock off all the drinking. But he couldn't stop smoking, which bothered Lynnette since her father was slowly shriveling with lung cancer. There were disagreements over money. There always seemed to be enough for scuba diving or a hunting trip, but Toby complained of tight finances for other things. Lynnette's idea of essentials ran more to nice, brand-name clothing for the girls. One time Lynnette borrowed several hundred dollars from her father to pay some bills and gave the checks to Toby to mail. Two weeks later the Thulins got complaints from the merchants. Where was the money? Lynnette checked Toby's coat and there were the envelopes, unmailed. And the money was gone from the checking account.

Toby talked for a while about rejoining the military, getting back with the guys and the regular paychecks, the structured life and travel. But Lynnette, who had moved around the region with her father the truck driver, said the last thing she would ever do, other than give up going to church several times a week, was pack up the girls and move all over the country again every few months.

Then, of course, there was Vietnam. Lynnette was sick of hearing how horrible it had been over there. Okay, fine, it was horrible. It was more than a decade ago though—and Toby had volunteered. How long was he going to cling to those nightmares? This was the Midwest in the 1980s, and things weren't going too well right here. Either forget this Vietnam business or get some help.

Toby did stop talking about it. He also stopped talking about practically everything else. The four females in his family began to see the man in their lives as a walking time bomb ready to explode verbally at unpredictable times.

These troubles didn't show when Toby first arrived in Ruthton that November. The Thulins began living in Rudy Blythe's big bank house, the one with the yard cluttered by repossessed farm machinery awaiting resale. With Susan and Rolph in Texas, Rudy needed only a bedroom at one end, and the Thulins had the rest of the place. It was a chance for them to start over financially. Rudy and Toby got along well. Rudy had his own tie-and-coat social circle and Saturday dinner out. Toby was a frayed-jeans-and-sweatshirt guy, puttering around the garage or wandering down to the ballpark to join a game. He went back to Iowa one or two weekends every month for National Guard duty.

To his small group of local friends, Rudy seemed very happy to be back in the country. He found himself drawn to Lee Bush, the bank's rural attorney. He'd often eat at their old place with the canoe and the pond outside Tyler where Lee, Lee's father, and Lee's grandfather had grown up. Before dinner, Rudy would paddle around the pond, dipping the oar and his hand in the old, cool water. He decided then to take Rolph on a two-week canoe trip in Minnesota's northern wilderness that summer.

Rudy also decided that, unfortunately, he had to sink some money into that Jenkins place. It hadn't sold, although Toby and Lynnette had considered buying it. But after seeing the holes Jim Jenkins bashed in the wall and floor while tearing out the plumbing, Lynnette said maybe someplace in town would be better after all. She also remembered Rudy telling her that one afternoon long after the repossession he saw Jenkins walking his old property, carrying a shotgun.

On one of his occasional checks at the Jenkins place, Rudy had found the roof leaking. So he hired Lyle Landgren and Dick Austin to fix it up in their spare time. They both commented on what a creepy place it had become, empty and without life for so long. Not long after that, there was a story in the papers about the protest by a couple of hundred farmers at the sheriff's sale of a foreclosed farm up around Ivanhoe. By law the sale had to be by public auction. The farmers gathered outside the county courthouse to jeer and shout and wave signs to disrupt the sale. They failed, of course. Abe Thompson, Lincoln County's sheriff, would not be kept from his duty. But down in Illinois that spring a bunch of farmers got together with some auto worker union members and broke up a forced farm sale by drowning out the auctioneer and forcing him hard up against a combine.

Once Susan had agreed to move back to Ruthton, she quit her job in Texas. The Blythes spent much of the summer of 1983 listing the house in Dallas, packing, and hauling possessions back north. Rudy continued to tighten operations at the bank. Susan helped wherever possible. Rolph and Rudy took their wilderness canoe trip together. It was great fun, according to Rolph.

With Susan returning to Ruthton, the Thulins had to leave the Blythe house. They did, but not together. Toby had Lee Bush serve Lynnette with separation papers in June. On August 8, she and the girls left for Fargo, North Dakota. Lynnette was going back to finish college, bitter but determined. Toby moved into another bank-owned Ruthton house, another repossession, in fact, from a young couple who also had separated.

Slowly word got around town. There was a new woman in Toby's life, Karen Rider, a divorcée with two children, Missy, twelve, and Casey, eleven. She had appeared in town after the Thulins' separation, moving to the Ruthton area from some little town in Iowa, Sibley or something like that. She rented a house in Lynd and got a job working with handicapped youngsters in Tyler, both just up the road from Ruthton. Karen, a redhead who wore large eyeglasses, was forty-two when they moved to Minnesota. She had met Toby several years before during a visit with a female friend to a National Guard camp. It turned out that Toby and Karen lived only a block and a half apart in Sibley. They would talk often there; that's all there ever was between them until the separation, Karen maintains. Each was lonely. Each sensed the other caring. Karen liked outdoor activities— camping, hunting, fishing. They talked wistfully of someday building a log cabin together in the northern woods. Karen also was eager to listen to Toby's stories of Vietnam. He liked her children, who needed a man in their lives. Even before Toby's separation he was attending Casey's football games. Karen had been married sixteen years to a handicapped professor, but Toby was the first man in her life to send her roses. He attached an anonymous card that said simply, "You're Neat!"

In late August several hundred local residents gathered not far from Ruthton for a public picnic. Mike Cable, the Lincoln County prosecutor, stopped by and noticed that Jim Jenkins was back in town. He'd been off in Texas or somewhere for a long time, Mike knew. Jenkins had his son Steve with him. Weird kid, shaved head, camouflage clothes, and a machete strapped to his leg. Word was, those losers were trying farming again, down near Hardwick. Better not let Rudy Blythe hear about it.

In early September Rudy had gone to the doctor complaining of occasional memory loss and dizziness. Maybe it was the long hours he'd been putting in. Maybe it was his weight, which had crept up to around 260 pounds. The forty-two-year-old banker was determined to go on a diet again. The doctor could find nothing wrong, but he suggested a specialist if Rudy was still concerned. He was. Some nights he had trouble sleeping; the phone would ring at all hours. It was some man—he didn't sound drunk—telling Rudy to make his dog shut up else he'd shoot it. Rudy would reply, accurately, that his dog was right by the bed quietly asleep.

On September 21 Susan set out by car from Ruthton for Texas with her friend Sharon Fadness. The Dallas house had not yet been sold. Susan would check on it, perhaps lower the price, and load a trailer with furniture and winter clothing. She'd be home in a week, in time to celebrate her birthday.

That same day, a Wednesday, Peggy Dobbyns, the secretary in the school maintenance garage in Brownwood, Texas, got a long-distance call from Jim Jenkins. He was calling from Minnesota about some pension money due him. Jim said he had found a farm. He'd bought some used machinery. Now he and Steve were waiting on credit checks from a local bank. They needed to borrow more money to buy cattle. Jim sounded very happy.

Toby didn't travel that weekend. A couple of times he had driven to Fargo to visit Lynnette and his girls. Karen said she understood. Things hadn't gone too badly on those visits, but that weekend late in September Toby stayed at Karen's house. She had thought she'd seen a pickup truck hanging around their place. Lynnette didn't have a white pickup truck, did she? Toby let Karen shoot the big shotgun out back a couple of times. Hunting season was coming. Toby started teaching Casey about the little shotgun he'd bought for him, emphasizing safety to the boy and his mom. "You're not beneficiary on my life insurance yet," he joked to Karen.

On Tuesday, September 27, Susan Blythe was due back in Ruthton. But she was running late. She'd be back Wednesday evening instead. In Ruthton at the welding shop that morning, Swen Borresen got a call from some guy over in Long Prairie. Jim Jenkins wanted to buy some cattle. He had given Swen's name as a credit reference. Swen said, accurately, that Jim had always been prompt in paying his bills there. But the fellow really ought to check with the local bank, the Buffalo Ridge State Bank.

Shortly after, the phone rang up the street at the bank. Toby Thulin took the call. Some guy in Long Prairie wanted to check the credit of a man named James L. Jenkins. Toby got the file.

Well, said Toby, the guy had declared bankruptcy back in 1980. Left a big debt at the bank. In fact, the bank still hadn't sold off the Jenkins house.

Thanks very much, said the caller.

A little while later the phone rang again. Rudy answered. It was a cattle dealer over in Long Prairie. A man named James Jenkins wanted to get some cattle from him and when he'd called a little while ago, a Mr. Thulin had said Buffalo Ridge had had bankruptcy problems with Jenkins. But now, the caller said, his would-be customer claimed never to have done any business with the Buffalo Ridge State Bank. There must be a different Jenkins, right?

Well, said Rudy, what's the social security number of your Jenkins?

The man read it off the loan application.

That's the same son of a bitch, said Rudy. And I wouldn't loan him the time of day.

The caller thanked him and hung up.

That night at dinner at Karen's house Toby was shaking his head at the nerve of some people. A guy named Jenkins, he said, had stuck the bank with a bad debt three or four years before. Then he declared bankruptcy. Now he was going all over this corner of the state looking for a loan and listing Buffalo Ridge as a credit reference. The bank had gotten a couple of calls checking on him. Some people, huh?

Wednesday after lunch Rudy took a call in his office. Somebody had seen the For Sale sign out at the Jenkins place. He sounded like a farmer. He wanted to see it right away. Well, sure, fine, but it'd have to be tomorrow. How about 10:00 A.M.? Rudy was in a hurry. One of his potential problem loans had been paid back, in full. Ninety thousand bucks! Wouldn't he have a lot to tell Susan that night? With the appointment made for the next morning, Rudy raced off to Pipestone to deposit the check. He picked up Rolph from school and zipped home to get the cake and things ready for Susan's surprise birthday party.

Susan phoned from dinner in Sioux Falls. Running late. But only seventy-five miles to go. It would be good to get home.

When Lyle Landgren cruised down the main street that evening, he spotted Toby unloading the bank's lawn mower from a pickup truck. Toby was annoyed. He had mowed Karen's lawn and was bringing the machine back when a state trooper stopped him. It seems the truck had been repossessed, but no one except the trooper had noticed that the registration sticker on the license plate had expired. Toby had got a ticket. Lyle laughed and took Toby with him on patrol for a few minutes. Toby and Karen wanted the policeman and his wife to come for dinner Saturday. They wanted company when they each quit smoking that day. Toby and Karen also had an announcement to make, and Lyle, who had heard some of Toby's horror stories about Lynnette, guessed what that meant.

He dropped Toby off back at the bank and cruised toward the Blythes'. Ah, Susan had returned. He waved. Elsewhere in Ruthton, Lyle found everything quiet. Darkness was coming earlier these days.

The sun was also rising a little later. So were the Blythes on September 29, 1983. They were tired and behind schedule. Rudy weighed himself: 251 pounds, down from the 264 of just two weeks before. Susan seemed in something of a rush; she hadn't even made real coffee. But, gee, it was good to have everyone back together again. Things would improve at the bank. Rudy was sure of it. Meanwhile, here was Rolph, his big Tigerboy, ready for school. Rudy and his son hugged each other hard.

Susan hadn't done the up-in-the-morning-get-Rolph-eighteen-miles-to-school-in-Pipestone-by-eight-thirty routine in a while. She was disorganized and slow, but she got to Pipestone all right and looked up as she passed by the First National Bank's digital time sign: 8:26. Uh-oh, she thought, it's going to be close. She'd promised to bring the car to Rudy by nine.

On her way back to Ruthton, Susan passed the Hartsons, Dick and Marlene, going the other way to open their business. Hartson lived across the road from the Jenkins place. As a neighbor, he'd kind of kept an eye on the property for the Blythes. In fact, just a month before, Dick had seen a couple of men in a white pickup on the Jenkins property. He'd phoned Rudy—the Hartsons had the nearest phone to that farm—but by the time the banker got out there, the strangers had left.

Susan arrived back in Ruthton a few minutes before nine. She was right on time to exchange vehicles. But Rudy's car was not in its usual spot by the bank. Nor was it by the house. He must have gone to the Jenkins place early. It would be just like him to go out there an hour early to make sure everything was ready for the appointment. Susan decided, on the spur of the moment, to drive out to the farmhouse.

It was cold with a misting rain as her car crunched its way slowly up the long, curving driveway to the Jenkins house. The cable, which was strung across the drive as a gate, was down. Rudy was there. Or somebody was. With the backyard hidden from the road, Susan didn't see her husband's car for a minute. Then there it was. The Ambassador station wagon that had made so many trips, back and forth to Texas. But whose vehicle was that? Rudy's car was pulled up, nose to nose, to a pickup truck. A white pickup truck.

Susan pulled in behind the station wagon in the farmyard and turned off the motor. Silence. Absolute silence. Usually that's what Susan liked about the place. But with the fog it seemed eerie somehow. Even the birds were quiet this morning. Must be the rain.

Susan didn't get out of the car. She surveyed the empty homestead through the drizzle. No one was there. Or no one was in sight.

Just then, she saw movement in the house. Someone—no, two people— had passed by the darkened, dirty stairs window inside, descending slowly from the second floor toward the front door.

Susan waited in the car. When the door opened, it was Rudy; even in the mist and rain she could spot him in that bright yellow rain slicker. And there was Toby. What was Toby doing here?

There wasn't much time to chat. Big Rudy was visibly annoyed. Someone was on his property when they shouldn't be. Rudy thought it might be that son of a bitch Jenkins. Rudy had referred to him so often like that around the bank that son of a bitch seemed like Jenkins's first name. It looked as if Jenkins was there. He liked white pickups. The truck had Texas license plates, or one of them anyway; the front plate was missing. And there was a Jenkins checkbook on the dashboard.

Damn, this pissed Rudy off. Can you imagine what the potential buyer would think when he got there in just, what, fifty-three minutes? A fruit-cake former owner hanging around the property nearly four years after he walked away from it? Hard enough to sell this lot when no one around had any money. Rudy wandered north alongside the garage, calling out into the woods.

"Hello. Anyone there?" There was no answer.

Susan was a little concerned as she stood with Toby by the car, so she kept an eye on her husband. Rudy had walked past the garage several feet and was nearing the edge of the woods. There is a slight incline there. So big Rudy looked shorter, standing in the tall, soggy weeds and looking around, calling out. There was no answer.

Rudy, his jaw set, came striding back toward the vehicles. He was opening his mouth to speak when Susan heard a funny metal noise back in the woods. "What was that?" she said. "Did you hear that, Rudy?"

Rudy didn't answer Susan's question. Maybe someone feeling less financial pressure, someone who hadn't wrestled and played football and been big all his life would have been frightened. But Rudy was a take-charge guy who could be very stubborn.

"Go get the sheriff," Rudy told Susan. Then he turned his head toward the woods and in a loud voice said, "GO GET THE SHERIFF AND TELL HIM WE'VE GOT TRESPASSERS ON THE OLD JENKINS PROPERTY."

"The Pipestone sheriff?" asked Susan.

"No," said Rudy, "we're in Lincoln County here. Go to the Tyler Town Hall and phone Abe Thompson from there."

Susan quickly jumped back into the bank's car. She made a U-turn toward the barn and headed down the drive. By then, Rudy was walking back toward the garage, and an unconcerned Toby was headed off down the path toward the other farm buildings.

In her mounting haste, Susan spun the car tires on the drive. Rudy's not answering her question had scared her. She turned to the north on County Road 7 and accelerated quickly, only to slow slightly at the Hartsons' drive. Try their phone? No, wait, not home. She'd seen them in Pipestone. Susan pressed the accelerator to the floor and pulled out to pass a slow-moving pickup. Damn farmer. Soon she would be doing seventy miles an hour. She looked back at the Jenkins house out the side window, trying to spot her husband. But the protective trees had already enveloped the scene.

The first shot blew melon-sized shatter marks in Rudy's windshield. Glass went flying inside the car and into Toby's hair. He ducked down in the passenger seat, terrified. The next missile from the woods came through the little triangular vent window, not the glass but the rubber stripping around it, creasing the chrome.

The bullet went straight to Toby's throat, right through the middle beneath his chin. It was a small neat hole about the size of a pencil eraser. In the back it was much larger. The .30-caliber slug shattered inside the veteran's neck and exploded out the back, tearing away the carotid artery and the entire spinal column. Toby's head jerked. His eyes flew wide open. The body convulsed violently once. Then it slowly began tilting to the right against the open door. *Bam!* A third bullet slammed into the door right where the head was. The metal stopped its flight. Toby fell backward until he hit the ground with a thud.

Rudy was hit by that first shot. The windshield sheared off the bullet's copper cover and slowed its velocity. It was the least lethal shot of the day. But for investigators it would be most helpful later. The nearly spent piece of lead flew into Rudy's lower back above the buttocks. He was crouching as he left the driver's seat. Then he was up and running, past the side door of the Jenkins house, along the little cement walk, across the yard toward the road and the Hartsons' place.

Rudy's shoes were slipping badly on the wet grass and bumpy terrain. As he cut across the overgrown lawn, a pair of booted feet moved swiftly away from the woods through the tall weeds of the empty farmyard. They went to the car, the passenger's side, and stood there for a moment. Then the boots moved quickly around the back of the station wagon, then faster past the side door of the house, and faster still along the little cement walk and into the middle of the big front yard.

Rudy was lumbering through the ditch, heading for its broad, steep banks. There were trees on three sides of the yard, but Rudy was running out in the wide open spaces with his big body wrapped in his bright yellow rain slicker.

The boots stood carefully spread apart. Rudy was bent over, still running but now desperately trying to hide amid the flimsy hip-high weeds. The man in the boots raised his arms and tilted his head ever so slightly. The target's broad waistline sat right atop the sight.

Take a breath. Let some out. Hold it. Squeeze. Squeeze. Perfect.

The two bullets tore across the yard almost simultaneously. Eighty-four feet later they struck just above the belt line on Rudy's right side barely a half inch apart. But because the forty-two-year-old father was running bent over, they tore up through the body, shattering and sending lead chunks slicing through arteries and vital organs.

Whoof! The air rushed from Rudy's lungs. The impact straightened him up. He whirled around. A third bullet ripped through his upper arm. A fourth zipped past his ear to harmlessly pierce the jacket's hood before sailing off over the empty Hartson house. By the time the 251-pound body slammed down on the wet, cold ground, his face looking up, his left arm pointing toward the Jenkins house, Rudy Blythe was gone.

It was a pretty normal day for Sheriff Abe Thompson. As he walked back to his desk with a brimming cup of fresh coffee, he instinctively readjusted the pistol on his hip. It always caught on the arm of his chair when he sat down.

The moment he set the hot cup down, both phones rang. The dispatcher got one. Abe took the other.

"This is Susan Blythe," said the caller. "We own the old Jenkins property near Ruthton. There's some trespassers there and—"

"What? Who is this?" asked the sheriff. He hadn't caught the name. The woman was talking too fast. And now, what the hell, the dispatcher was talking at him urgently from the door.

Standing in the Tyler Town Hall with a borrowed phone stretched over the counter and several local residents listening, Susan knew what the sheriff wanted to hear. If she had said, "Susan Blythe, the banker's wife," he'd have known right away. Because of her fear, now her anger was rising, too. These country people—a woman's always got to belong to somebody.... Then Susan heard the sheriff talking to someone else.

"What? The Jenkins place? In the ditch? Yes. Right. I've got her on the other line." Then, coating his voice with caution, back into the phone, "Mrs. Blythe, is that you? Where are you?"

"There are trespassers on the property and my husband said to call you from Tyler."

"Yes, I know," said the sheriff, reaching around to check that his holster was full. "I'm on my way."

"Should I wait for you here," asked Susan, "or at the property?"

"At the property," said the sheriff. Within seconds his cruiser was hissing down a quiet, wet Highway 75 at eighty miles an hour.

Susan was puzzled. And she wanted to stay that way. If she let her mind think too much about why someone else would be calling the sheriff's office about the Jenkins place, where her husband was, she would panic. She methodically put her mind to other things, driving slowly back down the country road. She was in no hurry this time.

Then she saw the truck, and began, unwillingly, to understand. It was parked by the Jenkins driveway in the middle of the road with its taillights flashing. A man was standing in the road, waving her over.

"Ma'am," he said through the open driver's window. "You can't go in there."

"Why not?" replied Susan, who kept inching the car along.

"You just can't, ma'am," he said. Then he flashed a badge. It was Paul Bartz. He said he was a part-time policeman. He reached in and turned Susan's steering wheel to the roadside. Susan got out to talk.

"You can't go in there, ma'am," he said, physically blocking the way. Oh, my God, thought Susan, it's a trick. These farmers have got Rudy, and I walked right into the trap too. She hadn't looked closely at the badge. "Okay," she said, stopping her resistance and turning around. "I'm okay." She started to walk back to the car. The man let go.

But Susan wouldn't face their rural reality without a trick of her own. She whirled around and flung her fist at the man's face. It bounced off his chest and she began flailing.

"Stop it!" the man yelled. "Your husband is dead in the ditch!"
Susan froze.

There, about twenty steps away, partially hidden in the matted grass, was the yellow jacket, still, very still. If you confront things that are wrong, Susan had always believed, anything can be fixed. But this, she knew instantly in her heart, this could not be fixed. Susan walked toward the yellow jacket. Someone had put a gray sweatshirt over Rudy's face. Susan knelt down beside her husband and lifted the covering. His mouth was open. He was a strange color. And his jaw was pulled back. When she'd left just a little while ago, Rudy had been full of life. Now he was an empty shell.

When the volunteer medical crews arrived, a sobbing Susan was holding Rudy's hand. "He was a very good man, you know?" she said.

"Yes ma'am," they said, standing around in a semicircle, their equipment bags ready.

"Can we have a look, please?"

"No!" shouted Susan. "Leave him alone. He's dead, can't you see that? They've killed him. That goddamned Jenkins." And she rubbed her husband's face.

Sheriff Thompson arrived then, siren wailing and lights flashing. Pipestone County's Deputy Sheriff Lyle Landgren came. And LeRoy Burch, Ruthton's mayor, who was a paramedic and Rudy's friend. But a sobbing Susan would let none of them near her husband. The big guy seemed so vulnerable now. He had protected her in that damned farmyard, probably saved Susan's life by sending her away. Now it was just Susan here in enemy territory. Just her and, oh, my God, Rolph! He's in school in Pipestone. He mustn't hear it from anyone but Susan.

Her fast, frightened thoughts were interrupted by the police and medics. "What happened?" they asked Susan.

"I don't know," she said through tears. "That son of a bitch Jenkins. Ask Toby. He was up there too." She motioned toward the house.

Susan didn't notice some officers break away from the gathering roadside crowd and creep up the driveway through the trees, their guns drawn. Nor did she see them walk down the driveway a few minutes later, their guns away, their heads down. Lyle broke off then and headed into town, to the bank. Paul Bartz stayed at the scene. His firsthand details would prove crucial. He had been driving south on the county road, had seen a small car flash by going north, and then, as he passed the old Jenkins place, thought he saw a bright color in the ditch, where bright colors do not belong in late September. As he turned his truck around on the narrow road, a white pickup roared down the Jenkins drive and raced by him to the south. An older man was driving, wearing a stocking cap.

"We just want to do our job," the paramedic was pleading with Susan.

"I know," said Susan, who was beginning to think it didn't matter anymore. Her world was ending in this godforsaken place. They began examining the body, squeezing the limp arm for a nonexistent blood pressure, prying an eye open to check the pupils, even trying chest massage. But with each push on Rudy's big chest, blood spurted up into the oxygen mask. Susan, wincing, moved her knee against Rudy's hip to quiet a gurgling sound there. She was going numb.

"He's not usually this overweight," she said to the bustling medics, who were not listening. "He's gone on a diet, you know."

When Lee Bush, the bank's attorney, drove up to the developing traffic jam by the ditch, the deputy was disturbed. "Lee," he said, "we've got one helluva mess here. We've got two dead bankers and a hysterical wife."

Lee knelt with his friend's wife in the ditch. "Susan," he said, putting his arms around her for several minutes. "Susan, we should go." He told her that the bodies—yes, Toby's dead too—would be there for hours while the police took pictures and sought clues to what happened.

"Well," said the new widow, standing up. "I've got things I must do."

The news of the two deaths spread quickly through the midwestern countryside and then into the general news stream: *In Minnesota, police said the president of a rural bank and his chief loan officer were shot to death today after they were lured to a farm the bank claimed in a foreclosure proceeding four years ago....*

Lynn Carpenter and three other women in the Buffalo Ridge State Bank were at the computer, posting quarterly interest payments to savings accounts, when Lyle Landgren walked in with a shotgun and said the bank was closing for the day. He took the four women into a back room and broke the news. There were gasps and sobs and stares. Lyle said no one could touch Rudy's or Toby's office until the boys from the state Bureau of Criminal Apprehension got there. He also wanted everyone to stay away from the windows. There were two men in a white pickup truck—they think it's Jim Jenkins and that boy of his, the one that always dresses like a soldier—seen leaving the farm after the shooting. They're still out there somewhere. There were reports they had grenades and maybe a grudge hit list.

By 10:05 that morning Special Agent Robert A. Berg of the state BCA was speeding toward the scene of a reported double homicide near Ruthton. Mike Cable was in court up in Ivanhoe, handling the last routine property-theft prosecution before the biggest case of his career blew Lincoln County's yearly law enforcement budget. Toby's buddies from the drill team up in Ada, Minnesota, or down in Sibley, Iowa, heard the news on the radio. They couldn't understand how a seasoned war veteran like Toby could walk into an obvious ambush.

Toby's wife, 225 miles away in Fargo, North Dakota, wouldn't get the news for several hours. Lynnette was in school, and Lyle and others had difficulty tracking down her new minister to break the news.

Karen Rider had been taking a shower at 9:10, mentally preparing for her afternoon class of retarded students. If Toby hadn't borrowed the bank's repossessed pickup the previous night, Karen would have driven him to work in Ruthton. But Toby wanted to tell Rudy about the truck's registration problem, maybe get that settled first thing. So he'd driven to the bank alone, and earlier than usual. Now Karen would take her daughter's forgotten gym shorts over to school and then zip down to Ruthton to surprise Toby for lunch.

When Karen walked up to the bank that morning, the door was locked and the sign said CLOSED TODAY. Funny, Toby hadn't said anything about that. Was this a state holiday or something? As she walked away, Karen heard a furious rapping on the glass. It was Lynn Carpenter motioning her to come in.

"I'll wait for Toby over there," Karen said, pointing to the café.

"No," said Lynn, "please come in here."

The lights were low in the bank. They were out altogether in Toby's and Rudy's offices. What was the deputy sheriff doing here? "Where's Toby?" Karen asked.

"Please come back here," Lyle said.

"What is it?" Karen demanded, louder. "Where's Toby? Where's Rudy?"

"I'm sorry, Karen," said Lyle. "There's been an accident. They're dead."

Rolph knew something was going on. The principal, Mr. Zorich, had taken him from class in the middle of the morning and kept him by himself in the school auditorium. Now he sent the eleven-year-old upstairs to get his coat and books. And there was his mother waiting downstairs by the front door. She looked as if she'd been crying.

"There's been a terrible accident," Susan said, kneeling down on the wet cement by her son. She had changed out of her bloodstained sweat suit. Her eyes were swollen. She felt herself swimming in a vast ocean with no land in sight. She was squeezing Rolph's hand very tightly. She wanted to make the awful news easier somehow, but it didn't come out right.

"Daddy's dead," she said.

There was a long pause. Then Rolph wrenched away violently. "No, no, no!" he screamed. "Not my dad! You're lying! Not my dad!" Rolph ran across the lawn in confused circles and ended where he wanted to be, in Susan's arms.

Susan could have used some hugs herself. She had come back to this hated place because she loved her husband and he had asked her to and twelve hours later he was gone, forever. Now she was alone, in charge of everything. What would she do for money and for Rolph and about running a bank?

From the ditch Susan had gone to the bank with Lee. She called Rudy's parents in Florida, but his father was at an investment club meeting. His mother was there, but she was alone except for the cleaning lady. Susan didn't want to tell her, but Dot was suspicious. She hadn't recognized Susan's voice at first. There was no choice for Susan now. "Rudy's been killed," she said, "and—" The line went dead.

By the time Susan got through to Rudy's brother, his mother had already called him. "I know," George said. Susan was feeling increasingly cut off from everybody. Sharon Fadness had arrived at the bank and that was a help. They had become much closer during the drives back and forth to Texas. Susan's anger would fade to a stolid determination in the months ahead, but for now she was still very angry and lost. And when a minister arrived and suggested that the destruction of Susan's life and the snatching away of her husband were God's will, Susan told him, quite bluntly, to leave.

Susan, Sharon, and Lee had then stopped by the Blythes' house. The police did not want Susan there, not while the killers were loose. They had to go for Rolph right away, but Susan needed fresh clothes. On the way out, she grabbed Rudy's birthday card to her and his pajamas, physical links to someone, somewhere.

Susan, Sharon, Rolph, and Lee went in Lee's car from the Pipestone school to Sharon's house in Ruthton. Rolph, in the back seat, was distraught. He kept yelling, "No, not my daddy!" and kicking the seat in front. Nothing would calm the boy, so a mile out of Pipestone they turned around to go for a sedative.

Then, suddenly, Rolph calmed down. "I'm all right," they heard him say, although he wasn't speaking to anyone in the car. He was talking to his father. "I said I wasn't going to cry anymore," Rolph recalled later. "He wouldn't like it."

For the rest of the day until they moved into a Pipestone motel, Rolph and Susan stayed, or rather hid, at Sharon's, first from the killers and then from the press, who flocked into town to interview anyone on the streets or in the café. Everybody said they were shocked about the shootings, couldn't understand how they could happen. In the city maybe, but not out here. Many of those interviewed mentioned the good things Rudy had done for the town. But a few, in a lower voice, allowed as how the bankers had been leaning on some folks pretty hard recently. "Who can know what these hard times do to some people?" said Duane DeBettignies, the editor. "Every man has his breaking point. But how are you going to blame a banker for bad times? He's got to run a business too."

A few people gathered at Sharon's house throughout the day, bringing food and solace and wondering about Susan's behavior. She walked about the house, talking in disjointed half sentences, believing herself remarkably coherent, and wondering when her parents' plane would ever arrive. But no one questioned Susan and no one interrupted her.

Rolph, clutching Rufus, struck everyone as quietly mature on That Day, as September 29 came to be known among family and friends. From a corner, the boy watched the morning's events change the adults, especially his mother. She was acting very strangely. Rolph was certain he was losing her, too. Sometimes, with his arm around Rufus, who sat loyally by his side, Rolph gazed at the TV set, at one point spotting minicam coverage of an ambulance crew wheeling his father's draped body from the ditch. That was before adults leaped to change the channel.

Karen's two children took Toby's death quietly and hard. Counting the painful divorce, he was the second man they had lost in their young lives. There were tears and then blank looks, until, sitting at a table in Lyle's house, they heard the deputy sheriff describe the Jenkins men to Karen. At the description of Steve—shaved head, tattoos, camouflage clothes— little Casey blanched. He had seen that man walking by their house several times in the last week. Lyle looked quickly at Karen, who soon arranged for the children to visit Iowa for a few days.

The manhunt began immediately, though it was severely hampered at first by the fog and rain. From the Jenkins farmhouse, Lyle Landgren had radioed to surrounding counties a description of the men, the truck, and the rear license plate, which Paul Bartz had noted as the white truck sped away—black letters and numbers on a white plate. Sounded like Texas. But the main radio tower wasn't working right that morning, so the garbled message didn't get very far at first. Only a few deputies were looking for a Texas pickup, something about speeding in Lincoln County.

Soon after the shooting a middle-aged man and a teenage boy dressed like a commando bought a hundred rounds of hollow-point, .30-caliber carbine ammunition from Harvey's Trading Post in Luverne, Minnesota, forty-three miles south of the ambush site. The men said they were going hunting. The same pair bought some .410 shotgun ammunition and a flashlight at a local hardware store. Both purchases were paid for with checks drawn on the account of a James L. Jenkins.

Soon after, Pipestone County Deputy Sheriff Ron McClure saw a 1978 white Chevrolet pickup coming at him on Highway 75. It probably wasn't the wanted one; this one was headed north, back toward Lincoln County. But as they approached, McClure noticed that the front license plate was missing. He stopped, spun around, and caught up with the truck. The rear plate was from Texas, KW3618. Officers would soon learn that plate number was registered to James L. Jenkins in Brownwood, Texas.

Deputy McClure followed the truck quietly without a siren or flashing lights. The truck wasn't speeding. The deputy saw two men—one of them, the driver, wore a tightly rolled stocking cap—look back at him occasionally. The truck seemed to be heading for Hardwick. McClure dropped back a little. Then the truck turned off on a dirt road and stopped. The deputy saw the passenger get out with a stick and look back at the road and then— Jesus, it was a rifle! Aimed at his car! McClure sped past the dirt road. He thought he heard shots.

He stopped. The passenger got back in the truck. It drove away. Just as the truck went over a little hill, McClure saw the brake lights go on. Ah- hah, he thought, they're going to wait there to ambush me. He radioed for help and waited, but by the time the cars and helicopter arrived, the truck had disappeared. McClure found a couple of .30-caliber carbine shells in the dirt.

For the state detectives who thronged Ruthton, unraveling murder and mayhem is old stuff. For Lincoln County's Sheriff Abe Thompson, however, much of this was new. "I've handled assaults and rapes and suicides and just about everything," he said in his Ivanhoe office, "but I tell you I'm learning a whole lot about murder real quick."

The sheriff knew Jenkins, of course. He'd served him a couple of times for bouncing checks or not making proper payment. Jenkins was a loner, but "a likable sort," Thompson said. "Nothing unusual. No trouble."

Abe knew he was up against a formidable fugitive. "He knows this country real well," said the sheriff in his meetings with the press, "all the little back roads and groves." Abe said he believed the killer or killers were still in the area. The FBI kept in touch in case it became an interstate crime.

The sheriff knew something of the psychology of the hunted. While the BCA boys methodically went about the business of vacuuming cars and clothes for fragments, sifting weeds for spent shells, prying into lives for personal details and motives, the sheriff would put a little public heat on the fugitives, make them feel alone, isolated, frightened. He wanted the Jenkins pair to feel they had nowhere to go. That could help run them down.

Abe was working on getting Jim Jenkins's full-face photo from the Texas Department of Motor Vehicles. He'd already gotten one of Steve, standing in his grandparents' kitchen looking goofy in army clothes, with his eyes closed and his tattooed arms holding up a couple of fresh-caught fish. Later, those pictures would go out to journalists for transmission all over the region, and maybe even the country. Abe also got the grandparents, Clayton and Nina Jenkins, to film a short emotional TV appeal to their son and grandson to turn themselves in. "We love you," the grandma said.

The sheriff repeated for countless tape recorders a description of the hunted pickup truck, while plainclothesmen, with backup from sheriff's deputies in surrounding counties, made thorough rounds of the fugitives' friends and the places the father and son frequented. In the newly leased Jenkins farmhouse near Hardwick, searchers found food, a gun, some instructions for making homemade bombs, and a telephone number with a 214 area code. Officials at the telephone company said the phone was in Dallas, Texas, under the name of Blythe, Rudolph H.

BCA Agent Dennis Sigafoos taped his interview with Darlene Jenkins. She said her ex-husband hardly ever did any shooting. He'd had a shotgun years before, but he'd gotten rid of it. Steve had a rifle, she thought, an awful-looking army thing with a military sling. But that was nothing. Steve had liked military things since, oh, golly, since he was little.

BCA Agent Michael Cummings poked around Rudy's bank office. He found the Jenkins file easily enough. The farmer had sold mortgaged property, then declared bankruptcy. But what was this back here? A message about a phone call from a Ron Anderson and something about a 10:00 A.M. meeting.

Does anybody in the bank know a Ron Anderson? Pause. No, there's no Ron Anderson around here.

At Clayton Jenkins's place, the couple cooperated fully. They perhaps hoped there was some awful misunderstanding. Did Jim or Steve do much shooting? they were asked. No. Well, Jim didn't, but Steve did. He used to go out back for hours at a time. Just by himself, you know. That was when the agents found the thick, Y-shaped tree branch. Someone had put a pair of pants on it and a blue shirt. The wooden limb was pocked from hundreds of rounds of rifle fire.

The judge signed the arrest warrants that night.

The agents also began a series of interviews with Susan, who remained a taut bundle of nerves—constantly working, talking lest she have a moment to confront what had really happened. Even much later, it was hard for her to speak of Rudy's murder—she came to call it The Ditch—without imposing on herself an icy impersonal tone. She was so eager to help the detectives—some of them saw it more as an obsession—that she would call them often with a freshly remembered detail or a suggestion for an investigative lead and then want to hear progress reports. They understood, bereaved spouses being a common encounter in their line of work, but it was distracting. They quietly arranged for Mrs. Blythe to get some professional counseling.

Rolph's counseling came from his mother. Everyone agreed he should resume normal activities as soon as possible. Two days after That Day, even with the Jenkins pair still on the loose, the youngster went off to football practice as usual; Rolph didn't see the unmarked car parked by the field with the large man watching his every move.

That first Sunday night without a father was an important one. Susan had wanted to have a few private minutes with the body and Rolph before the public memorial service. At the funeral home Rolph thought his father looked strange in the coffin. Susan showed Rolph how, looking down from the head of the coffin, the body looked like his father stretched out in his recliner chair in the living room; she didn't want Rolph building any illusions that the man about to be cremated was not really Rudy Blythe.

Inside, Susan wasn't all that calm. Even with her parents there, she felt hollow and lost. The memorial service would be the first time since Thursday that she had had to confront the physical evidence, final and unequivocal, of Rudy's death. She couldn't fully handle that yet, so she focused on details—how lovely the flowers were, had everyone been invited, were all the arrangements in order, are there enough chairs?

That weekend, in bed, when slumber freed her mind for some moments, Susan relived, detail by detail, the events of The Ditch. And then, as if looking down on herself, she said, "Oh, this is really just an awful, awful dream and I'm going to wake up now to reality." She woke up and looked hopefully around the room. She was in a motel room in Pipestone. Her mother was sound asleep in the semidarkness. Rolph and her father were next door. The police were just down the hall. Rudy was not in the bed. Just his pajamas. She began to scream.

CHAPTER SIX

Appointment in Paducah

Sundays are quiet in rural Texas. It is a peaceful time, as the Lord's Day was meant to be. But on Sunday, October 2, fear of a fall storm was strong in Paducah, Texas, the only town of substance in sandy Cottle County. Eighty percent of the area's sparse moisture comes suddenly from thunderstorms, but so does 100 percent of the area's tornadoes. There were reports of clouds that afternoon, a warning sign that sent a team of volunteer firemen scurrying off into the countryside as storm sentries to watch for those whirling black clouds that make people pray and hide, not necessarily in that order.

Paducah's radio-equipped sentries had fanned out of town several miles to the west and south looking for trouble in the sky. No one ever thought to watch the north, and Highway 83 running straight down from the Dakotas and Minnesota.

Joyce Hall was having a problem with her hair. She had washed it earlier that afternoon, but it was still wet, and limp. Every time she sat down to do something about it, someone would call on the radio to say all was clear, no funnel clouds over toward Matador or down toward Finney, or a local policeman checked in, or the phone would ring.

Joyce and her ten-year-old daughter Lucrezia lived with their cats Felix and Rocky in Paducah City Hall at the corner of Backus and Tenth streets. They occupied a tiny, windowless apartment across the marble hall from the drinking fountain and just down the dim passage from the potted plant. Joyce earned her keep there manning the radio for local police and firemen. She'd done it for years. It was a bother sometimes, but she liked being involved.

Joyce walked to her apartment door and looked down the hall to check the weather. It was getting dark early. Big drops were starting to fall on the empty pavement outside. A storm was very close. Joyce was not fully dressed, but no one ever came to City Hall on Sunday. She left the door open and went across the room to set her dresser mirror down on the table by the radio microphone. Joyce had her curlers and bobby pins there too. Lucrezia was on the floor near the door, jabbering away at the kitties.

With an ear to the radio and her back to the door, Joyce sat down and concentrated on her hair. She had her arms upraised wrapping her hair around the plastic tubes.

"Mommy," cried her daughter. "Mommy. Mommy. Mommy."

"Mmmmm," said Joyce, her mouth full of bobby pins.

Then, in the mirror over her right shoulder, Joyce saw him standing there silently watching her back—a six-foot-tall commando. His head was shaved. His arms were bare except for the tattoos. He wore camouflage gear and heavy boots. He looked empty.

Joyce turned in the chair and looked at him, afraid to be afraid for fear of what it might ignite.

"Is this the police department?" he asked.

"Yes, it is," she said, swallowing. "I'm the dispatcher. Can I help you?"

"I've come to turn myself in," he said.

Ronald Kay Simpkins, a part-time police officer, was the first to arrive. An excited Joyce had called anyone in authority to get down to City Hall. At first, given his appearance, she'd thought Steve Jenkins was an AWOL soldier from some military base. He started to cry pretty quick in her apartment and she got him a fistful of tissues. She was comforting him and telling him everything would be all right, but right away he had said something about accomplice to murder. Up in Minnesota or somewhere. Joyce forgot about her wet hair for a long while.

Kay Simpkins had frisked the boy while the rain came down hard outside. Then Randell Bockleman arrived. Randell had been a farmer for years but had seen the financial writing on the wall three years earlier, and he'd gone out and found himself a new line of work: town policeman.

When Sheriff Frank Taylor arrived, the three men began to question the teenager. Around Joyce he'd been bawling like a frightened little boy, but with the men Steve straightened up. No sign of fear, just calm, short answers. There's been a couple of murders, bankers, up in Minnesota, he said. He'd been behind the garage when it happened. Heard a bunch of shots, someone yelled, "He's got a gun," and then more shots. Steve said that when he came out, his father was walking back around the house from the front yard and he said, "I fixed that son of a bitch Blythe."

The three men didn't know about any Minnesota murders; they hadn't read that morning's *Avalanche-Journal* from Lubbock so they didn't know what to fish for in the kid's statement. The farmer-banker problem seemed credible enough. The kid said the banker had taken his dad's land away even though he'd made the payments on time. Sounded familiar.

"And speaking of your father," the sheriff said, "where is he, boy?"

It's still known as the old Goodwin house, even though no one, including Ernest Goodwin, has been able to live in the place for nearly twenty years.

It's a little over three miles north of Paducah on Highway 83 and six tenths of a mile east on a nameless gravel road that runs straight out of J. R. Bratton's front yard. The old farmhouse burned down long ago. Nothing was left but its cement slab foundation, now hidden behind a couple of cedars going wild from their civilized days of decorating a front door.

Pretty near everyone thereabouts knew where the old Goodwin place was, everyone except a couple of strangers who had arrived after dark on Saturday night. They were specialists in abandoned houses; in fact, one of the two men in that white pickup truck still felt he owned an abandoned place up in Minnesota, and the two of them had been staying in such places for the last couple of days on their way south.

Jim Jenkins was headed to no particular place. Just south, back to the Sunbelt where things seemed successful. Maybe he would know it when they got there, a safe, sunny place where things would work out right for once. It never occurred to Jim that the appointment was already set, and he was right on time.

The father and son didn't go straight to the Goodwin house. They turned east off 83, passed J. R. Bratton's yard, and parked by a cow pasture, or what passes for one in the arid parts of Texas, at the open end of a dusty, dead-end lane. From that little rise, a field-sized knoll really, anyone can see the landscape's spread. It was a good place to sleep; the two men dozed in silence for a few hours. The pink of Sunday's first light in the east uncovered a building of some kind about two hundred yards up the sandy drive. It looked like an abandoned garage. Probably the house burned down. They backed the truck in behind the garage, took some gear and their scant food over to the cement slab, and sat down behind the cedar trees, with a view of the surrounding county that could not see them.

They had heard the news of the killings and the manhunt on the radio during their long droning nights on the road. Many of the newscasts carried descriptions of them and their truck, and sometimes even their license plate number. Dot by dot, their pictures were flowing electronically into every newsroom in the country. No matter how far south they went, neither Jenkins could tell anymore when a smiling gas station attendant was just trying to be friendly or when he was stalling until the state police arrived.

Steve says he remembers his father growing more tired and irritable as the day wore on and the big country seemed to grow smaller around them. Steve says he suggested they turn themselves in, and he remembers his father saying he would never go to jail, and if he was going to die in a blazing gun battle, he wanted to take some others with him. His father grew even angrier when the son announced he was going to surrender—there was no point in going on. Steve says they argued for a long while that afternoon. Then they sat down on the cement slab for their last supper, half a can of cold beans each and a few swigs of warm Pepsi from a bottle they had bought two lifetimes ago in Pipestone.

Late that afternoon, as Rudy Blythe's friends and relatives were gathering back in Minnesota for a memorial service, Steve stood up to leave the cement slab. The sky was darkening in the west. Steve says his father had often threatened suicide since the divorce, saying there was not much to live for anymore, and sometimes he threatened to take his son with him. But this time, Steve said he was determined to leave. Somehow he managed to get the pickup truck stuck in the sand. Jim Jenkins helped his son out, but before the boy drove off, his father took the shotgun from the truck. For a man who planned a shoot-out until death, Jim didn't take much ammunition, and when Steve looked back across the flat land, his father looked very small.

Not long after, the storm arrived. Jim Jenkins sat out in the downpour, his denim clothes growing dark and heavy. That was the least of his concerns; Jim didn't have enough time left to catch pneumonia. His old farm was gone. His wife was gone. So was his daughter. His big Texas savings were gone. His new farm dream was gone too. The future of the forty-six-year-old man had died in that farmyard right along with those bankers. Now even Steve, his son, the one person who kept coming back to him no matter what, now Steve was gone.

Jim picked up the old shotgun and the new flashlight, and, aiming his tunnel vision down at the ground in the gathering twilight, shuffled through the sand from the safety of the bushes to the dangerous open area toward the end of the road.

The heavy rain had stopped. The Texas soil smelled fresh and clean, recharged to fuel new growth. The ground rose slightly beneath his feet as he approached the junction of the lane and the dirt road. After spending four days in a cross-country flight avoiding people as much as possible, Jim Jenkins was ensuring that he would be found, finally. He walked up the little knoll where he could see, or sense, the surrounding countryside. He turned the flashlight off.

Jim carefully removed his glasses then and folded them up. It was a natural step for someone about to go to sleep. But it was a step that would later come to haunt his son and his son's legal defense.

Jenkins stepped back a little and turned toward the west. That's where the wind comes from. That's where the sun sets on opportunity. With his left hand Jenkins moved the broad muzzle of the twelve-gauge shotgun up toward his mouth. He slid the cold, hard barrel between his lips and teeth. His right thumb moved to the shiny trigger, and he pushed it ever so gently.

"You sure it was this road?" said Sheriff Frank Taylor, turning east on the gravel road by J. R. Bratton's house. From the kid's description, it sounded like the old Goodwin place.

The kid in the back mumbled yes. Steve Jenkins was handcuffed, just in case. Kay Simpkins was sitting next to him. Randell, the town cop, was in the front seat with Frank, who was thinking. This bald little fucker in the back seat was awful cool and calm for someone claiming to be a murder accomplice. He'd been talking about how his father was threatening suicide. But that didn't ring right to Frank. Why would a boy leave his troubled daddy alone with a shotgun? Most sons would have stayed, or taken the gun away, Frank figured. Maybe this was all bullshit, another ambush setup right here on Frank's own turf.

Frank Taylor slowed his car to a halt, got out, and opened the trunk. He picked up his machine gun and returned to the front seat. Then he slowly drove toward the Goodwin house.

Frank was looking hardest, so he saw them first, a pair of booted feet sticking out in the road, very still. It was strange, almost comical. The man's right heel was propped atop his left toe. What Frank saw next was not comical. Most of the guy's head was gone. The sand was dark red.

Frank saw the shotgun. He held on to his own gun and looked around carefully. There was just one fresh set of footprints in the dirt, so the victim had come here alone after the rain. His clothes were soaking wet; he obviously had sat outside through the whole storm. The tracks came down from the old homestead, walking up on that knoll and facing west. Wonder what he was looking for out here in the open?

Then a few footprints back down the knoll, where the man stood a minute. The blast of the gun had blown him around toward the south, and he'd fallen back on the ground, stiff as a board. Whaddya suppose he'd want a flashlight for? It wasn't dark yet. And look, the glasses.

"Hey, boy, did your daddy wear glasses all the time?"

Yeah, well, he won't anymore. The poor bastard had put the glasses in his pocket.

J. R. Bratton drove up. He was puzzled by the small crowd on his property. The place had been quiet and empty just thirty minutes before when he drove by. J. R. saw the body and figured some excited dove hunter had accidentally blasted himself. Then he saw the handcuffed kid casually looking out of Frank's car. He knew that kid from somewhere.

Frank was busy checking out the area with Randell and radioing for the coroner and the Texas Rangers. No doubt old Leo would be arriving soon.

"J. R.," said Frank, "looks like you got some visitors. This kid says he and his daddy were involved in a couple of murders up north and—"

"That's it! That's the kid that's wanted," said J. R., who had seen two family photos and read an interesting story in that morning's newspaper about a farmer lashing out at a couple of bankers.

Sheriff Abe Thompson was at home in Minnesota when the call came. He had to look at a map to find Paducah—from the middle of nowhere in Ivanhoe, Minnesota, to the middle of nowhere in Paducah, Texas. When the two rural sheriffs talked, Steve Jenkins was sitting on a hard wooden chair in the Texas county's courthouse. He was making a voluntary statement, and Frank was getting it all down with detective Leo Hickman of the Texas Rangers.

After they'd read Steve his rights and started the interrogation late that evening, the kid said he was real hungry. Randell went out for food, and Steve wolfed down a big cheeseburger, a pack of french fries, and a vanilla milkshake, which struck Sheriff Taylor as kind of strange since he couldn't eat for days after his own father died, and the old man had passed away in a hospital, not swallowed the wrong end of a belching twelve-gauge.

Leo and Frank found the Jenkins truck parked near City Hall in the little lot behind the dentist's office. They found a small armory in the truck, including several guns, a steel helmet, ammunition, some kung-fu throwing stars, and a .30-caliber carbine that would attract the interest of Minnesota authorities. Looking at all those killing tools, some of the police were thinking how ironic it was to have this eighteen-year-old kid who was too young to buy a can of beer legally in Texas but plenty old enough to walk around with a deadly arsenal like this.

The truck and all the weapons and Steve were taken into Minnesota custody after Abe Thompson arrived the next day in a farmer friend's chartered plane. With him were two experienced BCA agents, Bob Berg and Mike O'Gorman, who would follow the Jenkins case to its end.

Right behind that private plane, landing at Paducah's little airport just outside town, came other chartered aircraft and then rented cars down the highway as the television crews descended. That Monday Paducah was like many of the country's obscure communities that are suddenly thrust into the national spotlight for a moment by an event over which they have no control. Some native son becomes an instantly notorious assassin and strangers with cameras and notebooks appear from nowhere looking for relatives, pals, and high school yearbooks. The trouble was that no one in Paducah knew anything about Jim Jenkins or Steve for the scrambling TV correspondents to interview them about. And Abe and Bob and Mike and Leo sure weren't talking in front of any cameras about what they knew. So instead there was a lot of scenic footage on the news that night, shots of the stained suicide scene, the Goodwin garage, the white pickup truck, and a clip of Cottle County Sheriff Frank Taylor outside his office saying, no, the kid didn't seem surprised when he saw his father dead in the road. But the sheriff firmly believed Mr. Jenkins's death was a suicide anyway, unless Batman sneaked up on him in a helicopter.

Sheriff Thompson and the two BCA agents questioned Steve for more than two hours on videotape. They went over all the events of recent weeks. They searched the truck, inventoried the arsenal, and began to form the legal and criminological hypotheses that would become the foundation of the case against Steve. The defendant had marked his eighteenth birthday on August 21, five weeks before the shootings, so he was an adult in the eyes of Minnesota law. He would be charged with a most serious adult offense: murder.

They took Steve home in Abe's friend's little plane. It was Steve Jenkins's first airplane ride, and he sat there, in handcuffs, his excited face glued to the window and the view of the big land where he had so recently been hiding.

Bob Berg and Mike O'Gorman, and for a while a few others, began the reconstruction of the Jenkins men's lives and movements and Susan Blythe's recollections and exactly what might have happened in those few fleeting seconds on that rainy morning in that farmyard near Ruthton. This was a grisly process, reenacting two deaths, firing guns at windshields, and reliving, emotionlessly, the moment of death to pinpoint the sequence of events and the killer's identity.

It is an all-consuming task, this conscientious reassembly of the past. The agents see that there are victims in everything, most of them unsung, painfully caught up in the crimes and their aftermaths. People like Jim Jenkins's parents, who worked hard all their lives, covered their son's bad debts, and who one day woke up and found they had an emotional choice: they could turn on their only grandson for the sake of their dead son or they could forsake their only child as a killer and support their grandson.

In one sense, the Jenkins case was an easy one. The bodies were there. The gun was there. A witness placed both men at the scene. But in another sense, the Jenkins case was very difficult. The evidence was pretty much all circumstantial. The only living survivor of the four, the only one who really knew what happened, said he didn't know what happened. He said he was hiding behind the garage the whole time and emerged only after two bursts of gunfire to see his father returning from the front yard saying, "I fixed Rudy."

Berg and O'Gorman went over and over the crime scene in Ruthton. They had found a note for Darlene Jenkins in Steve's wallet, apparently put there just in case something happened and Steve wasn't alive to talk. "I love you Mom," it said. "Tell gradma [sic] and grandpa and Mickey that I love them. I'm sorry that this happened Please forgive me and daddy I love all of you for being there and helping when I needed it. I wish things could be different If I could change what happened I would I wish I could be with you. I love you. Steve." The agents, along with Sheriff Thompson, had also gone over and over the whole situation with Steve during that long questioning on videotape in Paducah. He mumbled and kept his head down. But he was cool and assured.

The agents ran over the easy stuff with him at first: his date of birth and address and his childhood, much of which they already knew but which helped later to judge Steve's credibility. They hoped that as he respun the strands of the web they knew, he might fill in a gap or two. Steve talked about their problems in farming and working with his father in Texas and how he loved military things. All the clothes he had were camouflage and khaki green. He said he took his carbine everywhere, even to bed at night.

He talked about not getting into the marines because of his missing spleen. Steve explained why he'd quit high school halfway through his junior year; they had changed his shop teacher and he didn't think he was getting much out of it anymore.

From different angles the questioners gently but persistently came back to the morning of the murders and the days leading up to it. The only time Steve wavered was on the subject of his father's health. He had diabetes, you know. And night blindness. And his father sometimes said he didn't have much to live for anymore, not since his wife left and the banker took away the farm and now was telling everybody else around not to loan Jenkins any money. Steve got a little weepy then.

The agents made a note to check the eyeglass prescription. As the questioning progressed, they boosted the pressure a bit. They said, well, Steve, that was interesting, but they had some problems with that story. First of all, it didn't matter if you were there and pulled the trigger or if you were there and didn't pull the trigger. You were there. You were an accomplice. And in the eyes of the law you are equally guilty.

Steve said he shot no one. That may very well be, they said, but it would be a whole lot easier on him if he just said what really happened, you know, just came clean and got it over with. Steve stuck to his story. They had rented the land and house with the Texas money. Got some machinery, too. Then they had gone from bank to bank and cattle dealer to cattle dealer throughout September looking for money and cows. Time after time they had been turned down for credit. Steve said his father was real discouraged and blamed that son of a bitch Rudy Blythe for everything. Steve said he couldn't understand how bankers could get away with taking things that don't belong to them when other folks would get arrested for such stealing. Steve had heard that Rudy had taken away fourteen other farms. And then one day, the day before the shootings, Steve said his father came home from the last credit turndown and announced he had used a fake name to make an appointment with Blythe out at the old farmhouse the next morning. They were going to rob Rudy and scare the hell out of him, Steve remembers his father saying.

The agents said that really didn't fit with some of the things they had started to learn from other people. Steve said he didn't know about that, but he was scared as hell out there at their old farmhouse and he knew he didn't shoot nobody. The agents said they had a different idea of what happened. They thought that before the suicide Jim had made Steve promise that no matter what happened, no matter what anyone said, Steve should always maintain that his father did the shooting. How could anyone prove otherwise? With his father dead, Steve would be free. The agents and Sheriff Thompson said that would explain a lot of things, and that's how it looked to them. And Steve owed it to his father's name to let him rest in peace in his grave, to come clean with the truth.

Steve was crying now. He said he hadn't wanted to leave his father. The agents said they understood. They warned him about his conscience. Over the years, they said, "it'll eat you alive."

Later, reviewing the tape and watching Steve's reactions, the agents came to believe he almost broke then, almost said something that would have made life a lot easier for a lot of people in the coming months. There was a pause. But Steve stood steadfast. He didn't know about any other theories. When he had told his father he wanted to surrender, his father had said, Never—he wouldn't go to jail. They had argued, Steve said, and slept, and then Jim Jenkins had said his boy could go. He wouldn't stop him. But if Steve left, Jim said, he was going to kill himself. He took the shotgun from the truck because, he said, it would do "the best job." Steve only knew what happened out there, he said. He hadn't killed anybody ever.

"Well, fellas," said Thomas L. Fabel, "I'd say you have your work cut out." The tall, deep-voiced Fabel unfolded out of the chair where he'd been watching the Steve Jenkins videotape with O'Gorman and Berg. He was deputy attorney general of the state of Minnesota. He was also concerned. Fabel had learned during his legal career never to be too certain of anything, especially in the fields of law and human behavior. On this day he had more doubts about the accused's guilt than he felt comfortable with as a professional prosecutor. Fabel would be the government's point man on this highly visible case, which had even grabbed page one attention in the *New York Times*. Within hours of the ambush, Mike Cable, the local part-time prosecutor in Lincoln County, had asked for help, and Fabel himself was going to need a lot of it if they were to prove the charges against Steve Jenkins.

Things had quieted down in Paducah, the media's interest having evaporated within forty-eight hours. The Texas town got back to its slow decay except for an incident right around New Year's.

One bleak day two men showed up in a private plane at the community's little airstrip. They introduced themselves to Randell as Louis Taveirne and James Dwire from Minnesota, friends of the Jenkins family. They very much wanted to see the suicide scene, they said, because they were convinced Jimmy Lee Jenkins had left a suicide note that would clear his son of the Blythe shootings. It being nearly dark, the trip to the old Goodwin place was postponed until morning. But when Sheriff Taylor arrived for his 9:00 A.M. appointment, the pair had left word they had gone on ahead.

Taylor was a little worried about J. R.'s reaction should some more strangers, and northerners at that, be found strolling on his land. In addition, since the suicide, J. R. had put in some electric fence right by the old garage. Its steel strands ran from an old fuse box on a nearby pole. When the sheriff arrived, J. R. was already there. He hadn't said much to the strangers except "Howdy" and "Whatchall doin'?" But his eyes silently spoke deep suspicions to his sheriff friend. For people who'd never been there, these two fellows knew an awful lot about the layout. Frank and J. R. were chatting for a moment when Dwire and Taveirne suddenly shouted from over by the old fuse box. "Hey, sheriff!" they said. "Look what we found." And they came running over with a little piece of pink paper.

J. R. and the sheriff looked at each other silently again. They had both looked in that box several times since the suicide, even though it was a good two hundred yards from the body. In fact, the day after the suicide Frank had scraped a lemon-sized hornet's nest from the leaky metal box with his pocket knife. Now, ten weeks and several thunderstorms later, these two Yankees just happened into town and just happened to find Jim Jenkins's official suicide note on the unstained back of a TV repair bill an eighth of a mile from where Jim Jenkins had blown his head off. These visitors also just happened to have a camera along which they used to photograph Louis Taveirne handing the note to Sheriff Frank Taylor. The penciled note said: "I killed Rudy Blythe the SOB. Steve leaving. Won't listen anymore. A guy just as well be dead." It was signed by James L. Jenkins.

One newspaper headline of the discovery read: SUICIDE NOTE TURNS UP IN JENKINS MURDER CASE; SHERIFF HOLDS DOUBTS. What Sheriff Taylor was really holding was his temper. The two Minnesota men were, as Frank put it, "standing there pissin' on my leg tryin' to tell me it's rainin'." He told the men he didn't want their phony note and he suggested they remove themselves, fast, from this private property. "But, Sheriff," said Louis Taveirne, "what should I do with this note?" Frank Taylor paused only a moment before he told the stranger precisely where to put it.

Eight days after Jim Jenkins took his last steps in the Bratton's field, he was put in the ground. The funeral in Paducah was ignored by most of the town and all of the world. Faced with a $150,000 bond for Steve, the Jenkins family told mortician Pat Seigler on the phone that they wouldn't be bringing Jim Jenkins's body back to Minnesota, not right away anyway. Maybe next year.

The Reverend Emmett Autrey drove the long white hearse down the dusty little path that separates the neat rows of mounds out in Paducah's Garden of Memories Cemetery. It was late Monday morning. Nine people had gathered at the hole, freshly dug by Jimmy Branson. No one who ever knew Jim Jenkins was there. "But God knew him better than anyone," said the Reverend Autrey of the Missionary Baptist Church. "It is not our place to judge his thoughts, his emotions, his actions. We are here simply out of respect for another human being." Sheriff Taylor was there and Pat Seigler and the cemetery's caretaker, and two state troopers. Off to the side stood Thelma Martin and her daughter, Joyce Hall, the police dispatcher who first encountered the Jenkinses and the only one to send any funeral decorations, white plastic flowers.

Mere mortals, the minister said, face two final certainties—to die and to face judgment in the hereafter. "But that judgment," he said, "brings into it every secret thing." There was a moment of prayer before Jimmy Branson eased his growling backhoe up to the site and began pulling the soft dirt back into the hole. The little stone would read: James Lee Jenkins, Feb. 4, 1937-Oct. 2, 1983.

Eleven days later they dug up Jim Jenkins and hauled him two hundred miles to a lab in Dallas for a day before burying him in the Paducah sand again. Something about his eye.

CHAPTER SEVEN

Through the Looking Glass

"All rise."

Six dozen people stood for the entrance of a gray-haired gentleman in a black robe who would preside over the next few weeks in their lives.

The trial of Steven Todd Jenkins began on April 10, 1984, in the freshly painted courtroom on the third floor of the Lincoln County Courthouse in Ivanhoe, Minnesota, 15 miles northwest of the murder scene as the hawks fly. It was an overcast, drizzling, cold Tuesday, not unlike That Day back in September. Fog covered many fields and chilled drops of water dripped steadily off the bare branches of the trees, christening the old soil with the first sign of the new spring.

County Clerk Lee Smith had officially summoned eighty potential jurors to the three-story Ivanhoe courthouse from across the county's 540 square miles. Jury trials are rare in Lincoln County; it had been several years since the last one, some kind of a theft. Finding eligible jurors for a murder trial was no easy task near spring planting time. Back at the turn of the century, when Lincoln County had its last murder trial, it was easier to find jurors, there being four families or so on every 640-acre section, or square mile. But in 1980, Lincoln County's population was only 8,207. Twelve months later it was 8,168 and in 1982, 8,081. By trial time it was about 7,800. In the middle of the Jenkins trial, a new state study revealed that the number of Minnesota farmers had fallen to 94,385 from a 1935 peak of 234,000. The study also confirmed that the number of medium-sized, 180- to 500-acre farms, the economic foundation of many rural communities, was falling sharply. The number of small farms was increasing as financially pressed farmers and their wives whittled land holdings and took off-farm jobs to support their country life. At the same time, the number of large farms was increasing too, many with out-of-state owners.

The telephone lines crackled that rainy morning in Ivanhoe, where the thirty-one-page phone book contains twenty-five pages of instructions. And all the courthouse parking spaces on North Rebecca Street were filled before 9:00 A.M. The big news was not the trial itself; farm financial difficulties and tensions between farmers and their local financiers were old news. The big news in little Ivanhoe (pop. 761) was that the murder trial and the financial problems were big news elsewhere. A TV satellite truck parked out on the street proved it. So did three or four camera crews and the squad of guys with notebooks. Anyone who went over to the courthouse those days, and a lot of people seemed to remember some business they had to do over at the courthouse, saw the crowds outside the courtroom, including Blythe's widow and maybe even the kid himself. They saw the TV crews with their Japanese cameras and bandolier battery packs sprawled all over the steps, waiting and griping and swapping stories. That first trial night, and several other times during the three weeks of court sessions, townsfolk saw and heard Dan Rather talk about their town to the whole world. He even pronounced Ivanhoe right.

There was the usual sense of celebrity and excitement, when they saw little Ivanhoe on the map, in color, behind Dan Rather's shoulder. But there was also a sense of tension. Twelve people were going to have to pass judgment on this boy, on one of their own. Now, talking down at the café is one thing. It doesn't really matter. But getting up in front of a judge and saying, "Yessir, he did it," or "No, sir, this boy is innocent," that's quite another thing. Which is one reason why Swen Anderson did not want the trial moved out of Steve Jenkins's home county. It might just be a little harder to convict one of their own.

Forty-eight years and one day before the Jenkins trial began, the defense attorney, Allan Swen Anderson, was born in southern Minnesota, the first of two sons of a Swedish immigrant. It was not unusual in the Scandinavian ghettos that dot Minnesota, but Swen did not learn to speak English until the seventh grade. Critics of this eccentric attorney often maintain that he still hasn't mastered the tongue. Which could well be another Anderson ploy. For Swen Anderson is no fool, though it may sometimes serve his purpose for people to think so.

Anderson commands attention, with his large, broad nose, his left eye in an eternal squint, an old-fashioned flattop haircut, and a Stetson perpetually plunked down over his flaglike ears. He can swear up a tornado of words that accidentally on purpose spill into nearby ears. "I got a voice you can hear in five counties," he says, suddenly smiling. Swen often talks only in capital letters, as in, "THAT FABEL IS A GODDAMNED PUBLICITY HOUND." The words are hurled over his shoulder with an accompanying stare just as the target passes by.

"Yeah, he's a character," admits his wife, Liz, who often serves as secretary in Swen's law practice in Granite Falls, about fifty-five miles from

Ivanhoe. During this trial Swen would leave his motorcycle at home. After a near fatal bout with rheumatic fever, and high school graduation at age twenty, Anderson earned degrees from the University of Minnesota and St. Paul's William Mitchell College of Law (with honors) before becoming an assistant to his county's prosecutor. He inherited his boss's job seven months later. For twelve years Swen was elected prosecutor, then somebody ran against him. Swen lost, which was fortunate in the eyes of some. Gruff, grumpy, disorganized Swen, with all his keys on a rubber band, strewing papers about his office as he rummages through files, doesn't seem to fit the mold of a methodical prosecutor.

Swen's love of underdogs led him into legal defense work, especially in defense of folks who were a little bit different, semi-outcasts in a small town where the unwritten rules can be strict. These local pariahs, by some quirk of circumstance or life-style, swim against the small-town current and get snagged on the law. And maybe some folks feel if this unusual fellow isn't guilty of that particular crime exactly, then he ought to be. That gets Swen's dander up. When he takes on a client, he takes on the town too, if necessary. Swen usually gets his client off.

Swen Anderson took on Steve Jenkins as a client because he enjoys colorful cases and because another client, Louis Taveirne, was living with Steve's mother. And perhaps because some people were saying Steve was an oddball son of a sick father, neither of whom had done the farmer's cause any good, even if some bankers did have it coming. And certainly because Steve had become a real underdog. Other lawyers were not exactly swarming to help Steve. "He had everything against him," Swen recalls.

Pending the trial, Anderson even got Steve out on bail, $150,000 put up in the form of Louis Taveirne's local supper club. Swen promised the court that Steve would never leave his sight, which he didn't. The plainclothes police tailing both of them saw to that. Steve lived in the Andersons' home as another son; they already had four, plus an adopted daughter. Steve did odd jobs around Swen's storefront office, where the walls are covered with the lawyer's personal trophies: a stuffed shark, some favorite fishing poles, guns, an original U.S. Mail pouch, and a portrait of an Indian, another underdog.

Swen has a great deal of empathy for his clients. He warns them about the opening of any trial when the prosecution unleashes all its big guns in a barrage of overwhelming oral observations and evidence so convincing that even an accused saint could come to believe he had done whatever they say. "A trial is like a pancake," Swen tells his worried clients and prospective jury members during courtroom interviews. "You can't tell if it's done until you see both sides."

Anderson also demands a great deal of discipline from his clients. He toughens them by hurling insults during long periods of practice testimony. Clients are not to talk to the press. No show of emotion in court.

Do what you're told in public. Wear what you're told—long sleeves for Steve. It all adds up; Steve performs well for stern sergeants.

Early on, it seemed that Swen was prosecuting the deceased Jim Jenkins more than he was defending Steve. Swen had a handwriting analyst look at Jim's alleged suicide note. She found no indication of fraud and said that it came from a disturbed person. Swen hired a psychiatrist who interviewed Steve, his mother, his sister, his grandparents, and Louis Taveirne and then produced a fifteen-page report for the defense. It found Steve to be pleasant, courteous, cooperative, above average in intelligence, and "neat in every regard" with "an exceptionally good moral code." Steve was emotionally "overcontrolled" at times, except when the four-hour interview turned to his father, and Steve cried. The psychiatrist traced Steve's military fantasies to his father's tales of National Guard experiences, and he speculated that Steve, with his intense loyalty, obedience, and perfectionism, would have made an excellent marine, except that he seemed bothered by pictures of people being killed.

The psychiatrist devoted several pages to a profile of Jim Jenkins based on the same interviews. He found him to be "a depraved maniac," overly dependent emotionally on his parents, especially his mother, with strong feelings of masculine inferiority and inadequacy, and an inability to function well at work away from his authoritarian father. The psychiatrist referred to family stories about cruelty to animals, Jim's refusal to take orders at work, violent temper tantrums, and a crying, begging emotional dependency on his wife in which he became, in effect, Darlene's third child. Jim also had repeated delusions about his wife's sexual affairs. Jim felt the banker was out to ruin him financially, the report stated, and Jim sought to emotionally enslave, subjugate, and coerce Steve to stay with him and obey him, ending with a threat to commit suicide if his son left him alone in Texas.

According to the psychiatrist, Jim's perceived inadequate relationship with his own father prompted him to direct his furies toward men exclusively. He said that Steve, on the other hand, was considered likable by everyone, cooperative, with no disciplinary problems, and carrying a firm conviction that he must always respect his parents and never hurt anyone, even his father, whom he had come to see as sick and emotionally needy. Finally, however, Steve's inability to commit murder in a final shoot-out with police enabled Steve to make the emotional break with his father. In a final desperate act to hurt those left behind, Jim, by then a paranoid psychotic, committed suicide to leave a lasting emotional trauma on his disobedient son. The psychiatrist also stated that Steve's mother, his paternal grandparents, and his mother's boyfriend all believe very strongly that Steve not only did not kill anyone but could not kill anyone.

During pretrial hearings that winter Swen appeared to be building a defense of duress, that Steve didn't do the shootings and had to be with his father that day out of his abiding respect for elders, concern for his own father, and fear for his own safety from a mentally-ill dad, and that too many doubts dotted the state's circumstantial evidence to put a kid away for life.

Thomas Lincoln Fabel saw this one coming before it turned the corner. Generally considered the senior and most experienced criminal trial attorney in the state attorney general's office, the thirty-eight-year-old Fabel is a rangy replica of a bespectacled Clark Kent. He has the kind of neatness and precision—the unwrinkled suits with striped red tie, the fine-point pens with fresh notepad, the crisp files, the precisely placed paper clips—that can quietly intimidate those who aren't always so ready and so organized.

Tom had long ago opted for a legal career and the University of Chicago Law School, just as he had long ago decided that Jean Hoisser, his ninth-grade sweetheart, would be his wife. He is a staunchly religious man, perhaps not surprising for someone who has already died twice. At the age of sixteen at summer camp Fabel fell off a cliff and landed on the side of his head. Two times during succeeding days of surgery his heart stopped. Twice it was restored. His face and jaw required extensive reconstruction. The only sign today is a misbehaving hearing aid that sometimes goes beep in a quiet courtroom.

Although Fabel is one of the highest law enforcement officers in Minnesota, his second-floor office behind the state capital in St. Paul is modest, overlooking the building's back roof: a metal desk, a single light, a mug that says I LOVE ST. PAUL, two potted plants, some file cabinets, and a phone, which he often answers himself.

On one wall is a large state map so Fabel can see where he is going to try the cases he regularly takes on to keep his hand in trial work and because he feels strange asking subordinates to do that work without handling some himself too. On another wall are crayoned drawings by his three daughters. As he prepared for his long stay in a motel room near Ivanhoe, Fabel and his wife awaited the birth of their fourth child.

From his office, Fabel supervises five legal divisions from antitrust to public safety with twenty-three lawyers and fifteen investigators. Yet his presence out in the state is not always welcomed by the often part-time prosecutors. Tom's presence means that he and not the local man will be in charge, so Fabel must practice some tact as well as law. He must be aware too of simmering local resentments toward hotshot city lawyers coming to town to send a local fellow to prison. Resentment doesn't always show on the faces of jurors, but it can in their verdict.

Thanks to the work of O'Gorman and Berg, BCA technicians, and other investigators, Tom had a stronger case against Steve Jenkins than he had originally thought after seeing the boy's videotaped questioning the previous fall. After the detailed crime reconstructions and filmed reenactments, Tom had resolved his personal doubts over Steve's guilt. But convincing a jury that one of their local kids had brutally blasted two bankers into oblivion with premeditation was going to require some skillful presentations of circumstantial evidence. For a first-degree murder charge to stick, Tom Fabel and Mike Cable would have to do more than place Steve at the scene. They would have to prove, beyond a reasonable doubt, that he had pulled the trigger and that he had planned to do so.

Tom had considered a plea bargain to get something for sure. As usual, he discussed this option with the victims' relatives. They were inclined to think that the justice system ought not to be short-circuited by dealing. The trial should proceed.

The jury would have to be unanimous. Tom had always had great confidence in juries, especially their essential good faith and common sense. He would appeal strongly to those attributes. But he was aware of the jury's unpredictability despite the fact that during the *voir dire* he and Swen could get a sense of each juror's individual values and feelings, or the lack of them, and each lawyer could eliminate the most objectionable, from each man's viewpoint.

Tom knew that few people in that area were rich. He knew how much, generally, people resent needing financial help. He knew that deep inside the minds of some of those men and women waiting for their names to be called out in the courtroom, murder might be wrong, but killing a banker was not murder. Extreme perhaps. But understandable. It would take only one example of such thinking on the jury and Steve Jenkins would walk out that courtroom door a free man.

When Fabel stands up at the prosecution's table at the start of a trial, he likes to be well rehearsed, and he always remembers the trial lawyer's cardinal rule: never ask anyone a question without knowing the answer. For weeks before a trial, he pores over the documents, the police and BCA reports, the photographs, the legal precedents for disputed points, the transcripts of interrogations and interviews. He compiles lists of vital points to be made and countered. He visits the crime scene and makes vivid notes so his realistic descriptions will place the jury mentally on the scene. He orally rehearses portions of his presentation. He even scouts out nearby racquetball courts and potential players to keep the mind and body in shape come evening; stale tensions from long courtroom days, he finds, cause mental mold.

Tom would be helped by Mike Cable, the quiet thirty-three-year-old son of an Indiana geometry teacher. Cable had graduated from college and then worked seven long years in the steel mills of Gary to finance his evening law studies. Like Rudy Blythe, he preferred the life of smaller cities and towns. So he studied the region, borrowed $600 from his father, and moved to St. Paul, where a three-month search for work ended with a job offer from a small law firm in Ivanhoe. When the county prosecutor's job became vacant in 1977, Cable ran and won.

Mike would become the prosecution's designated Official Worrier. His role in the case was not to speak in court, but to sit at the shiny, old wooden table in front of the judge's bench and speak into Tom's right ear, the one with the hearing aid, to register an observation or reminder.

The first step in the trial was to pick a jury of twelve, plus two alternates, who would decide the fate of the kid whose face so many of them had seen before. Seven of the first thirty-eight candidates disqualified themselves; they had known the Jenkins family somehow. Others said they just didn't feel capable of rendering an impartial verdict.

Tom was efficient and friendly throughout this crucial questioning. Wearing his favorite gray suit and frequently touching the corner of his eyeglasses as if to adjust them, he would introduce himself to each batch of potential jurors. "I'm Tom Fabel. I'm here to help Mr. Cable for the next couple of weeks." He talked about how important this trial was. His questions often reflected his interest—and underlying concern—with the jurors' attitudes toward the defendant, who was legally an adult and was about to be tried that way. Cable had warned Tom first thing about that: he'd heard a lot of talk locally about why the state was picking on a teenage kid. "You know," Tom would say, touching his glasses, "in Minnesota an eighteen-year-old is considered an adult by law. Do you have trouble accepting that?" Some said no. Others said that might be a tad on the youngish side, while still others said they had seen some eighteen-year-olds who were adults and some who weren't. Tom would nod and maybe smile a little, and Cable would scribble something by that juror's name.

Both Tom and Swen were also concerned about hunters. Almost all the males in the countryside hunt to some extent, though not the women. Hunters are more likely to see nothing strange in a little boy pretending to shoot things until he got his own rifle for his tenth birthday, so Tom and Mike concentrated on making sure the hunters on the jury also belonged to clubs or hunted in sociable groups, not by themselves. One or two loners, identifying too strongly with a defendant like Steve, could deadlock deliberations or, worse yet, swing an impressionable jury to an innocent verdict with a plea for individual rights.

Tom was also looking for a leader on the jury because, as Tom knows from sad experience, a jury without a leader is a hung jury and a large waste of time. In this regard, Dave Koster, the pharmacist from Tyler, seemed like a take-charge kind of guy. But Tom couldn't appear too pleased with him. That would ensure the guy would be thrown right out when Swen's turn came to challenge selections.

Swen, for his part, was eager to line up two rows of red-blooded, all-American, National Rifle Association hunters who probably went through a stage when they played soldier every day and who had sons who did the same. He began by apologizing to all the would-be jurors. "I'll have to ask some blunt questions," he said. "It's not 'cause I'm nosy. My job requires it.'' He would mispronounce just about every juror's name the first time around, and maybe the second and third time. He'd apologize and fiddle with his pen and pad of legal paper, and put his little glasses on to check his notes and then rip them off from one side in a manner that drives opticians right up the wall. Swen would look across at the jury, sticking his head and chin out, raising his eyebrows, and pursing his lips.

"What kind of father did you have?" he would ask. "Did you obey him?" "Do you think grown men should occasionally cry?" Some did. Some didn't.

He was interested in their views on adulthood and teenagers before pointing at Steve and reaching the $64,000 question for each potential juror: "Do you see before you now a totally innocent person?" Swen would freeze in his tracks, pursing his lips and sticking his jaw out again, awaiting the response. "Yes," they said softly.

Swen was interested in this Koster fellow too—the small-town pharmacist spoke out every answer clearly—asking him, as he did the others, "Do you have the courage to doubt?"

Koster right away revealed in his answer what his major concern was. "You're in a pickle," he said. "You could lose business if he's innocent or if he's guilty."

Slowly a general portrait of the jury began to emerge: they were people who got most of their news from television but claimed not to pay much attention to it; who all belonged to a church and its affiliated social groups but preferred not to be president; who thought that a lot of eighteen-year-olds are really not adults despite the law; who often hunted; who felt obedient to their strict but loving fathers, who hardly ever cried but would have been forgiven for doing so if they had.

After two days of questioning and selecting, of trading vetoes back and forth, the prosecution, defense, and the judge reached agreement. They seated fourteen jurors, eight women and six men, including two housewives who wouldn't learn until later that they were alternates. There were two retired farmers, an active one, two nurses, a lab technician, a telephone repairman, and a former creamery manager. Dave Koster was on the list, too.

Both Tom Fabel and Swen were pleased. In private, Tom had been describing Steve's developing defense as "Barnum & Bailey," focusing on "This Is Your Life, Jimmy Jenkins." In pretrial briefs, he opposed the handwriting expert as unscientific and the psychiatrist's report as blatantly biased since he talked only to those who had a definite stake in portraying Steve as pure and clean and Jim as a crazed maniac. Tom also sought to exclude testimony on Jim Jenkins's anger and strange behavior as irrelevant, since Jim was not on trial. He figured that much of the detail in Swen's briefs about Jim chasing some beer-drinkers off his property with a shotgun years ago or his racial remarks about a Filipino emergency room doctor one evening were put in the defense's legal papers, not so much for the judge's eyes as for the eyes and ears of others. Such incidents might allay a widespread sympathy for the farmer, focus more on his craziness, and maybe plant some seeds of doubt about poor Steve's guilt in the minds of twelve TV news watchers and newspaper readers.

Just to keep things in balance, Tom included as exhibits some BCA investigative reports from interviews in Texas. These reports quoted Jim Jenkins's bosses and coworkers on how hard he worked, how reliable he was in the demolition work, and, in contrast, how strange and consumed by guns and talk of violence was his son, Steve, who preferred to remove old windows with sledgehammers instead of screwdrivers. And they described Steve's attempts to build a bomb to drop in one woman's gas tank.

Tom's legal strategy also pointed out that under Minnesota law, for Swen to claim a defense of duress, he would have to prove that Steve faced the threat of imminent death from his father if he failed to comply with the man's wishes to help in the killings. And Swen would have to show too that Steve feared his father might kill him then and there in the farmyard, not later that afternoon or at some future time. But during the Texas interrogation and before the grand jury, Steve's description of the events leading up to and away from the killings made no mention of coercion. In fact, because of his father's night blindness and the need to flee in darkness, Steve ended up doing much of the driving to Texas while his father slept.

So the duress defense appeared to be under considerable duress itself when Judge Walter H. Mann of Minnesota's Fifth Judicial District stepped from his Ivanhoe chambers to preside over the State of Minnesota, Plaintiff, v. Steven Todd Jenkins, Defendant.

The judge was sixty-eight and a thirty-nine-year veteran of courtroom combat, five of them as a private attorney, ten as a county prosecutor, and twenty-four on the bench. He had been appointed to the state court in 1960. In 1978 he became chief of the five judges in the Fifth District, tucked away in Minnesota's agricultural southwest corner. Over the years he had built a reputation for gentle firmness and fairness both among prosecutors and defense attorneys. The Steve Jenkins case, however, was his first murder trial in many years.

On April 10, the first day of the trial, Judge Mann mounted the steps to his chair and looked out over the pews full of spectators and reporters and relatives of the victims. He issued, in response to the state's pretrial motions, a set of rulings that shaped the proceedings and the form of the evidence the Jenkins jury would receive. He ruled out any lie detector tests of Steve, and the handwriting expert's personality assessment of Jim, saying the state of the art was too unreliable to be admitted as evidence. He also came down on the side of the state regarding testimony on Jim Jenkins's personality and behavior. The judge would allow testimony on the father's character only insofar as it bore on the son's actions. Anything about Jim's temper, for instance, would have to have occurred in Steve's presence or have been observed by a third party to demonstrate the nature of Steve's relationship with his father.

Swen expressed no shock at this ruling that devastated his defense plans. He rose and ripped off his little glasses and said he needed some clarification from the judge. The same limits existed for the prosecution, didn't they, should the state try to introduce evidence about Jim Jenkins's good character?

Yes, they did.

The trouble for Swen Anderson was that in most cases the only person who could testify about Steve Jenkins's presence at such a time and its impact on Steve Jenkins was Steve Jenkins himself. Although he hadn't announced it, Swen, for his own secret and strategic reasons, had no intention whatsoever of allowing his client to take the witness stand. Nor did the law require it. At the proper time the judge would instruct the jury not to read anything into Steve's silence. Swen, who was starting to act very fatherly toward Steve, rarely cared what anybody thought about him anyway, so all the whisperings and hallway suspicions that would follow this decision bothered him not at all. Only the real jury mattered, and Swen was going to do the absolute best he could with what he had.

Sitting next to him at the courtroom table was a dark young man, his black hair neatly brushed over his low forehead and his busy eyebrows shading small blue eyes. His hands were clean; he wore a small stone ring on his little finger. He kept his head down, looking at the table or at the legal pad where he wrote a few notes now and then with his left hand, rarely looking at the judge, the witnesses, the jury, or anyone but the Andersons and, during recesses, his mother downstairs in the hall. The clean-shaven youth wore nice sweaters and shirts, pressed trousers, and leather dress boots, not too well polished. Some days when the high school dropout entered the courtroom, his thin shoulders and 135-pound frame were covered with a varsity letter jacket that a few years before would have fit one of Swen's boys. If anyone had asked, Swen would have explained that Steve didn't have any clothes of his own or any money to buy a new, nonmilitary wardrobe.

"Mr. Fabel, you may proceed."

"Thank you, Your Honor. May it please the court, Mr. Anderson, ladies and gentlemen of the jury. This trial is now about to begin."

The jury was impaneled, the spectator section was jammed, and television crews—prohibited from advancing beyond the second floor—hovered downstairs. Tom began the prosecution's presentation by stressing how important and serious these days were for the jurors. He said there would be an opening statement by him and another by Mr. Anderson, although the defense could delay theirs until after the prosecution's case had been presented. Fabel called the opening statement a summary of what was to come, but he warned the jury that the summary was not evidence. Of course, all attorneys try to summarize their case accurately, he said, but just because a lawyer said some words didn't make them evidence. "Please remember that," the prosecutor urged.

Fabel said he would be calling a number of people to testify. The defense could cross-examine these witnesses and present its own case. But the defense was under no obligation to prove anything, the prosecutor said. That was the state's responsibility, to prove guilt beyond a reasonable doubt. Then there would be summations by both sides, instructions on the law from Judge Mann, and finally the case would be turned over to them for their decision.

"You can think of the evidence in a criminal trial as a bunch of little pieces," Fabel said, touching his glasses now and then as he walked back and forth before them. "It is not like TV. Rather I think it's more helpful to think of the evidence in the case like a bunch of little pieces of a jigsaw puzzle that you spread out on the kitchen table. When you first walk into the kitchen and you see the mess the kids made at the table, you say to yourself, 'How can that possibly make any sense?' But then you pick up the cover to the box and you see the picture. You see the picture that the manufacturer intended for all those little pieces to make when they are fit together in a proper way. And that is what the opening statement is. The opening statement is the cover of the box of that picture."

Fabel outlined the charges. There were six counts in the two murders. The first two were first-degree murder, both for the death of Rudy Blythe, one for premeditated murder, the other for intentional murder during a robbery with a deadly weapon. Counts three and four were second-degree murder, intentionally causing the deaths of Rudy Blythe and Toby Thulin. Counts five and six were felony murders, that is, the defendant intentionally committed a felony against the victims—assault with a gun or robbery—and that death was reasonably foreseeable as a probable consequence, though perhaps not originally intended.

Tom introduced the two victims, briefly described them, their family circumstances, their jobs, and how on September 29, 1983, they happened to be at the bank's farm, thinking they were meeting a possible buyer. "Instead, both of them were executed in cold blood. The question in this trial, ladies and gentlemen, is how did this execution happen. Who did it?"

Fabel described how Rudy Blythe's bank had loaned Jim Jenkins the money for his farm and cattle, how Jim Jenkins made all his payments until 1980, when he announced that his wife was leaving him and he was quitting farming, and the bank learned that many of the cattle had already been sold off. Then Jenkins changed his mind, said his wife was coming back and he wanted to try the farm again, but the bank didn't think he was a good credit risk anymore. So they took back the few remaining cattle. Jenkins declared bankruptcy, and the bank got the farm.

Then on September 28, Rudy Blythe got a call from a Ron Anderson. Rudy had never heard of Ron Anderson. But Anderson wanted to see the Jenkins farm. Ah-hah, thought Rudy, finally, a customer.

Now, the next morning at about eight, Jim and Steve Jenkins got in their pickup truck near Hardwick and headed for their old farm. In that truck, Tom said, they had a .30-caliber rifle, a twelve-gauge shotgun, a sawed-off .410 shotgun, some disarmed hand grenades, knives, and "other instruments of violent death." At eight-thirty they arrived. Keep in mind, now, they didn't expect Rudy for an hour and a half. They got out some guns. They took off one license plate. "Their plans went awry. For some reason Rudy and Toby decided to go out to the farm earlier than ten A.M."

Tom described Susan Blythe's morning, too, how she came to be at the farm, and how, when Rudy sent her for the sheriff, she last saw her husband alive, fifty feet away, walking toward the woods next to the garage and saw Toby, sixty yards away, walking by some old outbuildings. "Moments after Susan Blythe drove out of that driveway," Tom said forcefully, pointing to a large map of the farmyard, "Steve Jenkins began shooting at Rudy Blythe and Toby Thulin."

Tom talked about where the bullets flew and what they did and how desperately Rudy was fleeing for his life, and how frantically, moments later, the Jenkins men fled too, stopping only to purchase more boxes of ammunition and to fire on a pursuing deputy. "That is a narrative account of the picture that is going to be on the front of that jigsaw puzzle," Fabel said. "Over against that account as part of the state's proof you are going to hear the defendant's story."

Between Steve's questioning in Texas and in front of the grand jury the previous fall, the prosecution had a very detailed account of Steve's version. Methodically, Bob Berg and Mike O'Gorman had taken that version and laid it over Susan's account and over anything else they could find out. The overlay showed some crucial disparities, which Tom was going to drive home time after time.

Using simple declarative sentences, the prosecutor summarized for the jurors the Jenkinses' circumstances. They had returned to Minnesota from Texas. They wanted to start over once again with another milking operation. Obviously they needed money. They visited banks all over that corner of the state, and everywhere the story was much the same. After examining their application, the banks would discover the earlier bankruptcy. They would learn that Rudy Blythe's Buffalo Ridge State Bank had been left with some unpaid debts in 1980. The other institutions would decide not to issue a new loan. But the Jenkins men continued to try. They tried to lease cattle instead of buying them, planning to pay rent with their milk checks. But no one wanted to extend any credit. Jim Jenkins blamed Rudy Blythe for that.

On September 28 came word from one last cattle dealer, who had seemed a good possibility: no credit. According to Steve's story, his father then set up the ambush, using the name Ron Anderson. "According to the defendant," Fabel said, "James Jenkins said, 'We are going to go out there to rob Rudy and to scare the hell out of him.' End of conversation, according to the defendant. According to the defendant, there was no further discussion of a plan during the balance of that afternoon. According to the defendant, they visited a friend's house. No further discussion of the plan. According to the defendant, they went out to eat that night. No further discussion about the plan. According to the defendant, they went through a normal evening's activity. No further discussion of the plan. According to the defendant, they went home that evening and went to bed. No further discussion of the plan. According to the defendant, they woke up on the morning of September 29, 1983, and his father said, 'Let's go.' No further discussion of the plan."

Fabel summarized Steve's version of the farmyard events: how they had been surprised by Blythe's early arrival; how Steve had run and hid behind the garage, not knowing where his father ran; how he heard some faint conversations, someone walking near him alongside the garage, a second car arriving and then someone saying, in a loud voice, to go for the sheriff. One car left. Then, Tom said, Steve recalled hearing someone say, "He's got a gun," followed by several shots, a period of silence, and more shots. When he hesitantly emerged from behind the garage, Steve said he saw a body hanging out of the station wagon and his father returning from the front yard with Steve's M-1 carbine. Steve said his father handed him the pickup truck's keys and said, "Come on, let's get out of here," and Steve drove away.

Tom recalled in a distinctly disbelieving tone Steve's story of the flight and how his father wanted to stop and kill some other people and rob some places but Steve talked him out of it; their arrival in Paducah, Texas; and the end.

"Well," said Fabel, "that is the defendant's story. And obviously that is not consistent with the picture that the state says that it will prove. Just as obviously there are only four people who were ever out at that farm at the time the shootings took place, and three of them are now dead."

Tom reviewed some of the discrepancies and implausibilities. He noted how Susan had placed Rudy so far past the barn that both Rudy and Steve would have had to see each other if Steve had been crouching behind it. He said the state would show how unlikely it was that the Jenkinses had no further conversations to plan their robbery and how unlikely it was that anyone but Steve would pick up his favorite weapon—which he admitted he even took to bed at night—and fire it effectively.

Tom also made public for the first time how the BCA had identified that funny metal noise Susan had heard coming from the woods that morning as Rudy dispatched her for the sheriff. Two weeks after the killings, BCA agents had taken Susan back to the yard and had turned her away from the woods. Mike Cummings ran around back there, touching and moving anything he could find to re-create the noise. Finally Susan's eyes widened. "That's it!" she said. "That's the noise!"

Hidden beneath the matted dead grass were some old sections of metal gutter. Someone sneaking through the grass had run over them, creating that muffled, hollow sound: the killer was positioning himself to shoot. He was moving from the back of the garage around the chicken coop to the spot where agents would find three empty M-1 carbine cartridges.

Steve had said that he did not hear any noise; but it had come from just a few feet behind his hiding place. "If Steven Jenkins had been in this spot," Fabel said, "he would have had to hear the noise that Susan Blythe heard—unless that noise was made by Steven Jenkins."

Tom said he would submit evidence that Steve Jenkins was a good marksman, in good physical shape, and that his father, the only other man out there, did not possess the conditioning, the shooting ability, nor, ladies and gentlemen, even the eyesight to commit these crimes.

"That," said Fabel, shuffling his papers into a neat stack on the lectern, "is the big picture that we are going to get in bits and pieces over the next several days."

Seventy-five minutes after he began, Tom Fabel was done. The judge cautioned the jury, as he would every day throughout the proceedings, not to discuss the case with anyone, read any newspapers, or listen to any electronic accounts of the trial. Ideally, the jury would have been physically isolated from any possible outside influences, bused from a motel to court and back again every day throughout the trial. But the nearest motel was twenty-five miles away. And these folks had their own businesses and farms to oversee and planting time was fast approaching. And the defense had not requested such precautions.

After a recess Fabel and Mike Cable called their first witness, Sheldon Thies, an assistant Lincoln County engineer who had made the enlarged courtroom drawing of the crime scene showing the location and relationship of various key buildings, the vehicles, trees, and the bodies.

Swen, who was saving his opening statement until later, was growling when he began his cross-examination. He questioned Thies closely on some measurements—how long the car was, for instance, and how far the trees were from the garage.

Next came Sheriff Abe Thompson, who described the two phone calls that morning, his race to the scene, what he found, and how he identified the men by their driver's licenses and then photographed the bodies. Swen was on his feet to inquire how far the sheriff was from the bodies when he took the pictures.

"I would say ten feet," replied the sheriff.

"Ten feet?" said Swen, almost drawing the question mark in the air.

Fabel resumed his questioning, asking the sheriff to describe the criminal investigative activities at the scene that day and how he initiated the hunt for the Jenkins men. Then, suddenly, Tom produced two photographs of the defendant, showing them to the sheriff for identification and then asking him to point out the same man in the courtroom, which Abe did. Tom wanted to know when they were taken (six days after the murders), if they were official county photographs (yes), and what the lines were in the pictures on the wall behind the defendant.

"It's a height chart," said the sheriff.

Tom then simply offered the two photos as state's exhibits, which brought Swen to his feet again.

"Your Honor," he said, knowing full well now what his opponent was up to, though few others in the room did, "we would have no objection as to reading into the record the height. We would object to the photos as to relevancy."

The judge asked to see the pictures and heard Swen and Tom argue over their relevancy in an animated bench conference.

"The record may show," said Judge Mann, "that the objection is overruled."

As the two photographs were passed slowly down the twin rows of the jury, the jurors could see for themselves the same shaved commando with tattoos who frightened Joyce Hall that stormy afternoon in Texas. The eyes of most of the jurors went from the image of the menacing youth in the photos to the young man in the varsity letter jacket staring at the floor by the defense table. Fabel was making a point about this local boy without saying a word.

Swen's questions for the sheriff focused on details. Were any rings or watches missing from the bodies? Not that he knew of. Swen said he'd seen the victims' clothing, but Rudy's socks and shoes were missing. Did the sheriff know what happened to them? No, he didn't.

The judge then said it was time for lunch. And everyone left. Except that Swen and Tom and Mike and Merle Matson, the court reporter, and the judge met privately in the back, where, for the record, the defense attorney objected again to the photographs of Steve as prejudicial. This was not the last skirmish in chambers that Swen would launch—or lose—seeking to build a record for a possible appeal.

Within minutes the Eagle Cafe, four blocks away, was filled not only with the regulars from a handful of offices and businesses along the one block of Norman Street that constituted downtown Ivanhoe, but with chattering groups of strangers from the courthouse. The judge and Merle were at one booth. The jury, overseen by a bailiff, was at three adjacent booths or tables. Spectators and reporters vied for the remaining tables and revolving counter seats.

Louis Taveirne ate at the Eagle too. And Swen. The prosecuting team, Fabel and Cable, was back in its courthouse workroom munching bagged sandwiches and reviewing the upcoming testimony with the two BCA agents. By a few minutes after one, they were back in the courtroom. At about 1:20 the spectators would flood in. Susan Blythe came every day, often carrying a prayer book that she found provided increasing comfort, and set herself up on the inside end of the second pew from the back with Sharon Fadness at her side. "I want to know it all," she would say. "I have to know it all." It is a reaction familiar to those who counsel survivors of violent crimes. Darlene Jenkins was sometimes at the other end of the same bench, sometimes one or two rows ahead, with her daughter Michelle.

Fabel in gray and Cable in black would walk in with a tall stack of papers and books. The prosecution and defense, though barely three feet apart, pretended to ignore each other and looked up at the bench. Then in would come Merle, and a businesslike Judge Mann, who plunked down his documents and looked over the players before him.

"You may proceed, Mr. Fabel."

"The state calls Robert Berg."

Fabel established the witness's credentials as a state detective and submitted a series of slides from a projector. Up on the screen appeared an aerial view of the white Jenkins house with its red roof and a few maples with their brightly colored leaves. And the barn and a station wagon parked near the garage with the front doors open. Fabel had Berg identify the place and date and show where the bodies had been found and where some shell casings had been found. Other pictures showed the high weed conditions, different farmyard perspectives, and a close-up of the car, where something seemed to be hanging out of the right front passenger door.

When the next slide came on, a soft gasp flashed through the room. On the ground was Toby Thulin, father of three little girls, in unliving color. His face was pocked with little red wounds from flying pieces of glass, and below his chin was the neat little hole, a darker red, with a trail of fainter color running into his collar and up to his ear.

Fabel and Berg pressed on with other testimony and photos, and came inexorably to the color close-ups of Rudy Blythe's bloated body, clothed in his bloodstained garments. Berg inventoried Steve's military equipment and weapons, including the .410 shotgun with a hunting knife welded to the front and some throwing stars with specially sharpened points. Because he had never heard of such weapons until this trial, Tom had Berg explain these Oriental martial arts weapons. Berg identified a wide variety of other items that afternoon, from bullet fragments from Toby's body to the pair of eyeglasses found in Jim Jenkins's jacket pocket.

Fabel seemed finished then, but Mike Cable whispered something in his ear. And Tom had one more question. He recalled how hard Berg had said it was to wade through the thick weeds on the Jenkins farm. And he thought some jurors might have connected that difficulty with Berg's obvious limp.

With a little smile that anticipated the courtroom snickers, Berg explained there was no connection. He had recently broken his ankle in a volleyball game. Tom smiled too then. The prosecutor, who had once alluded in court to his own hearing aid, had just shown that another member of the visiting prosecution team was human too.

Swen's long cross-examination focused on details. He wanted more information on crime-scene measurements, and he wanted to know how much money Rudy had in his wallet (two or three dollars), if the spent shells might have been moved by weed removal (unlikely), and how frequent was the tendency of Steve's gun to jam. The prosecution claimed that only someone intimately familiar with this malfunctioning could have fired the murder shots. He also wanted to know if Rudy Blythe had any change in his pocket.

"Yes, there was a small amount."

"It is obvious, then, that Ruby Blythe had not been robbed?"

"Objection. Argumentative."

"Objection sustained."

What was the weather like that day? Swen wanted to know. Was it a little tough to see? Berg didn't think it was too bad, just a little slippery driving. What wcrc all those weeds at the crime scene? Berg said they were just weeds. Where were Rudy's socks? Had they or any clothes been vacuumed by technicians? Swen seemed to be trying to suggest that Rudy had not walked past the garage, past Steve's alleged hiding place, looking for the trespassers; if he had, some of those weed fibers would have been on his clothing. But Berg, a veteran of many witness stands and a former U.S. Army MP, was not about to be ambushed, even by a momentarily smiling Swen.

Susan took her customary place in the spectator section the next day, but before the proceedings began Mike O'Gorman appeared behind her. He had seen her often after That Day, seen her turn from an overweight, distraught new widow full of tears and fears to a slimmed-down woman under emotional control, almost too much control sometimes. Mike bent down and whispered, "You don't need to be here for this morning's testimony." Susan, knowing what he meant, waited outside until Dr. Brad Randall was done testifying.

"Bullet number one passed through the abdominal cavity," said Dr. Randall, who conducted the autopsy, "and, of course, the abdominal cavity contains the liver, stomach, and the intestines, and spleen." Using drawings and color slides taken twenty-three hours after the banker died, the forensic pathologist described in detail the wounds, fatal and otherwise, suffered by Rudy and Toby. Tom had to establish the medical cause of death for the record.

"This is a line diagram representing the bullet paths found in Mr. Blythe," the doctor was saying, pointing at the screen in the darkened courtroom. "Again, this is not a—"

The doctor's graphic testimony about shattering bullets and severed arteries stopped abruptly. He and everyone else had heard a kind of wheezing sound from the jury box. The lights came on quickly, and the judge dispatched Dr. Randall to examine a juror, Donald Guida. The elderly former farmer, who had a history of heart problems, looked pale and shaken. Following a recess, Judge Mann excused him from the jury.

Fabel called Cindy Sizer. She was the court reporter for the grand jury proceedings. Tom and Cindy read into the record lengthy portions of Steve's testimony from the grand jury transcript. Those portions described the Jenkinses' futile search for credit and talks Steve had five days before the shootings with Richard Hartson at his glass store. Steve had inquired what kind of bullet would pierce bulletproof glass. Then there was Steve's talk with Marvin Minette the day before the shooting about how to obtain dynamite. Steve had said he did not talk with his father about how they planned to rob and scare Rudy Blythe, and he described their movements leading up to their arrival at the old farm, how they parked there, got their guns out, and how he put on his camouflage shirt and floppy camouflage hat, and how his father picked up the M-1 and went to remove the rear license plate on his pickup truck. But they both heard a car slowing on the wet pavement of County Road 7. Steve said he ran behind the garage then. His father ran off too, but Steve didn't know where. Steve said he crouched there, hearing indistinct conversations, pauses, then three minutes later another car arrived, and there were more conversations with a loud command to go for the sheriff. Steve said he stayed crouched there, facing west, doing nothing. Then one car left. Seconds later, the shooting began.

Steve said that when he emerged following a second series of shots, he saw one guy lying there, sticking out of the station wagon, and then Jim Jenkins appeared wearing his usual blue jeans, denim jacket, and tightly rolled purple and white stocking cap and told his son to start driving.

Tom Fabel and Cindy Sizer continued to read from Steve's grand jury transcript about the men's flight, their shooting at the pursuing deputy sheriff, and the taking of some license plates from an old car on an abandoned South Dakota farm. Then Steve had said he asked his father a question. "Well, I had asked him what happened back there, at the place," Steve testified, "and then after we got going a ways there, he said about since he got these two that he might just as well keep going, take as many with him as he could." They stopped for gas only once, Steve said, and for food not at all, eating only the few cans of groceries that had fallen through a wet paper bag into the truck in the rain the night before the shootings.

Steve described the long inventory of weapons, when and where he had acquired the guns, the stars, the handcuffs, the machete, and why he had sawn off the .410 and welded a knife on the front. (It looked more military.) He said how much he had practiced shooting (a lot), and at what— cans, bottles, a refrigerator door, a big, old tree branch dressed up like a man, and a piece of wood about a man's height with a plastic milk bottle for a head.

Fabel had led the youth through memories of his father's interest in guns: Jim Jenkins had none. His father hadn't gone shooting or hunting in years. Bad eyes, you know. When his father said he wanted to kill Louis Taveirne, too, Steve talked him out of it, he said. He also talked him out of robbing a lot of gas stations for money along the way to Texas, Steve said.

"Were you afraid of your father?" Steve was asked.

"When he got mad," he replied.

"Did you love your father a lot?"

"Yes."

Fabel opened the next week of the trial with Susan Blythe, who recounted the purchase of the bank and general business dealings since moving to Ruthton as well as the events of that September morning. Then it was Swen's turn. Interrogating the widow of a murder victim before a jury while defending the alleged criminal is a tricky business. There may be some points to nail down, but it must be done carefully lest the poor woman collapse in tears and the defense attorney and defendant come out looking like bullies.

As usual, Swen had a lot of detail questions, running over the dates of the Jenkins bankruptcy, his financial record with the bank, whether Steve Jenkins had ever had an account there. Swen was trying to separate Steve from his father's bad relationship with the bank, to leave only the father with a murder motive of revenge. But Susan was not going to give this, uh, person defending her husband's assassin one inch. She had felt the first faint stirrings of sympathy for Steve in recent days. But for this sly, funny-talking lawyer who would thwart justice, she felt hatred and contempt. Her son Rolph, who was in court one day, felt the same. In fact, in the boy's regular nightmares about the murder, Swen became the menacing figure, not Steve Jenkins.

So when Swen asked Susan if Jim Jenkins had frequent overdrafts, she didn't know. And the bankruptcy, was that in 1980? Susan thought that was approximately right. Did she know Steven's age? No. Had Steve ever had an account at her bank? Don't know. Had he ever done any business there? Don't know. Well, would a bank normally have customers under age eighteen? Why not? she answered. Her eleven-year-old son had an account there.

Had she ever seen James Lee Jenkins write? Excuse me? Did she ever see James Lee Jenkins write? No. Did Steve ever have any loans at the bank? No, no. Do you know or don't you know whether Steve ever had any accounts with the bank? I said no, Mr. Anderson. He did not? I said no.

The tug-of-war went on. Swen questioned her on her husband's weight. Once she had said 260 and now it was 230. No, said Susan, she had said 250 before and 230 now; she had found a weight chart. And his height— once she had said he was six foot four and now, Swen said, scratching for any inconsistency and reminding her she had been under oath, it was six three and a half. He was a big man, Mr. Anderson. Yes, but why the difference? Sometimes, Susan said, she says she is five foot seven and a half and sometimes she says five foot eight. Well, which is it? I don't know.

But Susan knew exactly what Rudy had worn That Day. She was clothes conscious, unlike her husband. Like many wives of such men, she had tried to sharpen his wardrobe a bit.

When she had first been told she would have to testify as a crucial prosecution witness, Susan was very confident and wanted no directions. As the time neared, however, her confidence wavered. So her steeliness strengthened. She didn't know everything that was coming from Swen Anderson, but she knew what she was going to give him: no satisfaction nowhere nohow.

Swen pulled from a paper bag State's Exhibit No. 88. "Tell me if you recognize it," he said.

"These are my husband's pants."

"Do you know what kind of fabric it is?"

"I would consider that to be khaki twill."

"Do you know when he bought the pants, where he bought them?"

"Yes. I purchased them from L. L. Bean."

"What is L. L. Bean?"

"It's a sporting goods place in Maine."

"What? Maine?"

"Yes. Freeport, Maine."

"Other than the sight of blood and the bullet holes, is there anything different in these pants today than when you last saw them on your husband September twenty-ninth on the Jenkins farm?"

"Mr. Anderson, I wasn't concerned with my husband's pants; I was concerned with him."

"Did you notice any difference outside of the blood and the bullet holes?"

"I don't think so. I don't think so."

At the prosecution table, Fabel was looking just fine. On the inside he was incredulous. How could this magnificent opportunity slip by? Any self-respecting widow he had seen would be in hysterics by now, melting like butter in the heat of such a blunt interrogation and likely solidifying the antipathy of the jury toward the insensitive interrogator, especially a jury with a majority of females. Tom, who had just about had it with Swen's irritating coughs during the prosecutor's presentations, considered spilling his water pitcher to get a recess and to get to Susan. "Loosen up," he would have said, "just be yourself." But he didn't. It wouldn't have mattered anyway. She was being herself.

Swen tried to chip away at the credibility of Susan's memory. First the weight, then the height, then the color of the pickup truck she passed on the way to fetch the sheriff. So, a polite Swen thought aloud, maybe that noise Susan thought she heard back in the woods was a rabbit or dog or something. How loud was it, Mrs. Blythe? How loud is loud, Mr. Anderson? Maybe it was not loud enough for your husband to hear? Maybe, Swen continued, Rudy didn't walk as far back into the woods as she remembered, not far enough to pass the garage corner.

The next round of questions came from Tom Fabel, who was obviously trying to clear the air. Was the noise Susan heard consistent with the volume and the noise she heard two weeks later with the agents?

"Yes."

"Thank you. I have no further questions."

Piece by piece, Fabel and Cable continued their attempt to assemble a convincing portrait of guilt. Agent O'Gorman described the reenactment with Susan and fellow agent Cummings, who is about Rudy Blythe's height. O'Gorman established that when Cummings walked toward the trees, he appeared to shrink as he walked down a slight incline, as Susan had described. That point was well past the back of the garage, meaning Rudy would have seen anyone crouching down there, even someone wearing camouflage. Swen sought to point out how the police hadn't measured Rudy Blythe's pants legs and compared them to Michael Cummings's.

Fabel showed a videotape with agents walking where the tragedy's characters were said to have walked and reinforcing O'Gorman's statement about the incline, plus showing how if Steve was indeed hiding behind the garage, he would have had to see Rudy walking by. By the way, asked Tom, after the reenactment did O'Gorman notice the agents having to pull weeds off their clothes?

Objection.

Overruled.

No.

Swen, mispronouncing O'Gorman's name, had more questions about weeds. He thought if Rudy really had walked back there, he would have picked up some weeds on his clothes. Swen had some photos of his own, showing a man on the Jenkins farm wearing khaki twill pants with some burrs and weed debris stuck to them.

Tom objected, on the basis of no foundation. Was O'Gorman present when these pictures were taken? No. Did he know what month they were taken in? No. What year? No. Did he know the man? No. Did he know where that man had been before? No.

"Objection sustained."

Paul Bartz, the part-time local policeman, described driving down County Road 7 near the Jenkins place and glimpsing a flash of yellow in the brown grass. He slowed, and saw part of a leg. Making a U-turn, he saw a white pickup truck speed down the driveway and turn south. No front license plate. The driver he saw was an older man, mid-forties maybe, heavyset. The passenger was a kid, early twenties perhaps, dark hair, green shirt. Rear plate was black and white, likely Texas. Six digits, letters and numbers. He went back and checked the ditch. It was a man; he appeared to have been shot. Another driver came by and was sent for help.

Swen tried to shake Bartz's identification of the pickup truck driver, reminding him that under oath before the grand jury Steve had admitted he was driving. "That would not change my mind, sir." Was anyone wearing anything on his head? The driver was wearing a stocking cap.

Okay, said Swen. Now, what was Susan Blythe's emotional condition when she arrived? Hysterical and combative, said Bartz. He was unable to understand her, but he gathered she was worried about her husband and she mentioned Jenkins, something about goddamned Jenkins. Then Swen showed Bartz a copy of his police report. He'd written it the same day, September 29. The report indicated that Susan had said her husband saw somebody running in the woods.

"Like I say," said Bartz, "she was pretty incoherent and hysterical. But yes, I got the distinct impression that he had seen something."

O'Gorman came back briefly to reconstruct Susan's drive to phone the sheriff. Because she had passed the oncoming Bartz at high speed and because he noted the time, the agents could determine how long everything took from the time Susan left the farmyard until the body was found— three minutes and twenty seconds. Swen thought they had the killer running a mite fast, according to his calculations, which he got confused in going over there in court. And perhaps so too did his listeners, which was fine with Swen.

Jeff Schroeder was up next. He'd seen the speeding white pickup too. When he came over the hill in his car just before the Jenkins place, he'd seen a truck pulled over and Paul Bartz said to him did he know cardiopulmonary resuscitation and Jeff said no. So Bartz sent him to phone for help, but there wasn't anyone at home at the Hartsons'. Schroeder doubled back to the Petersons', where the missus let him in to phone. By the time he got back to the ditch, Bartz was administering cardiopulmonary resuscitation but it seemed to do no good. Looking around, Jeff saw a trail in the wet grass running from the side of the house across the front yard and down to the body in the ditch, the only remaining sign of Rudy's last frantic steps.

No further questions.

Now, said Swen, could Jeff positively identify the defendant as one of the men in the truck? No, but Steve fit the characteristics of one of them, the passenger. Did the truck cross the center line at all? Jeff hadn't had too much time to watch. The white pickup was coming awful fast. But the driver appeared to have the vehicle under control. Had Jeff noticed anything about the driver to indicate he had difficulty seeing? Not enough time to make that evaluation, just a second or two at the most. He was also asked about Susan's appearance and he said she was very upset, not quite in control of herself. "Shock, so to speak."

Tyler Police Chief Dan Fischer was up next. When he arrived at the Jenkins farm that September day, the ambulance crew was working on Rudy, and Susan was leaning over him talking and she said something about her husband and Toby showing the farm to someone. It was at that point that Dan realized there might be others around, and they went up into the farmyard and found Toby. No pulse in the neck. Dan sealed off the yard and the path through the tall wet grass toward the old shed.

Deputy Ron McClure told Fabel about getting the radio message at 10:10 A.M. to watch for the white pickup, which he spotted later that morning. It had no front license plate. He whipped a U-turn and came up behind— it was a white Chevy, all right—and he got the Texas license number, KW3618. Two male subjects. Passenger dark, very short hair. The driver wore glasses and a stocking cap.

At one point the pickup made a wide left turn onto a gravel road, and McClure lost sight of it for a moment behind the tall corn. Then he saw the truck stop and a passenger got out with a rifle. "And I knew exactly what was going to happen then.

"I heard two or three shots. I watched him come across. As I came into the intersection, he come across with a gun toward me, and then I observed him get back in the pickup. And as soon as he did that, I did a power turn around and headed back toward them to follow."

Swen wanted to know if there was anything besides the missing front plate that attracted Deputy McClure's attention, anything like, say, swaying back and forth or across the road. No, nothing. Had he measured the distance between the shooter at the pickup and where his patrol car was? No. Swen produced a transcript of McClure's interview with the BCA on September 29. The attorney wondered how come McClure could say approximately thirty yards then. "I was shook on September twenty-ninth." And why hadn't he measured it to begin with? "Probably an oversight on my part."

Tom Fabel had a rebuttal question for the deputy, thinking also of the pending charges against Steve for shooting at McClure's car. "If the defendant had been successful in shooting out your tires, as was indicated by his grand jury testimony, would that have prevented your vehicle from engaging in a high-speed chase?"

"I would object to that," said Swen. "I think it's speculative."

Judge Mann agreed. "Objection sustained."

"Well, let me ask it this way. Is your vehicle capable of a high-speed chase if a tire has been blown out?"

"No."

"Thank you. I have no further questions." Another day ended.

Lynnette Thulin was on the stand the next morning. She had brought her three daughters to court, as Susan had brought Rolph, to see the justice system at work. When one of them in the spectator section became disturbed at the questioning of their mother and the memories, it was Susan who offered motherly hugs.

Actually Lynnette, who was a couple of hundred miles away at the time of the killings and had been separated from Toby for nearly two months before his murder, had little to offer the jury. Fabel knew this. But he also likes to keep a trial from becoming too cold and technical, so he always tries to have at least one of the victim's family members testify to remind the jury that these deadly incidents leave real people behind.

To justify Lynnette's appearance, Tom's questioning focused on Toby's physical condition and mental attitude toward confrontations. He wanted to show that Toby would probably not run from a physical confrontation unless there were guns involved and he didn't have one. This would be a delicate process for Tom. He had to touch on Toby's military involvement and his veteran's status without going into it too deeply. He knew Toby had lied to several people about his membership in the Special Forces. What Tom wouldn't learn until much later was that Toby had been an airplane weapons mechanic. He had nothing to do with Gatling gunships or being a POW or even teaching little Vietnamese kids. The closest that that son of a World War II veteran ever got to combat, Toby's official military records would show, was a safe and secure air base in Thailand.

Lynnette described her marriage for the jury as being in the process of reconciliation following an August separation. She said what close friends they and Rudy were, and she recounted Toby's numerous physical activities with local teams, the National Guard, and, of course, his military combat training. Tom asked her if she'd ever seen Toby in a confrontational situation. Swen objected. Tom objected to the objection. But Swen's objection was upheld.

Tom started on another tack, this one more defensive, although it sounded innocent enough. The night before Lynnette was scheduled to testify the prosecution team met as usual after some exercise—O'Gorman regularly whipped Fabel in racquetball. Cable, the worrier, referred to an early BCA interview with Lynnette in which she recalled Rudy speaking of an encounter with Jim Jenkins at his old farmhouse one time when Jim chased him off with a shotgun.

This incident came as a bombshell to Tom, who hadn't seen that report or had forgotten it amid all his other cases. Such testimony would be a priceless gift for Swen, introducing the crazy-Jim factor that Tom had just gotten excluded and putting a gun in Jim's hands much more recently than even the defense could establish. The agents remembered the interview, but they had never been able to verify the incident. As professional detectives, it didn't sound right to them. It wouldn't be like Rudy not to spread that story around, so convincing was it about Jim Jenkins's lunacy. But the agents could find no one else who said they ever heard about it.

Confirmed or not, the story presented a strategic problem for Tom. Swen had copies of all police reports, so he could be ready to pounce. Tom could simply not call Lynnette to the stand, but he rejected that suggestion; he wanted living victims in evidence and he had already told the jury the other widow would be there. Changing course might raise suspicions.

There was, however, another alternative, a bold stroke but Tom liked it. It fit the classic legal theory that if there is damaging evidence to come out, bring it out yourself, then smile. The prosecutor would go ahead and produce Lynnette. Tom would steam along right behind her with an appropriate smoke screen to throw Swen off. If the defense attorney recalled the damaging though unverified Jim Jenkins story, Tom would just produce his "it-doesn't-really-hurt" smile and wade on through.

After the jury returned, he asked Lynnette if Toby had ever had any training in physical combat. Oh, yes, she said. When was he in the National Guard? She listed the years. Now, Mrs. Thulin, said Tom, while you were living in Ruthton did you ever have any contact with the defendant, Steven Jenkins? No, sir. Did you ever have any contact with any other member of the Jenkins family including James Jenkins? No, sir.

"Did your husband ever inform you of any contact that he had had with the—with either the defendant or with James Jenkins?"

"Objection, hearsay."

Perfect. A suspicious Swen was trying to cut off that line of questioning, just as Tom desperately wanted. Swen didn't know what was coming, but he didn't like the sound of it, which was the whole plan.

"Objection overruled," said the judge.

Oh, no, thought Tom. He'd have to make the next question even more objectionable. So he spoke slowly, trailing the bait carefully.

"Did you ever have any discussions with Rudolph Blythe concerning either the defendant or James Jenkins?"

"Objection, hearsay."

"Objection overruled. You may answer."

What? Tom did not want this to happen! Quick now, how could he qualify this, stretch it out?

"Yes, sir, I did," answered Lynnette.

"When did those conversations occur?"

"May I give the background?"

"Your Honor," interrupted Swen, "I would ask the witness be responsive to the question."

"Yes. The background question would be improper, Counsel. You may ask specific questions."

Tom was getting his phony smile ready. Time was running out, and he was hoping and talking at the same time. "When did your first conversation with Rudolph Blythe occur concerning the Jenkinses?"

"Okay. It was the second [job] interview that Toby and I had with Rudy. The board wanted to meet Toby, and we were to go with Rudy to the

Kronborg for supper to meet with the board. On the way we stopped at the old Jenkins place and Rudy took us into the house. He said that he frequently would stop to check to see if anyone had been there to vandalize it or anything. And while we were in the house, he showed me the destruction in the bathroom and in the plumbing downstairs in the kitchen. And he told me to be careful when I was standing in the bathroom—''

"Your Honor," interjected Swen, "I would object again on hearsay and irrelevant unless it is linked to Steve Jenkins."

"Objection sustained."

At last, thought Tom. "I have no further questions."

Swen could still unearth something in his cross-examination, of course. "Mrs. Thulin," he began, "I am just going to ask you one question. Did Rudy Blythe seem to have ill feeling against Steven Jenkins's father, James L. Jenkins?"

"I would say—"

"Objection. Calls for speculation."

"Objection overruled. You may answer."

"I would say he was cautious."

"I have nothing further."

When Tom Fabel rose to summon the next witness, Al Weathers, the prosecutor was smiling, this time genuinely.

Alvis Henry Weathers was a fifty-nine-year-old gunsmith from Brownwood, Texas. In his questioning Tom established Weathers's expertise with guns dating back to 1942, when the M-1 carbine was the officers' rifle. In fact, Al helped write the navy's training curriculum on the M-1 during his thirty-year hitch. Tom had Al detail the mechanics of the semiautomatic M-1, how it fired every time someone pulled the trigger, how the ammunition cartridge fit, and how the ejection process worked. Tom introduced a business receipt that showed that Al had worked on a feeding problem in Steve's M-1, back on February 15, 1983. He mentioned notes Al had made then that said the weapon should have gone back to the factory to repair ill-fitting parts that pulled out the empty cartridge after firing. He described how that led to misfiring problems, when an empty ejecting shell would jam in one position, blocking entry of the new cartridge. He showed how in the military, men are trained to rapidly overcome such occurrences. Al also looked at the seven empty shells found by BCA agents at the murder scene.

"Was there any evidence of jamming on any of the rounds?" Tom asked.

"One," Al replied. It had a distinctive scratch.

Swen's long cross-examination opened on marksmanship, how good a shot an expert is at a hundred yards, leading up to what an easy shot it would be for an expert like Al to pick off at that distance a man standing, oh, say, six foot four. He talked about what a cheap reproduction the murder weapon was and how it hadn't been properly cared for.

When Tom's turn came again, he focused on the sighting mechanism and how difficult it was for people like Al, with vision problems, to use peep sights like the murder weapon's. Also, isn't it true that while a six-foot-four-inch man might be an easy target at a hundred yards, a moving target is more difficult to hit?

"Absolutely."

Now, assume you're shooting at a moving target about ninety feet away. You fire two shots almost simultaneously and both hit the target within an inch or so of one another. Is that a good or poor shot?

"It would be excellent," came the reply, which pleased Tom, but then Al went on, "if it was intentional."

"If it was unintentional, sir, does that mean it would simply be random chance?"

"Random chance."

"And I assume there is as much chance of accidentally shooting yourself in the foot as of putting a second shot at that same spot. Is that correct?"

"Objection. It is leading and suggestive."

"Objection sustained."

Then Tom questioned Al about running and shooting and how both activities seriously compound the problems of accurate shooting—heavy breathing, blurred vision, disorientation. "It takes weeks to develop the stamina," Al said. The worse shape you are in, the more inaccurate would be the shooting.

Swen thought it would be impossible to put two shots so close together if you had to manually cock the malfunctioning semiautomatic. Right, Mr. Weathers? No, not impossible, said Al, which Swen did not want to hear. "I must tell you this," the witness added. "Normally when you have a manual operation, your sighting is a lot better than it is from your semiautomatic."

Tom had been making so much about all the training necessary to shoot well, and Swen knew pretty much what Charles Snow, top sergeant extraordinaire, was going to say on the stand about all of Steve's training. So Swen wanted to nail something down. But he hit his thumb instead.

Wasn't it true, Swen asked Al, that a man trained on the M-1 in the National Guard in the 1950s would be prepared to shoot the M-1 carbine too? Yes, they were the same guns functionally, just a shorter barrel on the carbine. And has it been your experience, Mr. Weathers, that qualified National Guard shooters are good or poor marksmen?

"It's been my experience," Al responded, "that the people trained by the National Guard were poor marksmen."

Swen then asked Al why this was. He had to get out of this one with something.

The training was not intense enough or long enough, Al said.

"Would the training have been sufficient to have hit a man at a hundred feet that weighed over two hundred pounds and was six foot four in height?" Yes, because it's an easy shot. No further questions.

Tom produced Roger Papke next. A crime lab technician, Papke talked about murder-scene measurements and ballistics. He set at 266 feet—nearly a 100-yard dash—the distance that the killer moved from shooting Toby to shooting Rudy. He traced the paths of the bullets and showed slides of test firings at the Blythe station wagon. The agents had wanted to know where that first bullet, the one that shattered the windshield, ended up. It was in Rudy's lower back.

Swen noticed that this fellow Papke wore glasses. Was he wearing them when he fired the test shots? Yes. Any difficulty making the shots? No. Any shots go off the mark? No. No further questions.

James Lansing, also from the crime lab, testified that the holes in the victims' clothing were made by the bullets; the fabric contained traces of lead. He linked the empty shells and bullet fragments to Steve's gun. He described the test firings on Steve's rifle and how it often malfunctioned, jamming with that poor ejection mechanism. Through a series of timely objections, Swen prevented the jury from hearing this expert's opinion on whether someone familiar with a particular gun could easily overcome its tendency to jam.

Tom called other witnesses as the days passed. Sheriff Thompson was back to produce a piece of the noisy rain gutter. Steve Wurster, an ambulance attendant, was called to say that he had not moved Rudy's body during the forty-five minutes they had performed CPR on him. Swen didn't care about the CPR. He wanted the twenty-eight-year-old to describe, over Tom's objection, Susan Blythe's condition in the ditch. "Very upset," he said. What else did he hear her say?

"She—before we even knew what had happened, she had made the remark that Jenkins had killed her husband."

BCA Agent Michael Cummings was called to produce a telephone message slip he had found on Rudy's desk by the phone. Barbara Jean Winsel, a bookkeeper-teller at the Buffalo Ridge State Bank, took the stand to say she had taken that message while Rudy was on another line. In her handwriting it said, "Ron Anderson is on 1." Beneath that in Rudy's handwriting it said, "10 A.M." That was underlined.

Swen began his cross-examination as usual. "Ms. Henshall," he said.

"Winsel," she corrected him.

Swen wanted to know if she knew the caller's voice, if it had been muffled. No on both counts.

Jerry Ihnen, Rudy's former bank manager, was called to establish how the bank came to own the farm. He said it was collateral on Jenkins's loans for machinery and cows. Everything had been going along fine, Ihnen said, payments on time until August 1980, when he'd received an anonymous phone call from a man asking if he knew Jenkins was selling off his milk cows. When Jerry called the sales barn, they confirmed it; thirty-two of Jenkins's seventy cows were on the block, and not for the good dairy cow price of perhaps $800 each but for the $400 to $500 slaughter price.

The sales check was made out to both Jim Jenkins and the bank, Jerry said. When the farmer came in to cash it, Jerry asked him why he'd done it. Jenkins said his wife was leaving him, and he wanted to quit farming and pay off the bank. A few days later he called Rudy and said the bank might as well come get his last few cows. He was leaving. The bank never accounted for the twenty-five missing cows. It took possession of all the property later from the bankruptcy judge.

Swen wanted to know about Jim Jenkins's walk (normal), ability to drive (don't know), eyesight (he looked at things and objects real closely). Did Jerry have any reason to believe Steve had anything to do with the missing cows? No.

Nancy Smith was questioned next about her café in Pipestone, the Mayfair, and two of her regular customers, Jim and Steve Jenkins. Over numerous objections by Swen, she said they would spend at least an hour there every day, eating the noon meal and sometimes breakfast and supper, too. Tom asked her about the men's normal behavior in the café.

"Objection, relevancy."

Overruled.

"They were just very quiet. They never spoke to each other nor did they speak to the waitresses."

Now, the murders occurred on September 29, Tom said. What had Nancy noticed about the behavior of the Jenkins pair the previous evening?

Objection.

Overruled.

"They happened to be in the café at nine-thirty. And I usually go over to lock up at about that time. We lock up at ten, but I usually go a half hour early. And when I walked in, they were talking."

"Was there anything about the way they were talking that struck you as noticeable?"

"Objection, leading and suggestive."

"Objection overruled. You may answer."

"They, you know, other days when they would come in, they sat with their back up against the wall and would just relax. That night when I came in, they were talking to each other, you know, hovered over the table." They were the only ones in the restaurant at the time. They talked all the time, too.

Thank you, Miss Smith.

"Miss Smith," Swen began, "did—was there any disturbance in the café on the twenty-eighth?"

"No."

"Any bad manners?"

"No."

"If you hadn't heard the next day that there were two killings, would you have remembered that evening?"

"About them talking together?"

"Yes."

"Yes, because when I walked in I said to the girls—"

"I'm sorry, I can't hear you."

"I'm sorry. When I walked in the café that night, I said to the girls that's the first time I've ever seen those guys talk...."

"Do normally people talk to each other in restaurants?"

"Yes, they do."

"Do they normally whisper so others can't hear them?"

"Not on the average, no."

"I have nothing further." Swen sounded tired.

Tom called the next witness and examined him with a rapid-fire sequence of questions. State your full name for the record, please. Richard Glenn Hartson. Lives on County Road 7 across from the old Jenkins farm. Age fifty. Married. Runs a glass business in Pipestone, D & M Glass. Known the Jenkinses for many years. Father and son had a good relationship. Saw Steve out hunting, but never the father.

Last time he saw them, Dick Hartson said, was the Monday before the murders. They came in, Steve all in camouflage gear. While Dick was out in the shop working on a tractor door, Steve asked him what kind of glass they used in banks. Dick said bulletproof and Steve asked what it would take to go through one. Dick recalled a supervisor who said a 30.06 wouldn't pierce it and Steve asked then what about an armor-piercing weapon. Dick paused and said, "Gol, Steve, I don't know. I have no idea."

Hartson described too the night Jim Jenkins flipped his truck in the ditch and Darlene Jenkins explained, "Jim's got bad eyes."

Under Swen's questioning, it developed that Hartson had talked with Jim on that Monday as well. Dick had said he hoped all would go well with Jim's new milking operation, you know, not have any trouble with the bank and all. That's when Jim Jenkins said he knew his wife had fooled around with his banker.

Tom knew his notes cold, and he wanted another crack at Hartson. Aside from that day, Tom asked, had Jim Jenkins ever expressed suspicions that his wife had been having affairs with other men?

Objection.

Overruled.

Yes.

How many?

Three or four.

When Jenkins mentioned Rudy Blythe that Monday, did he sound bitter? No.

Now, about the bulletproof glass, had anyone ever asked before what kind of ammo would pierce bulletproof glass?

"No, sir."

Swen wanted to make a point too. Had Steve Jenkins here ever talked to Dick at all about bankers or anything like that?

No.

Marvin Minette, a well-driller, was called next. He remembered meeting Steve Jenkins the day before the murders at a mutual friend's house. Marvin was out back drilling, and Steve, dressed like a GI in jacket and camouflage pants, came over to talk. Steve asked Marvin if dynamite was hard to get.

"What led up to that conversation?" Tom asked, knowing full well the answer.

"Nothing," said Marvin.

Then Steve asked about fertilizer bombs.

Swen wanted to know if that was the sum total of their conversation. Yup. Did Steve at any time say he was going to make anything? Nope. Did he say he was going to use explosives to hurt anyone? No.

Steven Shriver then recalled his friendship with Steve Jenkins, and how they would go hunting together and shoot cans and try for animals in the state park. Steve was a good shot, his friend said, though sometimes that M-1 would jam. Steve had a quick little movement of just pulling the chamber back, dumping out the old shell, and ramming in a new one. But even with that jamming problem, he usually hit his target on the first shot, Shriver said.

Tom asked him about Steve Jenkins's ability to run and shoot. Yes, he could. How far? Maybe fifty yards? No, more like fifteen.

Tom then read Shriver a similar question from his grand jury testimony when he had mentioned fifty yards. "Were those answers to the grand jury true?"

"I've never seen him run fifty yards, but it's possible."

Swen wanted to make a point about Steve Jenkins's taste in clothes, which Tom saw as ominous. "In the summer and fall of 1983," Swen said, "was it the style of some teenagers to wear camouflage clothing?"

"Objection, irrelevant."

"Objection overruled. You may answer."

"Some did. The boots and stuff were a lot cheaper than a lot of shoes or work shoes would be."

As the trial's second week neared its end, fatigue was starting to take its toll on the main players. Swen was increasingly mixing up names. As for Tom, when Agent Berg was recalled, Tom asked if he had participated in some test firing at the windshield of the Blythe vehicle on September 29, 1983, the date of the killings.

Berg signaled the mistake to the prosecutor. "Test shots fired at the windshield on September 29, 1983? No, sir."

"Excuse me," said Tom, correcting himself and moving on. He was more interested in Exhibit No. 77 anyway, a pair of eyeglasses that Berg identified as coming from Jim Jenkins's body and which were tested later by Dr. Theodore Fritsche, Jim Jenkins's eye doctor. Berg didn't say how the BCA agents had found the eye doctor of a dead man who hadn't left any records on all of his regional wanderings. The method: sheer luck, the kind of occasional good fortune that makes detectives believe in Providence. Bob Berg had no idea who Jim Jenkins's eye doctor was. But he did need a good explanation of Jim's eye disease, retinitis something or other. One day in Marshall, Berg happened to mention this to Lyon County Sheriff Don Stokke, who suggested the agent talk to a Dr. Fritsche, an outspoken local supporter of law enforcement. The doctor did give Berg a helpful rundown on the eye disease and, on the way out, Berg instinctively asked one more question: Did you ever treat a James L. Jenkins? The doctor remembered no such name, but he had a secretary check. And there, waiting, was the Jenkins file.

On the witness stand, the doctor said he treated Jim for the first and last time on February 26, 1981. His records for that visit included notations such as "Night blindness, never drives at night" and while in the National Guard twenty years earlier "at night person marching in front of him had to have a white T-shirt pinned on his back." Jim Jenkins told the doctor his mother had some eye disease, possibly glaucoma, and his father was a diabetic. The doctor's notes indicated that, wearing his existing glasses, Jim's vision was 20/200; in other words, "he had a severe visual handicap."

Dr. Fritsche's testimony was long and very detailed; Tom wanted it that way. The details of Jim Jenkins's eyesight problem were crucial to fingering Steve as the one who did the skilled shooting That Day.

The doctor said Jim had the early stages of cataract formation, limited depth perception, and such tunnel vision that he would have to keep shifting his head back and forth and up and down to cover the same field of vision others get at a glance. The best eyeglass correction possible for him would be 20/70 in the right eye and 20/50 in the left. The doctor noted too that Jim repeatedly tried to peek during the tests—a little cheating to better the results—so his actual eyesight may have been a little worse than results indicated.

The final diagnosis was that Jim suffered from retinitis pigmentosa, "an out-and-out hereditary disease that consists of a triad of constricted visual fields, poor night vision, and ultimate total blindness in a relentlessly downhill course."

Now, Doctor, what would be the effect of two and a half years' time on the visual abilities of someone with this disease? "I can say without hesitation that it would be the same or worse."

Dr. Fritsche recommended that Jim Jenkins take five thousand units of vitamin A a day and that he get dark glasses because, studies indicate, both might slow down the disease. The records also showed that within three weeks Jim returned to the doctor's office. He didn't like the prescribed bifocals—too impatient with the necessary head motions. He had gone back to his old single-lens glasses, which gave him corrected vision of 20/200. The doctor said that those glasses were the same ones that Agent Berg got from Jim Jenkins's body.

Tom had one other line of questioning. It seems that, in part as a result of his military training, Dr. Fritsche was something of a gun fancier. He owns several rifles including an M-1 carbine. What, Tom asked, was the doctor's experience with the effects of eyeglasses on the ability to use peep sights on such weapons? The doctor thought they were a real handicap to shooting.

Could that handicap be overcome? Oh, yes, sure. How? By practice, practice, practice.

Swen was a little worried about the inconsistency in who drove the pickup truck away from the farm: Steve said he did; Paul Bartz said an older man, Jim. Juries get troubled over such inconsistencies: if the kid lied about that, maybe he'd lie about other things, too. So it would be helpful here if Swen could link Jim's eye problems to mishandling a vehicle, since at least two policemen had testified that the pickup truck did not swerve.

Doctor, could someone with such eye problems drive as fast as seventy miles an hour on a tar road and stay on the right side?

"Yes, I think that would be no problem."

"Would the fact it was a little bit cloudy or rainy or foggy make a bit of difference?"

"Not a bit."

"How about meeting cars then two hundred feet away?" No problem. Farther than that? Yeah, sure, six hundred, seven hundred feet, no problem.

"Now, that's working with the spectacles Mr. Berg gave you, at least the left eye had a twenty/seventy and right eye was a twenty/two hundred?"

"That's correct."

Would some colors be easier for someone with these eyes to see on a human? Well, he would have a definite loss of color appreciation. Swen didn't pick up on that warning signal. He loved this boy Steve and he was getting a little desperate, though trying not to show it. Swen didn't know much about eyesight irregularities, but even someone nearly blind would have to pick up on anything as bright as Rudy's yellow rain slicker. Would this coat here, Doctor, be easy or hard for him to see? Swen looked around the courtroom to make sure everyone saw the bright yellow jacket.

As I say, said the doctor, his color appreciation would be limited. He wouldn't see the same fluorescent yellow there we see. On the other hand, moving against a significant background, he probably could see him up to 450 feet or so. Swen was on to something.

"Would the yellow be a better color than some others?"

"Interesting that you should ask, because the MPS scanner that we did, the fluorescence on [the coat] is the identical yellow, and he missed all of the yellow dots, so his appreciation for that particular yellow is somewhat diminished."

There was no audible explosion at that moment. Swen didn't look as if he had just stepped on a land mine. He couldn't. He went right on to the next question about peripheral vision. Well, now, someone in the National Guard, even twenty years ago, would have to have pretty good eyes. What would Jim Jenkins's have been back in, say, '61?

"The National Guard has a propensity to change its eyesight requirements depending on the need, as do most of the services, and I can tell you this from experience, when they really need men, they let the standards slip. Now, '61 the Vietnam War was just beginning. They might have lowered the standards."

Would Jenkins have trouble walking in the woods? Oh, yes.

Now this rain gutter here. It was lying in some weedy area. "Would that be the kind of thing Mr. Jenkins could trip over, James Jenkins, with his eyesight?"

"It sounds like something anyone could trip over."

Swen, not a little frustrated and annoyed, tried the shooting angle. People with this eye disease could compensate for it, right? Yes. Well, would his vision be such that as a proficient shooter, he could hit a moving rat at fifty feet?

A moving what?

Objection.

Overruled. Rephrase the question.

"Assuming that he was a proficient marksman, pretty good, could he hit a running rat, R-A-T, like a mouse that's big, a rat, could he hit a running rat at a rather short distance like fifty feet with a twenty-two rifle?"

"I would have to guess at that—I've had the same experience, and I'm a very proficient shooter, and I've missed many rats at the dump, but it's a tough shot," said Dr. Fritsche.

"Could it be done?"

"It could be done."

How about hitting a running man?

Objection.

Overruled.

"The answer is yes. Mr. Jenkins could hit the target with his eyesight at a hundred feet."

"Could hit a running man at a hundred feet?"

"That's what I said."

"No further questions."

Tom wanted to do a little patching work. About Mr. Anderson's driving questions, how is it possible to stay in one lane with this disease? No problem, with the signs and painted lines and experience driving. "Driving down a road is really no indication of driving skill. I did it when I was eleven."

About shooting with this disease, do you agree with your earlier statement that it would be very difficult, if not impossible, for Jim Jenkins to shoot the weapon with any accuracy unless he was a proficient shooter himself?

"I do."

Thank you.

Next was Dr. Michael B. McGee, a forensic pathologist who has handled some fifteen hundred gunshot deaths in his career. He confirmed the autopsy report and spoke about each bullet in the killings. The one through Toby's throat, he said, also carried with it a small piece of chrome it picked up when passing through the window vent. The windshield bullet was deformed by its impact with the glass and, flattened, continued through Rudy's clothing and into his back. The bullets test-fired through new windshields came out flattened almost exactly the same shape as the tear in the back of Rudy's rain jacket where he was first hit. From the angle of entry into his back, the doctor could tell the victim was crouched over. He was fleeing or hiding from something.

He described the four shots out front, two to Rudy's back—both fatally tearing up his insides, one severing the spinal cord—one in the arm, and one through the jacket. He could also tell that the victim was moving at the time of impact.

Perhaps as a legacy of his prosecutorial days, Swen let his personal curiosity take over his legal mind for a moment. Swen was very interested in where all four bullets had gone. Perhaps, too, he was trying to make more fog or set up more blind alleys of doubt for the jurors. But this was not Dr. McGee's first testimony as a police witness. First-timers might miss opportunities because they are nervous or seize up on the witness stand, but not courtroom veterans. Effortlessly, Dr. McGee seized the opening in Swen's questions to make quite clear for the prosecution how accurate the shooting was. During one response, he managed to squeeze in three references to a bullet that came very close to Rudy's head. Not the mark of an amateur shooter.

Swen Borresen described his blacksmith business then, and the Jenkinses' frequent visits for welding work. One time just before the shooting, he said, Steve came in wearing three grenades hanging on a chain.

"Three hand grenades?" asked a stupefied Tom.

Yes, said Borresen. He wanted the bottom holes welded shut.

What for? He said a table lamp or something ornamental. Who picked up the welded grenades? Steve Jenkins. How did he pay you? Cash. When was this in relation to the murders? About one week before.

Swen Anderson didn't care about the other Swen, so Ted Beard was called, all the way from his appliance repair shop in Brownwood, Texas. Did you consider yourself good friends with Jim Jenkins?

"Yes, sir, I sure did."

Did Steve and Jim have a good relationship? Yes, they never argued. Did he ever see Jim Jenkins abuse his son or boss him around?

"No, sir, I did not. He seemed to think the world and all of the boy."

Did you ever happen to see Jim Jenkins around a gun?

Yes, sir, said Ted Beard. It was right after Ted came back from elk hunting in Colorado. Ted was cleaning his gun and Jim was watching and said what a nice gun it looked like and Ted handed it to him. Jim looked through the sight toward a neighbor's house for a couple of minutes, moving his head around behind the sight.

"He handed me the gun back and said, 'I can't see anything through it.' And that is the only time I have ever seen the man touch a gun."

And did you ever talk about guns with Jim Jenkins again?

"Yes, sir, probably a little later the same afternoon I asked him if he would like to go deer hunting with me and my son. He said, 'Well, it wouldn't do me any good to go deer hunting with you. I would just be in your way because I can't see well enough to deer hunt.'"

Ted told how Jim couldn't see well enough at work to use surveying tools and how he walked kind of funny, as if he was feeling his way with his feet. Then at night he always, and Ted meant always, carried a flashlight and shined it right down in front of his feet.

A reassuring Swen wanted to talk with Ted about the rifle scope and whether Ted was taller than Jim (a little bit maybe).

"I am not trying to trick you or anything," the attorney said. He wanted to show how each user must move his head and adjust a rifle scope for his own eyes, like surveying tools.

Ted said Jim was a careful driver after he got the truck. Before then, people would drive him or Jim would just walk all over, in his funny, slow shuffling way.

Wasn't it true that Jim was employed down there in Texas as a night watchman? Well, now, Ted didn't know as how it was an actual night watchman. They had burglar troubles at one renovation site and Jim did stay overnight there a few nights to watch over the fuel pumps and all. But it was well lit. Was he armed? "Not that I know of."

Ted's hunting pal Jim Perry was summoned next. James L. Perry, Jim Jenkins's foreman, had vivid stories of his employee's poor physical condition. Jenkins was hired for cement work, Jim Perry said. They were putting in curbs and gutters for a parking lot over at the junior high school and Perry needed good, strong men to muscle that gray, hardening mud about in wheelbarrows and then to pack it into place while it was drying. But whenever Jenkins tried to lift the 150-pound wheelbarrow loads, he'd spill them or become breathless and then his lower legs would swell up. Jenkins was a hard worker all right, Perry could testify to that. But he sure couldn't handle much physical exertion.

As soon as Fabel began that line of questioning, Swen objected. The jury was excused. The two attorneys argued. Tom said it was crucial to show the "circumstantial improbability" that someone in Jim Jenkins's shape could do a 100-yard dash in the farmyard and then squeeze off four rifle shots right on target. Swen said the whole thing was quite prejudicial. The two attorneys did some test questioning of Perry. And then Judge Mann said, No, that kind of testimony would be ruled out. Moving cement about didn't relate closely enough to the alleged activities. Bring the jury back. Score another for Swen.

Working with Jim Jenkins, Tom asked Perry, did you notice his seeing ability?

"Yes, sir. He was looking at some blueprints in the basement, and he said everything was blurred."

Perry said Steve and his father got along well, and then he got into the gun stories. Doing his night-watchman duties, Jim Jenkins had been carrying a baseball bat and one night Perry loaned him a shotgun loaded with rock salt, but Jenkins returned it the next day, saying if he ever used it, he would get himself killed.

There was one other time. Charles Snow, the maintenance director, had a horse on his farm. It had been sick for several days, wouldn't get up. The vet finally said, best thing to do is put her to sleep. Jenkins and Perry and some others went down to the farm. Jenkins was standing over by the horse and Perry walked up to him with a .22-caliber pistol and asked if he would want to shoot it and put it to sleep.

The attorneys and judge conferred privately then. They all anticipated trouble with this line of answers. It was revealing about Jim Jenkins, but not strictly legally relevant. The last thing Tom wanted was to hand Swen grounds for a mistrial. The questioning resumed, carefully.

"Did James Jenkins make any statement about inability to use a pistol?"

"Objection. Relevancy and hearsay."

"Objection sustained on the first grounds."

"Were there any rifles present at that time?"

"No, sir."

"Thank you, Mr. Perry. I have nothing further."

The last prosecution witness was Charles Ray Snow, who was on his best behavior. Did you develop any weapons expertise during your army career and two wars?

"Somewhat, yes."

Snow recalled being impressed with Jim Jenkins's callused hands and hiring him, and what a good deal it was, because even after work, Jim lived

there at the maintenance yard and Snow got a night watchman for free.
Then when Steve came along it was even better because after a while Snow
started paying him for part-time, but the kid was really working full-time
just to be with his father. Snow said the two got along well together, sometimes seemed more like a brother-to-brother relationship than father-son.

"Did James Jenkins appear to dominate Steven Jenkins?"

"No way, no."

"Was the opposite true in any respect?"

"I think so."

Did Snow ever talk with Steve? Daily. Did those conversations ever involve military subjects or weapons?

"Almost all the time, yes."

"Who would initiate those conversations?"

"It started—probably Steve started to initiate the discussion, and then
later on because of his interest—and, after all, I spent more than thirty
years of my life in the military—I was more than happy to talk to him about
military experiences I had had. And he was exceptionally interested in
them."

Under Tom's questioning, Snow described how their relationship developed, how Steve bought the M-1 carbine with his first paycheck, and
how, because the kid was so interested, Snow taught him the military firing positions. Snow also recalled telling Steve he could get more stability,
more accuracy, by installing on the carbine a web sling, which is then
wrapped around the arm and is especially helpful when firing in the standing position. Snow was pleased to see Steve practicing these positions at
different times.

"What kind of shooter was he?"

"Superb. Excellent. He hit the can every time. Danced it right across
the pond." From the standing position, too.

Had Snow ever seen James Jenkins use a firearm? Never. How about
Jim's eyesight? He said he saw poorly. Lots of times, well, we had the two
of them down doing some demolition work at one school, and Snow gave
Jim the blueprints so's he'd know where the doors was to be cut, but
sometimes his measurements was way off. "I attributed that to poor eyesight."

Did you ever see James Jenkins run?

"Never seen him run. He was a hard worker, but he worked at his own
gauge, but never in a hurry."

"Did you ever see Steve Jenkins run?"

"Oh, yes."

"Did he have any difficulty running?"

"No. He was a good athlete."

"Thank you, Mr. Snow."

Swen just wanted to review a few things, to make sure Steve was respectful of his dad, which he was, which is important in this day and age.

Or ought to be. And check on the distance from Steve to that can in the pond. How big was the can? Beer can size. What else did they shoot at? Tree limbs, tree branches. Snow told Steve he could hunt all the rabbits, skunks, and armadillos he wanted. Swen wanted to know what an armadillo was. Swen said the M-1 must be a very accurate rifle. Snow said it was at that distance.

For Tom again, Snow said he remembered that Steve hit pretty much everything he shot at. Did he have a sighting problem? Well, not after Snow explained the proper procedure. Steve always wanted to put the front sight in the middle of the target, and Snow kept explaining that it should go at the bottom. They went over proper breathing, sighting, exhaling slightly, taking up the trigger's slack, and then squeezing off the round—the standard firearm training for all members of the military. "He seemed to have an excellent knack for being a soldier and firing a gun," Snow said.

That was it for the prosecution.

"Your Honor," said Fabel, "the state of Minnesota rests."

The jury was ushered out. Then, as agreed in the judge's chambers, Swen made a motion to have all six counts of murder dismissed because the state didn't prove each and every element beyond a reasonable doubt. As for the robbery part, Swen noted there was absolutely nothing to show that anyone was robbed. No watches or money missing. No robbery consummation, maybe just a trespass, which was a misdemeanor.

Tom disagreed, noting several points of law and the fact that Steve said they went out there to rob Rudy and, according to Statute 609.185 Subsection 3, whether it was consummated or not is irrelevant. He requested the dismissal motion be denied.

Judge Mann agreed with Tom. He ordered the jury members returned. It was time for the defense to present its case and for Swen's opening statement.

"Normally," Swen said, "I think the perfect defense is to call no one." But to buttress his claim that there was reasonable doubt on all six counts, Swen was going to call a few people who would testify about Jim Jenkins's physical abilities, coordination, that sort of thing. "There were two people at the scene," Swen said, seeking to redirect the jury's attention, "and one of the two was not the killer."

Swen said he'd be calling Eric DeRycke, a local attorney, to talk about how good Jim Jenkins could see. Gene Abraham, Darlene Jenkins's only brother and Steve's uncle, might be testifying. He's been a highway patrolman in good standing for some time and he might say that he had seen James Jenkins shoot the patrolman's revolver back in 1980 or so. There'd be a private investigator talking about rifle scopes. Finally, Swen said, he'd have Darlene Jenkins to testify on what her husband could do physically back in 1980 around the time of that eye exam that Dr. Fritsche described so well.

So, Swen said, those are the main areas. "Of course," he added, "in every case a defendant has a right to take the stand or not take the stand. And the fact that he does not take the stand is no inference of guilt. In fact, when they had the trial of Jesus, Jesus never took the stand. And that didn't make him guilty of anything. And the same is true here.

"One other thing," Swen added. "The next most important item will, of course, be final arguments where the prosecutor goes first. And I will go last, which means nothing as far as the order of arguments. But that's the way it will be."

Minutes after the trial recessed for that last weekend, Bob Berg and Mike O'Gorman were in a car speeding the 150 miles northeast to Brainerd, Minnesota. Swen's opening statement reference to Gene Abraham firing his service revolver with Jim Jenkins had stunned Fabel and Cable. Nothing had ever been said before about the state trooper testifying.

What the agents uncovered before they got home just before dawn Saturday disturbed Fabel greatly. Early Tuesday morning he met with Swen in Judge Mann's chambers.

It was "very, very distressing if true," Tom said. But BCA agents had interviewed Gene Abraham, and Steve's uncle said he didn't know he was going to be a witness, he hadn't talked with the defense in six months, he never said he saw Jim Jenkins use his gun—in fact, he never saw Jim Jenkins use *any* gun. If all this is true, Tom said, then Swen had no good-faith basis for saying that to the jury. If the prosecution had done such a thing, the state supreme court would deal harshly with him and any conviction would be reversed. Now, even if the false evidence was not introduced, the jury might speculate on how the prosecution maneuvered to deny the defendant this point.

Well, now, said Judge Mann, the jury had been instructed that evidence is only that which comes from witnesses and exhibits, not words uttered in opening statements. In fact, Tom had reminded the jury of that in his opening statement. Judge Mann didn't feel, objectively, that any harm had been done. What did Mr. Anderson have to say? Was he going to call Mr. Abraham?

No, said Swen. Mr. Fabel had some good points. You see, Swen had been told about this on Friday by Darlene Jenkins who remembered her husband saying it, and she remembered the incident too, shooting Gene's .38. "I guess I relied on that," said Swen, "and she may still be right, having remembered it." But the information was not true, and he'd be prepared to tell the jury the information was wrong, but he hadn't acted in bad faith.

Tom reiterated his concern. Swen offered to make a correction statement as long as he didn't have to say where the wrong information came from because, Swen didn't say, that same source was going to testify. Tom wanted any statement in writing so there'd be no dispute over phrasing later. Swen agreed to say whatever Tom wrote out, which he did when the trial resumed.

"Mr. Anderson," Judge Mann said to Swen, the jury, a packed courtroom, and two very calm prosecutors, "it is the court's understanding that at this time you may have an amendment to make to your opening statement."

"Your Honor," Swen began, reading from a piece of paper that did not carry his own handwriting, "I would like to correct my opening statement. Ladies and gentlemen, during my opening statement Friday I told you the defense would offer testimony from Mr. Gene Abraham, who I identified as a state trooper, and said Mr. Abraham would say James Jenkins shot a service revolver. That portion of my opening statement was based upon erroneous information, and therefore I want to tell you that Mr. Abraham will not be asked to testify because he does not possess the information that I had indicated, and that part of my opening should be deleted. Thank you."

"Gotcha!" mumbled one agent in the back.

"You may proceed with the defense," said the judge.

Eric DeRycke was called first. A Belgian immigrant, an attorney. In fact, he once represented James L. Jenkins. What type of legal work did you do for him?

"I defended Mr. Jenkins on a bad check charge." Score two points for Swen: the guy knew Jim Jenkins well, and Jenkins wrote bad checks, it seems. An unsavory fellow, maybe capable of murder, too.

Eric last saw Jim in the winter of 1981, when he got out of his car to walk through snow on an icy patch up the stairs to Eric's office. They were poor steps, too, not built right. But the man had no problem.

"Your witness."

"Mr. DeRycke," said Tom, "you have had as a client over the years a man by the name of Louis Taveirne, isn't that correct?"

"Yes, I have."

What legal work did you do for him? Well, his divorce and other small matters. Are you aware that Mr. Taveirne lives with the defendant's mother? Yes, he was aware of that.

Now, Mr. DeRycke, do you recall being interviewed on January 24, 1984, by BCA Agent Michael O'Gorman? Yes. Do you recall that Mr. O'Gorman asked you to estimate how long ago you saw James Jenkins? Not sure, but maybe. Do you recall telling Mr. O'Gorman your last contact was four years ago? Don't know. Might you have said that?

"It's possible."

"Fine. No further questions."

"Your Honor," said the defense attorney, "the state would call Jim Lenz."

"The defense," corrected Tom.

"Yes, the defense," said Swen. "Did I say something wrong? I'm sorry. The defense calls James Lenz."

Lenz was a farmer once, but he had to sell out—sold his cows to Jim Jenkins, in fact. Now he had a repair shop and sold auto parts and welding supplies. Last saw Jim the spring of '81. Saw Jim Jenkins run after a cow, no trouble. Saw him operate a crane, too, takes a lot of coordination, crane-operating does. And as far as James Lenz was concerned, Jim Jenkins was as good a crane operator as he'd ever seen. Seen him do welding, too. Jim Jenkins was a perfectionist. And mechanical work. Saw him strip down a crane once to replace some bushings. No sight problems. No walking problems.

Tom's turn. Mr. Lenz, you are a legal client of Swen Anderson's, aren't you? Yes. Now, when did you see Jim Jenkins do this crane work? Back when he was in the construction business. Okay, let's calculate backward on that, said Tom. That's two or three years on the Tyler farm and another four years up at Ruthton and he's been off that place since 1980. So all this work you saw him do must have been around 1973 or '74, isn't that correct? Somewhere in there.

Now, about the welding. Tom backdated the welding memories an equally long way.

"Did you ever see Jim Jenkins use a gun?"

"No."

Swen had another turn. Well, what was it you saw Jim Jenkins do in the spring of 1981? Lenz didn't see him do anything. He just stopped by the shop, wanted Lenz to build him something. Lenz forgot what it was exactly. Did he drive his own truck to your shop? Think so, yes.

Next up was Darlene Jenkins, the star attraction. As the media exposure accumulated, spectators flocked in growing numbers to the trial. Transmitted through the air as tiny electronic dots, the characters in the legal drama had been transformed into celebrities. Steve and his mother seemed to have been awarded the highest status. Some of the teenage girl spectators, even if they weren't lucky enough to get a number low enough to get courtroom seats, would hang around the courthouse, watching for Steve during recesses, then watching him and giggling and maybe saying, "Hi, Steve." Steve, maybe with a little wad of chewing tobacco tucked in his mouth, would continue to talk with his mother and Swen and maybe nod and say "Hi" back. Then he'd try to smother a smile.

That Tuesday morning when Darlene was to go on, the would-be spectators started lining up even earlier than usual, well before 7:30 A.M. There must have been more than a hundred people. When the bailiff went to open the door for the 9:30 proceedings, the crush was so bad that she got knocked down. A man fainted. The door got splintered.

The spectator benches were packed. Susan was there with her prayer book and Sharon Fadness when, at 10:15, wearing a proper black skirt and a white blouse with collar ruffles that reached for her chin, Darlene Jenkins took the oath. Swen had her dance quickly through her marriage, her son, her divorce, photos of her ex-husband on a driver's license and in the National Guard, and identification of his eyeglasses, Exhibit No. 77. He wore them all the time except sometimes in the barn when milking and when he was welding. She recalled how upset Jimmy was with his new bifocals, soon giving them up for regular glasses.

Do you fire a gun? Yes. What kinds? Darlene didn't know all the names, but she'd shot her brother's .38 and a .22 semiautomatic Marlin and her father's guns and shotguns and her son's M-1.

"How good a shot are you?"

"Objection, irrelevant."

"Objection sustained."

Now, is this an accurate depiction of your old farm? Yes. Did you at one time have a windmill there? Yes. Please mark where that was. Thank you.

And did your husband ever shoot at that windmill? Yes, he shot at the tail. Why?

"I suppose to hear the noise, like we all did."

"You could hear the metal ping."

"Yes, you could hear it. It would zing and ping."

How often did he do that? Free time, maybe a couple times a week with Steve's .22. Did he shoot anywhere else on the farm? Yes, out back where Jimmy dumped some silage. We'd all shoot out there.

"Could you point out where you used to shoot on the farm?"

"I don't think it's even on the board, Swen."

It was more of a garbage hole and the rats got into it. They were hard to hit. They see you, they take off real fast. But he got some probably at fifty feet.

She recalled how after they left the Ruthton farm and moved into a trailer in Marshall, the whole family would often go out to James Dwire's old gravel pit south of town and shoot with Steve's .22 at cans of all sorts. There wasn't much else to do. The targets were probably a hundred yards away. Jim wore his glasses then and he wasn't a bad shot, even without a scope. In fact, he shot a dog once. He shot the kids' dog.

"I was very interested to hear you had shot the M-1," Swen said.

"Yes."

"How did it function when you fired it?"

"It shot all right. It had, it had a lot of kick, though. I didn't like to shoot it."

Mrs. Jenkins, you said your husband could shoot as well as you. "Could you hit a coffee can at a hundred feet?"

"With what?"

"With a twenty-two."

"Oh, yes."

"I have nothing further."

Now, Mrs. Jenkins, Tom began, you've been here in the courtroom every day of the trial, haven't you? Yes. You've been meeting virtually every day with Mr. Anderson, haven't you? Pretty much. You've been traveling to and from the trial every day with him? No, I travel in a different car.

"You are now aware just how significant this whole shooting ability is to this trial, aren't you?"

"Yes, I would say I am."

"Now, do you recall, Mrs. Jenkins, being asked some questions about James Jenkins's shooting ability way back on October fourth, 1983, by Bureau of Criminal Apprehension Agent Dennis Sigafoos?"

"At that time, when everything happened—"

"Excuse me, do you recall being asked by him back on October fourth, 1983, about James's shooting ability?"

"I don't recall."

Tom had in his hand a transcript of that interview. He read a series of excerpts, questions about her husband's ownership of guns (none she knew of), about his interest in hunting (never went), in target practice (not at all), and her interest in guns (so little that she didn't know what guns her son owned). He asked her if she remembered her grand jury testimony in this same room and how she had been asked the same questions about her husband and guns.

"Do you recall being asked this question: 'Do you recall seeing him do any target practicing?' And your answer was 'No.' Do you recall that exchange in the grand jury?"

"No, I don't."

Tom asked Darlene if she recalled Agent Sigafoos asking her about Steve's M-1.

"I don't know. I have no idea what it is."

"It's your testimony right now that you and Steven went out and shot the M-1 together, is that correct?"

"We went out in the alfalfa field right in front of our house."

Tom wanted to make sure Darlene knew what Jim was in the National Guard. "A transportation unit, isn't that correct?"

"He was also in heavy equipment."

He wore glasses when they were married, right? Yes. Tom asked if it wasn't true that her husband's eyes got worse over the years.

"I suppose. Nobody's eyes get better."

"His eyes became noticeably worse, did they not?"

"Not to me, they didn't."

Tom ran through some of Agent Sigafoos's questions the previous fall about James Jenkins's eyes. Darlene had said his eyes were poor. He couldn't see anything in the dark. They were getting worse.

"Do you recall saying that to Agent Sigafoos?"

"I don't remember. Was—"

"I'm sorry. There's no question right now. Thank you, Mrs. Jenkins."

Next, Swen focused on clearing up some things. Jim had owned a shotgun at one time, but he sold it. After that he shot Steve's guns, but he never went hunting except for the rats. And she remembered Jim shooting her brother's .38, but that was a long time ago.

Kenneth Nordine was up next. As Swen promised, he talked about rifle scopes. He explained about moving your head behind one to get the correct position. Otherwise the target would just be a blur. Nordine talked too about his police investigative experience and how important it was to keep and study everything, even a victim's socks and shoes.

In his cross-examination Tom wanted to make sure that Mr. Nordine was getting paid for his services to the defense's cause. Yes. And Tom made the point that scopes have very little room for adjustment, kind of one-size-fits-all.

Swen wanted a few more questions. Was Mr. Nordine paid when he was a policeman? Yes. Did he ever testify as a policeman? Yes, maybe fifty times. Does his testimony differ because he was hired privately instead of working for the government? No, sir.

The defense rested.

Fabel was somewhat surprised. Nothing about the duress defense at all. Tom had been setting up for that. Swen didn't even get his favorite newspaper quote in, the one about how gun collectors are good Americans too. "Every police officer in the state," Swen liked to say in defense of Steve's practice targets, "takes target practice at a human profile." One reason Swen didn't get to use those lines was that Tom never introduced Steve's tree-branch target that was dressed like a human. Sheriff Thompson had it ready in the next building, but Tom never called for it. Maybe the subject would come up in the closing arguments, which Tom had to finish meticulously assembling that day. First would come some brief testimony by Agent Sigafoos, who had been urgently summoned by telephone and was en route by car at that moment to thoroughly rebut Darlene Jenkins's testimony.

Swen's cross-examination of Sigafoos was longer than Tom's initial questioning. The implication of the defense attorney's questions was that there was more to the Sigafoos interview of Darlene than met the eye, or the ear. Swen's inquiries weren't too clear on this issue. He mentioned one of Sigafoos's questions to Darlene that referred to James Jenkins's story of a Darlene Jenkins–Rudy Blythe love affair, a suggestion that no one took seriously. Agent Sigafoos said he took that to mean she thought it was preposterous.

"Your Honor," said Tom Fabel, "the state rests."

CHAPTER EIGHT

The End

"We have now arrived at the final phase of this trial," said a very tired Tom Fabel, who was by then running on adrenaline. It was like final exams back at college—a set time for the test, a long night of study beforehand, reviewing, remembering, organizing chaotic human events and thoughts into a rational, understandable order to convince his audience, even though the only place such human affairs ever happen in any rational, understandable pattern is in the next morning's newspaper. Tom's secretary, Nancy Haley, had not seen the boss so intense in a long while. She had driven down to Marshall with another attorney for the trial's end. Tom put her to work on his closing argument with a typewriter borrowed from the motel office. Her fingers flew over the keys until nearly dawn transcribing Tom's notes. He wanted a neat closing statement, as neat as his desk top back in the office, the ideas arranged, I, II, III with a common theme throughout.

Now, in his good-luck gray suit with the red tie, Tom thanked the jury for their diligence in this difficult experience. The next few hours were very, very important, he said, and he outlined like a friendly tour guide what would be happening—his closing argument, the defense's, the judge's instructions, and then their own deliberations.

"Every time I think of this final phase of the American jury system," the prosecutor said, "I am amazed once again at the infinite wisdom that is embraced by the whole process. For weeks now you have been sitting here doing nothing but listening. All the talking basically is being done by lawyers and experts, people that are familiar with the courtroom. All of us that are participants in this trial are people that have gone to law school, and we have taken tests and we have done everything else to learn about the law so that we can participate in the trial. And yet when that final, most important moment arrives at the trial, the case is taken out of our hands, and it's handed to you. The reason for that is that you people bring to this courtroom something that no school in the world can give any person. You come to this courtroom with all of your lives of common experience, all of your lives as good citizens of this county, collective experiences which are as different from one another as the faces that you have. And together you are able to bring to bear upon this whole decision-making process one important quality: common sense.

"That is the most important thing that you will be asked to exercise today. Please don't forget that. Above all, the process of decision making in a court of law is a sensible, rational process. Your decision should be one which is guided by your good common sense."

In plain, commonsense sentences, Tom ran down the six counts again. He had a suggestion on how they could work through this complex process. First, Tom said, look to whether the defendant's grand jury testimony was completely true. If they believe that, then the first four counts of intentional murder would be inappropriate. But he could still be guilty of the robbery and assault.

If, however, they found Steve's grand jury testimony not completely true, then they should decide next if Steve was the shooter. If they found Steve was the shooter, then they must decide on premeditation.

Tom ran through the evidence then, attempting to destroy Steve's claims to credibility one by one: Jim Jenkins announces one day that they will rob and scare Rudy Blythe the next day. Nothing more is said throughout the day, throughout dinner, throughout the evening, throughout the drive to the farm. When the pair was surprised at the farm, Tom recounted from Steve's story, Jim Jenkins grabbed Steve's favorite gun and ran. Hiding behind the garage, the youth didn't know where his father was and heard nothing but talking, no gutters rattling, no arguments, no threats. Just the shots. And when Steve emerged he found the bodies.

Even if they believed "all of those things," Tom pointed out how Steve admitted having all the deadly weapons and helping in the felony, the assault and robbery. Mike O'Gorman was correct back in that Texas questioning; it is as wrong to help a felon as it is to do it yourself. When you go out to scare someone with all these weapons, Tom said, death is reasonably foreseeable.

"Now, I expect Mr. Anderson to argue to you," Tom said, "that these are merely the toys of a child." Tom paused. He picked up the murder rifle from the pile of weapons in evidence. "Some toys," he said. Then the prosecutor looked over at the eighteen-year-old looking down at his boots, his left hand cradling his cheek. And the jury's eyes turned there too. "Some child," he said.

Tom emphasized the implausibility of much of Steve's story. You've heard, he said, from many people—Ted Beard, Jim Perry, Charles Snow—how close Jim and Steve were. Would they come up with such a drastic plan as robbery on the farm and not talk about it? Extremely doubtful. If they were going out there to rob Rudy, does a person rationally rob someone by running fifty yards away with a high-powered rifle? No. Tom moved over to touch the shotguns.

"Now, if James Jenkins did indeed plan on robbing Rudy Blythe or just scaring him well, what would be the far, far, far more logical weapon for him? For him, a man who, as you know, had a very limited eyesight, for him who, as you know, doesn't use guns. Right there! That's what you rob and scare the hell out of somebody with. You do it from a short distance. You walk up to them and say, 'What are you thinking about doing, not giving us a good credit reference? I want you to get off our backs, and we want your money, too.' That's the kind of weapon you use for that. Not that [pointing at the M-1]. Not that. And certainly not from the distance of forty to fifty yards away from where the car came in. That doesn't make any sense."

He asked them to consider the murder weapon's history. Who bought it? Who trained with it? Who carried it everywhere? Who was that gun's best friend? Steve Jenkins. Not James.

Is it likely that with a strange car arriving, Jim Jenkins, who couldn't see well, would grab Steve's gun and run off across the open farmyard he knew so well to hide by the chicken coop where the shooting began? Extremely doubtful. "One of the problems, of course, in a case like this is that there aren't any eyewitnesses left around to tell us whether that happened or not. All we can do is work on circumstances."

Now, what was it that brought Toby and Rudy back to the car so far so quickly? Steve said he heard nothing after Susan left, nothing except two series of shots. "Something had to put them in the car. Something scared those men. Someone said, 'Toby, get back here.' Someone said, 'Hey, what are those guns?' Someone had an argument. Something happened. Keep in mind the men that we are talking about. Rudy and Toby. Big, strong, athletic men. Are they going to run away from just trespassers? No. They saw something that scared them. There was a confrontation. Somebody shouted a warning. Something happened, ladies and gentlemen of the jury. The evidence doesn't tell you what, but the circumstances tell you that something had to have happened to bring Toby back, to get Rudy into the car, and to cause them to try fleeing. Defendant says he heard nothing. Can that be true?"

Now, if the jury decides that Steve Jenkins is lying, they must ask themselves a question. "Why? Do you lie because the truth is actually better for you than your story? Or do you lie because the truth is much, much worse? What does common sense tell you about that?"

Tom detailed the fine shooting. Marksmanship, ladies and gentlemen, marksmanship. Three shots in the backyard, all would have hit their targets but for an intervening object. And physical exertion, the chase. Then four shots in the front yard, not random sprays all over the universe either. But four precisely placed shots. "And what did you hear about your two candidates for being shooters?" Tom recapped Steve's passion for guns and his marksmanship and everyone testifying to his father's lack of interest in firearms.

"Oh, but there was one exception," Tom said, "Darlene Jenkins. Yesterday Darlene Jenkins told you that shooting was a family hobby of the Jenkinses back in the seventies." He contrasted that with her earlier testimony to the grand jury under oath.

Tom detailed the physical abilities of the father and son, the running and then the eyesight. The young defendant fresh from his Texas training under a Vietnam veteran or the aging diabetic with a 63 percent field of vision in his left eye and only 20 percent in the right eye, his aiming eye? The youth who rarely missed his targets or "the man who had to feel his way along the street because he had difficulty walking?"

Then, as he talked, as he spun out how improbable it was that the overweight diabetic with no interest in guns could do the shooting, Tom got the flash of an idea. When he came to the part about young, athletic Steve in training, Tom, clutching the murder weapon, dramatically threw himself onto the floor and sighted across the courtroom. The only sound then was the happy yells of children down the street at recess.

"Use your common sense, ladies and gentlemen of the jury. That's what you are here for."

Tom turned to the question of premeditation. Usually, when you think of premeditation, Tom said, you think of Agatha Christie, where someone plans a murder for months and months. Well, that's not the only kind. You can use those strange conversations of Steve's as one indication they were planning something, the conspiratorial talk at the café, taking all the guns out to the farm, that could be premeditation. Think for a moment more carefully about what happened at the farm. Toby, the wrong man at the wrong place, is shot.

"The defendant ran over and checked to see who that human being was. He evidently figured out that it wasn't Rudy. Who knows. Maybe his father told him. Maybe he knew himself. Maybe he didn't care. But in any event, from the moment that he leaves here until the moment he arrives at that spot, there is one thing in his mind. He is pursuing a man as a hunter would pursue an animal. As he leaves the car in this direction carrying that M-1 rifle, he knows what the M-1 does. He has just seen evidence of a dead man. He has used it many times himself. He has got one thing in mind, and that is the death of Rudy Blythe. As he runs out to the sidewalk, he has that one thing in his mind. As he runs down the sidewalk past the house, he has that one thing in his mind. As he rounds the front of the house and into the front yard, he has that one thing in mind. As Rudy Blythe comes into his sight, Rudy running for his life, he has that one thing in his mind. As he pulls up in the shooting position and brings the rifle to his shoulder, takes a deep breath, and expels it, he has that one thing in his mind. And as he pulls the trigger on four consecutive occasions, he intended one premeditated act. That was the death of Rudy Blythe. It is not necessary that premeditation exists for any specific length of time."

Toby's death was intentional, Tom said, second degree. Rudy's death was carefully calculated, however briefly, therefore first degree.

Tom knew from the fog-inducing questions of Swen's cross-examinations that Steve's defense and Swen's final argument would rely on reasonable doubt. One hundred different lawyers would give you one hundred different definitions, Tom said. The judge will talk to you of that later. "But keep in mind always that what we are talking about is a commonsensical standard. Proof beyond a reasonable doubt is not proof beyond all doubt whatsoever. It is a high degree of certainty, and that is what the evidence in this case produces.''

Tom had a story to tell then, a story that probably each one of the jurors could understand, even from this city fellow. The story, which Tom had been polishing for more than six weeks, dealt with his family—his wife and three little girls back in St. Paul. Now, Tom has to do a lot of traveling and, of course, he calls them regularly and, well, let's imagine an imaginary conversation. Tom asks his wife what the girls did that day. She says, Why, they went to school, of course. Then Tom says, How do you know they went to school? She might think her husband had been working too hard, but she humors him. She says she got up in the morning with them as usual and packed their school lunches. Annie was fussing with her hair as usual. Jessica came roaring into the kitchen late and in a mess, as usual. Little Leah was still sleeping. Jean saw them run down to the corner and jump on the school bus. At three-thirty, Tom says his wife says, she saw the children get off the bus and Annie had a new library book and Jessica had a math paper and they went off to play before their mother found the uneaten carrots in the lunchpails. That's how Mrs. Fabel knew they were in school.

''Now, you see, my wife didn't see the kids get off the bus up in front of the school. She didn't see them walk into their classrooms. She didn't see them as they sat there for seven hours, but she knew they were in school. And if she had to base an important decision in her life upon whether they were there or not, she could do that with a good degree of certainty. She never saw them, but the circumstantial evidence led her to but one commonsensical conclusion. That's the same that happened in this case.''

Tom wanted to touch on Swen's anticipated closing statements. There were hints of improper investigative work. You know, Rudy's shoes and socks, which were examined and then returned to the widow. Maybe the defense might claim that if Steve were such a super marksman, he could have drilled the pursuing deputy sheriff instead of shooting at his tires and missing. Well, Steve and Jim Jenkins were trying to disable their pursuer, not kill a policeman and attract forty-five more patrol cars. ''It is a red herring,'' Tom said, ''and don't let it confuse you.''

Just use your own rock-solid commonsense standards, Tom said. Don't be overwhelmed by sympathy or emotion. Remember that the word *verdict*, like so many words in our language, comes from Latin, the words *veritas dictum*, a true statement. ''That's what you are to issue—a true statement.''

''I ask in the name of the people of the state of Minnesota that you perform justice, that you render true verdicts. I ask that you render verdicts of guilty on count one, the premeditated murder of Rudolph Blythe, and guilty on count four, the intentional killing of Deems Thulin. Thank you very much for your attention.''

Tom sat down then, exhausted and emotionally drained. Judge Mann called a brief recess before it was Swen's turn.

The defense attorney was obviously impressed when he got up to speak. ''You have just listened to one of the most competent prosecutors in the state of Minnesota do an excellent job—Mr. Fabel,'' he said. ''And in my forty-eight years of life this has probably been a very important—the most important moment, and it will also be in this case your most important moment.

''Detail in this case is everything,'' said Swen. ''In every case the state must prove guilt beyond a reasonable doubt. This means that you jurors can act as human beings and don't have to be like God, human lie detectors. It's for you to go strictly on the evidence. And if there is evidence of guilt beyond a reasonable doubt, convict. And if there isn't, acquit. In this case it will be our posture that the reasonable doubt is tremendous.''

Swen talked about circumstantial evidence and how murky it could be and how all of its inferences must point toward guilt. ''Let's start out,'' he suggested with a smile, ''by mentioning the one thing which Mr. Fabel never mentioned at all. And I don't blame him, because it's the cross of his case. And that is motive. Motive.'' Swen said he saw all the motive for murder on the father's side—losing the farm to the bank, believing his wife had an affair with the banker, discovering the bank was putting out poor credit references, ''which I suppose the bank has a right to do. I am not saying the bank didn't. But again that was hatred and it would create motive.''

But the kid was only fourteen when the farm was lost, Swen said. ''And I don't know any fourteen-year-old boy that is going to cry if Daddy sells his milk cows. Kids aren't that gung-ho for milking cows. And [Steve] never had a checking account in that bank. He never had a savings account in that bank. Where was his motive? And he never saw the banker Blythe or the banker Thulin.''

Swen touched on the ability to kill. He recalled Darlene Jenkins saying how her husband had shot his kids' dog. ''If you can kill your family dog— most people can't—that shows something,'' said the attorney. And how about the boy shooting at the deputy's tires, which showed he was a good marksman and trying to disable the car, even if he did close his eyes. Swen dropped that last phrase in out of the blue. ''I can tell you,'' Swen said firmly, ripping off his glasses, ''that those two bankers, they may have been killed by someone with poor eyes, but they surely were not killed by someone with closed eyes. No way.'' Swen noted that if the boy was such a good shooter, he could have killed the pursuing deputy. That would have made more sense, since a live policeman could radio for help. ''But he couldn't do it,'' Swen said. ''He didn't do it. And I think that is a solid inference the boy could not kill.''

Swen also found it interesting that the kid didn't destroy any evidence, the guns and army helmet and stuff. And he turned himself in. That shows respect and trust in the law and Swen said he liked that. He also liked the idea of the boy talking his father out of killing or robbing anyone else. "That should have some consideration."

Now about premeditation. Swen saw none whatsoever in this case. If they'd gone to the farm for the sole purpose of killing Rudy Blythe, why take off the license plates? Why didn't they have any food if there was so much premeditation? And no money. And no gasoline.

As for the vision, Swen suggested that was a prosecution smoke screen. "Mr. James Jenkins was not a blind person that needed a cane and seeing-eye dog." Sure he had defective vision and terrible night vision, but the shootings were in daylight. And the eye doctor had said fog and clouds made no difference. Swen reviewed the icy sidewalk testimony and Jim Lenz's about Jim Jenkins running a crane real good. Concrete examples, not hot air, that's what Swen said he liked best in a trial.

Getting Rudy Blythe was not all that hard, the lawyer said. "It was an awful easy shot because there was no zigzag running." Swen suggested, considering the path of the bullets within the banker's body, that Rudy had stopped and turned to look at the shooter, which made it an even easier shot. He also quoted Steve's grand jury testimony that Steve and Jim Jenkins had shot together in Texas, and since the only gun they had in Texas was Steve's M-1, that was a good inference that Jim Jenkins knew about operating the M-1.

Swen knew he had a problem with Darlene's apparent switching. So he touched on that. Maybe the contradiction was just a misunderstanding on what Tom and Darlene meant by targets. Darlene did testify, after all, that her husband didn't hunt but did shoot at the windmill. "But he hit it and he killed the family dog. And he did kill a rat."

As for the Jenkinses' conspiratorial conversation in the Mayfair Cafe, "I ask you, if somebody was really planning to join into a robbery, would it be discussed in a public restaurant?"

Swen noted that Jim Jenkins had taken one, not two, green bath towels that fatal morning. The towel was to be a mask for the robber, Swen said. It was obviously a one-man operation. Of course the father would tell Steve to run and hide. Dressed like a Vietnam commando, Steve would stick out, too easy to identify.

On motive again, it probably wasn't really robbery. Bankers carry credit cards, Swen said, not cash. Jim Jenkins really just wanted to cause trouble for the hated banker, to screw up any sale of the house. If robbery was the motive, Swen suggested, Jim Jenkins would have robbed Rudy and sent the banker walking off across the plowed fields while the robber escaped. And then perhaps anyone else, whoever went out there to consider buying the place, he'd be saying to himself, "Is that farmer going to stick his gun in my face too?" Swen called that "a feasible theory."

Yes, sure, the kid did what he was told—drove to the farm, got the guns out, ran and hid. "Is that enough to be proof beyond a reasonable doubt of intentional aiding another in committing a felony where death would be reasonably foreseeable?" Swen's voice indicated he had an answer. "Every church in this area, every school, every civic group teaches people to honor their mother and father and obey them."

As for Rudy not seeing Steve allegedly hiding behind the garage, Swen suggested that the banker hadn't gone as far back as Susan remembered. The gutter noise would be far more likely to have been caused by a stumbling middle-aged man with poor eyesight, perhaps seeking his hidden son, than an athletic young man. Swen's idea was that Jim Jenkins emerged from the woods with the rifle, that Toby saw him and ran to meet Rudy at the car, and that Jim waited to open fire until he had two still targets in the car.

The shooting there was not as good as the state claimed. The shot through the windshield was obviously aimed at Toby and missed, hitting Rudy instead. The fatal one for Toby wasn't superb marksmanship at all; it was a lucky ricochet off the vent window chrome strip. Nor did the pattern of hits and near misses out front scream supermarksman to Swen. It was erratic.

Jim obviously chose the M-1 over the shotgun because there was more ammunition in the M-1 clips. A shotgun holds only five shells. A person with bad eyesight would be concerned about having plenty of bullets on hand for his anticipated misses.

The bunk about the bombs and bulletproof glass, Swen said, was easily explained as a curious young kid asking questions.

Swen brought up the next matter. "Susan Blythe I think is a fine person," he said. But her testimony left some serious questions that contributed to all the doubt that Swen saw in this case. It was quite feasible that she misjudged how far her husband walked alongside the garage. If her husband really had gone behind the garage, his clothing, the pants, for instance, and the socks, although they were missing, unfortunately, would have picked up those sticky burdock seeds.

"When Susan got back," Swen continued, "she was hysterical and combative. I don't blame her for being hysterical and combative, but it could affect her ability to give accurate testimony and judge distances. And the only thing the state has to prove the boy was behind here, and somehow got chased out around here, is the testimony that Susan Blythe thought on the second visit some twelve days later that her husband had walked behind the garage."

Wouldn't you think if Rudy really did walk behind that garage, and if Steve really was the cold-blooded killer the prosecution claims, wouldn't you think you'd have found Rudy's body back behind the garage instead of way out front? See, that's the problem with circumstantial evidence. It can be read so many different ways.

There are some other problems with the prosecution's case, Swen suggested. Jim Perry taking his new maintenance employee with the bad eyesight and making him a night watchman. Swen skimmed over the discrepancy between Steve claiming to have driven the getaway truck and two other witnesses saying it was the older man. This made Steve more believable because the boy knew it could hurt him, yet he told the truth anyway. Swen thought the chase actually proved that Rudy was chased by Jim Jenkins, not the kid. The boy could have caught the banker. "I don't know anybody that's forty-two that's as heavy as Rudy Blythe and could outrun a kid."

Swen said he'd tried to point out all the many areas of reasonable doubt using concrete examples and not just talk. The jury might think of more during deliberations. If they did see this reasonable doubt, then they must find Steve not guilty on all four charges concerning death.

The accomplice question was more difficult, he admitted. "One of the big problems with the lad being just barely eighteen and being under the dutyship of his father is that the more obedient the boy is in honoring his parents, the more difficulty he has in these situations. It is really very tough. It is really very tough indeed when, if you obey your parents, you are a criminal. And if you disobey them, you are a delinquent." It was going to take quite a bit of soul-searching to convict Steve on this one. Of course, if they didn't have any reasonable doubt, then they should convict him. But the jurors had committed themselves at the start to being honest and truthful.

Swen Anderson thanked the jurors for going through this terrible and difficult trial with him. He knew they were aware that this young boy's life was in their hands. "Do what you can on this. Do it as honestly as you can."

Swen dropped his notes and glasses on the defense table as he walked back. Sweating, with baggy eyes, he turned and seemed to be addressing a friend in the spectator's front row. "I did my best," he said. Then, for a moment, Swen smiled.

That was at 1:10 P.M.. After lunch the jury had instructions from Judge Mann. He warned them to give a true verdict and not to let personal opinions about the advisability of certain laws influence their thinking. He told them they were the sole judges of the facts and the sole judges of the truthfulness of witnesses and the weight given each. If a juror's recollection of testimony differed from anything the judge or either lawyer had said, he should abide by his own judgment. "Sympathy, passion, or prejudice must not in any way enter into your deliberations," the judge warned.

He told them about the two kinds of evidence: direct evidence, such as eyewitness testimony, and circumstantial evidence. In order to convict on circumstantial evidence, he said, the circumstances must all concur that the defendant committed the crime. "If the circumstances, no matter how strong, can be reconciled with the belief that the defendant is not guilty, then the defendant should not be convicted. It is not enough that the circumstances coincide with and render possible the guilt of the accused. They must exclude every other reasonable theory.''

The judge reread all six counts for the jury and defined their terms. He reminded them that in the United States all accused are presumed innocent until proven otherwise beyond a reasonable doubt. ''Absolute mathematical certainty'' is not required, he said. But reasonable doubt cannot be manufactured from imagination, conjecture, or speculation. They should draw no inferences from the fact that the defendant did not take the stand.

He stressed that any verdict must be unanimous. They were to elect a foreman, examine the facts, discuss them, listen to each other calmly and dispassionately, and avoid any arbitrary position. They could change their views but should not surrender their honest conviction solely because of others' opinions or merely to return a verdict. ''Remember also, the question is never 'Will the state win or lose a case?' The state loses the case only when injustice is done, regardless of whether your verdict is guilty or not guilty.'' He then excused the alternate juror and sent the remaining seven women and five men into their little jury room. At 3:41 P.M. the deliberations began. The waiting began everywhere else.

''This is completely excruciating, absolute agony,'' said Swen as darkness fell on the back steps of the courthouse. The defense attorney was huddled there with his wife, Steve, and Darlene Jenkins. ''I love this kid too damned much for my good. It's hard to be objective. I tried to put on a dignified proper defense. It could go either way.'' One week later Swen would be back in a courtroom. The next time would have nothing to do with murder charges. Swen would be in court then seeking, successfully, to adopt Steven Todd Jenkins, making him in the eyes of the law Steven Todd Anderson. Darlene Jenkins agreed to the step, she said, because she felt the boy never really did have a father before. Twenty-one months later, Steve would lose this father too; on February 2, 1986, Swen Anderson, at forty-nine, would die in his sleep.

In a short time, the wait for a verdict became a long one. The Eagle Cafe sent over the jury's supper and they worked right through the meal. First off, Dave Koster was elected foreman. Naively, Dave thought that all twelve jurors would have their minds made up, and one or two votes would end the whole ordeal. Over the protest of some, Dave did hold a vote right off. The results settled nothing. In fact, the vote was just the beginning.

A few feet away, a score of people began their verdict vigil. Relatives, reporters, and local police lounged around the courthouse, quietly swapping stories as the hours ticked by.

Judge Mann waited in his chambers. With the judge's permission, Tom Fabel, Mike Cable, and the agents gathered at Mike's house fifteen miles away for a few hours and a few beers.

Susan stopped by during the evening to thank them, whatever the final outcome. She felt a little uncomfortable among them on their turf, so she left after a polite period, and the men didn't try to stop her. Susan was feeling more comfortable with herself, though, those days. As psychologists often tell relatives of violent crime victims, the trial can take the form of a drawn-out funeral. It was hard to face all those sad facts every day, to poke at the scars. But Susan and the others told themselves that the real end was near when they could go on with life, scars and all. Eventually, the storm would pass. The tears would stop.

Come August, on their wedding anniversary, Rudy's ashes would be buried in a small town in rural New York State. He did end up in the country after all. Despite her initial fears, Susan was running the bank successfully without her husband. She commuted daily from a rented house in Pipestone, where Rolph was still in school. Her bank was for sale, and Lee Bush would handle that. Some offers fell through, but the final one was firming up. In early June she would be free of those loan payments and that responsibility, although for sentimental reasons Susan would deposit a substantial part of Rudy's life insurance payments in the Buffalo Ridge State Bank as a sign of support for the town and her husband's dream. "Rudy would have wanted that," Susan would confide, "and you know, surprisingly, I did too." Surprisingly too for Susan, the people of Ruthton were going out of their way to be nice and helpful and friendly. The Girl Scout troop even planted a tree in memory of the man who financed their train trip to Duluth.

Susan found herself—actually, her friends noticed it first—with a different attitude toward life, certainly a different shape. She had lost her extra weight. "I lived a pretty sheltered life," Susan said. "I was Betty Boop all my life, so much so that I didn't see and hear a lot of things and a lot of people." She was more religious after the shootings and didn't rail so much against the fates and fearful forces. "What choice do you have?" she would say. "You deal with the cards you are dealt." Susan also found herself wandering back out to the Jenkins farmhouse a few times, part of a migration route she developed to revisit familiar family touchstones. Perhaps it was just to make sure they were there before going on to new places. At the Jenkins place Susan walked along the same farm paths where she, Rudy, Rolph, and the dog had strolled and run. Susan always ended up out front in The Ditch, where she would stand and pray a little and mentally report to Rudy on what she was doing and thinking.

The Jenkins house would soon be sold, for a song, to a family with children. By early July, Susan had sold the Dallas house and repaid Rudy's father. She decided to stay in the Midwest. She bought her own modest bungalow on a shady street in Minneapolis, where Rolph would attend a private school, and she could do Junior League work, and someday, who knows, maybe even go out on a date again.

Getting Rolph through this time was more difficult. For a long while he desperately clung to Susan. If something unforeseen could snatch away one parent, then it could happen to the other. There was a tough time, too, in court that day when Rolph had felt like crying as Swen questioned Susan. The links between mother and son were very strong, if unspoken. Neither one would give that man the satisfaction of their tears. Until later, alone.

There were bad dreams and bad thoughts, too, for Rolph. Susan found him sobbing once. The eleven-year-old remembered his father That Day after breakfast. Rolph went over and hugged him before the man left for work. "And I'm always thinking," Rolph said, "maybe if I had held on to him longer and tighter, maybe he wouldn't have died."

At first, Rolph thought he might like to be a policeman and catch bad guys, or maybe a prosecutor. A year later he wasn't so sure. A few months after that he wrote a theme titled "My Adventure." It was about the two-week canoe trip he and his father had taken in northern Minnesota that final summer. The theme described a violent storm that descended on their canoe in mid-lake, the wind, the whitecaps. But they got the tent up on an island, changed their clothes inside, played checkers, and read books. "All of a sudden," Rolph wrote, "we couldn't hear the rain anymore. We stuck our heads out of our tent and saw a beautiful sunset on the horizon."

Rudy's parents, still retired in Florida, often thought the pain of losing a son was past. "You expect parents to go first," said Rudy's father. Then his wife would be reading or painting and would see her husband sitting in a funny position and when she checked, the old man would be crying again.

Toby's mother still had the radio he brought home from the war. She wouldn't part with that for anything. She still lived with her handicapped son and she still taught music, although she couldn't take on as many students as before.

Toby's father was getting old too. He didn't go to the trial; he was afraid what he might say or do to the defendant.

"No matter how you cut it," said Larry Thulin, "as a parent you have a favorite child. And he was it." Mr. Thulin left a light burning by his son's photograph at night where his second wife would find him sitting sometimes.

Lynnette Thulin continued her audiology courses after Toby's burial, the only time Toby's two women ever saw each other. They were only brief glimpses really; friends kept the two females separated at the funeral home. Lynnette and Lynnette's children had a range of feature-length nightmares, as did Karen Rider and Karen's children.

Not long after the trial, Lynnette's father died; the lung cancer won out. Mother and daughter shared tips on coping with widowhood. As the months passed, Lynnette began learning from friends about a different Toby. "I knew he was no saint," she said. "He had a lot of problems, but we loved him."

Like Susan, Lynnette would feel sorry sometimes for Steve Jenkins. Sometimes she would think about all the problems she had encountered and feel sorry for herself. "Time helps me sit back," she said, "and laugh and cry and sort out the garbage and throw it away." She credits religion with carrying her through many difficult times. Religion and Toby. "He was my first love," she said. "There's only one of those in a woman's life. I'd do it all over again, even knowing what would happen."

Karen would not let go of her Toby either. "Ours was a mature love," she said. "I may have another relationship in my life, but there won't be another like Toby." Karen stayed in Minnesota for the trial, although it was suggested she avoid the courtroom. It was very difficult. Every day she'd see places and people and things that reminded her of Toby or, worse yet, the Jenkins family. There were some letters in the local papers, too, sympathetic to the poor Jenkins kid. Thursdays were the worst times for Karen, like sad anniversaries every single week, until one week over coffee Susan told her, "You can't throw away one seventh of your life. You've just got to get on with living."

Karen's two children were growing up quickly, scarred from their losses, but good kids nonetheless. Their nightmares seemed to dwindle after the three of them left Minnesota to settle in a house trailer in a small Colorado town where life would be peaceful and Karen could work more with handicapped youngsters.

Meanwhile, that day in April 1984, the waiting outside the courtroom continued. Sheriff Abe Thompson was relaxing with his deputy, Vernon "Seeds" Dahl. To avoid every law officer's standard nightmare, a repeat of the Jack Ruby incident in Dallas, they had already made their contingency plans for a guilty verdict—get the kid out of the courthouse as quickly as possible. If Steve was found innocent, they wouldn't need any plans; the kid could walk out of there himself.

George Briffett, the janitor, went about his accustomed custodial rounds with unaccustomed company. Shifting groups of men and women sat, stood, talked, read, dozed. A few strolled outdoors in the warming spring evening. No one had expected an immediate verdict; there were, after all, six complex charges. But the absence of a decision after eight hours caused some concern. Would it be a hung jury and they'd have to do everything over again? Whatever it was about, the delay indicated considerable wrangling.

"Now, I'm not easily scared," muttered Sheriff Thompson, looking over at the accused teenager, "but if I was him, I think I'd be quaking in my boots right about now." Steve was wearing boots, all right. He didn't appear to be quaking, although he had started to smoke.

At 11:48 P.M. a flurry of activity erupted. The prosecution team returned to the building. The defendant's group made its way upstairs. The courtroom filled. The jury entered. And so did the judge. But it was a false alarm. Judge Mann wanted to tell the jurors that they could continue to meet until 1:00 A.M. or recess and resume in the morning. They should talk it over back in their room. They did. Recess time was set at 12:01 after the now ritual warning from the judge on talking about the case with anyone. They should return at 9:00 A.M. sharp.

Everyone ran into storms on the way home that morning. Thunderstorms rumbled all around Lincoln County, the warm falling water helping to thaw the ground. Tom Fabel rode toward his distant motel to the rhythmic beat of the windshield wipers. Every minute or so his tired face was bleached an unnatural white by broad beams of lightning. His face might have been brighter had he known then that he was just three months and one day away from becoming a father again—finally a boy.

Swen Anderson hardly slept that night. He had farther to drive home, farther to drive back, and, it seemed, more at stake.

There was no formal court session at 9:00 A.M. on April 26. Everyone just fell automatically into his or her assigned place and assigned role of deliberating behind a barrier or waiting in the audience.

Within minutes, the judge received a written note from the jury foreman: "We would like the definition of unconsidered or rash impulse. Could it be given in writing?" This referred to the judge's instructions in which he said an unconsidered or rash impulse, even though intended to kill, is not premeditated.

To Tom, this was good news. It meant the jury had decided Steve committed murder and was deciding now if he planned it in advance. To Swen, this was good news too. It meant the jury was having some real problems deciding on guilt.

The judge had the definitions typed out from a *Webster's New Collegiate Dictionary*. The attorneys read them. The papers were sent to the jury. The wait continued.

The normal business of the courthouse continued too, with deeds being registered, property taxes being paid, and certificates for marriages, divorces, births, and deaths being filed. County officials were increasingly worried, however. They estimated the trial would cost more than forty thousand dollars, or nearly six dollars for every living person in the county.

Then at 11:19 word flashed out from the third floor: "There's a verdict!" Excitement swept the building. Reporters ran for their regular seats. Susan and Sharon took their places. Lynnette was across the aisle. Darlene was nearer the front. When Tom Fabel and Mike Cable walked to their seats, the courtroom was full.

At 11:25 the jury walked in silently. At 11:28 Swen entered with Steve, who looked calm and cool as usual. At 11:29 the judge entered, his black robe billowing out behind him.

"Ladies and gentlemen of the jury," said the judge, "have you reached a verdict?"

Dave Koster rose reluctantly. "We have, Your Honor."

The pharmacist handed the verdicts to the bailiff, who carried them to Judge Mann. He opened them and read them silently while the courtroom waited. There were three pieces of paper—two verdicts plus a note from Dave Koster. If it's all the same to His Honor, the note said, could somebody other than the foreman read the verdicts out loud? The judge made no mention of the note but handed the verdicts to the court clerk, Lee Smith, to read.

"State of Minnesota. County of Lincoln. In District Court. Fifth Judicial District. Number K-83-254. State of Minnesota versus Steven Todd Jenkins. We the jury find the defendant guilty of the charge of murder in the second degree as charged in count four of the indictment. Deems A. Thulin, victim."

A gasp swept the courtroom. The clerk picked up the next slip of paper.

"State of Minnesota. County of Lincoln. In District Court. Fifth Judicial District. Number K-83-254. State of Minnesota versus Steven Todd Jenkins. We the jury find the defendant guilty of the charge of murder in the first degree as charged in count one of the indictment. Rudolph H. Blythe, Jr., victim."

A louder murmur. The judge spoke.

"Is this your true and correct verdict as read, Mr. Foreman?"

"Yes, it is."

At Swen's request, Judge Mann then had the clerk poll each member of the jury on each verdict. While this long process was under way, Lynnette was in tears, Susan was staring straight ahead, Steven was still looking down, and Dave Koster was thinking. It had been an extremely arduous process, the pressure eating away at each juror every minute, and their emotions reflected that. Dave had wanted a verdict vote right away. There was some debate, but he got it. The secret ballots were unanimous: Steve Jenkins had been involved in the murders somehow.

Did he do the shooting? A vote. Ten said yes, two said no. The discussion, which was to become a debate, began. They pored over their notes and memories, mentioning what struck them, where they noted discrepancies, what they believed, and who they didn't. The jurors never even discussed Darlene's testimony. They decided right off she had been protecting her son. They were very impressed by Fabel's presentation, such simple organization. Several jurors commented on Fabel's dramatic closing argument, including the attorney throwing himself on the floor to aim the murder weapon. And the father's poor eyesight. And all that kid's training.

And some of the discrepancies. Who lied? Who would benefit by lying? For instance, who was driving when they left the farmyard? Why would a part-time policeman and the other guy lie about who was driving?

The two dissenting jurors slowly came around. All right, it was decided: Steve had done the shooting. But did he plan it?

Maybe Jim Jenkins and Blythe just got into an argument out there, some pushing and shoving, name-calling maybe. You know what bankers can be like. Jenkins, too. And the kid just opens up to protect his dad. Sure the kid talked about bulletproof glass and making fertilizer bombs, but he's accused of shooting, not bombing. A vote. It was nine to three that Rudy's murder was premeditated.

Wait a minute. Why take the license plate off if you're going to kill the guy? Well, he didn't have to plan it for months to be premeditated. What do you mean? He could have planned it for just a minute. That's premeditation, Fabel said. No, it was—what did the judge say?—a rash act. No. Let's get a definition from the judge.

When the judge's dictionary definition was delivered that morning, the unanimous verdict came quickly, which is not to say it made all twelve feel good. The jurors were comfortable with the decision but worried about its impact. Some saw a kid's life going down the tubes. They didn't like feeling responsible, until someone noted they hadn't sent the kid out there to do the shooting. The foreman had said he was worried about choking up while reading the verdicts. Maybe he'd ask the judge to have someone else read them.

"Marcella Rieth, is this your true and correct verdict as read, murder in the first degree, Rudolph Blythe?"

"Yes."

That concluded the polling of the jury. They were excused.

An appeal, sometimes taking years, is automatic in capital crimes in Minnesota: Steve's wouldn't come for nearly seventeen months. The defense—Swen would give way to a public defender—would claim there was no evidence of premeditation, that the judge should have sequestered the jury (though Swen didn't seek it himself), that the presence of a sheriff's deputy behind the lawyer's table was intimidating, and that the exclusion of his psychiatric testimony made a proper defense impossible. The Minnesota Supreme Court would disagree, however, upholding the verdicts in December 1985.

On that first verdict day the judge set May 22 as a sentencing date. At that time he would speak at length about the tragedy of the deaths and the tragedy of Steve's life. He would criticize a certain military officer, whose skills were honed in the duty of his country training young men to be soldiers, for teaching yet another teenager some of the mechanics of firing a deadly weapon accurately. The sentencing was a formality, since first-degree murder carries a mandatory term of life, which in Minnesota means a minimum of seventeen and a half years. Judge Mann, impressed with Steve's new family life with the Andersons, would rule that the ten-year sentence for Toby Thulin's murder and the five years for firing on Deputy McClure's car could be served concurrently.

Given the seriousness of the crime, however, Judge Mann revoked bail at the end of the trial. The teenage defendant Steven Todd Jenkins was to be turned over to law enforcement authorities for transportation to begin his imprisonment at least until the year 2001, when he would be thirty-six.

"Court's adjourned."

Everyone stood as the judge left. Steve was calm, though noise and people and pandemonium began crowding around him. He remained calm until Seeds Dahl, the big beefy deputy, walked toward him, according to Sheriff Thompson's plan. Dahl reached around his back to his belt and pulled out a pair of chrome handcuffs like the ones Steve used to carry.

Steve broke down then, sobbing and clinging to his mother. Darlene Jenkins and Steve stood there hugging and crying for several minutes while dozens watched.

Four feet away, reporters prodded Fabel for a reaction. "There is no sense of elation or victory, no sense of vengeance," he said. "It is the sad culmination of a tragedy for three separate families that began last September twenty-ninth, and we can only hope now that the families can begin to put their lives back together again."

Deputy Dahl put his large right hand on the back of Steve's neck. "Okay, boy," he said, and a crying Steve was gently pried from Darlene. They went out the courtroom door, the three of them together, Darlene hanging on Steve's arm, and they moved down the long metal stairs.

At the bottom Swen was expressing his love for the boy to the television cameras and vowing a thorough appeal. But his last few words were ignored as all the cameras and bright lights swung toward the newly convicted murderer.

"Seeds, will you wait for me?"

"If you hurry, Swen."

The mob grew as the deputy and Steve burst out the heavy courthouse door into the sun. Cameramen connected to their crewmen by black wires tried to run backward through the pushing crowd, attempting to get a head-on shot of the youth and the officer. Microphones on long poles waved in faces. Seeds was not taking his time out here in the open. Down the sidewalk, around to the right, back toward the sheriff's garage and a waiting patrol car. Steve was put in the back with Dahl. Swen got in the front. Doug Pedersen, another deputy, drove. At 11:51 the police car moved off toward the jail.

Back upstairs Tom Fabel was packing his briefcase. "I'm awfully sad about the human condition that brings these things to pass," he said, "but I'm going to enjoy going home now and putting my arms around my wife and kids and reminding myself that life is not all death and sadness."

In the hall George Briffett was leaning on his big broom, surveying the afternoon's work ahead. The refuse included cigarette butts, coffee cups, soda cans, potato chip bags, candy wrappers, newspapers, dirty dishes, and a crumpled pink Kleenex. "There's so much to clean up," he said.

All that while, Lynnette Thulin sat alone on a bench outside the courtroom. Her eyes were swollen. But the tears had stopped.

"Amen," she said.

**ARTHUR T.
VANDERBILT II**

TREASURE
WRECK

THE
FORTUNES
and FATE
of the
PIRATE SHIP
WHYDAH

mouth Bay is very
...al and full of Flatts
...hin and on the Sea
...d very dangerous
...Browns Bank and
Monument
...d very Rocky
a great many
...lds go in for a
...rbour in bad Wea
many Inletts in
...Bay and a place of
...ts for small Vessells and
...h Iron Oar here

Bay

Plymouth
Bay

Plymouth

Clarks I.

XI

Monomet
high Land

Rocky ground

Gurnethead

Channell oway

Browns Sunken
Island

20

5

7   10   30

10

7

3

3

3

3   F

XI

2

Barnstabl
reason of
Run a Sho

Note that
Bors are b
are set don
Water an
there is th

Barnst

Buzards Bay is very dangerous
Ebbing and Flowing is but small

Buzard Bay
IX †
2

Sandwich

2

Woodshole
2
3
...fts
5   5   5

...arpets in Cove

5

12 →
...ch at Horseshoe
...d to Westward
Horse Sho

Tuggynist
bit order

2   2   4

5

5   5

3
Tuggynist Point

Dry

Dry   Dry

2

2

North Cha
3 Coarse Sand
Southacks C
Horseshoesa

3

Barnstabl

Barnstable

9 feef
2

Race Point
10

2 7 X

High Land of C. Cod

5   35

25

30   25   15

20   10   Griffins I

ARTHUR T.
VANDERBILT II

Stony ground

Crab Bank

Stony ground

Stony ground

ny not dangerous by Great
wry Flatts Unfull have
above got of again   James I.

D'h of Water at some
the Depths of Water
int at high and low
known from Fathoms
atF placed by them

l 7 Bay
thorn Sand

12F

Yarmouth

Billingsgate

Eastham

The Pirate Ship
Whido 2 lost
Table Land

The Place where Icame
through with a Whale Boa
ordered by y Govern to lo
y Pirate Ship Whido Bella
cast away y 26 of April 1717
One Hundred & Two Man

2 the Seal 2 sunken
Channel w

Bishops & Clarks

Channel way

Old Ros

Dry

As a small boy, Arthur Vanderbilt was enthralled by the story of the pirate ship Whydah. *This fabulous ship was laden with a king's ransom in gold—or so the legend went—when it was sunk off the shores of Cape Cod by a raging storm. For years young Arthur roamed the Cape's outer beaches vainly searching for a piece of eight or a gold doubloon from the ship's priceless booty. As he grew to manhood, he dismissed the story as nothing more than local folklore.*

But in 1984, two and a half centuries after the purported wreck, the Whydah *was discovered—and its treasure surpassed even its mythic proportions. Millions of dollars' worth of pirate gold, long buried in the shifting sands, was recovered and a small boy's daydream became a grown man's delight.* Treasure Wreck *is one of those books—rare in fiction, even rarer in fact—where things work out just as they should.*

CHAPTER ONE

The Spanish Main. November 1643. Half the Spanish treasure fleet, dispatched from Seville in August, had anchored for several weeks at Veracruz on the Gulf of Mexico before sailing on to islands of the Greater Antilles. The rest of the galleons had sailed for Nombre de Díos and Portobello on the Isthmus of Panama, then to Cartagena on the northern coast of South America, and later to coastal outposts of Central America.

At each of these ports along the Spanish Main, the riches of the New World had been gathered in anticipation of the arrival of the king's annual flotilla of treasure galleons. For weeks, mule trains bearing bags of gold bars from the mines of Nuevo Reino de Granada and silver ingots from Peru had made their way down steep mountain passes. The bags of gold and silver, and chests of precious stones, were loaded on the backs of Indians who struggled for days under their weight, traveling east along paths through endless jungles. Canoes packed to the gunwales with the treasure of two continents were poled down malignant rivers to the coast.

There, once a year, in these sweltering outposts along the coast, where not a breath of air stirred and the stagnant smell of pestilence lay over the harbors, "the spectator would remain thunderstruck," one Spaniard wrote, "at the streets crammed with chests of gold and silver."

For a hundred years, Spain had been draining riches from the New World. From the time of the *conquistadores*, who, with a few hundred men and a few dozen horses, had plundered the Aztecs of Mexico, the Carib of the West Indies, the Mayas of Yucatan, the Chibcha of Colombia, and the Incas of Peru—from that time Spain had claimed sovereignty over the islands of the Caribbean, over Mexico, Central America, and South America. And, with the sacking and pillaging of these ancient Indian civilizations and the mining of the wealth of their lands, the Spanish Empire had become the greatest power in the world.

During the next century, a million pounds of gold, tons of bar silver and cast flat pigs of copper, coffers of pearls from the island of Margarita, topazes and emeralds, and chests of tobacco and indigo, all poured down to these squalid shanty ports, "things so marvelous," Cortés wrote eagerly to King Carlos I of Spain, "that they cannot be described in writing, nor can they be understood without seeing them."

When the dark holds of the ships had swallowed so much of the gold and silver that the stately Spanish galleons were wallowing in the Caribbean swells, the annual fleet rendezvoused and the treasure was tallied. After taking on provisions, the sixteen galleons paraded out to sea, their flags and pennants flying, and began their slow voyage back to Spain.

The ships would beat their way against the currents and prevailing winds through the Straits of Florida and then thread a course through the uncharted *bajamar*—the shallow sea between Florida and the Bahamas. This would be the most difficult part of the journey; the trade winds and equatorial currents that had all but swept them into the Caribbean on their voyage from Seville made it equally difficult to leave this so-called Spanish lake. Once the Bahamas were behind them, the ships would sail north with the trades and the Gulf Stream, and near Bermuda catch the westerlies across the Atlantic to the Azores and Spain.

On November 15, 1643, as the treasure fleet tacked through the passage of shoals and coral reefs off the northeastern coast of Hispaniola, the shallow turquoise waters began to turn pewter gray. A cover of clouds hung as low as the hills of the tropical islands. All afternoon, the wind gusted up and heeled the heavy galleons bucking through the whitecaps, strengthening as the fleet clawed its way on through the channel.

After dark, a howling wind bore down upon the passage off a furious ocean. The treasure fleet had sailed into a hurricane.

With their towering gilded sterncastles and short keels, dangerously laden with treasure, the galleons pitched wildly in the storm. On board, Jesuit priests prayed to Our Lady of Carmen, the patroness of those who risked their lives at sea.

Gale winds blew out mountains of canvas. Masts cracked. Stumbling down the backs of forty-foot waves, plunging into the troughs, lifted again toward the heavens, the ships lost sight of each other in the black fury of the night.

By morning, the hurricane had blown north. As the sun bore through a rushing floor of clouds, the captain of one of the galleons, *Santísima Trinidad*, scanned the ocean to the horizon. He could see none of the sister ships. Each of the fifteen other galleons had sunk. For a hundred miles, wreckage floated on the waters of the Bahama Banks. And somewhere beneath these shallow waters lay millions of dollars' worth of gold and silver and jewels.

Eight years after the loss of the Spanish fleet, William Phips was born to a poor Maine couple with twenty-five other children. At an early age, William was apprenticed to a ship's carpenter and, after learning his trade, settled in Boston, where he found work in a shipyard. Later he became the captain of a sailing vessel. Around the harbor and in the taverns of the seaport, young Phips heard sailors talk of treasure galleons that had gone down in the West Indies. One wreck in particular sparked his imagination: the loss of the fleet of heavily laden Spanish galleons on November 15, 1643.

Phips was infected by gold fever. In 1683, at the age of thirty-two, after several fruitless years of trying to raise money to salvage the Spanish treasure, Phips left his wife and home and sailed for England to enlist the aid of King Charles II. Phips's presence and persuasiveness, perhaps bolstered by his belief in an astrologer's prophecy that he would find "a mighty treasure," was enough to convince the king to gamble that this rugged sailor might actually recover part of the huge lost hoard. King Charles gave Phips the use of a frigate of 160 tons burden, H.M.S. *Rose of Argier*, which Phips outfitted with diving bells and other equipment for the expedition and manned with a crew of ninety-five that he rounded up along the waterfront.

The *Rose* sailed from the Downs on September 5, 1683. It was immediately obvious that a more dangerous crew had never been assembled, even from the scum of London's quays. Sailors were stealing so much from provisions stored for the entire voyage that, before the ship started across the Atlantic, Phips had to anchor off the west coast of Ireland to replenish supplies. The private stores of wine, brandy, and cheese belonging to the king's two agents, who were sent on the voyage to protect the Crown's interests, were pilfered. Members of the crew smoked in the powder room and drank themselves into stupors, and, as noted in an account of the voyage kept by one of the king's agents, "For swearing and cursing I bless God I never heard the like before in all the ships as ever I have sailed in."

When the crew learned that the agents were complaining to Captain Phips, they threatened to maroon the two on a tiny Caribbean cay. Phips refused to discipline the men, telling the agents that the ringleaders were "some of the best men in the Ship and if I should punish them I am afraid that their consorts will mutiny."

Upon reaching Boston Harbor on October 27, the troubles that had been confined to the *Rose* on the high seas were brought ashore. Although the *Rose* was on a private enterprise and was therefore not a man-of-war, the crew fired shots across the bow of each vessel entering the harbor until that ship struck its colors; then the crew demanded from the captain of each ship the cost of the shot. The nights were filled with drunken carousing and brawling on the streets and in the taverns of Boston. Before the *Rose* finally weighed anchor on January 15, 1684, for its voyage to the West Indies, Captain Phips had been summoned to court more than once because of fights started by his men.

On the Bahama Banks, days and weeks went by without spotting anything like "a Rock wch...apeeres Like a boate Keele up," which was said to mark the location of the wrecks. The crew rebelled, demanding that Phips join them on a pirate cruise around the Spanish Main. Phips, who was a giant of a man, rushed at the sailors, knocking them down left and right with his bare fists, and quickly quelled the mutiny.

Within a week, however, the crew, ashore on an island, plotted to take over the *Rose* and maroon Phips. The captain, who was aboard the ship when he was warned of the mutiny by one of the few loyal sailors, aimed the ship's cannon at the men on shore, threatening to blow them to pieces. "Stand off, ye Wretches, at your Peril," he shouted, as he prepared the ship to sail, calling out that he would leave them to die on the island as they had planned to leave him. The mutineers fell to their knees on the beach and begged for his mercy. Not about to test his luck a third time, Phips dismissed every sailor at the closest port and assembled a fresh group of men to join him on the treasure hunt.

Continuing his search around Puerto Plata off the northeastern coast of Hispaniola until his provisions and patience were depleted, Captain Phips returned to England in the fall of 1685.

King Charles had died, but Phips, again exhibiting what must have been extraordinary self-confidence, secured the support of the second Duke of Albemarle, who in turn enlisted the assistance of a number of other noblemen. He was outfitted with two new ships, the *James and Mary* of 200 tons burden and armed with twenty-two guns, and the *Henry*, a small frigate of fifty tons. On July 18, 1686, Phips obtained from the Crown a warrant to "all such wrecks as shall bee by him or them found in the Seas to the Windward of the North side of Hispaniola" with the right to retain "all such Riches, whether Gold, Silver or Bullion or of what other kinds soever, as shall be found therein," except for the one tenth to be reserved for the Crown.

By January of 1687, Captain Phips's divers were searching the shallow waters around Puerto Plata near the Bahama Banks, but without finding any evidence of the lost galleons.

Captain Phips sent out an expedition of two crew members and three divers to the Banks on January 17 with orders "to goe on the bank and make a search for a wreck" if they could "gett a slatch of faire weather."

The crew returned on February 7, dejected, discouraged. The divers met with Phips in his cabin to present their report. They had searched the Banks as thoroughly as possible, they assured him, until one evening when their boat was "amongst a parcell of boylers [rocks that were washed by the waves so that the water seemed to boil] they knew not off where; they were forced to Anchor all night & by Gods blessing it being very small breese of wind all night in ye morning they gott Cleare of them."

Phips was so disheartened by the report that he told the men he would prepare his ships to sail the next day to Jamaica.

At this point, one of the sailors slipped a large bar of silver onto the table.

"Why? What is this? Whence comes this?" asked Phips.

The sorrowful countenances of the crew suddenly changed. This was *treasure*, they cried out. They had found the wreck!

"Then thanks be to God!" Phips exclaimed. "We are made!"

The ecstatic crew now told the captain how the boat had searched the north side of the Banks, and then the south side, finally coming to anchor a mile and a half south of the Banks. They set off in a canoe to explore among the "boylers." On the trip back to the boat at the end of the day, one of the men saw through the shallow crystal waters a violet-hued sea feather. A diver jumped overboard to fetch it, thinking that Captain Phips might enjoy seeing this beautiful coral formation. The diver quickly surfaced without the sea feather. There, in nine fathoms of water, were scattered great cannon and other unusually shaped, coral-encrusted objects. One of the fifteen Spanish galleons had been found.

Within three days, the divers had brought up large casts of silver, three thousand pieces of eight, and a great quantity of plate silver.

The discoveries were first counted in individual "peeces of Eight." As the treasure trove was mined, the bullion and coins began to be recorded by weight. One day, for example, "baggs of Coyne Money Weighing 1139 lbs" were brought aboard the *James and Mary*.

Phips and his crew scoured the wreck of the Spanish galleon for six weeks, stopping only to let a storm pass and to observe the Sabbath. Day after day, the divers brought up from the bullion room of the wreck seemingly unending loads of silver in the shapes of pigs, sows, and bars, bags and chests of pieces of eight, plate silver, gold chains, and jewels, all encrusted with coral from nearly forty-five years in the sea. Other members of the crew combed the waters with long-handled rakes, finding coins that lay scattered among the galleon's ballast. The wealth from the sea was astonishing. Even "a bad day's work," caused by sickness of the divers, resulted in the recovery of 3931 dollars and 1500 half dollars.

Fearing an attack by a French privateer that had been spotted standing off the harbor at Puerto Plata and concerned about the coming of "fresh gales" with "many Tornadoes and great swelling seas" in which they could lose all their treasure just as the Spanish galleons had, Phips left the wreck and sailed for England on May 2, 1687.

On June 6 he arrived in the Downs to a hero's welcome "with such Treasure as to the Honour as well as Profit of the Nation no Ship ever perform'd the like." The *James and Mary* was put under heavy guard, and the Comptroller of the Mint was summoned to weigh the salvage, "being wett, sandy dirty and rusty." The comptroller certified it to consist of "37,556 lbs 4 oz of bars and cakes of silver, and 347 lbs of plate; and of gold 25 lbs; 7 oz 9 dwt." The New England individualist had brought back to London a mighty treasure indeed.

Captain William Phips was knighted by King James II, "in consideration of his Loyalty, and good services in a Late Expedition," and named the Provost Marshal General of New England.

Sir William Phips returned to Boston a knight, a hero, and a wealthy man. He lived with his wife in a "fair brick house" at the corner of Salem and Charter streets in Boston and soon was appointed the first royal governor of Massachusetts.

The Phips treasure created a sensation. In the taverns and inns of London and New England for years to come, there was talk of his unfaltering conviction that he would find the galleons, of his perseverance, and the sheer quantity of gold and silver he recovered. And, for generations, the tales of his remarkable expedition would lure many other adventurers to the Spanish West Indies in search of ghost galleons still at the bottom of the sea.

CHAPTER TWO

If William Phips could do it, a young Englishman reasoned several decades later, he, Samuel Bellamy, could do it too. Like most pirates, Captain Samuel Bellamy is a historical phantom, a man who suddenly appears with no past, and just as suddenly disappears into the sea mists.

Young Samuel Bellamy—Black Bellamy, as he was called because of his jet black hair and swarthy good looks—came from the West Country of England, that rugged seacoast of Cornwall and Plymouth known for its seafarers.

Each year, West Country fishing boats brought many poor seamen to Newfoundland to fish, under contracts providing that they had to pay for passage home at the end of the season. The masters charged so much for food, clothing, and provisions that most fishermen found themselves bound for the next fishing season, and the next, and the next. Although there is no record of his early years, it is possible that this is how Samuel Bellamy found his way to the New World.

Or perhaps Bellamy was one of the many sailors serving on English privateers, sailing the seas to plunder French shipping, who suddenly was without work when England's war with France over the Spanish succession ended with the treaty signed at Utrecht in 1713.

Whether a fisherman or a sailor, Bellamy's life at sea had been a breakingly hard one, as it was for all seamen of the day. Conditions were harsh and dangerous; discipline severe, often unreasonable. Later, Bellamy would call those men who lived by society's rules "Cowardly whelps," and those in power, "Villains" who robbed the poor "under the cover of Law."

It was not surprising that an intelligent, disaffected sailor like Samuel Bellamy would be fascinated by the tales he heard of the fleet of ten Spanish galleons that had recently sunk off the coast of Florida in the hurricane of July 30, 1715. Like Phips, he became obsessed with seeking his fortune by salvaging this sunken hoard, said to consist of 2290 chests of newly minted silver coins. He too would become wealthy and be knighted and live the life of a gentleman.

Early in 1716, Samuel Bellamy acquired an old sloop and set out to seek support for his expedition. On his way to the Caribbean, he moored his sloop in Eastham Harbor on outer Cape Cod, staying for a while at Higgins Tavern in the Southern Parish of Eastham. There the young seafarer met fifteen-year-old Maria Hallett.

Together, day after day, they wandered out past the village along cart paths through the scrub pines, across sandy moors of salt-spray rose, through silver-green beach grass to the bluffs overlooking the sea. As they lay on the sand on those sunny days, watching waves roll in to shore, Samuel Bellamy told Maria of the treasure that would be his. He would return with his sloop's hold full of doubloons and ducats, guineas, and pieces of eight. When he returned, he would take Maria to the Spanish Main and make her his princess of an island of the West Indies.

The surge of the surf was a call to Samuel Bellamy to be on his way. From the bluff above the beach, Maria watched as his sloop sailed out the harbor through the inlet to the sea. She watched when she could no longer distinguish its shape as a ship, and long after it had become a part of the sea and sky.

Day after day, as the ocean sparkled in the summer sun and still later as the sound of autumn roared in the breakers, Maria returned to the bluffs to watch the sailing ships pass off the coast, waiting for Samuel Bellamy's treasure-laden sloop to return.

That winter, a disgrace to the God-fearing Halletts of Eastham, hidden in the barn of Elder John Knowles, Maria gave birth to Bellamy's child. The baby choked on a piece of straw and died. Maria was found, and the village selectmen put her in the Eastham jail to be tried for murder. Time and again, captivated by the charm of the young girl, her jailors let her escape. The sheriff didn't mind; all he had to do to find her was to look out across the moors where she would be walking on the bluffs. Mystified by her ability to escape from jail at will, convinced she was a witch, the townspeople drove her out of town.

Maria built a hut on the moors of the tablelands above the beach, where, from her doorway, she could scan the sea. There she continued her vigil, waiting for Samuel Bellamy's return.

Sailing down the New England coast early in the spring of 1716, Bellamy had met forty-year-old Paulsgrave Williams, a goldsmith living in Newport, whose father, a successful merchant, had been the attorney general of Rhode Island. Williams joined the treasure voyage to the Caribbean, and the two adventurers became close friends.

After several weeks of diving off the eastern coast of Florida near Vero Beach, amid other groups of divers, the patience of Bellamy's crew was as drained as the stores of supplies. No bar silver had been raised; not a single Spanish coin had been found.

The thought of returning to New England empty-handed was intolerable. The idea of shipping out again as sailors was unacceptable. In this paradise of azure seas and steady trade winds, of narrow shipping passages, uninhabited islands, and hidden cays and coves, the lure of piracy was irresistible. Merchant vessels sailing the trade routes of the Spanish Main had to pass through the Straits of Florida, or Crooked Island Passage in the Bahamas, through Windward Passage between Cuba and Hispaniola, or Mona Passage between Hispaniola and Puerto Rico, and there, waiting for them, would be a swift pirate sloop. In those years, several hundred pirate ships haunted the Caribbean. "North and South America are infested with these rogues," wrote the governor of Bermuda in 1717. And the governor of Jamaica complained that "there is hardly a ship or vessel coming in or going out of this island that is not plundered." Now, too, Samuel Bellamy and Paulsgrave Williams decided to give up their treasure expedition and "go upon the account." They would try their luck as pirates on the high seas.

"In an honest service," pirate captain Bartholomew Roberts later would say, in words that must have reflected Samuel Bellamy's thoughts, "there is thin rations, low wages and hard labor; in this, plenty and satiety, pleasure and ease, liberty and power; and who would not balance creditor on this side, when all the hazard that is run for it, at worst, is only a sour look or two at choking. No, a merry life and a short one shall be my motto."

Undoubtedly, they were encouraged by Captain Benjamin Hornigold. Recognized as a founding father of piracy on the Spanish Main, old Captain Hornigold would brag most about the orphan from Bristol, England, who had found a berth on a merchant ship, deserted in the Caribbean, worked his way to New Providence in the Bahamas, and joined Hornigold's crew. Edward Teach was his name.

Dressed in black, with a greasy black beard that hung to his waist, his chest crossed with a bandolier holding three brace of cocked pistols, with ten-pound cutlasses, additional pistols, and daggers hanging from his belt, slow-burning matches smoldering in his hair and beard and under his hat, Teach—Blackbeard, as he was called—seemed to merchant seamen, as he boarded their ships, the Devil himself.

Hornigold recognized the talents of this hulking, drunken, intimidating man, and in 1716 gave him command of one of his prize vessels. Teach soon split off on his own to terrorize the Caribbean and the eastern seaboard. It must have seemed to Captain Hornigold a good time to teach his trade to other beginners, so, in the spring of 1716, Samuel Bellamy, Paul Williams, and their diving crew joined the pirate band of Captain Hornigold, commander of the sloop *Mary Anne*, and Captain Louis Lebous, master of the sloop *Postillion*, who together worked the waters of the Caribbean. Captain Lebous's *Postillion* was manned chiefly with Frenchmen, while Captain Hornigold's crew consisted primarily of Englishmen. Each sloop was mounted with eight guns and had a crew of eighty to ninety men.

That spring, captains Hornigold and Lebous led their pirates on a cruise around the Spanish Main "to Portobello...then...for the Havana, and from thence to Cuba, where they met with a Pink, an English-man Master, and took out some Powder and Shot and some Men." In May 1716 they captured a ship "to the Leeward of the Havana" on a "voyage with Logwood to Holland." The pirates "kept the Ship about 8 or 10 Days and then having taken out of her what they thought proper delivered her back to some of the Men who belonged to her." They took "without any resistance" two Spanish brigantines off Cape Corrientes (near the southwestern point of Cuba) "laden with Cocoa from Maraca." The Spaniards "not coming up to the Pirates' demand about the ransome were put a-shoar and their Briganteens burn'd."

The pirates sailed on to the "Isle of Pines [off the southwestern coast of Cuba], where meeting with 3 or 4 English Sloops empty, they made use of them in cleaning their own, and gave them back." From there "they sailed to Hispaniola in the latter end of May, where they tarried about 3 months."

The two pirate ships dropped anchor in a lonely bay, sheltered by reefs from the Atlantic rollers. It was here in this tropical paradise, in June 1716, that a dispute arose among the pirates. Captain Hornigold and some of the English pirates had refused to attack an English ship. The rest of the crew, "some being for one Nation and some for another," demanded that every merchant ship be taken.

A pirate crew elected its captain and could just as easily depose him. "They only permit him to be captain," a contemporary history of piracy reported, "on condition that they may be captain over him." The crew shared the ship and shared its treasure, and all major decisions were made by a show of hands. And so it was that the crew of the *Mary Anne* voted to pursue all ships on the high seas, regardless of nationality, and "Bellamy was chosen by a great Majority their Captain."

Captain Hornigold "departed with 26 hands in a prize Sloop, Bellamy having then on Board about 90 men." Paul Williams was elected Bellamy's quartermaster, the second in command, responsible for the crew of the *Mary Anne* and the division of plunder.

A pirate captain, as one contemporary pirate remarked, must be "a Man of Courage, and skill'd in Navigation, one, who by his Council and Bravery seems best able to defend this Commonwealth, and ward us from Dangers and Tempests of an instable Element, and the fatal Consequences of Anarchy." Bellamy's character must have been dominating and recklessly brave to win the support of a band of seadogs only weeks after meeting them, and especially to have overthrown one of the very fathers of piracy.

The new pirate leader was led to the great cabin of the *Mary Anne* where the quartermaster, speaking for the crew, pledged their loyalty. Then, the quartermaster presented a sword to the captain, saying, "This is the commission under which you are to act; may you prove fortunate to yourself and us.''

There remained one more formality: Pirate crews were governed by a code of laws developed over the years by the buccaneers of the West Indies and signed and sworn to by each pirate before a cruise commenced. The articles of the contemporary pirate crew of Captain Bartholomew Roberts were probably similar to the articles agreed upon when Samuel Bellamy became captain:

i. Every man shall have an equal vote in affairs of moment. He shall have an equal title to the fresh provisions or strong liquors at any time seized, and shall use them at pleasure unless a scarcity may make it necessary for the common good that a retrenchment may be voted.

ii. Every man shall be called fairly in turn by the list on board of prizes. But if they defraud the company to the value of even a Piece of Eight in plate, jewels or money, they shall be marooned. If any man rob another he shall have his nose and ears slit, and be put ashore where he shall be sure to encounter hardships.

iii. None shall game for money either with dice or cards.

iv. The lights and candles should be put out at eight at night, and if any of the crew desire to drink after that hour they shall sit upon the open deck without lights.

v. Each man shall keep his piece, cutlass and pistols at all times clean and ready for action.

vi. No boy or woman to be allowed amongst them. If any man shall be found seducing any of the latter sex and carrying her to sea in disguise he shall suffer death.

vii. He that shall desert the ship or his quarters in time of battle shall be punished by death or marooning.

viii. None shall strike another on board the ship, but every man's quarrel shall be ended on shore by sword or pistol in this manner. At the word of command from the quartermaster, each man being previously placed back to back, shall turn and fire immediately. If any man do not, the quartermaster shall knock the piece out of his hand. If both miss their aim they shall take to their cutlasses, and he that draweth first blood shall be declared the victor.

ix. No man shall talk of breaking up their way of living till each has a share of 1,000 [pounds]. Every man who shall become a cripple or lose a limb in his service shall have 800 pieces of eight from the common stock and for lesser hurts proportionately.

x. The captain and the quartermaster shall each receive two shares of a prize, the master gunner and boatswain, one and one half shares, all other officers one and one quarter, and private gentlemen of fortune one share each.

XI. The musicians shall have rest on the Sabbath Day only by right. On all other days by favour only.

Each of the pirates of Captain Bellamy's crew, if ever captured, was ready to claim that he was a forced man, that he had been taken prisoner and forced to join the crew. Some volunteers even requested that the pirates go through the motions of forcing them to join, so that if ever captured they would have witnesses and a defense.

With the exception of captives with special skills—such as surgeons, sailmakers, and carpenters—pirates rarely forced seamen into service, for there were always volunteers. Men like Thomas Baker, "by Trade a Taylor," who had left his home in Holland to go to sea at the age of twenty-nine, and Peter Hoof, a thirty-four-year-old Swede who had been a sailor for the last eighteen years, Simon Van Vorst, a young sailor from New York, and Hendrick Quintor, a twenty-five-year-old mariner from Amsterdam, all might claim that Captain Bellamy had told them they "must be easy" or he would put them "a-shoar on some Moroon Island," but their actions made it clear they were volunteers.

Crews comprised seamen who had had enough of the severe discipline on board merchant ships of the day, sailors who had been flogged with the tarred rope or cat-o'-nine-tails, who had been keel-hauled, towed from the stern of a ship, dunked from the yardarm, branded, or subjected to any of the other punishments meted out by sadistic officers. Other recruits came from the ranks of sailors tired of the back-breaking labor that was their lot. "Six days shalt thou labour as hard as thou art able," went an old sea saying, "the seventh, holy-stone the main deck and chip the chain cable."

Joining these discontented seamen were deserters from warships of the Royal Navy, runaway apprentices and indentured servants, escaped prisoners of war, debtors, adventurers, and the hundreds of privateers suddenly without a livelihood when England and France ceased hostilities in 1713. "Peace makes pirates," it was said.

All were drawn by the same magic vision of easy riches. In a day when sailors were little more than slaves, pirate ships were returning to port with enough booty to reward each member of the crew with over a thousand pounds, a staggering sum equivalent to the income of the English gentry. In an age in which the lower classes had no way to rise above their circumstances, there was no shortage of men eager to join a pirate crew like Captain Bellamy's.

An outlaw, ever on the alert, Captain Bellamy sailed the Caribbean, unheard of for weeks, lurking in the coastal shallows, suddenly skimming along under a press of sail, his cannons roaring, swooping out of the dawn to plunder a cumbersome merchant ship, just as suddenly lost again among the endless isles along the Windwards.

So terrorized were sailors by the tales they had heard, that their only reaction upon seeing a pinnace or sloop bearing down on them, flying the Jolly Roger, was to surrender at once. They had heard of the pirates who captured two East Indiamen in the Red Sea in 1695 and, annoyed by the talk of one of the captive captains, sewed his lips shut with a sail needle. They had heard all about another captain and his crew who had been sewn up in a mainsail by pirates and flung overboard. Twenty bodies were found in the sail when later it washed up on shore.

Their dreams were haunted by scenes of pirates stuffing sailors' mouths full of oakum and then setting the oakum ablaze, pirates pulling out sailors' tongues, slicing off their ears, lopping off their heads, lashing them to the capstan and whipping them to death with a cat-o'-nine-tails, cutting out their hearts and making shipmates eat them, forcing their victims to walk the plank or throwing them directly into shark-infested waters, setting them adrift in small boats with no provisions, marooning them on tiny coral islands. "It is a common thing among privateers," one observer reported, "to cut a man in pieces, or tie a cord around his head and twist it with a stick until his eyes pop out."

The penny-pinching owners of the merchant ships manned them with as few sailors as possible. When pirates overtook a ship, firing a shot across its bow, with the pirate crew shouting war cries and swinging cutlasses through the air, the merchant seamen would come to and lower their flag, giving little thought to fighting to protect their employer's cargo. Their best hope was to give the pirates whatever they wanted, and pray that they would soon depart.

Because of this reputation, the work of pirates by the time Samuel Bellamy went upon the account had become very easy indeed: a chase, a shot of the cannon, and the ship and its cargo were theirs. There is no record that Captain Bellamy and his crew ever used force or violence to capture any of the scores of vessels they plundered.

At sunrise on November 9, 1716, Abijah Savage, commander of the sloop *Bonetta*, sailing from Jamaica to Antigua, spotted "two large Sloops betwixt the Islands of Saint Thomas and Saint Cruise [St. Croix]." The breezes were light, but it was soon clear that the two ships were pursuing *Bonetta*. The *Mary Anne*, commanded by Samuel Bellamy, and the *Postillion*, commanded by Louis Lebous, each "Hoisting a black flag at the Mast Head," immediately "fired a Canon Ball." This was enough to convince Captain Savage to strike his sails. The pirates didn't even have to board his ship; Captain Savage had his longboat lowered into the water and was rowed to the pirate ships.

The pirates helped themselves to what they wanted from the *Bonetta*, including "Several of their Cloaths, and other things particularly a Negro Man, and an Indian Boy belonging to Mr. Benjamin Wickham of this Island, who were then on Board." Captain Savage and his crew and passengers were held captive on the island of St. Croix, "where the pirates anchored for a great part of the time."

During the sixteen days he was held captive, Captain Savage watched as the pirates "took a French Ship, and Six Sail of Small Vessels, all of which (after taking from them what they thought convenient) they discharged."

Shortly before releasing him, Captain Bellamy told Captain Savage that what his pirates were looking for was a larger ship to engage in longer expeditions. They wanted "a Ship of Provisions, and to exchange their Sloop for a Ship, which if they could but get fit for their Turn they would go further believing they should be able to Conquer and make a Voyage."

Such enthusiasm of Captain Bellamy and his crew caught the imagination of one passenger aboard the *Bonetta*, John King, who decided to join the pirates. He was, as the captain of the *Bonetta* later testified, "so far from being forced or compelled by them . . . that he declared he would kill himself if he was restrained, and even threatened his Mother who was then on board as a Passenger."

Plying to the windward, the pirates reached Saba, where "they Spy'd 2 Ships, which they chased and came up with." The larger ship, *Sultana*, was commanded by Captain Richards and the other by Captain Tosor, both bound for the Bay of Honduras. Having plundered the ships "and taken out some Young men [who] Cry and express their Grief upon their being compelled to go with Bellamy," they freed the rest, giving them back Tosor's ship and converting the *Sultana* into a man-of-war under the command of Captain Bellamy. Paul Williams was elected captain of the *Mary Anne*.

On December 16, 1716, about twenty leagues off Saba, the *St. Michael*, a Bristol ship bound for Jamaica, was captured by Captain Bellamy and Captain Lebous. The *St. Michael*'s crew was held captive by the pirates on the island of Blanco until January 9, 1717, when the ship was returned to its master, James Williams, after the pirates had plundered it. The pirates took on board the *Sultana* as new recruits fourteen men of the crew of the *St. Michael*. One of these, Thomas Davis, a twenty-two-year-old Welsh boy who, at age seventeen, had gone to sea as a shipwright, was forced to join the pirates because "he was a Carpenter & a Single Man."

Captain James Williams entreated Bellamy to let Thomas Davis go, and Davis begged Bellamy for his freedom, crying that "he was undone by being detained among them." One of the pirates, hearing Davis lament his condition, said, "Damn him, He is a Presbyterian Dog, and Should fight for King James."

Davis begged the pirate captain to promise that he be set free with the next vessel attacked, a plea Davis continually renewed. Bellamy replied that if the crew consented, he would let Davis go. The captain then called a meeting of the pirates and asked "if they were willing to let Davis the Carpenter go." The crew, "by reason he was a Carpenter, expressed themselves in a Violent manner, saying, 'No, Damn him, they would first shoot him or whip him to Death at the Mast'" before they would let him go.

"To his great sorrow and grief" Davis remained a prisoner aboard Bellamy's ship. With another forced member of the crew, Thomas South, a thirty-year-old sailor from Lincolnshire who had been his shipmate aboard the *St. Michael*, he plotted how they "would run away together," at the first opportunity. The pirates tried to make Thomas South a member of the crew, offering him arms, "but he told them He would not use any, for which he was much threatened."

In late February or the beginning of March in the year 1717, Captain Bellamy and his crew pursued on the high seas for three days and nights "in the Windward Passage in the West Indies, a Free Trading Ship called the *Whido*, bound from His Majesty's Colony of Jamaica, to the Port of London, which Ship then was Owned and Navigated by His Majesty's Subjects of Great Britain, having her own Cargoe on board, and displaying English Colours."

Built as a merchant slaver, the handsome three-hundred-ton galley was named for the trading port of Whydah on the Gold Coast of West Africa. There, in the early eighteenth century, a thousand captives a month were taken by the Royal African Company for the slave trade to the New World. The pirates "thought they had lost her, but came up with her the third day." Other than firing two chase guns at the pirates, *Whydah*, "with 18 guns mounted and fifty men," offered no resistance to the pirate sloop flying the "large black Flag with a Death's Head and Bones a-cross."

Bellamy's pirates swarmed over the *Whydah*, taking hostage the ship's captain, Lawrence Prince, and his crew, and ransacking the hold. There, below deck, they discovered an astonishing cargo accumulated on a successful slaving voyage along the Guinea Coast, "consisting chiefly of Sugar, Indigo, Jesuits Bark [cinchona, from which quinine was made], Silver and Gold."

All the treasure the pirates had stored between decks on the *Sultana* was transferred to the *Whydah*. There, "Captain Prince was treated civilly." He was given *Sultana* and "above Twenty Pounds in Silver and Gold to bear his charges," and allowed to load her "with as much of the best and finest goods as she could carry... Seven or eight of the Whido's crew joyned" the pirates; "the Boatswain and two more were forced, the rest being Volunteers."

Bellamy could well afford to be generous with his captives. After less than a year upon the account, the *Whydah*'s hold was laden with treasure. "It was a common report in their Ship," one of the crew, John Brown, would later testify, "that they had about 20,000 pounds in Gold and Silver." And Peter Hoof, another member of the crew, would later report that at the time "the money taken in the Whido, which was reported to Amount to 20000 or 30000 Pounds, was counted over in the Cabin, and put up in bags, Fifty Pounds to every Man's share, there being 180 Men on Board. Their Money was kept in Chests between Decks without any guard, but none was to take any without the Quarter Master's leave."

The crew mounted an additional ten cannon and swivel guns along the bulwarks, giving the *Whydah* twenty-eight guns, a staggering number for a ship of a hundred feet and three hundred tons burden. The men also stripped off the protective lead sheathing around the hull to increase the ship's speed. Several tons of shot for her cannon had been stored in the hold, along with a number of water barrels, each weighing a ton.

With such a ship, pirating was even easier than before. When a cargo vessel spotted the *Whydah* bearing down on it, with its twenty-eight cannon uncovered, surrender was immediate. Bellamy didn't even have to waste a shot across the bows.

Off Petit Goave on the southern coast of Hispaniola, the *Whydah* stopped an English ship laden with sugar and indigo, taking several of the crew and as much of the cargo as the pirates wanted, and then returning the ship to its captain. Several days later, the pirates captured the *Tanner*, bound from Hispaniola to Old France with a cargo of sugar. Below deck, the "Pirates found 5000 Livres," which they added to their sea chests between the decks of the *Whydah*. John Shuan, a twenty-four-year-old French sailor aboard the *Tanner* caught by the lure of the pirates' life, "declared himself to be now a Pyrate, and went up and unrigged the Main top-mast by order of the pyrates."

Later in the year, Samuel Bellamy planned to go "a-pyrating" around the vast Indian Ocean, sail the Red Sea, anchor at the pirate haven of Madagascar, and capture some of the ships of the Dutch East India Company he had heard so much about, ships whose holds were said to be filled with huge cargoes of diamonds and silks, spices, rugs, and bar gold.

But first, what a sight it would be for Maria Hallett: the *Whydah* storming up the coast of Cape Cod, with every sail set and the lee rail awash.

CHAPTER THREE

Like many of the brethren of the coast who cruised the emerald green shallows of the Caribbean during the winter, Captain Bellamy and Captain Williams steered north late in March, up the coast of the colonies toward New England.

The ships bound to and from England and the Leeward Islands would be off the coast of New England in the spring, replenishing their supplies, and trading cargoes of gold and amber, slaves, skins, and elephants' teeth for bolts of cloth and iron kettles. There the pirates could stalk the coasting vessels, sailing on to Cape Sable and Newfoundland for their own fresh supplies and recruits, later bartering their illicit goods with eager merchants in Newport, Connecticut, and New York. "The pirates continue to rove on these seas," wrote the governor of the province of Massachusetts

Bay in 1717, "and if a sufficient force is not sent to drive them off our trade must stop."

The *Whydah* and the sloop *Mary Anne* followed the Gulf Stream's oceanic current north, through its steep seas and sudden squalls of wind and rain. For four days and three nights off the coast of Virginia, they battled a violent thunderstorm. In his *General History of the Robberies and Murders of the Most Notorious Pyrates*, published in 1724, Daniel Defoe describes this storm in such detail that it seems likely he had talked about it with a member of the pirate crew:

"At the first appearance of the sky being likely to be overcast, Bellamy took in all his small sails, and Williams double-reefed his mainsail, which was hardly done when a thunder shower overtook him with such violence that the *Whidah* was very near oversetting. They immediately put before the wind, for they had no other way of working, having only the goose wings of the foresail to scud with. Happy for them the wind was at W. by N. for had it been easterly, they must have infallibly perished upon the coast.

"The storm increased towards night, and not only put them by all sail, but obliged the *Whidah* to bring her yards aportland, and all they could do with tackles to the goose neck of the tiller, four men in the gun-room, and two at the wheel, was to keep her head to the sea, for had she once broached to, they must infallibly have foundered.

"The heavens, in the mean while, were covered with sheets of lightning, which the sea, by the agitation of the saline particles, seemed to imitate. The darkness of the night was such as the scripture says, as might be felt; the terrible hollow roaring of the winds, could be only equalled by the repeated, I may say, incessant claps of thunder, sufficient to strike a dread of the Supreme Being, who commands the sea and the winds, one would imagine in every heart; but among these wretches, the effect was different, for they endeavored by their blasphemies, oaths, and horrid imprecations, to drown the uproar of jarring elements. Bellamy swore he was sorry he could not run out his guns to return the salute, meaning the thunder, that he fancied the gods had got drunk over their tipple, and were gone together by the ears.

"They continued scudding all that night under their bare poles; the next morning the mainmast being sprung in the step, they were forced to cut it away, and at the same time, the mizen came by the board. These misfortunes made the ship ring with blasphemy, which was increased, when, by trying the pumps, they found the ship made a great deal of water; though by continually plying them, they kept it from gaining. The sloop, as well as the ship, was left to the mercy of the winds....

"The wind shifting round the compass, made so outrageous and short a sea, that they had little hopes of safety; it broke upon the poop, drove in the taveril, and washed the two men away from the wheel, who were saved in the netting. The wind after four days and three nights abated its fury, and fixed in the North, Northeast point, hourly decreasing."

When the skies over the ocean cleared, the crew set up jury-masts. "All this while the *Whidah*'s Leak continued, and it was as much as the Lee-Pump could do to keep the water from gaining, tho' it was kept continually going." The ship's young carpenter, Thomas Davis, still the pirates' prisoner, discovered that the leak was caused by some oakum "spewing out of a seam" in the bow, a simple repair.

The two ships hailed each other. Bellamy and Williams agreed to head to the Outer Banks off the coast of the Carolinas to check their ships. Southerly winds a day later forced them to revise plans and set their sails straight for New England. There they would rendezvous at Block Island off Rhode Island and visit Paulsgrave Williams's family, sail to Cape Cod to see Maria Hallett, and then on some deserted beach overhaul the ships.

The tension of battling the storm was broken. Off the southern coast of the colonies, it began to feel like spring. The crew "passed their time very jovially," and one of the pirates suggested that to celebrate their good fortune, they should put on a skit, "The Royal Pirate," a plan heartily endorsed by the rest of the crew, which already was celebrating the end of the storm with rounds of rum punch.

The quarterdeck was cleared. Roles were assigned. The treasure chests below deck were ransacked for "Thracian" togas and scarves, chains of gold, rich silks and brocades for costumes.

As the luffing canvas groaned and the long Atlantic swells rolled unceasingly past, with rapt attention the pirates watched the drama of Alexander the Great. One of the *Whydah*'s gunners in particular was drawn into the spirit of the play. As Alexander raised his arm to point to the heavens, the gunner looked up to see what he was pointing at, "creak'd his Neck," lost his balance, and fell against the bosun. When Alexander wept, the gunner began to cry. When Alexander captured the hero of the play, a pirate playing a pirate, he exclaimed, "Know'st thou that Death attends thy Mighty Crimes, And thou shalt hang Tomorrow Morn betimes!" The gunner, convinced he was watching a real kangaroo court, raced to the stage to the hero's defense. "They were going to hang honest Jack Spinckes," he shouted to his comrades, "and if they suffered it, they should all be hanged one after another, but, by God, they should not hang him, for he'd clear the decks." "Taking a grenade with a lighted match," the gunner "set fire to the fuse and threw it among the actors." Other pirates in the audience who, like the gunner, had become swept up in the drama, rushed with drawn cutlasses to help save the hero pirate.

Before Captain Bellamy could call a halt to the melee, the pirate playing Alexander had lost his arm, the hero had broken his leg "with the bursting of the shell," and "Alexander the Great revenged the loss of his arm by the death of him who deprived him of the limb." Those in the audience who had rushed onto the stage were thrown into irons for a day with the gunner, and Captain Bellamy decreed that forever after "The Royal Pirate" never be enacted aboard the *Whydah*.

Several days after the storm, the *Whydah* lost sight of the sloop *Mary Anne*, but according to the agreement between the two captains, the *Whydah* cruised the coast off Virginia for ten days.

She was well positioned in the shipping lanes. On Sunday, April 7, 1717, five leagues east of Cape Charles off Virginia, at about eight o'clock in the morning, the *Whydah* bore down upon the *Agnes*, a ship "bound from Barbados to Virginia laden with Rum, Sugar and Molasses & Sundry European Goods." Captain Bellamy "commanded the Master to come on Board." After the crew of the *Agnes* was aboard the *Whydah*, "the greatest part of the Cargo was plundered by the Pyrates, [and] carry'd on board their Ship."

The pirates that same day plundered three other merchant ships "of what Goods they thought fit" and took six of the crew "and two Men Servants, who voluntarily joyned with the Said Pyrates." They then put the rest of the captured crew aboard one of the ships and set them free, but kept as a prize the snow *Ann*, a one-hundred-ton transatlantic carrier that looked like a brigantine, with two masts and all sails square-rigged. Captain Bellamy ordered eighteen of his crew to man the snow along with ten sailors of the *Ann*'s crew who had joined the pirates.

The *Agnes* proved to be "so leaky that the Men refused to proceed farther" with her. Bellamy directed Thomas Davis and another of the *Whydah*'s carpenters to board the *Agnes*, "who by his Order cut away the Masts and bored a hole in the bottom of the Vessel, and so destroyed her."

Captain Bellamy and his pirates had told the master of the *Agnes* that "they intended to Cruise for ten days off Delaware Bay, and ten days more off Long Island, in Order to intercept Some Vessels from Philadelphia and New York bound with Provisions to the West Indies." Thereafter, the *Whydah* would head for Green Island "to the Eastward of Cape Sable" off the southern coast of Nova Scotia. There, on a sheltered beach, they would careen the *Whydah*. The ship would be run onto the beach on a high tide and, with a block-and-tackle system attached to stout trees above the beach, would be hauled on its side. Then, the many months' growth of seaweed would be scraped off the hull, the barnacles burned off, and the holes made by the voracious teredos plugged, with planks replaced and seams recaulked and tarred. Finally, the entire hull would be coated with a mixture of tar, tallow, and sulfur to inhibit further damage.

Fair winds brought the pirate ships and the prize snow to the coast of Rhode Island, where Captain Paul Williams captured a sloop out of Boston commanded by Captain Beer, sailing with cargo to South Carolina. Williams had Captain Beer rowed to the *Whydah* to meet Captain Bellamy.

Although Williams and Bellamy wanted to return the sloop to Beer, their crews insisted that his ship be sunk. Bellamy apologized, explaining that under the pirate code, he could not veto a general vote of the crew. Then, for several hours, he urged the hostage captain to join his crew, expatiating on his philosophy of piracy:

"Damned my Blessed," he said, "I am sorry they won't let you have your sloop again, for I scorn to do any one a Mischief, when it is not for my Advantage. Damn the sloop, we must sink her, and she might be of Use of you. Tho' damn ye, you are a sneaking Puppy, and so are all those who will submit to be governed by Laws which rich men have made for their own Security, for the cowardly whelps have not the Courage otherwise to defend what they get by their knavery; but damn ye altogether. Damn them for a pack of crafty Rascals, and you, who serve them, for a parcel of hen-hearted Numskulls. They vilify us, the Scoundrels do, when there is only this Difference: they rob the poor under the cover of Law, forsooth, and we plunder the Rich under the Protection of our own Courage. Had ye not better make One of us, than sneak after the Asses of those Villains for Employment?"

Captain Beer replied again and again that he could not break the laws of God and man to become a pirate.

"You are a devilish Conscience Rascal, damn ye," Captain Bellamy sneered. "I am a free Prince, and I have as much Authority to make War on the whole World, as he who has a hundred Sail of Ships at sea, and an Army of 100,000 Men in the Field; and this my Conscience tells me; but there is no arguing with such snivelling Puppies, who allow Superiors to kick them about deck at pleasure, and pin their faith upon a Pimp of a Parson, a Squab, who neither practices nor believes what he puts upon the chuckle-headed fools he preaches to."

Captain Beer was rowed ashore at Block Island. He would find passage to Rhode Island and reach his home in Newport by the first of May.

Captain Williams anchored off Block Island for several days to be with his mother, his sister, and his niece, regaling them with tales of his adventures on the high seas since he had left home. The pirates of the *Whydah* and the prize snow sailed on toward Cape Cod.

On Wednesday, April 24, 1717, the pink *Mary Anne* of Dublin, Ireland, under the command of Captain Andrew Crumpstey, with a cargo of Madeira wine, sailed from Nantasket, bound for New York. As the *Mary Anne* sailed between the Nantucket Shoals, and Georges Bank, the crew on watch between four and six o'clock on Friday morning sighted two sails off the stern.

By nine-thirty that morning, the two ships, with the "Kings Ensign and Pendant flying," overtook the cumbersome cargo ship. Bellamy ordered the *Mary Anne* to strike her colors. Lowering a longboat into the sea, seven crew members from the *Whydah* rowed to the *Mary Anne*.

Hearing the commotion, Alexander Mackconachy, the plump old sea cook, had climbed up from his galley and watched in horror from behind a mast as the seven pirates boarded the *Mary Anne*, five of them armed with muskets, pistols, and cutlasses.

Swinging a cutlass, one of the pirates, Thomas Baker, approached Captain Crumpstey and ordered him to climb into the longboat with all the ship's papers and with five of his crew, and to row to the *Whydah*. The pirates directed the mate, nineteen-year-old Thomas Fitzgerald, the cook, and crewman James Donavan to remain aboard.

Amidst the confusion of taking the ship, one of the unarmed men from the *Whydah*, Thomas South, hurriedly whispered to the mate of the *Mary Anne* that he was being held on the *Whydah* against his will and that he intended to escape as soon as the opportunity arose, words given credence by his behavior, which the pink's crew noted was "civil and peaceable."

Learning of the cargo stowed in the bulbous hull of the ninety-ton pink, four more pirates from the *Whydah*'s crew rowed over to the *Mary Anne* to bring some wine back to the flagship. But because the anchor cable was coiled in the hatchway, "they found it difficult to come to the Wines in the hold, and so returned to their own Ship without any wine, Except five bottles of green wine which they found in the pinks cabbin."

The longboat was hauled aboard the *Whydah*. Captain Bellamy hailed the *Mary Anne* and ordered his seven crew members who had taken command to "Steer North-West and by North." After an hour, he again hailed his pirate crew and commanded the broad-beamed *Mary Anne*, which was lagging behind, to make haste. Out of earshot of the captain, twenty-five-year-old Jamaican-born John Brown swore that he would "carry Sail till she carry'd her Masts away."

In the meantime, several of the pirates were amusing themselves by teasing the old cook. Simon Van Vorst threatened Mackconachy, saying that "if he would not find Liquor he would break his Neck," and Thomas Baker said he would shoot the hapless old cook through the head because he steered to the windward of his course, telling him that he "would make no more to shoot him, than he would a Dog; and that he should never go on shoar to tell his Story." Baker also told the hostages that Captain Bellamy and his crew had "got a Commission from King George to act as privateers." Even Simon Van Vorst had to laugh at that, saying, "We will stretch it to the World's end."

All the while, the pirate crew was drinking "plentifully of the Wine on board the Pink." They ordered Fitzgerald, the mate, "to reef the top-sail" and "Damn'd the Vessel and wished they had never seen her," for the *Mary Anne* was leaking badly and all hands, including the pirates, were "forced to Pump hard."

The ships continued sailing north by west until four o'clock in the afternoon, when the *Whydah*, the snow *Ann*, and the pink *Mary Anne* lay to, "it being very thick foggy weather." A sailor had been in the *Whydah*'s crow's nest all day, searching for the darker blue of the channels' deep water. Another had spent the day taking repeated soundings. Bellamy had taken on as a member of his crew John Julian, "an Indian born at Cape Codd," and a man named Lambeth as pilots to guide the ships past this coast. Even so, he was worried. He knew enough about the waters off the Cape from his stay at Eastham to understand just how treacherous they could be. Finding the channels through these shoals, even for John Julian and Lambeth, would be difficult enough in fair weather. And now, a fog was coming in, and clouds were piling up along the horizon.

Early that evening, the sloop *Fisher*, bound to Boston from Virginia, encountered "within a few leagues off Cape Codd," as one of its mariners recalled, a ship "of twenty eight guns called the *Wedaw*, which asson as they came near, haled us and Demanded from whence we came." Captain Bellamy called over to Captain Robert Ingols of the *Fisher*, "We are of the Sea," and asked if he "was Acquainted here." His luck was holding; Captain Ingols responded that he knew this coast "very well." Bellamy ordered Ingols and his mate to come aboard the *Whydah*. Four armed pirates boarded the *Fisher*. Bellamy instructed his men on the new prize sloop to follow his light.

As night fell, the *Whydah*, the snow *Ann*, the pink *Mary Anne*, and the *Fisher*, all "put out a Light a-Stern." The convoy began to beat its way up the most dangerous coast along the eastern seaboard.

CHAPTER FOUR

Jutting thirty miles into the ocean from the shores of "his Majesty's Province of the Massachusetts-Bay" lay the sandy peninsula of Cape Cod. The outer coast of the Cape, which faced the North Atlantic, was guarded by a line of shoals stretching far out to sea. Submerged, shifting, and treacherous, a double line of these sandbars lurked two to three fathoms beneath the surface of the water half a mile to a mile and a half off the coast. Here, the shoals formed and broke apart and formed again. Waves gathering strength over hundreds of miles of troubled sea were tripped by these shoals and crashed down upon them. Surf erupted into spray and seething white water foamed over the bars before the waves rolled on toward the shore, their greatest force spent.

Sailors learned that there was little hope if they were storm driven toward these shoals. When trapped on a bar, no ship could long withstand the pounding of surf. During the next two centuries, more than three thousand vessels from seaports all over the world foundered on the shoals and sank. Half the wrecks that occurred along the entire Atlantic and Gulf coastlines piled up on this lonely forty miles of outer beach. Here was the graveyard of the Atlantic.

That Friday evening, as the *Whydah* and its prizes sailed up the Cape's outer coast, the pirates who "had the government of the Pink" divided themselves into two watches, assigning the three hostage members of the *Mary Anne*'s crew to different watches.

When night fell, nineteen-year-old Thomas Fitzgerald, the mate of the *Mary Anne*, was at the helm. With the night came wind, and with the wind, long, low, rolling thunder, a sudden rain squall, and lightning. By ten o'clock, "the weather grew so thick, it Lightned and rained hard, and was so very dark" that Fitzgerald had "lost sight of the Pirate Ship, Snow and Sloop."

The *Boston News-Letter* of April 29 to May 16, 1717, would later report that "the Pyrates being free with the Liquor that the captive had, got themselves Drunk and asleep, and the Captive master in the Night, thought it a fit opportunity to run her ashore on the back side of Eastham."

Such was not the case. Andrew Crumpstey, the master of the pink, was not even aboard the *Mary Anne*, having been taken to the *Whydah* that afternoon. And Fitzgerald seemed as shocked as the pirates when suddenly, above the gale winds, came that sound which haunted sailors: the roar of the surf under the lee bow.

"Being among the breakers," the crew "thought it most proper and necessary to weere [come about before the wind] the Pink," to force her back into deeper water. But "before we could trim the head sails we run ashoar."

The flat-bottomed *Mary Anne* had struck a bar in the seething shoal water. One of the pirates, Thomas Baker, quickly "cut down the Fore-mast & Mizen-mast of the pink" to reduce the pressure on the hull. In the howling northeast gale, sodden strips of sail and tattered rigging beat the sides of the stranded ship. The full force of the breakers began crashing against the *Mary Anne*.

Helpless, the seamen knew that it was just a matter of time before the pink split apart. "For God's sake let us go down into the Hould & Die together," one of the pirates shouted against the gale. The others followed. Stumbling down the ladder of the pitching ship, they pulled the hatch cover closed above them.

The hold was black, save for the flickering arc of light from a sea lantern swinging crazily on a beam. Empty bottles of wine and wreckage from the ransacking of the ship that afternoon rolled back and forth in the dirty bilge. The *Mary Anne* heaved and groaned as the seas pounded over her deck.

Huddled together, wet and cold, shivering, the pirates "in their Distress" begged Thomas Fitzgerald "to read to them the Common Prayer Book."

With the roar of the storm filling the hold, the young mate began to read:

"Grace be unto you, and peace, from God our Father, and from the Lord Jesus Christ.

"Repent ye; for the Kingdom of heaven is at hand."

Clutching their bottles of Madeira wine, the pirates cried out in terror as a giant wave exploded over the ship and shook its timbers. The long, horrible, hissing undertow mingled with the wind, sounding as if it would suck the ship down to the bottom of the sea.

The cook glanced over at the band of ruffians trembling in the deep shadows of the hold. He wondered where they had come from and what crimes they had committed, what trail of misery and lawlessness lay behind them. Surely it was God's will that they now must die. But why must he, Alexander Mackconachy, die too, and Thomas Fitzgerald and James Donavan?

Drunk, scared, the pirates fell to their knees and tried to pray, repeating words after Fitzgerald. "Amen! Amen!" the pirates cried.

Repeatedly, the storm and the sea joined forces to attack the pink. Down in the hold, the wildness of the night surrounding them, Fitzgerald continued:

"Deliver me from mine enemies O God, defend me from them that rise up against me. O deliver me from the wicked doers, and save me from the blood-thirsty men."

He looked up from the *Book of Common Prayer* to the pirates, who were covering their eyes and ears with their hands, burying their heads between their knees. Drunk from the wine, with the lantern swaying above them, the pirates began to fall into troubled sleep as the storm raged on.

Ten miles up the coast, the *Whydah* was beating its way north, its sails double-reefed, its mainsail furled.

At the height of the storm, Captain Bellamy offered the captain of the snow *Ann* his ship and his freedom if he would guide the *Whydah* safely to Cape Cod Harbor (now Provincetown Harbor) at the tip of the Cape. The captain of the snow, "suspecting that the pirate would not keep his promise, and that instead of clearing his ship, as was his pretence, his intentions were to plunder the inhabitants of Provincetown," ran his snow straight toward shore, trusting that with its shallow draft he could head back out to sea before grounding, as the heavier pirate ship struck the outer bars.

Bellamy's only thought must have been of the sea chests stored between decks, filled with thirty thousand pounds of gold and silver divided into bags, "fifty pounds to every Man's share," of the sacks of indigo and Jesuits' bark, the gold dust and jewels and ivory tusks, that remarkable treasure that he had worked for nearly a year to accumulate on the Spanish Main. Against the onslaught of rain blown horizontal by the gale and the sheets of spray and crests of waves lashing the decks, he yelled for the anchors to be lowered. A crew of pirates wrestled with the capstan, lowering two anchors, each weighing a thousand pounds, with their huge flukes and rings big enough for a boy to climb through, and feeding out fathom after fathom of heavy iron chain.

Dropping anchor while being driven toward the outer bars off the Cape was the last-minute maneuver many captains would attempt in succeeding years after they had lost control of their ships, a last effort that failed almost as often as it was tried.

The anchor cable pulled taut, holding the ship off shore. But the *Whydah* at the end of the iron cable was no longer able to ride over the waves. Sails blew out with an explosive roar. Pirates hacked at the rigging with their cutlasses and knives to lower other sails. The three-hundred-ton ship stumbled into mountains of water that swept over its decks, each wave threatening to swamp the galley. The anchor cable held, but the anchors began dragging, pulled by the *Whydah* as it was shoved by the tempest closer and closer to the shoal waters.

Captain Bellamy's only thought now was of saving himself and his crew. He ordered a small sail set. "Cut the cables," he shouted. Axes swung, the heavy line attached to the iron cable parted, leaving the precious anchors at the bottom of the sea.

It was no use. It was impossible to sail into the teeth of the gale. As soon as the pirates cut the anchor cable, the *Whydah* "ran a-shoar," striking the shoals with a jolt.

According to a sermon that was later preached by Cotton Mather, as the crew realized that they must swim for their lives, the "Barbarous Wretches horribly Murdered all their Prisoners (whereof they had a great Number) aboard; lest they should appear as Witnesses against them. The doleful Cries heard unto the Shore, a little before they Sank; and the Bloody wounds found in the Bodies afterwards thrown ashore; were two great Confirmations of this Report." "Alas!" Reverend Mather moralized, "how far the Wickedness of Men may carry them!"

Such nonsense could have been imagined only by the divine who had observed storms not at sea but from the study of his manse in Boston.

As the *Whydah* heeled drunkenly over to leeward, pirates and prisoners tumbled over the slanting, drenched decks, entangled in the fallen rigging, the snapped lines and torn sails. Water cascaded through gunports. The ship broached and the *Whydah*'s broadside was exposed. Waves swept men overboard. Heavy cannon ripped loose from their carriages and tore across the gun deck, smashing through the bulkheads. The slatting of the sails sounded like peals of thunder aboard the ship. Even if the pirates had had any intention of killing their prisoners, they never could have carried out such a plan amid the madness of the storm.

Breaker after breaker climbed out of the ocean, thundering aboard. The *Whydah* was lifted, rocked, pounded farther onto the shoals. Pirates who climbed into the rigging to escape the seas were ripped from their perch by a mountainous wave that poured tons of black water over them. Within "a quarter of an hour after the Ship struck, the Main-mast was carried by the board." Decks were splintered. Spars cracked and tore away. By morning, "she was beat to pieces."

The bodies of the pirates and prisoners that the waves brought ashore were indeed mutilated and beaten, but by the fury of the sea, not the wickedness of the pirates. More than a century and a half later, the steamship *Portland* sank in the record gale of November 26, 1898, with the drowning of all of its more than one hundred fifty passengers and crew. The marine reporting agent stationed at Highland Light in Truro reported that, for days, some of the surfmen whose duty it was to patrol the Cape's outer beach "were made almost nervous wrecks by their almost nightly contact with the disfigured and unfortunate victims thrown up to their feet by the sea." The sea took its same toll on those swept from the *Whydah*.

This, Cotton Mather was sure, was "what the Compassion of our God has done for New-England, in the Inflictions of His Justice on an horrid Crew of PIRATES.... The Good People of the Cape, saw a Marvellous Deliverance, in the Time of Tide, when these Monsters perished. Had it not been Just as it was, they had reach'd the Shore alive; and have made their way thro' the Blood of the Inhabitants, which Lived between Eastham, and the Hook of the Cape, where they would there have met with Vessels to have served them, in a Return to the Trade, which they had hitherto been upon. The Delivered People said, Blessed be the Lord, who hath not given us a Prey to their Teeth!"

Surely "Providence raised the Wind & Waves for our deliverance," concluded the advocate general of His Majesty's Province of Massachusetts-Bay.

"At break of Day" the next morning, Saturday, April 27, the first to awake in the hold of the *Mary Anne* ventured tentatively up the ship's ladder, pushing the hatch aside. The storm had passed. The skies were clearing.

To his amazement, the early-rising sailor "found the Shoar-Side of the Pink dry." The *Mary Anne* was right on the beach, having been driven ashore on Pochet Island, across from Slut's Bush, which was an overgrown piece of swampland in the middle of what was then the Isle of Nauset, and which had been given this intriguing name in 1626. That year, the *Sparrow Hawk* had been wrecked in this same area. One of the passengers, a Mr. Fells, had brought with him to the New World a woman he described as his maid and housekeeper, but who was suspected of being his mistress. When it became obvious that she was pregnant, the couple was ostracized by the rest of the ship's company and forced to camp out alone on this section of the Isle of Nauset, forever after called Slut's Bush.

The first of the *Mary Anne*'s crew to arise that morning looked out over Slut's Bush to the mainland. Upon hearing the sailor's shouts of joy, the others scrambled up to the deck of the *Mary Anne*, rejoicing at their good fortune, and "all of them jumpt out upon an Island."

Far in the distance up the coast, the masts of the snow and the sloop *Fisher* could be seen riding safely at anchor in deep water. The great flagship *Whydah* was nowhere in sight. Soon the two ships slipped their cables, and, working their way northward up the Cape, disappeared.

The pink was "bilged on shoare, so that it [was] impossible to get her off." The pirates were stranded. But they were alive.

There on the beach, in the lee of the *Mary Anne*, "they tarryed till about Ten a Clock, and eat Sweetmeats and other things" taken from the chest that Hendrick Quintor and John Shuan had carried out from the hold of the *Mary Anne* and broken open. They washed down their breakfast with "the wines which came out of the Pink."

At first, the pirates "were in as bad a condition as before, being fearful," as Thomas Fitzgerald supposed, "lest they should be Apprehended." As they drank more of the Madeira wine, their fears disappeared. John Brown strutted up and down, ordering the prisoners to address him as "Captain," and telling them that the other pirates "on Board were his Men." As they lay back in the sun after their breakfast, the pirates laid plans "to get to Boston and there Ship themselves as Sailors," with the hope of eventually meeting up with the rest of their comrades.

Around midmorning, they spotted two men in a canoe paddling toward their island. John Cole and William Smith from the Southern Parish of Eastham had seen the wreck from the mainland, and had set out to explore. When they landed and found the ten bedraggled men, they offered to paddle them to the mainland and take them to their homes, suggesting on each of the several trips to shore that the canoe be carefully ballasted with casks of Madeira wine.

At John Cole's house, the rescue was celebrated by breaking open the wine. It was only then that the old sea cook, Alexander Mackconachy, believing that his ordeal was over and that he was safe, stood up and cried that the seven were "Bellamy's men, so help me!"

Expressing no alarm, John Cole walked to a back room. There he ordered his young son to run to the home of the justice of the peace and tell him that there were pirates at his house.

Cole returned to his guests and asked them "to tarry and refresh themselves." But now the pirates were wary. They asked him the way to Rhode Island, apparently hoping to find refuge there with Captain Paul Williams's family, and then "made great haste from his house." The cook, who was quite pleased with himself, noted that "they looked very sorrowful, and made all imaginable speed in order to escape from the hands of Justice."

Justice Joseph Doane, the local justice of the peace and representative of the Great and General Court, pursued them with a deputy sheriff and assistants. They caught up with the pirates at Higgins Tavern in Eastham where they had stopped, a mile or two from Cole's home, to fortify themselves for their trip to Rhode Island. The pirates "talked in divers Languages"—Hendrick Quintor and Thomas Baker were Dutch, Peter Hoof was Swedish, John Shuan was French, John Brown was from Jamaica, Simon Van Vorst from New York, and Thomas South from England—but the justice realized that they all "were in a great hurry to go to Rhode Island."

Justice Doane and his men tied the hands of the dejected pirates and marched them, along with the three men from the *Mary Anne*, who he assumed were also pirates, down King's Highway, straight to Barnstable jail.

There were still two men abroad, however, who in the blackness and confusion of that stormy Friday night had been swept from the *Whydah* and miraculously cast onto shore alive: Thomas Davis, the twenty-two-year-old shipwright of the *St. Michael* who had been taken prisoner by Captain Bellamy in December of 1716, and John Julian, the Cape Cod Indian Bellamy had hired to help pilot the *Whydah* through the tricky shoals off the coast of the Cape.

How they survived the nightmare of the North Atlantic, how they found each other in the savage storm, remain mysteries. Perhaps carried ashore on a spar, the two survivors scaled the hundred-foot tableland bluffs, which the storm surf was attacking, and crossed the rain-lashed moors. John Julian was then in his own backyard, and they headed straight to the farm of Samuel Harding, near Duck Pond, in the present village of Wellfleet.

"At 5 morning," the two weary travelers of the night roused Harding and told him of the wreck. Harding at once understood. Without offering the two men food or rest, he had them help him hitch a horse to a wagon, and the three made their way in the gusty wind and rain back to the shore. There, they loaded the wagon with salvage and returned to the farmhouse, hiding the plunder deep in the recesses of Harding's weatherbeaten old barn, returning again and again to the beach before Saturday's sun rose over the troubled sea.

CHAPTER FIVE

It did not take long for news of the wreck of the *Whydah* to reach Boston. On Sunday, April 28, 1717, Colonel Buffet of Sandwich scribbled on a piece of paper everything he had heard about the wreck from Justice Doane and immediately sent a messenger, riding post, to Boston.

When this news reached Boston, Samuel Shute, the new governor of the province of Massachusetts Bay, undoubtedly had dreams of the remarkable good fortune of a former governor, Sir William Phips, who had recovered the fabulous treasure from the sunken Spanish galleon. What an accomplishment it would be for him to salvage a cargo of pirate gold right on the shores of Cape Cod! Governor Shute summoned the man he knew could do the job: fifty-five-year-old Captain Cyprian Southack.

As a young boy Southack had assisted his father, a British naval lieutenant in the service of King Charles II, in the Battle of Southwold. He had sailed to Boston at the age of twenty-three with a commission from the Admiralty Board, had served ably on Sir William Phips's ill-fated expedition to Nova Scotia against the French in 1690, and in 1704 commanded the commonwealth's ship, *Province Galley*, in an expedition against the French and Indians in Maine and Nova Scotia. A skilled cartographer, Southack in 1694 presented to King William III his "Draught of New England, Newfoundland, Nova Scotia and the River of Canada" for which the king bestowed on him a gold chain. In subsequent years, he issued "A Draught of Boston Harbor," a map of the St. John River, a chart of the St. Lawrence River, and in 1717 a chart of the English plantations from the mouth of the Mississippi to the St. Lawrence. During this period, he had commanded a number of ships to protect the New England coast from piracy.

Governor Shute and Captain Southack acted quickly. Less than three days after the governor learned of the wreck, Cyprian Southack was aboard "his Majesty's Sloop *Nathaniel*," as he wrote in his journal that evening in his cabin, the small sloop tacking through the choppy waters of Barnstable Bay (now Cape Cod Bay), "being bound on a Wreck cast ashoar on the backside of Cape Cod being by Information a Pirate Ship."

The next morning, the seas were still running too high after the great storm to sail from the bay into the ocean. Knowing the coast well, Captain Southack understood that even under ordinary conditions "it is very dangerous to have [to moor] a Vessell on the Seaboard side," where the *Whydah* was wrecked. "At 1 afternoon I came to Anchoar at Cape Cod Harbor," a harbor of twenty fathoms "wherein," as the Pilgrims described it, "a thousand sail of ships may safely ride." The curved sandy finger of Long Point off Provincetown, protecting the harbor on the west and south, had beckoned seafarers for centuries into one of the best anchorages on the Atlantic coast. Here, where sixteenth-century fishermen from the coast of Brittany and the Bay of Biscay knew they could ride out any storm, where the Pilgrims, after beating their way past the "dangerous shoals and roaring breakers" off the Cape's outer shore, "rode in safety" on reaching the New World, here in the harbor Captain Bellamy had tried so desperately to reach several days before as the *Whydah* was battered toward the coast, the sloop *Nathaniel* now swung easily at anchor.

Cyprian Southack lost no time that afternoon in sending his two deputies, Mr. Little and Mr. Cutler, by whaleboat to the neighboring village of Truro to get horses and ride across the dunes and moors to the wreck. By seven o'clock that evening, Little and Cutler had reached the ocean beach and dispersed a cluster of townfolk salvaging bits and pieces of wreckage. Lighting a bonfire of driftwood and broken planks, they established their watch.

Meanwhile, Southack that afternoon had "visseted" several of the ships in the harbor "and on board one of them found a Yung man boling [belonging] to the ship the Pirritt Took 26 April in South Channell, Saileing from Nantaskett the day before at 3 After noon." He learned of the recent captures the *Whydah* had made, and some of the details of the wreck, all of which he would dutifully record in his journal and report in his daily letters to Governor Shute.

The next day, Friday, May 3, at four o'clock in the morning, the hour at which he liked to begin his day, Cyprian Southack climbed down a rope ladder into the old, shallow-draft whaleboat he had commandeered on his arrival at Cape Cod Harbor, and with the eight men whose assistance he had enlisted in the name of His Excellency, Governor Shute, cast off from the *Nathaniel*.

In the chill dark of early morning on Barnstable Bay, they rowed the whaleboat down the coast, beaching at Truro. There Southack strode across the moors to Captain Pain's house, where he expected a horse to be waiting for his ride across the Cape to the site of the wreck. But there were no horses to be found that morning in Truro. The captain returned to the whaleboat, which his crew rowed out to deeper water, steering south down along the Cape.

As a cartographer familiar with the New England coast, Southack recalled that an early English navigator, Captain Bartholomew Gosnold, who had explored the waters around Cape Cod in the spring of 1602, had referred to the outer forearm of the Cape as an island, perhaps the first record that there was a passage of some significance through Cape Cod.

A half mile north of the present border between the villages of Orleans and Eastham meandered Boatmeadow Creek, a tidal inlet from Barnstable Bay that worked its way east through meadows of salt hay. Another tidal estuary, Jeremiah's Gutter, choked with cordgrass and rushes, wandered away from Town Cove, west through these lowlands. Town Cove, in turn, led to Nauset Harbor and out to the Atlantic Ocean. Only at the highest of tides had the headwaters of Boatmeadow Creek and Jeremiah's Gutter ever met, and it was at such times that the early colonists had used this passage as a canal across the Cape.

Because of a rare alignment of sun and moon, that morning was the very height of the spring tides. Tidal waters surged into every inlet and cove and harbor along the coast. Time would be saved if the whaleboat could be navigated through this old passage across the Cape from Barnstable Bay to the Atlantic Ocean. Captain Southack decided to try.

With his long steering oar over the stern, the Captain guided the whaleboat in toward the shores of Barnstable Bay up the mouth of Boatmeadow Creek, and into the shallow inlet through the salt meadows. The creek twisted and narrowed, the flooding tidal waters gurgling beneath the boat. When the oar blades hit the banks, the men stood up and poled the boat through the channel, pushing off from the banks of sedge and the muddy bottom.

Loaded with nine men and the salvaging "geer" from the *Nathaniel*, the whaleboat grounded. But once the men got out of the boat, the creek was still just deep enough to float it, and they hauled it with a length of line fastened to the bow.

Farther across the Cape, where Boatmeadow Creek met the flooded marshlands of Jeremiah's Gutter, the whaleboat grounded again and could no longer be dragged. Here the men lifted the boat with small ash bars slipped through pieces of leather fastened on each side, slowly portaging the whaleboat as they slipped on the eelgrass and sank in the soft ooze of the marsh. Soon the water deepened, and again they commenced poling and then rowing the whaleboat through the Gutter, finally reaching the open waters of Town Cove and Nauset Harbor.

Out past the crashing breakers at the inlet to the Atlantic, plunging through seas still churned by the storm of April 26, the whaleboat bucked up the coast to the scene of the "Pirritt Rack."

A driftwood bonfire fed by his deputies marked the spot. Holding the boat offshore, watching for a break in the waves, Captain Southack, resting on his steering oar, suddenly cried, "Now!" and the men bent to their oars. The whaleboat shot in on the back of a wave, in past the breakers, where Mr. Little and Mr. Cutler and Justice Doane helped the crew run the boat up the beach out of reach of the surf.

Fourteen hours after he had left the *Nathaniel* that morning, Captain Southack reached the beach where the *Whydah* had been wrecked. For fourteen hours, the fifty-five-year-old captain had helped steer, row, pole, drag, and carry the old whaleboat on its torturous trip. Now he was exhausted, covered with the mud of the marshes, and soaked from the spray that drenched the whaleboat as it fought its way out through the inlet to the sea. As the beach and dunes were fading in the black of dusk, he stood close to the bonfire that roared at the bottom of the tableland bluffs, its flames leaping in the gusts of wind.

Where was the wreck? the Captain asked his men. Mr. Cutler and Mr. Little pointed up and down the beach.

"The Pirate Wreck all to pices," Southack would record in his journal the next day, "North & South Distance from each over 4 miles." Caught in the heavy seas off the Cape's outer beach, the *Whydah* had "turned bottom up," and in the few days since the wreck, the timbers of the once proud flagship had been scattered up and down miles of beach.

Even more distressing was the report of what Justice Doane had encountered when he first reached the beach: "that there had been at least 200 men from Several places at 20 miles distance plundering the Pirate Wreck of what came ashoar." During the last five days, hundreds of Cape Codders from miles around had flocked to the scene with their horses and carts and stripped the beach of every bit of wreckage they could carry away.

Early in the eighteenth century, colonial authorities had decreed that the finder of any part of a cargo from a wrecked vessel must report such finding to the town clerk, whose responsibility it was to salvage the wreckage and hold it for its owner. This was the law.

It was a law that was never obeyed. To a Cape Codder, anything washed on their shores was a gift from the sea. Wrecking was their business as much as fishing and "whale fishing." In fact, in September 1854, when Ralph Waldo Emerson visited the Cape and stopped at Nauset Light on the bluffs high above the outer beach, "Collins, the keeper, told us he found obstinate resistance on Cape Cod to the project of building a lighthouse on this coast, as it would injure the wrecking business. He had to go to Boston, and obtain the strong recommendation of the Port Society."

Wrecking was in the blood of Cape Codders from birth. A young schoolmaster who in 1860 came to teach the sixteen students on Monomoy Point, a ten-mile finger of sand and dunes extending off the shores of Chatham beyond the beach where the *Whydah* was lost, was surprised to discover that his young pupils were wreckers. One of the students seated close by the eastern corner window, "where he could look up from his slate every fifteen minutes to scan the ocean horizon," took on the self-appointed task of keeping a lookout for wrecks. The schoolmaster noted that "the young gentlemen were quite orderly; and were duly amenable except on particular occasions, as, for instance, on news of 'wreck ashore,' when they were apt to leave pretty suddenly, forgetting even to say 'by'r leave.' "

Though less active since the end of the age of sail, Cape Cod wreckers have never become extinct. In 1974, for instance, some Barnstable residents stripped the sloop *Trull*, which had grounded on the flats of Sandy Neck. And in August 1982, when the 73-foot New Bedford dragger *Venture I* stranded on the shoals outside Chatham Harbor, seven men on a Sunday worked for several hours to remove her 1000-pound bronze propeller, electronic equipment, and fittings, despite the threat of legal action by the ship's owner.

An old English prayer captured the Cape Codder's feelings about wrecks: "We pray Thee, O Lord, not that wrecks should happen, but that if any shall happen, Thou wilt guide them onto our shores for the benefit of the inhabitants."

Although disturbed by how completely the *Whydah* had broken up and by how thoroughly the wreckage washed ashore had been picked over, Captain Cyprian Southack was not discouraged. Early on Saturday morning, he managed to row through the heavy surf out to the wreck, where he could "see her Anchor where She Struck first where I hope to get Something if any riches in her," but he reluctantly concluded that with the foul weather and "a great Sea . . . we can do nothing as yet."

Although the diving operations would have to be delayed a day until the weather cleared, Southack set his crew to gathering "pieces of cables and other things" from the wreck strewn along the beach, and to carting them the three and a half miles across the Cape to Billingsgate (Wellfleet Harbor on Barnstable Bay), where they would later be taken by ship to Boston.

As his men were gathering the wreckage, Southack counted the bodies of the pirates lying up and down the beach. "There has come ashoar 54 white men and five negros out of the Pirate Wreck Dead."

At two o'clock that afternoon, Captain Southack ordered the whaleboat and six men to return to Cape Cod Harbor, with orders to sail for Boston with his reports and letters to Governor Shute.

Galled by how little he had been able to accomplish, Cyprian Southack was now ready to teach the Cape Codders a lesson or two about respect for the law and for "His Excellency Samuel Shute Esq—Captain General and Governour in Chief in and over His Majesties Province of the Masachusotts Bay in New Eng. And Vice Admiral." Now it was time for the wreckers who had secreted what they had recovered in the root cellars beneath the trap doors in their kitchen floors, for those who had hidden treasure in their attics or in those tiny secret rooms behind the fireplace where the early settlers hid from Indians, who had locked it in their barns, buried it in their fields, now it was time to return the plunder to the governor's agent, Captain Cyprian Southack. In a stern notice he that day composed and copied and posted on church and meetinghouse doors, Southack warned "all persons that have found or taken up any thing" from the wreck to "bring in the Same to me at Mr. Willm Browns In Eastham or where else I Shall order Or they will Answer the Same at their Utmost peril. . . ."

Cape Codders greeted this warning with the same responses with which they greeted Southack and Messrs. Little and Cutler when later they came knocking at their doors. "To what wreck was the good Captain referring?" some asked in astonishment. "Did his notice pertain to them?" they questioned. Others welcomed him to try to find whatever part of the treasure he thought they might be hiding.

Captain Southack had of course first stopped at the farm of Samuel Harding. Harding exhibited the same Yankee ingenuity in dealing with Southack that had characterized his actions a week before when Thomas Davis and John Julian led him back to the wreck of the *Whydah*. He didn't deny that he had cargo from the wreck, but assured Southack that he was holding the salvage for Thomas Davis until after his trial in Boston; surely, he told the Captain, it would be an unpardonable breach of faith to renege on this commitment.

This Southack found absolutely infuriating. He lost no time in writing to Governor Shute: "I find the said Harding is as Gilty as the Pirate Saved."

The weather on Sunday was no better, the wind from the southwest bringing more rain. Southack nevertheless gathered his men and rowed out to the wreck in the whaleboat, but the sea was still too turbulent for them to see anything or to attempt a dive. Frustrated again, Southack returned to Provincetown to the *Nathaniel*, moored in Cape Cod Harbor.

All week long, storm winds blew over the Cape and whipped the raw gray sea to whitecaps, still preventing the salvage of the *Whydah*'s treasure. The weather was, at least, keeping the villagers off the beach.

Monday, May 6: "at Pirate Wreck this morning wind at S.E. and rain, a very great Sea on the Wreck; nothing to be done."

Tuesday, May 7: "at Pirate Wreck this morning, wind at E. Small gale & foggy, a great Sea on the Wreck. Nothing to be done there."

Wednesday, May 8: "at Pirate Wreck this morning wind att S and fogg Strong gale & great Sea, nothing to be done on the Wreck."

Unable to reach the wreck, Captain Southack sent Mr. Little and Mr. Cutler "on the cruise by land and Sea to See what they can find among Inhabitants." By Tuesday, the man who had been sent from Boston to salvage a fabulous pirate treasure "ordered Several Pieces of the Wreck to be burnt for the Iron work." On Wednesday he noted in his journal that "the Gentlemen have been crusing but can find nothing, nor the people bring in nothing." Only a few timid villagers brought to Southack's lodging a cartload or two of "small things but of little value."

Captain Southack's frustration with the weather, the wreck, and especially with the "Inhabtances" of Cape Cod was clearly evident in his next letter to Governor Shute, which he wrote on Wednesday afternoon in the parlor of Justice Doane's home.

Eastham May the 8, 1717

Maye itt Pleass Your Excellency
Sir, Captt. Gorham, Mr Litle, Mr Cuttler and Mr Russell, Gentt'men that I have Deputed, have Rid at Least Thirty miles a moung the Inhabtances, whome I have had Information of ther being at the Pirate Rack, and have Gott Concernable Riches out of her.

The Cape Codders who, Southack knew, were making fun of him behind his back now would be sorry: "I shall Mention their Names to Your
Excellency in Order for a Warrant to me for bringing them for boston before Your Excellency, or as You Pleass, Sir, for all thes Pepol are very stife
and will not one [own] Nothing of what they Gott, on the Rack."

Southack explained to the governor how the wreckage from the *Whydah* had been carried off, beginning with Samuel Harding. Then he described the most outrageous affront of all to the office he represented: The
coroner, who had done a "deal o' diggin" to bury the dead pirates cast up
on the shore, demanded payment for his services. Southack was outraged
that public money should be spent to bury criminals. He refused to pay
the coroner a cent, and told the coroner exactly what he thought of him.
The coroner laughed, and as payment for his work seized £83 worth of the
200 pounds of miserable salvage that Southack had struggled to gather
along the shore during the last several days. Southack was furious.

Having vented his frustration in writing to Governor Shute, Captain
Southack awoke the next morning to the sound of the southwest wind's
roaring through the cedars and under the eaves of Justice Doane's home.
With renewed determination he was "att Pirate Wreck this morning att 4."
But again, the wind, "at S.W. Small gale," and the "fogg," and "the Sea
being so great could see nothing for the Sand making the water thick and
muddey," made salvage impossible.

With little else to do, Southack returned to Justice Doane's house and
wrote to Governor Shute, warning the governor that some of the pirates
of Captain Bellamy's crew had escaped the storm in the snow and the sloop
and were said to be heading north, where they would be a danger to shipping.

Not all the pirates, however, had sailed north. The sloop *Swan*, sailing
to the Cape to bring Captain Southack and his pirate treasure back to Boston, was captured and boarded in Barnstable Bay by none other than Captain Paul Williams, Bellamy's "Cunsatte," and robbed of all its stores
before being allowed to proceed to Barnstable Bay.

It was now a week since Captain Southack had taken his whaleboat
across the Cape and reached the site of the wreck. Nothing had been accomplished. Southack began to feel sorry for himself. The only cooperation he had received from any Cape Codder was the "plum Posset" Justice
Doane's wife had given him to soothe his "Soar throte" and the "Indie-
Kachoo bandanie" (West Indian bandana) that the good Justice gave to
him for his sneezing and nose-blowing, for Southack, exposed day after
day to the Cape's "frisking gales" and rain and "fogg," had come down
with a sore throat that developed into a heavy cold in his chest.

Monday, May 13, 1717, the wind was "NE small gale." Twelve days after he had left Boston and seventeen days after the wreck of the *Whydah*,
Southack realized his mission had failed. If the great treasure still lay be-

tween the decks of the wreck, the seas off the Cape were much too rough for his divers to reach it. He had salvaged from the wreck of a treasure-laden pirate ship the occasional cartload of sandy line and tattered sails—less than might have been recovered from a fishing boat. His luck with the "wine Ship" *Mary Anne* was equally pathetic. The town folk of the Southern Parish of Eastham had the Madeira safely stored away in their cellars.

Southack ordered the remaining cartloads of salvage from the *Whydah* to be hauled to the shore of Barnstable Bay, wrote a final report to Governor Shute, and returned to Boston, leaving Cape Codders to speculate that he had found Bellamy's gold and had secreted it away, that he had taken a Creole mistress and sailed to England to lead the life of a country squire. Old Cyprian Southack, they chuckled, was himself the King of the Wreckers.

As much as it must have delighted Cape Codders to consider this fate of the arrogant "foreigner," there was no substance behind their imaginings. In 1718, Southack was commissioned by Governor Shute to prepare a report on the need for a lighthouse at the entrance to Boston Harbor, and later that same year was sent to adjust the boundaries of Nova Scotia. Several years later, he was selected to be a member of the Council in Nova Scotia. And, of course, he continued mapping the coast of New England, including a detailed map of Cape Cod and the waters surrounding it, noting where "the Pirate Ship Whido lost." He published the highly regarded *New England Coasting Pilot* in 1720, and in later years *A New Chart of the British Empire in North America* and a *Map of the Sea Coast of New England*. His maps and charts were relied on by navigators for the next hundred years.

At no time, from his return to Boston to his death in 1745 at the age of eighty-three, did Southack's lifestyle reflect access to a pirate hoard. In fact, not long after he returned to Boston, he ran a personal advertisement in the *Boston News-Letter*:

> To be sold by Capt. Cyprian Southack at his Hill, Sand for plaistering, or for Brick-work, at One Shilling a Cart Load, Mould Two shillings a Cart Load, and Gravel Three Pence a Cart Load: There being Two very good Cartways to fetch it, one over against the Bowling Green, the other by Mr. William Young the Glazier's House.

No man with a cellar full of bags of pirate gold would be selling sand and mould—or gravel at three pence a cart load! All that Cyprian Southack took from his hunt for the treasure of the *Whydah* was a head cold and a desire to forget those "stife Pepol" of Cape Cod.

On Saturday, May 4, 1717, a week after the great storm, the seven pirates from the *Mary Anne*, along with the two survivors of the *Whydah*, Thomas Davis and the Indian, John Julian, "were brought upon Horseback with a Guard" from Barnstable to Boston. They were imprisoned in Boston's stone jail, placed in heavy irons in a dungeon with walls four feet thick.

Boston Town knew just how to deal with pirates.

It was to Boston that the infamous Captain William Kidd had sailed in June of 1699 when he learned that an English naval squadron was searching for him. The English Admiralty had notified all the governors of the American colonies to arrest him on sight so that "he, and his Associates, be prosecuted with the utmost Rigour of the Law." Kidd, however, was certain that he would receive protection from the Earl of Bellomont, who was the "Captain General and Governor in Chief of Massachusetts."

Fifty-four-year-old William Kidd had been a respected and prosperous New York merchant sea captain who once had served honorably in the king's service as a privateer against the French. On a trading mission to London in 1695, Kidd had been offered by the Earl of Bellomont a privateer commission to attack pirates in the Red Sea, who had been crippling the trade of the East India Company, and French ships wherever encountered, since England and France were then at war. Kidd accepted this assignment reluctantly. But with a letter of marque and a commission from King William III, he set sail in a specially outfitted fighting ship, the *Adventure*, with the blessings of the Crown, Lord Bellomont, and several other backers who were among England's most powerful men.

At some point during his three-year voyage from London to New York to the Indian Ocean and around the Red Sea, Kidd crossed the fine line between privateering and piracy, even attacking a ship under English command. Word got back to London, and the order to capture him was spread to every port.

Kidd was confident that he could convince Lord Bellomont he had acted within the terms of his royal commission, and that, with his ship's hold full of treasure, his royal backers would be pleased with the magnificent return on their investment. Yet he was cagey enough to take some precautions. Before sailing to Boston, he buried a treasure chest on Gardiners Island off the eastern tip of Long Island. To Lord Bellomont's wife, Kidd sent ahead an extraordinary enameled box with four large diamonds set in gold.

Anchoring outside of Boston Harbor on July 2, 1699, Captain Kidd had delivered another gift to Lady Bellomont: gold bars sewed up in a green silk bag. This she at once sent back to him. Kidd should have realized then that something was wrong. On July 6, Lord Bellomont had Kidd captured. On July 17, the Provincial Assembly resolved that "the said Captain Kidd be put into the Stone Prison, be ironed, and company kept from him.''

Bound in irons, the captain who had sailed the seas for the last three years was held for seven months in solitary confinement. Finally, on February 6, 1700, he was locked in the steerage cabin of an English naval ship and taken to England. Incarcerated in Newgate Prison, Kidd was kept in solitary confinement for another year, until May 8, 1701, when his two-day trial began at the Admiralty Session of the Old Bailey.

Accused of killing one of his gunners in a fit of rage, Captain Kidd was charged with "being moved and seduced by the instigations of the Devil... [to] make an assault in and upon William Moore upon the high seas... with a certain wooden bucket, bound with iron hoops, of the value of eight pence, giving the said William Moore...one mortal bruise of which the aforesaid William Moore did languish and die," and accused also of five counts of piracy.

Captain Kidd continually requested that his trial be deferred "for want of two French passes that would vindicate" him and which were in the Lord Bellomont's hands. His requests were denied.

The Admiralty Court had little trouble finding Captain Kidd and several of his crew guilty and sentencing them to "be severally hanged by your necks until you be dead."

"My Lord," Kidd said after the verdict was declared, "it is a very harsh sentence. For my part I am innocentest of them all, only I have been sworn against by perjured persons." In so saying, Captain Kidd spoke the truth. The passes that would have supported his claim that he had seized ships as legal privateering prizes were found in the British Public Record Office 219 years later.

Kidd was hanged at the execution dock at Wapping on the edge of the Thames and then, as the piracy laws of the day required, his body was chained to a post until the tidal waters of the Thames ebbed and flooded over it three times. Then his body was painted with tar and bound in chains, and hung from a gibbet in Tilbury Point, there to swing for years over the waters, to serve, as the Admiralty Court had stated, "as a greater Terrour to all Persons from Committing ye like Crimes for the time to come."

Since the capture of Captain Kidd, Boston had become known as a "hanging port." Plagued by pirates, Massachusetts had enacted strict laws making any act of piracy punishable by death. So strident was the town's hatred of piracy that it became something of a ritual for New England pirates to force their hostages to curse the Reverend Cotton Mather, the pastor of Boston's Second North Church, who frequently preached sermons about the evils of piracy. Pirates were fond of telling their captives that they would never be taken to Boston alive but "if they should ever be overpower'd, they would set Fire to the Powder with a Pistol, and go all merrily to Hell together."

On Monday, May 6, 1717, the pirates of the *Whydah* were interrogated. Each described how he had been captured by Captain Bellamy, how he "and every one of the other Prisoners were forced to Join the Pirates," and how Captain Bellamy had threatened to set them "ashore on a Moroon Island" if they "would not be easy."

Of keener interest to the governor than the pirates' stories was their account of the treasure on board the *Whydah*. Each was carefully questioned on this subject. Young John Brown stated that "It was the common report in their Ship, that they had about 20000 Pounds in Gold and Silver." Thomas Baker reported that "they had on Board 20000 or 30000 Pounds, and the Quarter Master declared to the Company, that if any Man wanted Money he might have it."

"The riches on board were laid together in one heap," Thomas Davis explained, although he did not know the amount of the treasure. Peter Hoof knew more: "The Money taken in the *Whido*, which was reported to Amount to 20000 or 30000 Pounds, was counted over in the cabin, and put up in bags, Fifty Pounds to every Man's share, there being 180 Men on Board.... Their Money was kept in Chests between Decks without any guard."

Having learned what they were after, the representatives of the governor left, and the pirates were brought back to their cell.

All summer long, the young sailors who had roamed the seas at will— the "free princes" of the seas as Bellamy called them—sat alone, manacled in a damp dungeon. Undoubtedly they entertained hope that as soon as he learned what had happened to the *Whydah* and the *Mary Anne*, Captain Paul Williams would rescue them. In fact, Williams and his crew lurked off the New England coast all summer. When they took a ship commanded by Captain Thomas Fox in July, the pirates questioned their hostages "whether any thing was done to the Pirates in Boston Gaol." Captain Fox responded that he knew nothing about them. "A Dutch-man belonging to the Pirates," asked Captain Fox about "his consort, a Dutch man in Boston Prison." The pirate swore "that if the Prisoners suffered they would Kill every body they took belonging to New-England."

But as the imprisoned pirates waited for a midnight tap on the bars of the dungeon, or for a smuggled message, or for Captain Williams's men to storm the old stone prison, as the weeks went by and their muscles grew soft, it became more difficult to convince themselves that their comrades would come.

In October, they learned that seven out of eight of them were to be tried for piracy.

The exception was Thomas Davis, the young shipwright. Davis had been kept in the cell with the other prisoners and was concerned that "the Pyrates in Prison suspect that he will make such discoverys as will not be pleasing to them" and was therefore "fearfull least they should hurt him, if not deprive him of life, to prevent his Testimony against them." He begged to be freed "from his Chains and Imprisonm't with the pyrates, and that he may have some Apartm't seperate from them."

Seth Smith, the prisoner-keeper at the Boston jail, recognized that Thomas Davis was a different breed from the pirates. He took Davis aside and advised him "that if he would be ingenuous & make a confession, he might save his Life, and be a good Evidence against the other Pirates in Prison." Thomas Davis told him that "he was abused by several of the Pirates that were Drowned, and was glad he had got away from them, but knew nothing against the rest of the Pirates in Prison."

A judiciary court of admiralty was assembled and held in the courthouse in Boston on Friday, October 18, 1717. The judges of the court were especially appointed to "Try, Hear and Adjudge Cases of Piracy, Robbery and Felony Committed on the High Seas" and included Samuel Shute, the governor and commander-in-chief of the province, Lieutenant Governor William Dummer, seven members of "His Majesty's Council" for the province, Vice Admiralty Judge John Menzies, the commander of His Majesty's ship-of-war, the *Squirrel*, and the collector of the plantation duties.

The sheriffs brought the prisoners into the courtroom, and, "having held up their hands at the Bar, the Indictment Exhibited against them by Mr. Smith, His Majesty's Advocate, was Read to them" by the notary public:

"That such Persons, as shall be . . . found Guilty of Piracy, Robbery & Felony committed in, or upon the Sea or in any Haven, River, Creek or Place where the Admiral or Admirals have Power, Authority or Jurisdiction, by their own Confessions, or their Refusing to Plead, or upon the Oath of Witnesses by Process founded on the Authority of His Majesty's Commission or Commissions by the said Act directed and appointed, shall be Executed and put to Death."

After the indictment was read, the king's advocate, Mr. Smith, moved that the prisoners should plead guilty or not guilty as the law required.

Simon Van Vorst, on his behalf and for the rest of the prisoners, asked the court's permission to consult an attorney before pleading, so that they "might be well advised what to do." The court granted this request. Thereafter, the prisoners each pleaded "not guilty." John Shuan, the Frenchman, made it known to the court through sign language that he did not understand what charges were being brought against him. A Boston merchant who spoke French was sworn in and read Shuan the indictment. Shuan also pleaded "not guilty."

Mr. Smith addressed the court.

Piracy, according to Mr. Smith, was a combination of "Treason, Oppression, Murder, Assassination, Robbery and Theft," a crime that is committed "in remote and Solitary Places, where the weak and Defenceless can expect no Assistance nor Relief; and where these ravenous Beasts of Prey may ravage undisturb'd, hardened in their Wickedness with hopes of Impunity, and of being Concealed for ever from the Eyes and Hands of avenging Justice.

"That the Prisoners are all and each of them Guilty will evidently appear to your Excellency from the Testimonies of three Persons, who belonged to the Vessel.... The Witnesses are here in Court, and I humbly move that they may be examined and interrogated."

The court asked the prisoners if they had any challenge or objection to make against the witnesses. None being offered, the witnesses were sworn in.

First appeared Thomas Fitzgerald, the mate of the pink *Mary Anne*, who testified as to the capture of the *Mary Anne* on April 26, 1717, when the pirates "all Armed with Mosquets, Pistols and Cutlasses" had "forcibly taken Command of her," with the exception of Thomas South who, soon after he came on board, told Fitzgerald of "his Intention to make his escape from the *Whido*, as soon as he could." Like South, John Shuan was unarmed, but "was very forward & active on board the Pink." Fitzgerald told how the pirates plundered the cargo of wine and recounted the events of the storm and the shipwreck and the apprehension of the pirates the next day by Justice Doane. The mate's vivid account of these events included a detailed report of how Simon Van Vorst had threatened to break the cook's neck "if he would not find Liquor" and how the pirates joked that they had "got a Commission from King George" and would "stretch it to the World's end."

The next witnesses were James Donavan, mariner of the *Mary Anne* and brother-in-law of Andrew Crumpstey, the late captain of the *Mary Anne* who had died aboard the *Whydah*, and then the pink's cook, Alexander Mackconachy. Their testimony corroborated Fitzgerald's report of the capture of the *Mary Anne* and that "Thomas South's Behaviour in the Pink was civil and peaceable" and that he "behaved himself Civilly." They also told how Thomas Baker threatened to shoot the cook "thro' the head, because he Steer'd to the windward of his Course."

That afternoon, the pirates were called before the court and asked "what they had to say for themselves."

Simon Van Vorst explained that he had been forced by Captain Bellamy to become a pirate and to join the *Whydah*'s company. He explained that he had considered telling the mate of the *Mary Anne* that he wanted to escape from the *Whydah*, but that "he understood by the Mate's discourse that he inclined to be a Pirate himself, and therefore he did not discover his mind to the Mate."

John Brown also alleged that he was forced to join the *Whydah*'s crew, but could produce no evidence to confirm this allegation.

Thomas South testified that he was a member of the crew of a ship out of Bristol, England, and "that he was taken by Capt. Bellamy, and forced to tarry with him, otherwise was threatened to be put upon a desolate Island, where there was nothing to support him."

Thomas Baker explained that he and Simon Van Vorst were both captured from the same ship, and that "he attempted to make his escape at Spanish Town [the old Spanish capital of Jamaica], and the Governour of that Place seemed to favour his design, till Capt. Bellamy and his Company sent the Governour word that they would burn & destroy the Town," if Baker was given refuge.

Hendrick Quintor also alleged that he was captured by Captain Bellamy when his pirates seized a French vessel, that Bellamy had agreed to let him go when they reached the coast of Crocus [Caracas, Venezuela], but later changed his mind, and so he was forced to "Continue among the Pyrates."

Peter Cornelius Hoof's testimony followed the same lines: that he was taken by Captain Bellamy from a vessel under the command of John Cornelius, and that Bellamy's crew swore "they would kill him unless he would joyn with them in their Unlawful Designs."

John Shuan's story was told to the court by his interpreter. Shuan explained that when he went on board the *Mary Anne* "he did not carry any Arms with him; and that he hoped by going on board the Pink he should the sooner make his escape from the Pyrates, for that he had a better way of getting his living than by Pyrating."

After the pirates had completed their testimony, His Majesty's Advocate "in a very handsome and learned Speech" summed up the evidence and presented his concluding remarks.

"May it please your Excellency:

"Their pretence of being forced out of the respective Ships and Vessels they belonged to, by Bellamy and Lebous, if it [is] true, can never excuse their Guilt, since no case of Necessity can justify a direct violation of the Divine and Moral Law, and give one the liberty of Sinning.

"That they acted freely and by their own choice is most plain and obvious, for when they had the fairest opportunity, that could have happen'd, to make their escape, if they had intended it, by means of the Weather, Wind and nearness of the Shoar, they were obstinately resolved rather to hazard the Vessel and their Lives, than lose company with the *Whido*. . . .

"As the English Trade is in the utmost danger at present in America from the prodigious Number of Ships exercised in Piracies and as Providence hath wonderfully preserved us by destroying their Capital Ship with her Numerous Crew, and hath no less wonderfully delivered into the hands of Publick Justice the Prisoners at the Bar, to teach others by their Exemplary Punishment to abhor the barbarous and inhumane practices, which have been fully proved against them, and whereof they stand convicted, [I] humbly move His Excellency and the Honourable Commissioners to proceed to pass Sentence of Death upon all and each of them, they being all equally Guilty. To show the least Pity in matters of this kind, where the Proofs are so full and Pregnant, and not the least presumption in favour of the Prisoners, would be the greatest cruelty.''

The courtroom was cleared. Upon reviewing the trial and the evidence that had been presented, the judges found Simon Van Vorst, John Brown, Thomas Baker, Hendrick Quintor, Peter Cornelius Hoof, and John Shuan guilty of piracy, robbery, and felony as set forth in the indictment. But the court concluded that Thomas South indeed had been taken from his ship and "compelled utterly against his Will to joyn with the Pirates." The judges therefore were of the opinion, and accordingly voted, that "Thomas South is Not Guilty."

The prisoners were led back to the courtroom.

"Have you anything further to say why Sentence of Death should not be Pronounced against [you] according to the Law?" they were asked.

The pirates could offer no other testimony than what they had already presented at the trial.

As president of the court of admiralty, Governor Shute pronounced its decree:

> The Court having duly considered the Indictment & the Proofs of the several articles contained therein, together with your Defences, Have found you Simon Van Vorst, John Brown, Thomas Baker, Hendrick Quintor, Peter Cornelius Hoof and John Shuan, Guilty, of the Crimes of Piracy, Robbery and Felony, as is set forth in the Indictment, And do therefore Adjudge and Decree, That you Simon Van Vorst, John Brown, Thomas Baker, Hendrick Quintor, Peter Cornelius Hoof, and John Shuan, shall go hence to the Place from whence you came, and from thence you shall be carried to the Place of Execution, and there you and each of you, shall be hanged up by the Neck until you & each of you are Dead; And the Lord have Mercy on your Souls.
>
> Thomas South, The Court have found you not Guilty.

South kneeled, and thanked the court. "And after he was duly Admonished and had Promised Amendment of Life, he was dismissed and taken out of the Bar."

Then "Charge was given to the Sheriffs to take Special Care of the Condemned Prisoners."

The judiciary court of admiralty was adjourned for a week until Monday, October 28, 1717, at 9:00 A.M., when the sheriffs of Suffolk County brought the Welsh boy, Thomas Davis, from the jail to Boston's courthouse.

When Mr. Smith, the king's advocate, moved the court that the prisoner plead guilty or not guilty, Thomas Davis requested that he be assigned counsel. John Valentine was admitted as his attorney. Davis then "held up his hand at the Bar, and pleaded 'Not Guilty.'" The court was adjourned until Wednesday so that Davis and his attorney could review the indictment.

At nine o'clock that Wednesday morning, after the opening of the court, Mr. Smith presented his case.

"May it please Your Excellency, the Prisoner at the Bar is arraigned before You, for Crimes of Piracy, Robbery and Felony by him committed on the High Sea, in Confederacy, combination and conspiracy with others like himself, i.e., Profligate and Felonious Persons; And has pleaded Not Guilty. . . .

"I humbly move, the Nature of the Crime the Prisoner is charged with, and the manner of proof adduced to convict him, may be duly considered, and if his guilt shall plainly appear by his own confession, the evidence of Witnesses, and violent necessary presumptions, that he may by Sentence of this Honourable Court suffer the Punishment which the Law inflicts."

The "Kings Evidences were called into Court."

Owen Morris, a sailor, testified that he "knew the Prisoner at the Bar" and that "he belonged to the Ship *St. Michael.*"

"In the Month of Sept. 1716," the sailor explained, "[we] left Bristol bound to Jamaica, & in Decemb. following the said Ship was taken by two Pirate Sloops, one commanded by Capt. Sam. Bellamy, & the other by Loues Lebous, about Twenty Leagues off Sabria. They detained the Prisoner because he was a Carpenter & a Single Man, together with Three others of the Ships company. The Prisoner was very unwilling to go with Bellamy, and prevailed with him by reason of his Intreaties to promise that he should be discharged in the next Vessel that was taken. The Prisoner reminded the said Bellamy of his promise . . . and then the said Capt. Bellamy replied, If the company would consent he should go. And thereupon he asked his company if they were willing to let Davis the Carpenter go? Who expressed themselves in a Violent manner, saying, No, Damn him, they would first shoot him or whip him to Death at the Mast."

Thomas South, who knew just how Davis must feel, was the next witness.

"[I] thought it not prudent to be too familiar with the Prisoner," South explained to the court, describing the period they were both held aboard the *Whydah*, "because it might tend to create a jealousy in the Pirates that [he and I] (whom they suspected because he was a forced Man) would run away together. Capt. James Williams commander of the Ship *St. Michael* (whose Carpenter the Prisoner was) Intreated the said Capt. Bellamy when he took him to let the Prisoner go. But the Ships company would by no means consent thereto by reason he was a Carpenter; and Swore that they would Shoot him before they would let him go from them."

The court then asked Davis "to speak for himself."

Thomas Davis described how he and "fourteen other Prisoners were put on board the *Sultan* Galley, then under the said Bellamy's command who had taken her from Capt. John Richards: And afterwards took another Ship called the *Whido*, in which Ship to [my] great grief & sorrow, [I] was forced to come upon this Coast, where she was cast-away."

He told the court how he and "John Julian only escaped Drowning." As this account showed, he pointed out to the judges, "he was no way active among the Pirates, only as he was compelled by them."

Other witnesses confirmed that the defendant was of good character. After a short debate in their chambers behind the courtroom, the judges were quite convinced that there was good proof that Thomas Davis "was forced on board the Pirate Ship *Whido* which excused his being with the Pirates," and that there was "no evidence to prove that he was an accessory, but on the contrary that he was forced to stay with them against his will." The court therefore voted that "the said Thomas Davis is Not Guilty."

When Governor Shute announced "that the Court found him Not Guilty of the crimes for which he was Indicted," twenty-two-year-old Thomas Davis fell to his knees and bowed his head.

CHAPTER SEVEN

The ordeal of the six imprisoned pirates of the *Whydah* had just begun, for frequently to study them and to save their souls came the famed Puritan ecclesiastic Cotton Mather.

Forever mindful of his imposing family heritage—his father, Increase Mather, and grandfather, Richard Mather, and maternal grandfather, John Cotton, had been towering Puritan religious leaders and statesmen of New England—Cotton Mather felt himself from birth ordained to carry on the Christian leadership of his forebears. He developed an impressive piety at a very early age, noting later in his life that he prayed as soon as he could talk. Indeed, while still a child he began his efforts to achieve a world of godliness, showing his less pious seven- and eight-year-old schoolmates their errors, rebuking them for their "Wicked Words and Ways," and writing out short prayers for them which he "Obliged them to Pray." Young Cotton was surprised when the other students beat him with their fists, though many historians, Samuel Eliot Morison among them, have noted that the "young prig" got exactly what he deserved.

Cotton Mather, however, was not one to stray from his genealogical obligations of righteousness and missionary fervor. He continued his reading of fifteen chapters of the Bible every day—five in the morning, five at noon, and five at night—and preparing for his life's work in the Lord's service. Upon entering Harvard College at the age of twelve, its youngest student, he was again hazed by his classmates, whose lives he tried to better.

Mather became a Puritan clergyman, preaching his first sermon at the age of sixteen, presiding over the Second North Church in Boston from 1685 until 1722, and living a life of ceaseless activity in his zeal to attain the impossible goals of purity, goodness, and godliness that he set for himself and others: praying strenuously, sometimes through the night; wrestling daily with Satan, who tormented him with doubts; fasting, preaching, caring for the sick, and setting down his thoughts and principles in over four hundred published books and pamphlets.

But no matter what he proposed, no matter what good he attempted to do in his community, Cotton Mather encountered opposition. In a moment of frustration, he once announced to the Boston community that he was through with offering suggestions for good works; from then on, he would limit his proposals to people and places far from Boston. When a parishioner questioned whether Mather was in fact conceding defeat to Satan, the busy divine immediately began again his efforts to relieve the poor; find money, food, and firewood for widows and their children; spread books, instructions, and food; maintain a small school for Negroes; and pursue through all his days the activities he believed were essential for a man of God to undertake.

Mather was aware constantly of his human limitations, and agonized over the disparity between the goals he set for himself and the life that he led. He repeatedly accused himself in his voluminous writings of being a "vile" sinner, "feeble and worthless," beset with spiritual "diseases . . . so complicated," he told the Lord, "that I am not able so much as distinctly to mention them with thee; much less can I remedy them."

If Cotton Mather saw himself as an indescribably filthy sinner, his assessment of the rough band of pirates that had been marched from Cape Cod to Boston on May 4, 1717, can easily be imagined. Just as he had made an investigation of the witch trials at Salem Village, Mather now studied and tried to save the curious band of buccaneers cast up on the shores of Cape Cod, or, at the very least, to prepare them "for a Return unto God."

The good minister, who frequently preached sermons about the evils of privateering and piracy and the wickedness of pirates, had learned that New England pirates forced their hostages to curse him as part of their punishment. The bedraggled crew of the *Whydah* learned why when the plump, pasty-faced, bewigged, fifty-four-year-old preacher paid his first visit.

"The Pyrates now strangely fallen into Hands of Justice here," Mather noted, "make me *the first man*, whose Visits and Councils and Prayers they beg for." Certainly after their trial, if not before, the pirates of the *Whydah* were shrewd enough to realize that it was Cotton Mather who had the power to save their lives, and so they not only welcomed his visits, but made every effort to convince him that they had abandoned their wicked lives as a result of his good work.

After their convictions, the pirates were held under guard at the North Meeting House as a warning to all who were about to sail from Boston

Harbor. There, Mather labored to "Improve the Time" of the prisoners, bestowing "all possible Instructions" upon them. "All the Riches which are not Honestly gotten," he lectured them, as they must have thought about the bags of gold and silver that lay in chests between the *Whydah*'s decks, "must be lost in a Shipwreck of Honest Restitution, if ever Men come unto Repentance and Salvation."

A gray, coming-of-winter Friday afternoon, November 15, 1717, was the time set for "the Execution of these Miserables."

The pirates were released from the Boston jail in the custody of dozens of "Mosketeers and sheriffs." The admiralty marshal held high his "silver Oare," an ornate symbol of the Admiralty Court's jurisdiction over crimes on the high seas, and then began leading the solemn procession through the streets of Boston, mobbed with spectators, on toward the Harbor to Scarlett's Wharfe.

Cotton Mather "took a long and sad walk with them, from the Prison, to the Place of Executions." He spoke to each of the pirates as they were led through the streets. The minister "successively bestowed the best Instructions I could" and "prayed with them, and with the vast Assembly of Spectators, as pertinently and as profitably" as he was able. Perhaps Mather did help ease the dread of their impending fate: Death at the gallows might well have begun to seem a preferable alternative to further lessons from the sanctimonious bore.

"Your determined Hour is now arriv'd," Mather declared as they left the jail, turning to thirty-year-old Thomas Baker, the tailor who had left his home in Holland a year before. "You Cry in the Destruction which GOD this Afternoon brings upon you. I am come to help you what I can, that your Cry may turn to some Good Account. How do you find your Heart now disposed?"

"Oh! I am in a dreadful Condition! Lord JESUS, Dear JESUS, Look upon me!" Baker responded in the manner he had mastered after many such meetings with Mather in prison.

"You are sensible, That you have been a very Great Sinner?"

"Oh! Yes; I am!" Baker consented again. "And is it possible that Such a Sinner should ever find mercy with GOD! O GOD, wilt thou pardon Such a Sinner!"

"My Friend," Mather assured him, "this is the very First Thing that I am to advise you of. There is a Pardon to be had! Mark attentively, Every word that I Speak unto you."

Thomas Baker listened most attentively, straining to hear those words he wanted to hear above all others: that Reverend Mather would pardon him; that he would not be hanged, that he would be set free to lead a new life. Such words were not forthcoming.

"I perceive you are in a very Great Agony," Reverend Mather stated, ending his lesson to Baker. "But, the Strait Gate must be Entered with Such an Agony."

Seeing that he had done as much as he could for Thomas Baker, the Minister turned to "Poor Vanvoorst."

"I have been a very Great Sinner," Van Vorst confessed.

"Of all your past Sins, which are they, that now Ly most heavy upon you?" the good preacher inquired.

"My Undutifulness unto my Parents; and my Profanation of the Sabbath," the pirate responded.

This, from one of those "Barbarous Wretches" who had been engaged in the most monstrous acts of piracy, astounded the minister.

"Your Sinning against a Religious Education, is a fearful Aggravation of all your Sins. I pray you, to count it so," Mather counseled.

"I do, Syr."

"But I wish," Mather continued, "that you, and all your miserable Companions here, were more sensible of the Crime, for which you are presently to be chased from among the Living." Mather shook his head in disbelief. "You are Murderers! Their Blood cries to Heaven against you. And so does the Blood of the poor Captives (Four-score, I hear,) that were drown'd, when the *Whidau* was Lost in the Storm, which cast you on Shore."

"We were Forced Men," Simon Van Vorst protested once again.

"Forced!" Mather scorned. "No; There is no man who can say, He is Forced unto any Sin against the Glorious GOD. Forced! No; You had better have Suffered any thing, than to have Sinn'd as you have done. Better have died a Martyr by the cruel Hands of your Brethren than have become one of their Brethren.

"Say now; What think you of the Bad Life, wherein you have Wandered from God? Can you say nothing, that your Worthy Parents, (whom you have so kill'd!) may take a little Comfort from! have some Light in their Darkness?"

"I am heartily sorry for my very bad Life," Van Vorst confessed. "I dy with hope that GOD Almighty will be Merciful to me. And I had rather Dy this Afternoon, I would chose Death, rather than return to such a Life as I have Lived; rather than Repeat my Crimes."

Mather was not convinced the pirate had learned his lesson. "'Tis a Good and a Great Speech; But such as I have heard uttered by some, who after a Reprieve, (which you cannot have) have returned unto their Crimes. I must, now Leave you, in the Hands of Him who Searches the Heart; and beg of Him, Oh! May there be such an Heart in you!"

As the procession passed, crowds stepped back as if the prisoners were dangerous beasts.

"Gold!" they shouted. "Where are the bags of gold?"

Some charitable soul handed John Brown a mug of rum which he drank in a gulp. Others called out from a safe distance, "Throw a doubloon! A piece of eight! Here! Here!"

Cotton Mather walked next to John Brown, the Jamaican who had joined the pirates in the winter of 1716, and who was now just twenty-six.

"Brown, in what State, in what Frame, does thy Death, now within a few Minutes of thee, find thee?"

"Very Bad! Very Bad!" Brown exclaimed.

"You see yourself then a most miserable Sinner?"

"Oh! Most Miserable!"

"You have had an Heart Wonderfully hardened."

"Ay," Brown agreed, "and it grows harder. I don't know what is the matter with me. I can't but wonder at my Self!"

"There is no Help to be had, any where, but in the admirable SAV-IOUR, whom I am now to point you to."

"Oh! God be merciful to me a Sinner!" Brown tried.

"A Sinner. Alas, what cause to say so! But, I pray, What more Special Sins, Ly now as a more heavy Burden on you?" Mather questioned.

"Special Sins!" Brown cried. "Why, I have been guilty of all the Sins in the World! I know not where to begin. I may begin with Gaming! No, Whoring, That Led on to Gaming; and Gaming Led on to Drinking; and Drinking to Lying, and Swearing and Cursing, and all that is bad; and so to Thieving; And so to This!"

Mather hastened his efforts as the procession approached Boston Harbor.

"Ah! But what shall I do to be Reconciled unto GOD!" the thirty-five-year-old Swede, Peter Cornelius Hoof, pleaded with the minister, knowing that time was short.

"A Reconciliation to GOD is the Only thing that you have now to be concern'd about. If this be not accomplished, before a few minutes more are Expired, you go into the Strange Punishment reserved for the Workers of Iniquity.

"You go, where He that made you, will not have Mercy on you," Mather warned. "He that formed you, will show you no favour.... If you were to Live your Life over again, how would you Live it?"

"Not as I have done!"

"How then?"

"In Serving of GOD, and in doing of Good unto Men." Hoof had been the perfect student on the commoner's bench at the North Meeting House. Cotton Mather was delighted.

"GOD Accept you!"

"My Death this Afternoon, 'tis nothing, 'tis nothing," the pirate moaned. "'Tis the wrath of a terrible GOD after Death abiding on me, which is all that I am afraid of."

"There is a JESUS, who delivers from the Wrath to come; With Him I Leave you."

Mather talked briefly with the twenty-five-year-old Dutch sailor, Hendrick Quintor, and finally, turned to the "last among the Sons of Death," the "poor Frenchman," John Shuan. Shuan could understand no English, so Mather spoke to him in French, assuring him that "I commit your Spirit into the Hand of JESUS CHRIST, your Redeemer."

The damp winds of November carried from the harbor the smells of tar and salt water. The captive sea rovers saw the masts of a fleet of merchant ships, fishing boats, and whalers moored out in Boston Harbor, the very ships that would have been prizes for the *Whydah* had the flagship not hit the shoals.

The admiralty marshal waved his silver oar. The procession stopped. The pirates, the minister, the "Moskoteers and sheriffs," and the gazing crowds had reached Scarlett's Wharfe. Throngs of people gathered along the shore, and a hundred small boats filled with spectators had anchored just off the beach to get a good view.

The pirates were rowed to Charlestown Ferry, a small strip of shoreline between the ebb and flood of the tide. Off a point of land below Copp's hill, a gallows had been erected with a scaffold suspended from it by ropes and blocks.

Standing in the bow of a small boat in front of them as the pirates mounted the scaffold and the hangman's ropes were adjusted around their young necks, Cotton Mather, holding his Bible, his black robes blowing in the wind, offered a prayer.

On the scaffold in their last minutes, the pirates seemed very penitent. But John Brown, maybe realizing that any more sanctimonious acting was futile, maybe having been given too much rum by the crowds as the procession made its way through the streets, appeared to Cotton Mather to have lost his mind. He broke out in furious oaths, "which had in them too much of the Language he had been used unto." Then he began reading prayers, "not very pertinently chosen," Mather carefully noted. Finally, Brown made a short speech to the hundreds of spectators gathered at the harbor, "advising Sailors, to beware of all wicked Living, such as his own had been; especially to beware of falling into the Hands of the Pirates; But if they did, and were forced to join with them, then, to have a care whom they kept and whom they let go, and what Countries they came into."

"In such amazing Terms," Mather noted, "did he make his Exit! With such Madness, Go to the Dead!"

The other pirates said little. Simon Van Vorst sang a Dutch psalm with all his heart, accompanied by Thomas Baker. Then Van Vorst exhorted the young to lead a life of religion and keep the Sabbath and respect their parents.

And then there was silence.

The ropes holding the scaffold in midair were released.

The scaffold dropped.

As in other executions, there was "such a Screech of the women" present that it could be heard far away.

The bodies of the young pirates twitched, dancing the jig of death.

After the crowd had gone home, long after the end of the day, the six pirates of the *Whydah* swung above the breaking waves.

"Behold," Cotton Mather said, "the End of Piracy."

CHAPTER EIGHT

Here the story surrounding the sinking of the *Whydah* and the recovery of her treasure is lost in history.

"One Hundred Two Men Drowned" had been buried back in the dunes of Cape Cod's outer beach where Maria Hallett's hut was said to be, for the *Whydah* had wrecked at her very doorstep. Goodie Hallett's meadow, Lucifer Land, as this expanse of sand and dunes came to be called, was said to bring bad luck to those who crossed it without reciting a prayer.

The bodies of John Brown, Simon Van Vorst, Hendrick Quintor, Thomas Baker, Peter Hoof, and John Shuan swung above the breaking waves of Boston Harbor, a warning to sailors leaving port. And there they hung until, over the years, they decayed and disappeared.

After Thomas Davis was found "not guilty" of piracy, he disappeared forever from recorded history. And John Julian, the Cape Cod Indian, vanished from the records soon after he had been marched to Boston with the pirates and Thomas Davis. He may have escaped, or perhaps he died from his ordeal.

Cyprian Southack had reported that on "29 April Came to Anchor sum Distance from the Pirritt Rack Ship, a Very Great Sloop. After Sending his boat to the Pirritt Rack Thay Came to Saile and Chassed several of Our fishing Vessells, then stod in to Sea which I believe to be his Cunsatte [consort]." This was Captain Paul Williams and the crew of the *Mary Anne*, examining the wreck of the *Whydah*, and probably, with the high seas, experiencing no better luck than Cyprian Southack would have in spotting the treasure beneath the waves.

Captain Williams returned to the wreck a month later. After capturing a sloop and a schooner, he sailed into Cape Cod Harbor on May 24, 1717, about ten days after Cyprian Southack returned empty-handed to Boston. Along with such other pirates as Louis Lebous and Blackbeard, who had sailed north for the summer, Williams haunted the waters off New England for several months. Given the readiness of pirates to attempt to salvage treasure wrecks, it would not have been unusual if he, or any other pirate who learned of the wreck of the *Whydah*, attempted to salvage its cargo. But, like a late afternoon fog, time obscured the fate of the great treasure of the *Whydah*.

And what of the Cape Codders? A pirate ship capsized in their backyard. They learned from its two survivors that it was filled with the treasures of the Spanish Main. Several hundred Cape Codders swarmed to the scene and stripped the beach of every bit of wreckage. Certainly, if treasure was found, the lucky wrecker would not have revealed his good fortune to anyone, but would have secreted the plunder away. Was there a Cape Cod family that lived well for generations without any visible source of income?

Or had other members of the pirate crews survived the storm? Two of the one hundred forty-six men aboard the *Whydah* are known to have reached shore. "One Hundred Two Men Drowned" had been buried back in the dunes. It was not unusual that not all of the bodies were recovered. In the wreck of the steamer *Portland* in 1898, in which not a single passenger or crew member survived, only sixty bodies of over one hundred fifty passengers were ever recovered. Bodies from other wrecks have been found miles down the coast from where the disaster occurred. Weeks after a wreck, a surfman patrolling a beach might come upon a hand thrust out of the sand, the rest of the corpse having been buried by the action of the sea.

But isn't it possible that at least one other of the unaccounted-for men on the *Whydah* made it to shore? Perhaps an unknown survivor, a pirate, was clever enough to realize he would hang if discovered, and therefore remained hidden. If Thomas Davis and John Julian were in satisfactory condition after reaching land, able to set out for the home of Samuel Harding two miles across the windy moors, and immediately return with him to the beach to begin removing load after wagon-load of salvage, another survivor could have helped himself to the rich plunder of the *Whydah*, hiding his treasure nearby.

In October 1849, Henry David Thoreau left Concord, Massachusetts, to explore Cape Cod. "Wishing to get a better view than I had yet had of the ocean," he spent several weeks on the Cape, returning in June 1850 and again in July 1855.

In the chronicles of his visits, Thoreau describes the wreck of the *Whydah* and quotes a historian of Wellfleet as reporting: "For many years after this shipwreck, a man of a very singular and frightful aspect used every spring and autumn to be seen travelling on the Cape, who was supposed to have been one of Bellamy's crew. The presumption is that he went to some place where money had been secreted by the pirates, to get such a supply as his exigencies required. When he died, many pieces of gold were found in a girdle which he constantly wore."

Another story that has been passed down and become an indelible part of Wellfleet's local history is that of "two redcoated strangers" who tethered their horses one night long ago past the last house at Gull Pond, held a chart up to the moonlight and dug a hole, while a scared little girl, presumably the reporter of these events, "held her breath and peered at them over a window-ledge." The strangers were never seen again.

As for Maria Hallett, the record is much clearer:

When a dead calm held a ship in port, sailors would say that "the Old Woman has got the cat under the half-bushel," a reference to their belief that Goodie could stop the winds by putting her black cat under a "berry-bushel."

She could whistle up a tempest or hurricane. Her cat and black goat would ride on the backs of porpoises, following the ships of Wellfleet, Truro, and Eastham out to the fishing banks. When seamen would see them in the wake, they would report, "Thar be Goodie Hallett's familiars waitin' to pick up souls. Reef sail, a squall's to wind'ard!" And soon the sky would darken with storm clouds.

When a skipper caught Goodie Hallett's fancy, the "little old woman of Nauset" would whisk him from the deck of his ship at night, bridle him, and ride him up and down the Cape, returning him to his ship before morning, trembling from exhaustion.

For a century after Captain Bellamy's drowning, his lover lived inside the whale that capsized whaleboats and with a twist of its flukes stove in the hulls of ships. In northern waters, when the whaling brigs were trapped in ice with sailors freezing in the rigging, Goodie Hallett sat in the whale with the Devil, drinking hot rum and playing cards for sailors' souls.

On wild winter nights of sleet and wind, she hung a ship's lantern on the whale's tail and piloted it close into the bars along the Cape's outer shore where the *Whydah* had sunk, luring lost ships to their destruction. Cape Codders blamed her for many of the three thousand ships driven to their doom along the Cape's outer beach.

And even now, when a storm breaks upon the coast, there are those who know that Goodie Hallett, her black cape blowing about her, will be wandering the bluffs above the beach, watching beyond the waves for the *Whydah* and its prizes making their way up the coast of the Cape.

CHAPTER NINE

Every once in a while through the centuries, the *Whydah* has been sighted. Reverend Whitman reported in 1793 that "the violence of the seas moves the sands upon the outer bar so that at times the iron caboose of the ship, at low ebbs, has been seen." Cape Codders reported to Henry David Thoreau in the mid-nineteenth century that they had seen the iron caboose many times at low tide. In 1923, John Nickerson spotted the remains of the *Whydah* barely out of the water at an unusually low tide, and as recently as the early 1950s, there were reports of sightings off the Wellfleet beach.

During the last decades of the nineteenth century, several industrious Cape wreckers earned a living dragging for lost anchors. In those days, as many as a hundred schooners might be anchored off the Cape, waiting for the wind to change. After several days, the ships' huge anchors would become lodged in the sand. In a high sea and strong wind, it was difficult to break the anchors from the sand before being driven toward the bars—so difficult that the captains would often cut their anchor cables and sail away. At other times, the cables snapped and the anchors were lost. Or, driven in a gale toward the Cape's outer beach, every captain would try dropping anchor to hold his ship out from the breakers, as had Captain Bellamy. The bottom of the sea just beyond the bars was therefore scattered with anchors and anchor chains.

The wreckers would sail two schooners out to the anchoring grounds, dragging a quarter mile of one-and-a-half-inch whale line between them. The line hugged the bottom, held down by two sixty-pound sinkers. As the ships sailed parallel courses, the line, which was limber yet strong enough to play a hundred-barrel sperm whale, would snag any obstruction on the bottom of the sea, and the two ships would be drawn together. Then the wreckers pulled straight up on the line, and a messenger—a heavy, hinged, lead collar—was fastened around both parts of the line and slid down into the water to tighten the whale line around the object.

The real work then began. The line was made fast to the capstan through a block-and-tackle system, all hands manned the capstan bars, and slowly the object would break loose from the sand. After an hour or more of exertion, the object was at the surface and then on board. An anchor or cable could be sold to outfitters in Vineyard Haven or Boston for two to five cents a pound, a tidy profit for several hours of heavy salvaging work.

It was by just this method that, at the turn of the century, Captain Webster Nickerson of Chatham one day landed three anchors and two cannon off the outer beach. It was believed at the time that the cannon were from the pink *Mary Anne*, and that one of the anchors, with a thin shank, tremendous flukes, and a ring big enough for a boy to pass through, was from the *Whydah*. But that was all, and the *Whydah* had drifted into the folklore of Cape Cod, when on November 7, 1982, Barry Clifford, a thirty-seven-year-old Martha's Vineyard diver and salvager, announced that he would find the ancient wreck.

For five years, he had researched the history of the *Whydah* and lined up investors for a treasure expedition. He had spent most of the summer and fall of 1982 working with sophisticated metal-detecting equipment, making hundreds of passes over the outer bars off Wellfleet's Marconi Beach, and, using Captain Cyprian Southack's chart as a starting point, conducting surveys from the beach. From his research and field work, he was convinced that seven hundred yards off the Cape Cod National Seashore, in twenty feet of water, under five to ten feet of sand, lay the remains of the *Whydah*.

Out of several test holes at the site he recovered a clay pipe stem, two shards of gray glazed pottery, and some brass, chisel-type nails, which, when tested, dated to the early eighteenth century. Printouts from his electronic surveys revealed large pieces of iron hidden under the sand, iron objects that probably weighed from 1000 to 2000 pounds apiece, which, he concluded, must be cannon and anchors from the pirate ship. Moreover, his electronic equipment indicated that the underpinnings of the ship were held together by thick cords of rope, not the metal cables used in a later day.

"We are absolutely sure this is the *Whydah*," the diver told reporters. "There's no question. This is the most famous pirate ship in the world and we've hit it. When we tried to figure out how much it could be worth, the amount went right off the calculator." The newspapers reported him as speculating that, if intact, the treasure would be worth at least $80 million and perhaps as much as $400 million.

"I first heard about the *Whydah* when I was a kid," Barry Clifford explained with contagious enthusiasm. "My uncle, Bill Carr, who was a kind of a soldier of fortune himself, told me the tales of the *Whydah*, the pirates, and the treasure on board. I think I knew even then that some day I'd have to try and find it."

A football star, marathon runner, rodeo rider, power-lifting champion, and speed skier while attending Western State College of Colorado, Clifford graduated, as he said, "a terrific skier with a degree in sociology. I had no idea what I was going to do with my life. All I knew was I was having a lot of fun and I didn't want it to stop."

He married a champion skier, they had two children, and he worked as a Boy Scout administrator and then as a high school physical education teacher. After his marriage ended, he began buying land and building houses on Martha's Vineyard. "Between 1971 and 1978 I built a million dollars' worth of property. Making money was never that difficult for me."

In his spare time, he dove the waters of the Cape and Vineyard looking for lost ships. He had discovered the *Agnes Manning*, a four-masted schooner that sank in the late 1800s off Pasque in the Elizabeth Islands, and the wreck of the 105-foot *General Arnold*, which sank off the coast of Plymouth in 1778.

When the classes of schoolchildren he spoke to asked if he had ever been scared while diving, Clifford replied that yes, on one occasion he had been very frightened, but that he would rather not talk about it. Invariably, the children begged him for the details, and he would tell them about the day he was diving on the *Agnes Manning*, the day something snared him on the wreck. Turning, he saw through the cold green waters that his diving belt was hooked by the long finger of a human skeleton. On that bony finger, he told the wide-eyed students, was a gold ring. To free himself, he had to snap the finger off. Later, he said, he found that "the ring fit perfectly," and he would then hold up his hand to show the children the gold ring he wore.

It was after researching the wreck of the *Whydah* for several years that he tracked down Captain Cyprian Southack's letters and journal, which, he said, was like finding a compass. "He told us where the ship was and why he couldn't get to it. I said, 'Oh my God, I can't believe it. The treasure is still there!'" It was Clifford's belief that the Cape Codders had merely salvaged the flotsam and jetsam that washed ashore when the *Whydah* broke up, that the treasure immediately had sunk to the bottom of the sea and there remained.

Clifford made "an absolute commitment" to search for the wreck of the old pirate ship, arranging his real estate and building business so that he could devote the next five years to his quest, searching for the lost pirate gold.

On November 22, 1982, Clifford filed suit in the United States District Court in Boston, laying claim to the wreck and any treasure he might find on it. Two days later a deputy United States marshal, television cameramen, park rangers and reporters watched as three of Clifford's divers swam a half mile out to sea off Wellfleet, where they anchored a large orange buoy. Attached to the buoy in a waterproof container was an order of the court, naming Clifford guardian of the wreck until title to it could be awarded in accordance with federal laws. Also attached to the buoy was a poster to ward off the claimants that Clifford's attorney predicted would soon "be crawling out of the woodwork," warning that tampering with the wreck was a crime punishable by imprisonment and fines. "We're watching," Clifford said.

He told reporters that he would spend the winter preparing for the salvaging operation. He had an operating budget of half a million dollars a year, and predicted that the entire salvage operation would "take a minimum of three years, and probably five." A grid map of the site had been prepared, and everything taken from the sea would be labeled with a number noting exactly where it was found. His attorney added that the purpose of the exploration was not merely to find pirate gold. "We want to make that clear. It's not like we're going down there to rip the ship apart and take off with the gold. This is an archaeological project." Clifford had already talked with officials of the Cape Cod National Seashore about displaying artifacts from the wreck and founding a maritime museum focused on the discovery of the *Whydah*.

Just as in the days of Governor Shute and Cyprian Southack two and a half centuries earlier, the Commonwealth of Massachusetts, learning that a pirate treasure off its shores might have been located, lost no time in asserting its claim. The attorney general rushed to file suit in the Barnstable Superior Court to have the shipwreck declared an underwater archaeological resource, and an action was begun in the United States District Court to give Massachusetts rights to one quarter of whatever Clifford salvaged.

Clifford's attorney was just as quick to dispute the claim, saying that the questions surrounding the salvage may go "all the way to the U.S. Supreme Court. The state does have title to the sea bed. That's no problem. But we don't think that means the state has title to whatever drops on the sea bed."

Under a law enacted in Massachusetts in 1973, the Board of Underwater Archeological Resources had been created to oversee the excavation of any historically significant shipwrecks in coastal waters of the state. According to one of the sponsors of the law, "we did have [the *Whydah*] in mind. I felt that once it was found, we ought to have some kind of law." In 1983, the board was funded so that it could oversee Clifford's salvage operations and protect the state's share of the treasure, which the press was estimating might be worth as much as $50 million.

On February 25, 1983, the board met to review Clifford's plans for salvaging the *Whydah*. Several days later, his company, Maritime Underwater Surveys, Inc., was granted a special permit to explore a two-square-mile area of the ocean off Wellfleet, and to salvage whatever was found. The permit required allowing a member of the board to observe the salvage at any time, meeting with the board regularly so that it could monitor and evaluate the operation, and hiring a marine archaeologist approved by the board. Although still in court disputing the Commonwealth's claim to any of the treasure, Clifford readily agreed to these conditions.

Exploration of the site began on May 13, 1983.

The area Barry Clifford had selected to search for the *Whydah* was the two square miles of ocean surrounding the spot Captain Cyprian Southack had marked on his map: "The Pirate Ship Whido lost."

"Every time I look at the map," Clifford remarked, bending over a copy of Southack's chart, "I see something different. That old Cyprian Southack knew what he was doing. It's a very accurate map. Amazingly so. If anyone back in 1717 could be believed, it was Cyprian Southack." Clifford took the various points described by Southack and "it all just triangulated. Boom."

It was exactly two miles from this site to the location noted on an 1858 map of the outer Cape as the homestead of "S. Harding," probably a descendant of Samuel Harding, the first man to reach the wreck of the *Whydah*. With the help of surveyors, Clifford located the site of Harding's house, even finding old pipe stems and pottery on the property. "At 5 morning, Came the English man that was Saved out of the Pirate Ship, Came to the house of Samuell harding, Two miles from the Rack,"

Southack had recorded in his journal. It was "3 miles 1/2 by land from the Wreck to Billingsgate," the old sea captain noted in describing the cart loads of wreckage hauled across the Cape; the site selected by Clifford was exactly three and a half miles cross-country from Billingsgate, now Wellfleet Harbor.

Treasure hunting had changed from the days when William Phips scanned the Bahama Banks off Hispaniola for the spot where the Spanish galleons went down, and from the days when Captain Cyprian Southack peered over the side of his whaleboat through the heaving sea, looking for bags of gold.

Barry Clifford's expedition was based on state-of-the-art electronic technology that had been developed for military navigation and oil exploration.

Over the bottom of the sea, in a grid pattern defined by buoys, for weeks on end one of Clifford's supply boats towed back and forth a magnetometer that could sense vibrations in the magnetic fields around iron objects. Readings were transmitted through a cable to the towing vessel, where an operator noted each anomaly, or "hit," as the crew called them. The hits were registered on a printout and plotted on a grid map.

Bottom-penetrating sonar, using sound waves and echoes, was also used to locate buried objects. A "boomer" was towed behind the search vessel, sending out sound pulses that penetrated the sand and were reflected back by whatever hard objects they struck. A computer measured the minute variations in the time it took for the sound waves to return, and created an echo picture of the object that revealed its approximate shape, size, and depth under the sand.

After an area of the sea had been carefully surveyed and the hits recorded, an aquaprobe—a very long, thin tube—was inserted into the sand in spots where anomalies had been pinpointed to determine the depth of the objects. Exploratory holes could then be blasted in the sandy floor of the sea by propwash deflectors. These devices, nicknamed mailboxes, were two large elbow-shaped metal tubes that fit snugly over the twin propellers of the search vessel. The ship was securely anchored over the place where the hole was to be dug, and the engines started with the propellers in gear. The powerful streams of water from the propellers were directed straight down through the curved metal tubes, with the giant water jets blowing a crater in the sea bottom. Within a half hour, the mailboxes could excavate a hole about twelve feet deep and thirty feet wide. A conveyor lifted material from inside the hole to the boat, where artifacts could be separated from the sand and mud.

After the holes were dug by the propwash, divers could do more delicate digging, using their hands or Ping-Pong paddles to fan away the sand. Underwater metal detectors located smaller objects, and various blowers and airlifts dislodged the sand from the artifacts. Electronic ranging devices employing radio signals from fixed points could help the divers return day after day to within three feet of a particular spot where they were working.

But even this type of equipment did not make treasure hunting simple. The magnetometers could not obtain accurate readings through too much sand, the penetrating sonar equipment would have to be right above an object to detect it, and the mailboxes, unless used with the greatest care, could "be as destructive," Clifford commented, "as driving a bulldozer through the Museum of Fine Arts.... We've got to be very careful and proceed very slowly or we could make a hell of a mess.

"People get the idea that you just put on tanks, dive down, and there's a mermaid sitting on a treasure chest," Clifford said as he laughed, pushing back his baseball cap, "but it's not that easy." In fact, this particular stretch of coast, with its treacherous currents, tides, and storms, made the search an especially difficult undertaking.

A few miles down the coast, a pair of brick lighthouses had been erected in Chatham on the bluffs overlooking the sea. In 1870, the lighthouse keeper noted in his log that the towers were exactly 228 feet from the edge of the fifty-foot bank that dropped to the ocean. In December 1874, he measured again; the distance from the towers to the bank was now 190 feet. From then on, he kept measurements after each storm. Three years later, the distance was 95 feet. Six months later it was 84 feet. Alarmed by this rate of erosion, the federal government ordered construction to begin across the road on two new lighthouses. The work began none too soon. Four months later, the distance to the bank was down to 59 feet, and on December 15, 1879, the old south tower went over the bank, followed within a year by the north tower. In less than a decade, the sea had chewed 228 feet into the land, straight through a fifty-foot bluff.

On the tableland above the very beach where the *Whydah* foundered, Guglielmo Marconi in 1902 erected four transmitter towers for his first successful transatlantic wireless station. From the towers, a hallway led eighty feet seaward, ending one hundred feet from the edge of the sea cliffs. Today, the remains of the hallway stop after twenty feet, right at the brim of the cliffs. The sea since 1902 has claimed 160 feet of the tablelands, which at that point are well over a hundred feet high. With an average annual coastal erosion rate of three and a half feet along these outer shores, the beach where the Cape Codders had scurried about to salvage wreckage from the *Whydah* in 1717 was probably over nine hundred feet out to sea in 1983.

What the sea stole from one part of the coast it gave to another. The ceaseless offshore currents carried tons of sand and silt to the great Provincetown hook and to the long sandy finger of Monomoy Island, which grew as rapidly as other sections of the beach were destroyed. So strong were these offshore currents and so great the quantity of sand they carried that the divers found that the holes they blew in the sand with the wash from the ship's propellers, holes that were ten feet deep and thirty to fifty feet wide, were covered over within a day, so that they were indistinguish-able from the rest of the floor of the sea.

This was the coast where the divers would be working, twenty feet be-neath the surface of the ocean. Every part of the centuries-old wreck either had been carried away by the currents or had drifted down through ten to twenty feet of sand before reaching a floor of clay and cobblestones.

Every morning, Barry Clifford and his men loaded their gear aboard a twenty-five-foot Boston whaler named the *Andrew Crumpstey* after the master of the pink *Mary Anne*, captured by Captain Bellamy several hours before the *Whydah* sank. Clifford gunned the twin 150-horsepower out-boards so that the boat hydroplaned over the shallows of Nauset Harbor. The *Crumpstey* bounced and slapped out the inlet to the ocean, and, at forty knots, raced the three miles up the outer beach, just where Cyprian Southack had rowed in his whaleboat nearly three centuries before.

Anchored half a mile off the beach was the mother boat, the sixty-foot *Vast Explorer II*, built for the navy as an ocean research vessel in the 1970s. Most of the crew members were friends from Barry Clifford's college days, reunited after almost twenty years for the ultimate adventure. There was John Levin, a retired judge from Colorado who used to arm himself and go out with the police on drug raids; Robert McLung, Clifford's college roommate, who had been the sheriff of Aspen; Bill Dibble, a Marine jet pilot who had flown more than one hundred missions over Vietnam; Todd Murphy, a member of the Green Berets' combat scuba team; and Trip Wheeler, a rodeo rider and motorcycle racer.

Twenty-two-year-old John F. Kennedy, Jr., the son of the late President, was the first mate of the *Vast Explorer* that summer. A graduate of Brown University, Kennedy had met Clifford on Martha's Vineyard several years before and found his confidence infectious. "That optimism spreads to everyone," Kennedy explained. "We started talking about diving, and through a shared interest in it we became friends. He was telling me about the *Whydah*, and he said, 'If you want to do some diving, that's fine.' How often do you get to do something like dive a shipwreck?"

Veteran treasure salvor Mel Fisher was a consultant to the expedition. It was Fisher who helped salvage the great Spanish fleet that Bellamy had sought before he turned to piracy. And it was Fisher who would salvage the *Nuestra Señora de Atocha*, the richly laden Spanish galleon whose sinking in 1622 devastated the Spanish Court and caused a depression in Europe.

After three weeks of electronic survey work and charting, Barry Clif-ford reported that he and his crew had found "small hits all over the place" in a scatter pattern of wreckage. "I'm positive we will hit the wreck. We have found about one hundred and fifty anomalies under the sand. We're pinpointing those now," using a computer to assist in plotting each of these hits on maps and charts.

It was like working with a modern-day treasure map. "We have to excavate every X before we know what is where. We are pretty sure we know where the main concentration is. We have got the wreck; we're positive we've got the wreck."

The crew's hope was to discover something that would prove conclusively that it was the *Whydah* they had found. "Our goal this summer is to ID the ship. If we find the pot of gold at the end of the rainbow in the process, well, that's OK too.

"We are getting really itchy. I guarantee you that I'm going to find the *Whydah*. This is not any kind of a show or a Barnum and Bailey act. I have completed every salvage project that I have started."

Yet by early summer, some were saying the *Whydah* expedition had indeed turned into a show. Clifford had tried to downplay his project but by June, he was "chomping at the bit." "It is just too much fun not to let everyone in on it," he said as he invited the press and television crews to watch his divers at work.

A flotilla of small boats and planes filled with sightseers surrounded the *Vast Explorer* each day, with groupies on the shore spying on the divers through binoculars. "For a while," Clifford said, "I couldn't go anywhere without people mobbing me. It got to be a little annoying. But then I realized people were looking at me as some kind of hero. I was doing something they couldn't do. They were rooting for me."

The staff archaeologist, Edwin Dethlefsen, remembered that when he arrived in the summer of 1983 "there was a great deal of excitement. They threw a big lawn party. There were lots of pretty girls around. Barry was handing out T-shirts and caps with the company logo on them. It was a very festive atmosphere. I thought, 'Gee, this might be interesting.'"

Soon, however, Dethlefsen began to worry about the operation. "The whole thing was thoroughly disorganized." In Dethlefsen's opinion, the public relations aspects of the expedition had taken precedence over the search for the *Whydah*. Dethlefsen soon resigned from the project.

As the summer wore on and the press grew skeptical, Clifford seemed to become even more confident. "We're going to find the *Whydah*," he said. "If it's out there, we're going to find it, unless Bellamy's ghost drops the anchor on me. We believe in what we're doing. This is not just hype. This is the real thing. I've sacrificed virtually everything to get involved in this project and if I didn't believe I would be successful I wouldn't be out there. You have to make a hundred percent commitment and that's what I've done."

By the end of July, in the midst of all the publicity the expedition was receiving, the first of several other treasure hunters emerged. The Board of Underwater Archeological Resources received a petition for the salvaging of the *Whydah* filed in the name of Old Blue Fishing Company. The principals of Old Blue included William Crockett of Chatham, who worked as a contractor in home renovation and said he had been doing field work and research on the *Whydah* since 1971; Donald Chalker, who had been a diver with the offshore oil industry; Kirk Purvis, experienced in vessel recovery; and Dr. David Switzer, a marine archaeologist at Plymouth State College.

The men had conducted preliminary surveys of the waters from the Marconi beach in Wellfleet to Nauset Light in Eastham. Within a one-mile radius of Clifford's site, they had discovered eight wooden wrecks, none of which they believed to be the *Whydah*. The site Old Blue Fishing Company selected was a half mile to the south of where Clifford was working, 800 to 2000 feet off the beach. The wreck of the *Whydah* was believed to be scattered in a northeast pattern over this site. "It is a classic type of wreck where she hit the barrier beach, breaks up, and comes right in," Crockett told the board.

Crockett relied on many of the same documents that Clifford had examined but interpreted them differently. The *Boston News-Letter* of April 29–May 6, 1717, had reported that the *Whydah* was "cast onshore in a storm on the back side of Cape Codd, against the Middle of the Table Land." The tableland, Crockett believed, was a two-and-a-half-mile stretch of ocean bluffs near the present Eastham-Wellfleet border. Crockett had found two nails and three pottery fragments in this area that he presented to the board, and that the board determined were over one hundred years old.

Yet another group, the Ocean Marine Diving Company, headed by William Daniels of Chatham, told the board that it intended to apply for a site, "but you can rest assured," the men said, "it is a long way from [the] sites" of Barry Clifford and Old Blue Fishing Company. Daniels added that in 1969 he dove in the area Clifford was exploring, and he did not believe the *Whydah* was there, suggesting also that Old Blue Fishing Company may have located the pink *Mary Anne*.

At the same meeting of the board, Barry Clifford requested an extension of his search area. "We have discovered parts of the wreck to the south and possibly to the north," he told members of the board. "We'd like to at least be allowed to explore the possibility of these being related to the ship and our site. It would be tragic to divide what may be the only pirate ship in the world that has been found."

Clifford asked permission to work in the three-mile area south of his original claim, the same location Old Blue Fishing Company was after. "I am sure there are parts of the wreck in the area," Clifford continued. "We've done specific mag work in this drift pattern. I think the historical evidence is the strongest evidence here," he said, referring to Captain Southack's report that the wreckage was scattered for four miles down the beach. "It is very important that we secure this area." The board told Clifford that his original permit had been for a specific wreck, and that if he could document that "it broke up, it falls under your permit."

With renewed determination born of the new competition and the doubts being cast on their work, Barry Clifford and his divers decided to try to find a cannon or anchor to identify the wreck. "If we are able to determine the identity of the ship on the first dig," Clifford said, "we will cover it up and request a meeting with the Board. We're simply trying to ID the wreck site. I think it is going to take several years to completely survey the area. What we have got here is a sand wreck. There is nothing visible at all. In order to come up with artifacts, we are going to have to dig."

At the bottom of the first test pit, beneath ten to twelve feet of sand, the divers on August 4, 1983, retrieved a ship's rudder strap, a twenty-eight-foot mizzen stay used to support the front mast of a ship, bronze chisel-point nails, and fire brick. The finds were certainly not bags of coins or bar silver, but Clifford was as ecstatic as if they were. "It is perfect," he exclaimed. "It is like a time capsule. Historically, it is exactly where it should be." The artifacts would have to be tested to determine their age, but they appeared to be the kind of materials that indeed could have come from the wreck of the *Whydah*.

The board soon assigned the area to the north of Clifford's site to Ocean Marine Diving Company. A one-mile claim to the south of Clifford's was granted to Old Blue Fishing Company. A buffer zone of four tenths of a mile was established between each claim where no one was allowed to dig.

Clifford filed suit against the other two diving companies, calling them "claim-jumpers" and "thieves," and warned of a "gold rush" by more treasure hunters that could damage the coastline. The Ocean Marine Diving Company filed with the Wellfleet police a complaint against Clifford when early one morning the *Vast Explorer* was observed anchored right in the middle of its claim. "It is a big deal," William Daniels objected. "They can work all night there." Clifford responded that the *Vast Explorer* often moored there because the divers that lived on board frequented the Wellfleet Beachcomber, a disco several hundred yards down the beach. Clifford in turn accused Daniels of purchasing the artifacts he had shown to the board. Daniels scoffed at the air of mystery Clifford had created around his discovery of the treasure chart of Cyprian Southack, which Daniels said could be found on the placemats of half the restaurants on the Cape.

In November, the United States District Court in Boston approved the claim of Massachusetts to one fourth of whatever treasure was salvaged from the *Whydah*. But even more depressing for Barry Clifford was the end of the summer and the end of the diving season. "This is not a good time for me. I get so restless when the winter closes in, and everybody goes away."

When the diving season began again late the next spring, Clifford for several months seemed to shun publicity as much as he had courted it the previous year. As it happened, the first day that summer that television crews were aboard the *Vast Explorer*, July 19, 1984, would be the turning point in his expedition. He had promised to take NBC reporter Nancy Fernandes and her television crew out on a dig to do a feature on the *Whydah*. Clifford tried his best to delay. He was afraid that once again—but now in front of national television cameras—his crew would come up only with bomb shells, relics from years of artillery practice at an old army camp in Wellfleet. To distract the television men, he took them out to sea in the *Crumpstey* to watch some whales, reluctantly returning to the *Vast Explorer* as the morning wore on.

The mailboxes of the *Vast Explorer* blasted out a test pit. Once the sand had cleared, the divers put on their scuba gear and went overside, their air bubbles popping to the surface. They entered the test pit. "It was just filled with treasure!" Clifford recalled. "It was that simple."

NBC reporter Nancy Fernandes was watching on the TV monitor aboard the *Vast Explorer*. "There was a big piece of something. The diver said it was a cannon. When more sand was blasted away the other artifacts became visible."

On the deck of the *Vast Explorer*, Clifford chipped at one of the encrusted masses recovered from the test pit. "At first I'd thought it was an odd-shaped shell. But as I succeeded in loosening it, I could see it wasn't. I held the coin in my hand and flipped it over. There was a silver cross on it and clearly visible, a date: 1684."

A summer storm had stalled over the Cape all morning with thunderheads lifting over the horizon. "The sky had been pitch black. And when I found the coin, there were terrific claps of thunder—the spirit of Sam Bellamy, perhaps? I'll never forget it: black sky, black ocean, and white cracks of lightning in the sky; the white cliffs of Wellfleet on the shore nearby."

As the crew passed the silver 2-real piece from hand to hand, "the whole project changed at that point. We all went crazy. I felt like I was breathing pure oxygen. It was like being on the highest mountain, breathing the purest air."

In the twenty-foot test pit, the diving crew discovered cannons, heavily encrusted cannonballs, old swivel guns, a flintlock pistol, a rusty cutlass, silver "pieces of four," a trigger guard from a musket, and even a shoe "with toe prints still in the leather."

Clifford and his crew were stunned by what they had found. "At that point we just closed the pit back up. We left the pit filled with treasure. We found much more than we ever expected. You could see all the stuff sticking out of the sides of the pit. The ship had never been touched. It scared the hell out of us.

"We dug in the area we thought would do the least amount of harm and in this area the pit is completely filled with artifacts. This is way beyond me. I never expected to find this concentration."

News of the find was broadcast nationwide by NBC, and the AP wires carried the story: "Wreck Found off Cape Cod May Contain Pirate Treasure."

Clifford was convinced that the ship of his dreams had at last been discovered. Three of the coins were dated 1715, and one was a 1684 French coin with a hole through it. "So we've got four coins suggesting that we have a wreck that has circulated money before, unlike a Spanish galleon that would have had all one mint basically coming out of one area. This suggests very strongly to us that we have the right wreck. Not only that, this is exactly the point where Cyprian Southack said the wreck was. Eventually there will be enough circumstantial evidence and there won't be any reasonable doubt at all."

Barry Clifford was in his element. A week after the discovery, on July 26, 1984, at a special meeting of the Board of Underwater Archaeological Resources, dozens of reporters, photographers, and television cameramen pushed and shoved, scribbling down every word Clifford spoke as flashbulbs popped.

Out of a white plastic pail he pulled two cannonballs, each about three inches in diameter, and held them up for everyone to see.

Then he held high above his head an x-ray of a piece of iron about three feet long and four or five inches wide. "I'll say this," he began. "I don't expect everyone to agree with me. I'll stake it on whatever reputation I have, bad or good." The x-ray, he explained, showed the end of a heavy cutting sword. "Of course we know very little about the pirates. We do know that they were flamboyant."

He pointed to a dark circle in the x-ray at the tip of the sword. "Without question, this is a coin. It's exactly three centimeters wide and that's the same width as a gold doubloon." The coin was embedded in the tip of the sword.

"That to me suggests more than anything the spirit of what these pirates were about.

"I'm not going to ask anybody to agree with me. All I'm asking is for your help. We've got a highly concentrated wreck there, a highly concentrated scattering. We've dug in one small spot with the least amount of concentration that our magnetometer suggested. We're going to need as much time as possible. We're not planning on digging any new test pits. We're not planning on excavating. Those are the furthest things from our minds until we identify the perimeter of the wreck. If it is a pirate ship, and I'm saying that it is, then we have an incredibly rich find archaeologically."

And then, a shroud of silence settled over the *Whydah* expedition.

For the next two months, Clifford worked to line up a group of experts, headed by Michael Roberts, a marine archaeologist who had been director of the marine archaeology program at Harvard University's Peabody Museum, and including twenty-five other marine archaeologists and preservationists. He retained the Maritime Archaeological and Historical Research Institute, which took over the archaeological investigation of the wreck. "We realized that we really needed the best in archaeologists. The wreck warranted it." At the same time, a lab was set up to begin work on the preservation of the artifacts that had been recovered.

In September, Clifford and his team of archaeologists blasted out two more test pits, one close to the first, and the other where preliminary surveys seemed to indicate the presence of a section of the ship's hull. Shortly thereafter, the Board of Underwater Archeological Resources held a closed session to discuss security for the wreck. It was not until early December that the veil of secrecy surrounding the diving operations was finally lifted.

In his first public comment since July, Barry Clifford reported that in the initial test pit, his divers had discovered over three thousand silver coins of the Spanish empire, including 2019 Mexican coins and 996 Peruvian coins, four gold coins, gold and silver jewelry, three cuff links, and a candlesnuffer, a collection of which clattered onto a table as Clifford emptied out a bag of pirate coins. "Imagine the sound of these down in the bilge of the ship when they counted them," Clifford remarked. In addition to this treasure were a flintlock pistol, a three-thousand-pound cannon, six cannonballs, 580 musket balls, and four trigger guards. From the two pits blasted out in September, the divers had recovered an encrusted mass of four cannons, an eight-foot-long anchor, silver coins, a silver bar, gold bars cut up for division among the pirates, gold dust, brass shoe buckles and cuff links, a sword sheath, and a mortar jar with the letter "W" scratched on its bottom.

The cannons were dated by archaeologists as having been made in the period 1680 to 1800. The flintlock pistol, with barrel and lockplate fashioned of brass inscribed with a decorative sea serpent, bore the gunsmith's mark of John Brooke, whose London workshop was in operation from 1703 to 1715. The trigger guards, the archaeologists concluded, could not have been made after 1720. And the 656 coins with legible dates were minted between 1638 and 1716.

"We have several million dollars in treasure," Clifford noted. A single coin was valued at $40,000. He had yet to begin exploration of the areas where artifacts were thickly concentrated. "We're probably in the ballast, up toward the bow of the boat. If we dug seven and a half test pits a day it would take the next ten years to complete the excavation. They probably had ten tons of treasure on this thing. We have barely scratched the surface."

At last, Barry Clifford's expedition had located where the pirate ship had broken apart, but for many months he could do nothing about it. The 1985 diving season, which held so much promise, was delayed while Clifford waited to receive a permit from the Army Corps of Engineers, which regulated all work in navigable waters. Through June, July, and August he waited, fairly bursting with the "enthusiasm anybody involved in a treasure hunt" would have. As soon as the permit is granted, Clifford reported, "We're in the water. We're sitting at the dock, ready to leave!"

Finally, on September 6, 1985, he received the permit that enabled him to begin bringing up the pirate treasure. That very day, his divers were in the water. Now, they knew just where to look. From the test pits, the divers brought up a dozen navigational tools, pewter eating utensils bearing a royal African seal, a swivel gun, a gold ring, a casket of East Indian jewels, and small gold bars with knife marks indicating the pirates had cut them to divide into shares. The divers suctioned gold into plastic bags from the brilliant layers of gold dust that ran through the wet sand "like chocolate through ripple ice cream." And the first several dives of the day brought up two thousand more silver coins dating from the 1600s and early 1700s.

A month later, after $14 million of treasure had been salvaged, a several-hundred-pound hunk of clay and sand was hauled aboard the *Vast Explorer*. Embedded in the mass was an eighteen-inch bronze bell. Thick layers of incrustation and corrosion were chipped away. There, inscribed on the bell that had chimed the watches, were the magic words: "THE WHYDAH GALLY 1716."

The treasure was there. There should never have been any doubt about that. Neither the wreckers nor centuries of tides and storms had taken it away.

And the treasure would always be there for those who knew how to look, for as much a treasure as the bags of Spanish doubloons and silver pieces of eight and chests full of ivory and coffers of rubies, is the story of young Captain Samuel Bellamy going upon the account, of the voyage and wreck of the *Whydah*, of Cyprian Southack's attempt to salvage the pirate hoard and Cotton Mather's efforts to save the pirates' souls, and of Maria Hallett, wandering the dunes of Cape Cod, waiting.

Captain Bellamy's beloved *Whydah* had finally been found, the only pirate ship ever to have been discovered. Two and a half centuries dropped away. The treasure, the plunder from the year-long pirate cruise on the Spanish Main, could now be divided.

MOVE YOUR SHADOW

Joseph Lelyveld

MOVE YOUR SHADOW

Joseph Lelyveld

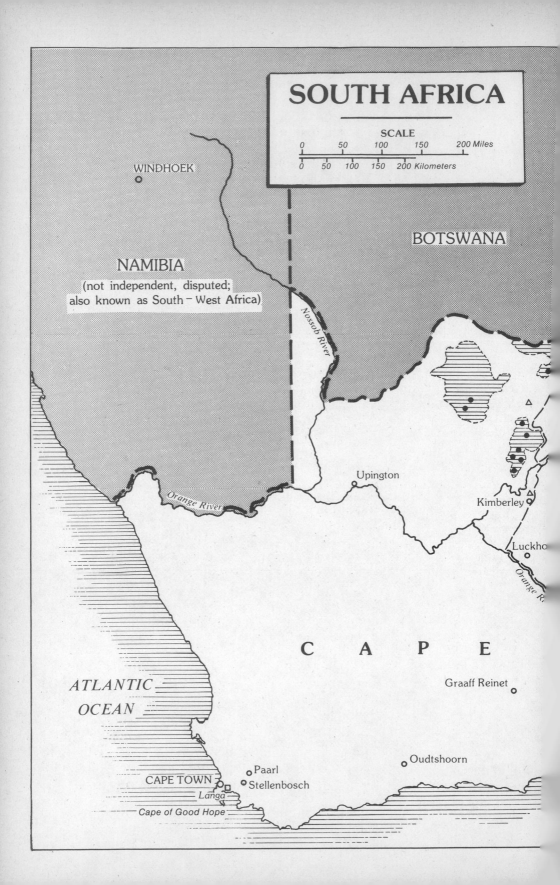

SOUTH AFRICA

SCALE

0   50   100   150   200 Miles

0   50   100   150   200 Kilometers

WINDHOEK

BOTSWANA

NAMIBIA
(not independent, disputed;
also known as South – West Africa)

Nossob River

Upington

Kimberley

Luckho

Orange River

Orange R

C A P E

Graaff Reinet

ATLANTIC
OCEAN

Oudtshoorn

Paarl
CAPE TOWN
Langa   Stellenbosch
Cape of Good Hope

ZIMBABWE

MOZAMBIQUE

Limpopo River

Pietersburg

T R A N S V A A L

KRUGER NATIONAL PARK

Sun City

erust

Mmabatho

Nelspruit

MAPUTO

PRETORIA
□○ *Soshanguve*
WITWATERSRAND

SWAZI-
LAND

□ ○ JOHANNESBURG
Soweto

Potchefstroom

lerksdorp

Vaal River

Welkom

ORANGE FREE STATE

Harrismith
Phuthaditjhaba

Blood River

Nqutu

Ladysmith

BLOEMFONTEIN

Ekuvukeni

N A T A L

Onverwacht

LESOTHO

Pietermaritzburg

□ *Inanda*
○ DURBAN

Umtata

eenstown

INDIAN OCEAN

ing

Frankfort

William's Town

Mdantsane

ahamstown

EAST LONDON

w Brighton

RT ELIZABETH

Don Pitcher

LEGEND

Black "National States"
(Homelands)

▦	Transkei
▨	Ciskei
▧	KwaZulu
▤	Bophuthatswana
▦	Qwaqwa
▦	KwaNdebele
▧	Lebowa
▨	Gazankulu
▨	Venda
▦	KaNgwane

△ Existing "Black Spots"

● Resettlement Areas

□ Black Townships *(italic)*

○ Major Cities

○ Other Cities, Towns

From Pulitzer Prize-winning correspondent Joseph Lelyveld comes this poignant, powerful and timely look at South Africa and its pervasive racial policy.

Expelled from the country in the mid-1960s, Lelyveld returned 14 years later to report on the evolution of apartheid. With a novelist's eye for detail and ear for dialogue, he portrays individual blacks and whites trapped by a government responsive only to the privileged, and chronicles the brutality and violence of a nation at war with itself.

In this remarkable book, we meet the black migrant workers, the "coloreds" of Cape Town, white racial theorists, courageous Afrikaner clergymen opposed to apartheid, and dozens of other players in this complex drama. Move Your Shadow, a classic look at a land and its people, vividly describes a country over which a shadow grows larger and more ominous by the day.

PROLOGUE

Wena azi lo golof? Mina hayifuna lo mampara mfan.
    Have you caddied before? I don't want a useless boy.
Tata lo saka gamina.
    Take my bag of clubs.
Noko wena lahlega lo futi bol, hayikona mali.
    If you lose another ball, there will be no tip for you.
Susa lo-mtunzi gawena. Hayikona shukumisa lo saka.
    Move your shadow. Don't rattle the bag.

> —J. D. Bold, *Fanagalo Phrase Book, Grammar and Dictionary, the Lingua Franca of Southern Africa*, 10th edition, 1977

CHAPTER ONE

Out-Kicked

When they are out to demonstrate their decency and goodwill white South Africa's racial theorists are inclined to lose themselves in a riot of euphemisms and analogies. A lot of words get spilled as the urge to be understood clashes with an aversion to being understood too well. But when being understood is no longer an issue, language can be used sparingly. The letter informing me I had a week to clear out of South Africa was a model of economy. "You are hereby instructed," it said, "to make arrangements for yourself and your family to leave the Country on or before the 28th April, 1966."

We had been there only eleven months, but the message had long been expected, ever since an official had canceled a lunch in Pretoria, explaining that he would be compromised if he were seen again with someone the Cabinet had decided to expel. When the snub was finally made official, my immediate reaction was relief. A weight had been lifted, and as we walked out of the terminal at Jan Smuts Airport to our plane for Rome—two days ahead of the official deadline—I had a feeling of lightness. Possibly it occurred to me at that moment to wonder whether I would ever set foot in South Africa again. But since I had now been officially certified as "one of South Africa's most notorious enemies in the world," an Afrikaans-language newspaper would later say, that would have been tantamount to wondering whether the regime would crumble and fall in my lifetime.

Fourteen years later, when the suspicion that I might be reconstituted as a persona grata in South Africa hatched itself almost instantly into a compulsion to return, I could remember the sense of relief I felt on leaving as vividly as I could recall anything about the place. It was a memory I willed upon myself almost daily to check my headlong flight from Manhattan, where I thought I really belonged, and another uprooting of my family. The white regime hadn't crumbled, and even with the transformation of Rhodesia into black-ruled Zimbabwe, then taking place on its northern frontier, it wasn't about to do so. But the whites' old urge to be understood gave me a slight opening. My work as an editor in New York occasionally brought me into contact with South African diplomats who seldom failed to say the diplomatic thing: that my expulsion had been an aberration, or that those had been the bad old days, or that I would be astonished by the changes. Getting carried away, they sometimes seemed even eager to make me a witness. What may have been intended as no more than a civility—or, at most, a suggestion for a brief visit—I took as a sporting wager, even a dare.

I had long had a craving for going back, not only to South Africa but practically anywhere I had worked as a reporter. There was something irresistible about returning to a story you had once covered; it was like a trip in a time machine, one of the few ways a newspaperman could inject a little coherence and resonance into a vagabond life. As I rummaged through fading memories, I knew that no story I had ever covered, no place I had ever been had gripped me as wholly and intensely as South Africa.

I didn't need to remind myself that there had been places I had enjoyed more. It was a time of silence and fear in South Africa then, when apartheid was being elaborated as an ideology and the security apparatus, having crushed the main black nationalist movements, was stamping out the few sparks of resistance that white radicals had managed to ignite. To a newcomer the supporters of the government seemed a monolith; its enemies, a subdued, if not cringing, mass. The first South African to be executed in the apartheid era for an act of political violence, a white romantic named John Harris who had foolishly imagined he could shake the regime by leaving a bomb in a railway station, had just gone to the gallows singing "We Shall Overcome." Finishing with the radicals, the security apparatus seemed to be switching its focus to slightly larger but nonetheless minuscule coteries of white liberals who still ventured to speak and act on the premise that South Africa was a multiracial country.

Those we knew were the most admirable people we had ever known: brave but often despairing or frightened. Some had been hauled off to prison for solitary confinement and police interrogation; others lived in fear that they would be. Terrible things had happened to their relatives, lovers, and friends, including betrayals under police pressure. The thought of going into exile occurred to many, but most carried on in causes they deemed hopeless, partly because they loved their land, but mainly because they knew that silencing themselves would be an unforgivable compromise. And always there was the awareness that their own suffering, which came from too much clarity, the moral equivalent of a hormonal imbalance, was nothing to that of the blacks; that probably it would be irrelevant in the long run.

All that moral clarity, as harsh in its way as the glare from the South African sun, was a large part of what wore me out in the country. It wasn't the problem of the color bar that gripped me—"the color bore," an English journalist once wrote—or even the great mystery of how it would turn out in the end. Least of all was I preoccupied by South Africa's supposed strategic significance for the West. It was the place itself, its actual workings. I had not especially wanted to go there initially; as a fledgling correspondent I had focused my aspirations on Asia. South Africa was an assignment—until I landed there and realized, in something like three hours, that it was already starting to get hold of me.

I had just flown in from what was still called the Congo in transit to what was still called Rhodesia. Five months earlier I had been in Mississippi; a few months before that I had covered race riots in Harlem, Rochester, Jersey City, and Philadelphia. What I saw looked familiar, yet like no place I had ever been, so startling did it seem in its most ordinary aspects, in the tiny rituals and gaping contrasts of its daily life. My memory has blurred, and I can no longer recall precisely what made me realize that here was a weird social order as well as an imminent conflict. It was something commonplace, I'm sure, the sight of a black nanny with a white child carried as a papoose on her back; a black policeman checking a pass; maybe a white postman with a black caddie to shoulder his mail sack; or beer-drinking blacks sitting on a curbside in front of a segregated bus stop, where whites, who seemed privileged in nothing but their skins, steeled themselves against their human surroundings. Whatever it was, it happened that afternoon in a lower-middle-class white neighborhood called Troyeville.

Up close, apartheid was not only a caste system but a statement about reality amounting to a denial, which then sought to be self-enforcing. That statement insisted, against all the evidence, that there was such a place as "white South Africa." It existed as a legal concept, but not anywhere in the external world that I could find. The first story I filed from Johannesburg concerned a black choral group that had been denied permission to sing Handel's *Messiah* to a white audience because it had been scheduled to perform with a white orchestra. In the mind of some white official, that constituted illicit race mixing. When the sponsors of the concert proposed as a compromise that the chorus be accompanied by an organist instead of an orchestra, official permission was forthcoming, though the only available organist was also white. "We had to promise that he would play only on the white keys," one of the sponsors wisecracked. Apartheid in those days was often nearly funny; the reality it created seldom was.

In the fourteen years after my expulsion—the headlines in the Afrikaans press had proclaimed that I had been *uitgeskop* ("out-kicked")—I had lost much of the feel of the place, remembering mainly my own tautness and alertness when I lived there; forgotten, too, its physical and cultural scenery and most of its political rituals and arguments. What had lodged near the surface of my mind was a series of stark images and, because reporters remember quotes, small shards of dialogue. One in particular involved blacks in a courtroom.

There had been fifty-six black men in the dock, wearing large numbered placards around their necks so they could be identified. Their trial, on charges of belonging to an underground black movement called Poqo, took place in a courtroom in Port Elizabeth on the Indian Ocean coast. I remembered the trial because of the white prosecutor's cynical cross-examination. The accused came from the same small *dorp*, or rural town, where they represented a significant fraction of the adult black males. The prosecutor's tactic was to demonstrate that they were dissatisfied with their lives and therefore likely "terrorists." In response, the defendants attempted to deny that they could ever be unhappy as black men in South Africa.

"You have no objection to being ordered around by white men?" the prosecutor taunted.

"I have become so satisfied that my health keeps improving," number 23 replied.

"Are you satisfied with your wages?"

"I have never complained, not on a single day."

"Do you want better wages?"

"No, Your Worship."

"Are you satisfied with your house?"

"It's a very beautiful house."

The white prosecutor's scornful questions showed that he knew it was reasonable for black men to rebel, unreasonable for them to claim they could be happy; that they were held in check only by the power of the state, which he represented. Every other white in the courtroom had to know it, too.

The cross-examination of number 23 was a caricature of the political exchanges blacks could have in that period. Conversation was inexplicit, steeped in irony, with kernels of meaning hidden between sardonic throwaway lines. What kept conversation in check was the seeming omnipresence of informers, known among blacks as *impimpis*. Invariably, when there was a political trial or wave of arrests, someone discovered the exorbitant price of trust. While visiting Port Elizabeth for the Poqo trial, I met two blacks at the seaside cottage of the playwright Athol Fugard. Because he vouched for me to them, and them to me, we were able to speak with more than normal candor. How was it, I asked, that black security policemen and the state witnesses in political trials were never assaulted in the black townships? "To do something like that," one of the men said, "you would want at least two men, wouldn't you?" Pausing to indicate that my question was hypothetical and not intended as incitement, I gestured toward the only other person in the room, the man's best friend. "How do I know," came the mumbled reply, "that he is not an *impimpi*?"

I got many of my clues to black life from black journalists, in particular Ernest Cole, a remarkable photographer, who had managed with fierce persistence to get himself reclassified as a colored—a person of mixed race—so he could maneuver more easily as a photo-journalist inside the system in order to document what it did to black lives. Other clues came in conversations with servants at the apartment complex where we lived, including a woman of astonishingly serene character named Dinah Diba-koane, whom we hired to look after our two girls. Shortly before we left, she went back to her own children, for she was due to have another. On a Sunday morning we drove Dinah past Pretoria, onto a little track that wound across the veld. Soon we reached the top of a slight rise and looked down on a small encampment of shanties knocked together from scraps of rusted metal siding interspersed with brand-new metal boxes that gleamed in the autumn sun. It had a name, Boekenhoutfontein, an officially des-ignated resettlement site for Pretoria blacks, like Dinah's family, who had been deemed "badly situated" because they lived too near the "white areas" where they worked. In their new setting it was hard to believe that they were in the same country, precisely the doubt the authorities wanted to instill. There, with guilty qualms but no alternative, we deposited Dinah with her family.

There was nothing secondhand, and nothing metaphoric, about my most immediate and painful collision with black life in that time. It is difficult to write about now, although the memory is nightmarishly vivid.

In a driving rain, at night, he came through the windshield. For an in-terminable moment I thought I had killed him. We were at the end of a 400-mile trip from Durban, lost in the thickening traffic of Johannesburg, driving past the movie palaces on Commissioner Street, where overdressed Saturday-night crowds came tripping out of the rain.

I had stopped for a light and was shifting out of first gear when I heard a scream, then a thud and the sound of glass shattering. A black man, dressed in black trousers and a black jacket, was lying on the pavement a few feet to the right of the car, which had veered to the left when I slammed on the brakes. I had never really seen him until I bent over to take his pulse, which was strong. I covered him with a blanket from the car and tried to direct traffic around him. A white policeman appeared and started asking questions. White bystanders stepped forward to make sure I was all right, to tell me they had seen the man step out from between parked cars, that I could not have avoided him; in their solicitude for me some even pressed little papers with their addresses into my hand, in the event I needed wit-nesses. Black bystanders stood back, watching silently from a distance. By the time I had sent my family home in a taxi, the policeman was bending down to make chalk marks on the rain-slick roadway to show the point of impact and the swerve of the car. No one paid attention to the form under the soggy blanket. The man breathed regularly and occasionally opened his eyes but didn't respond when I tried to put questions to him.

I covered him again, this time with my raincoat, then found another po-liceman sitting out of the rain in his wagon, reading a comic. Barely look-ing up, he said the black ambulance had been called. I asked him to call again. "They'll come," he said, returning to the comic. They came an hour and a quarter later. A white ambulance, I knew, would have been there in minutes. I phoned the emergency room an hour later. "It's nothing serious," the voice on the other end assured me. "Just a knock on the head." I asked for the patient's name. The voice said it was Clifton Roche. Nothing could be done that night, I told myself. It was still pouring, my car had no windshield, and even if I could get there, I wouldn't be able to find the man's family in the township at night. First thing in the morning, I would go to the hospital, speak to Clifton Roche, get his address, and find his relatives. I would also arrange for a good neurologist to examine him.

In the morning the hospital had never heard of Clifton Roche. "*Ja*, it's always like that," a pipe-smoking officer in a cardigan said when I went to police headquarters to ask for help in finding the man. "The hospitals let them go, and we find them dead a few days later." Still, he promised to see what could be done. We called regularly, but at increasing intervals, over the next ten days or so. The officer was unfailingly courteous. "Your Bantu has not been found," he would say. "You don't have to worry. No action will be taken against you."

We didn't stop worrying all at once, but Clifton Roche, if that was his name, gradually became a memory. When it forced its way into my mind, my preoccupation was with what I had done, rather than with his fate, which seemed unknowable. I would ask myself why I hadn't gone with him to the hospital that night. Only occasionally did I ask myself what would have happened if I had stepped out from between the cars and Clifton Roche had knocked me down. It had been an initiation into white South Africa.

As the incident showed again, this was an idea rather than a place. Clifton Roche may have been there, but he remained an object of indifference. Whites were privileged only in fact, not in theory. They had rights, went the theory, because they resided in the white country. Blacks could be privileged in their own country or, rather, their own countries. While it was all right, if not exactly desirable, for Afrikaners, the dominant white group, to live in the same cities and streets as English-speaking whites, even Jews and Greeks, such intermingling would not do for blacks. So far as possible Zulus and Xhosas and all the other tribal groups had to be kept separate. This, it was to be understood, was not merely for the convenience or safety of the whites but for the fulfillment of the blacks. White supremacy—which had only recently been flaunted under the banner of *baasskap*, from the Afrikaans *baas* for "master" and *skap* for "state of being"—was now said to have been annulled. But there was something called "white civilization" that had to be preserved. Its preservation required that blacks not go to universities attended by whites and that their own so-called universities be located outside the white country, in their own countries, wherever those were.

It was all very logical and very moral, but only one man, it seemed, could explain it without getting entangled in contradictions. Fortunately the chief

ideologue was also the prime minister, who had only recently been preserved for the nation, the white nation, after two bullets had been fired
into his head by a would-be white assassin. I never got closer to Hendrik
Verwoerd than the press gallery in Parliament, from which I would watch
him as he contemplatively fingered the scar that one of the bullets had left
next to his eye. At that distance he seemed icy and smug, but those who
got near enough generally found him a kindly man. What they never found
there was the slightest glimmer of self-doubt. Verwoerd dealt only in revealed truth, and although he was undoubtedly a humble and pious Christian by his own lights, he made sure that he did the revealing when it came
to matters of black and white in South Africa. "He would have made a
good impression on the Synod of Dort," Harold Macmillan later wrote in
his memoirs, comparing the discourse he heard in Cape Town as Britain's
prime minister in 1960 to a seventeenth-century church gathering in Holland, where the doctrine of strict predestination was dogmatically upheld.

I never suspected that much of what I took to be the temper of the Afrikaners derived from the temper of their leader, a self-made Afrikaner who
had been born in Amsterdam two years before his family emigrated to
South Africa, then educated largely in English schools in Cape Town and
Rhodesia. At the time of the Boer War, which erupted ten weeks before
the end of the nineteenth century and dragged on for the first two and a
half years of the twentieth, the Afrikaners were a frontier people whose
nationalism hadn't yet hardened into a doctrinaire creed. The spirit of in-
dcpcndcncc among them was so strong that it proved impossible to maintain discipline in armies that regularly humiliated the imperial superpower
in the early months of the struggle. Individual fighting Boers—the word
simply means "farmers"—came and went as they pleased, deciding for
themselves which battles were worth fighting. Arriving in the aftermath of
the war, Verwoerd's family had tasted none of its bitterness: the concentration camps in which 26,000 women and children died, the loss of farms
and sons. But those who could never forgive or forget took him as their
leader. It was Hendrik Verwoerd who finally led them out of the Commonwealth, reviving the legacy of the white republics that were crushed
when he was an infant in Holland. Verwoerd had no tolerance for dissent,
no tolerance even for tolerance. As a result, dissident voices among Afrikaner nationalists were nearly as hard to hear during my abbreviated first
tour in South Africa as black nationalist voices.

A soothsayer and visionary rather than a rabble-rouser, the good doctor
set minds at ease. (He had started out as a behavioral psychologist, writing
a thesis called *"Die Afstomping van die Gemoedsaandoeninge"*—"The
Blunting of the Emotions.") There was a plan, *and* it was moral, *and* it
would work: The Bantu would be in his "homeland," and all would be
right with the world. Blacks could not be allowed a permanent foothold
in "white South Africa" because it would be a denial of their rights to keep

them there as a disenfranchised majority. Insisting that they belonged in "their own countries"—even if most of these so-called countries existed only in his mind—was actually to champion black nationalism. Thus it was for the sake of the blacks as well as for the preservation of the white nation that no mixing could be allowed: not in a boxing ring or on a soccer field; not in a jazz club or a concert hall; not even in the workplace, where whites had been relying on nonwhite labor since they arrived at the Cape of Good Hope in 1652. True to his principles, his guest Harold Macmillan was astonished to discover in 1960, Verwoerd had no black servants in his official residence in Cape Town.

"So you are left with the taut South African present, which daily becomes more inward, more fragmented, more dreary." That was my sense of the place as I recorded it in a valedictory article after my expulsion. In September 1966, fewer than three months after that article appeared, Verwoerd was stabbed to death on the front bench of the white Parliament by a parliamentary messenger with a history of incarceration in mental institutions who apparently had none of the political motivations that might easily have been adduced for his act. But by then I was at last heading for Asia, and if I thought about South Africa at all, it was not to wonder whether the spirit of Verwoerd still reigned: I assumed it did.

Relativism occasionally crept into my reaction to news reports from South Africa. When there was a new uproar about a political detainee who had died in the custody of the security police, for instance, I couldn't help reflecting that with the advent of the various Latin American death squads and the Ayatollah's Revolutionary Guard, South Africa had suddenly slipped into the second division when it came to state terror; that this was so from a global perspective even when you considered the shooting of youthful protesters in Soweto or the vicious killing of Steve Biko, the young black leader who was pummeled into a coma and then hauled, naked and manacled, on a 700-mile journey in the back of a police van to Pretoria, where he died.

Of course, a global perspective is easily used to belittle the sufferings of particular groups. If it can be shown that someone in Gdansk or Kampala or Lahore is worse off than someone in Cape Town, then anyone in Cape Town who vents his unhappiness is convicted of a lack of global perspective. Nevertheless, from the distance at which I was following these events, it was the emergence of the student protests and of Biko rather than their suppression that stirred me. Once again blacks were making themselves heard. This was the generation that Verwoerd had intended to educate for a life of meager privileges and low horizons in the "homelands" since, as he put it, there could be "no place for [them] in the European community above the level of certain forms of labor." And now it turned out that they had read Frantz Fanon and Aimé Césaire, some of them at least, and were standing up to denounce the legacy of the great white seer and demand their birthright. Without Verwoerd at the helm, the Afrikaners seemed a bit wobbly in their response, uncertain of how to justify the system he had elaborated.

On the strength of that uncertainty, I asked my editors if I could explore the possibility of returning. The matter was taken up discreetly in Cape Town by John Burns, who had gone to South Africa ten years after my expulsion as the first resident correspondent *The New York Times* had been allowed to station there after me. In that sense Burns was to be both my predecessor and my successor. "Do you think, Mr. Burns," the foreign minister, Pik Botha, asked once my name had been broached, "that a condemned man has the right to choose the witnesses at his execution?"

I took the joke to be doubly ironic, a way of promising that I would be disappointed if I thought I would see the crumbling of white power. But I also took it as an accolade. Five months later my visa finally came through.

My time machine seemed to have landed me in Oz. Or was it Brobdingnag? No, it was Bophuthatswana. This was to be my first weekend in South Africa in nearly a generation, and now, I was given to understand, I was not in South Africa at all. I was in Bophuthatswana—alleged to be a sovereign and independent nation for the 2 million black South Africans of Tswana origins who, by virtue of its existence, were no longer deemed to be South Africans. This new black "nation" was at least seven fragments, scattered across three South African provinces, surrounded by the huge holdings of white ranchers and farmers. Three times on the drive from Johannesburg I had crossed its border without running into anything that remotely resembled a border post. There were small "Bophuthatswana Border" signs, but they were superfluous; a glance out the window could always tell you which country you were in. If you saw fields that were empty except for cattle and grain, it was obviously South Africa. If they were full of people in tribal villages and desolate shantytowns, it was the "national state." But now I was in neither a village nor a shantytown. I was in a glossy casino resort called Sun City that seemed to have taken some of its decorative cues from the Peachtree Plaza Hotel in Atlanta. Here, where whites and blacks mixed as freely as they might there, a black and a white were to fight for one of the world's two heavyweight championships. Hendrik Verwoerd, I wondered, where is thy sting?

From ringside it seemed likely that Verwoerd was revolving in his grave over this bizarre fulfillment of his vision, which nonetheless was turning into a festival of white South African, mainly Afrikaner, patriotism. Gerrie Coetzee from Boksburg, South Africa, was to fight Mike Weaver from the wrong side of the tracks in Gatesville, Texas. A crowd of about 17,000 screamed in good-natured frenzy as the theme from the movie *Star Wars*

blared over huge quadraphonic speakers and a chorus girl dressed in orange
ostrich plumes and sequins danced down the aisle, bearing the South African flag as honor guard to the contender. Another chorus girl brought
Weaver and the Stars and Stripes. They were followed by chorus girls with
the Bophuthatswana flag and even a flag for Sun City itself, until finally
there was a lineup of eleven dancers, mainly but not exclusively white,
swinging their bottoms and kicking their heels in the ring. Floyd Patter-
son, the last black heavyweight champ to be defeated by a white, got a cheer
as he climbed through the ropes. Then came the anthems, including that
of Bophuthatswana, with the thousands of whites standing at solemn attention. Finally, when the chorus girl holding their flag gave the signal by
thrusting its staff into her navel and raising it high, they burst into a full-
throated and passionate rendering of their own *"Die Stem"* ("The Call")
so that Coetzee would be left in no doubt of his duty:

> *At that call we shall not falter,*
> *Firm and steadfast we shall stand,*
> *At thy will to live or perish,*
> *O South Africa, dear land.*

The poor lug perished in the thirteenth, dropping with a thud in a
stunned and suddenly silent arena. To those of his countrymen who had
been intent on viewing the fight as a racial allegory, he had presented a
chilling foreshadowing of their destiny. In far-off Soweto blacks were rejoicing over the Afrikaner's defeat. A mood sodden with anticlimax and
regret descended on the casino, yet there was no apparent bitterness of a
racial kind as Afrikaners and Tswanas brushed shoulders at the slot machines and fast-food stands. On the platforms cantilevered over small lagoons in the dimly lit lobby, a few voluble young whites threw themselves
into earnest, boozy colloquies with young blacks, which gathered intensity
as the evening wore on but seemed to be largely one-sided. Out on the patio a middle-aged Afrikaner tried to catch the eye of the black barmaid.
"Mrs. Weaver, Mrs. Weaver," he called in a bantering tone. She took his
order with a wary smile that seemed to show there had been no offense.

The nearest thing to a confrontation occurred at the entrance to the
casino when a uniformed black security man informed a leather-jacketed
young Afrikaner that he could not proceed farther in running shoes. It was
not farfetched to imagine that it was the young man's first encounter with
black authority.

"Why can't I?" he demanded, asserting his whiteness but looking
around with noticeable uncertainty for support from his friends.

"That's our rule," the black man said.

"What's the reason for the rule?"

"Look," said the guard, who was trying to unclog the entrance and get
the line moving, "I don't want to talk."

Not knowing how to step back without humiliating himself, the young white persisted. "What did those shoes cost?" he asked, pointing to the cop's brogans. "Mine cost nineteen rands."

And when that was met by silence: "Don't you want my money?"

The man in uniform was now insulted. "I don't need *your* money," he replied. "I get paid."

The kid in the leather jacket was now as beaten as Gerrie Coetzee. His forefathers had fought blacks for half a century and built one of their frontier republics in this area on a constitution prohibiting "any equality... either in church or state," then had been ground down in a filthy war with the British and lost their republic, but had clung to the principle so hard and nurtured their grievances and sense of destiny so fiercely that decades later they reversed the tide of history. But now the long struggle had brought the Afrikaners to the point where a young member of the tribe could be turned away from a casino entrance by a black cop.

CHAPTER TWO

Spear-Shield

The black room service waiter who brought my breakfast in the Carlton Hotel in Johannesburg late on the morning after the fight managed to "sir" me four or five times. The servility got under my white skin; for the first time in years, I felt the urge to protest, "I'm not from this place." Instead, I grabbed the check. As I did so, the waiter dropped his patter and spoke up in a natural voice, forgetting the "sir." He was saying something real, but I didn't get it. "Look there," he said again, pointing to a rooftop a block and a half away and a dozen or so stories lower. "They're making an arrest."

Once I had my glasses on, I could make out three blue figures, policemen obviously, facing three blacks while several other blacks looked on from a distance of maybe twenty yards. One of the policemen seemed to be studying something at chest height, probably a reference book.

"Is it a pass-law arrest?" I asked.

"Must be," the waiter replied, over his shoulder, sounding suddenly neutral.

I then had some breakfast. The next time I looked two of the policemen had one of the blacks against a wall. Slowly and methodically they were beating him on the head and shoulders. The blows came one by one, not all in a rush. When the man ducked, they waited till he raised his head; then one of them would slam him again. At that distance, in the glare of the morning sun, the scene had a surreal quality. Except for the faint beep of a distant horn and the hum of the air conditioning, there were no sounds; on the streets below, the light Sunday morning traffic moved quietly, and quiet family groups, black and white, dawdled by shop windows. I didn't have to move my head to shift my glance from them to the quiet bashing beyond their view on the rooftop. Seen in this way, the bashing no longer looked surreal but normal.

Finished with the man by the wall, the three figures in blue turned to the others. One of the policemen ambled over to a man standing by what looked to be a laundry tub, and struck the man on the side of the head. The other two were chasing a third black to the far side of the roof. Their prey tried to dodge, then crouched with his arms over his head near the parapet. Together they hauled him to his feet. Then one held him while the other aimed three sharp blows at his face. The one who was doing the holding got in an awkward backhanded left before they dropped him, returning to the laundry tub to slug the man there, who had made the mistake of remaining upright. Then the policemen left, taking no one with them.

I showered, dressed, and went downstairs. Crossing the street, I walked a block, and went to the rooftop I had been watching. There I found a half dozen or so men crowded into a little room with bunks, watching another two who were playing checkers with Pepsi and Coca-Cola bottle tops. My appearance provoked no discernible surprise or interest. Awkwardly I mentioned that I was an American staying at the Carlton and that I had witnessed their encounter with the police. A large silence was the reply. I tried to chip away at the silence with questions. A compact man with a shaved head and pencil-line mustache spoke for the group, furnishing minimal answers. Yes, the police sometimes came to check their reference books. Yes, they were in order. Yes, they worked in the neighborhood. Downstairs at a restaurant called Chez André. No, they were not normally assaulted like that when the police came. No, the men were not surprised it had happened.

I had just about run out of questions and hadn't gotten anything like an explanation. What was it all about? "Maybe," the spokesman replied, without showing the least sign of feeling or lifting his eyes from the checkerboard, where play was continuing, "they didn't like the way their brother was beaten last night."

Less than an hour later, at an elegant lunch in a green park of a garden in the white suburbs, I mentioned the random vindictiveness of this epilogue to the Coetzee fight to my hostess. I was back now in Johannesburg's Chekhovian precincts, where great privilege and great social conscience occasionally converge. My hostess was Helen Suzman, a liberal member of the white Parliament who had battled against every apartheid law and expansion of arbitrary state power for nearly three decades—in the darkest period, for thirteen consecutive years, as a tireless minority of one speaking for all those who had been silenced. A woman without illusions, she understood immediately why the victims had no interest in lodging a complaint. The police would testify for each other, she said, and the blacks would be lucky not to be jailed for assault; not just their jobs but their status in the urban areas as migrant workers could be made to depend on their taking their lumps quietly. It had been, after all, a lesson in helplessness.

That did not mean they took it meekly or with resignation, I thought later, trying to work out their attitude on the basis of the terse answers I had gotten. Being unsurprised meant being unforgiving, it seemed to me. It meant keeping score.

For the next three years I was still regularly astonished by South Africa. It was a particular kind of sensation, a cheap thrill maybe, available to outsiders who can maintain access of a kind on all sides of its various racial and political divides—as few South Africans can. In a day I could travel through several worlds, could look at the same landscape through several sets of lenses. Often I would fill up, reaching a state of supersaturation in which I felt I couldn't absorb another impression. Sometimes my head would throb from having heard too many discordant views earnestly or bitterly argued; other times, especially when talking to the sorts of whites who seemed complacent in their privilege, I could taste the small and possibly snide satisfaction of knowing that in my short time there I had traveled far more deeply into their country than they would in their entire lives.

In its spaciousness and harsh beauty, South Africa was still gripping as a land. It was still absorbing, too, as a political conflict. But what made it different was its many ways of looking at itself: of explaining, rationalizing, and forgetting. And it was there—on the level of perception and expression—that South Africa seemed new when I returned. Something had definitely slipped loose, but whatever it was, it wasn't political power.

In the years that elapsed between my two lives there, the white settler or colonial regimes in the key buffer states of Rhodesia, Angola, and Mozambique had collapsed on its borders, and the black population inside had risen by 90 percent, compared to only a 30 percent rise in the number of whites (whose share in the total of about 32 million had thus dipped from 18 to 15 percent). Yet white power seemed more entrenched than ever. The old Verwoerdian trick of changing attitudes without changing practices, of annihilating white supremacy in theory without losing its advantages, had been marvelously refined. Black trade unions were getting legal rights. The brown-skinned minorities, the mixed-race coloreds and the Indians, were being offered a junior partnership in a national government that would continue to exclude blacks.

In the evolving white ethos, South Africa had already transformed itself into a meritocracy. If it also happens to be a racial hierarchy, that isn't a grotesque imbalance of power. Instead, it should be seen as an outgrowth of history and culture, of natural selection and maybe also biological destiny, although that thought can no longer be spoken out loud in polite company.

The word "apartheid," literally "separatehood," was coined as an election promise in 1948 by the political party that has governed ever since. But now that word is shunned, even resented, by the party's high priests as if it were an epithet fashioned by the country's enemies. "Apartheid, whatever that is supposed to mean," sneered an editorial in *Die Burger*, the party newspaper in Cape Town. As if Daniel F. Malan, the paper's first editor, had not become prime minister on the apartheid platform. As if he had not promised "to make South Africa a white man's land." "Apartheid, the propaganda concept of the past few decades," grumbled *Rapport*, another pro-government newspaper.

Yet the promise of 1948 has been sculpted into the landscape. The areas in which whites, browns, and blacks once lived in proximity have nearly all been cleared and sorted out. Before apartheid one third of Cape Town's whites lived in neighborhoods where coloreds also lived. Now the exceptions to the rule of racial exclusion are so few as to be statistically invisible. There is still some tidying up to be done—"black spots," meaning black-owned land in legally proclaimed "white areas," to be expropriated—but the racial checkerboard is firmly in place.

"They don't need their laws anymore!" exclaimed J. N. Singh, a fiery leader of the resistance to apartheid in the forties and fifties, after taking me on a tour of neighborhoods in Durban from which Indians had been driven. "They've done it! Whoever comes into power will not be able to change *this*." His gesture took in a major Indian township called Chatsworth in which the racially displaced of Indian origins had been regrouped. In another part of the city, close to the seafront, the lot on which his family's home once stood was now the corner of a shopping center parking lot in a white neighborhood.

In the eastern Cape industrial town of Uitenhage, the Reverend Allan Hendrickse, a Congregational minister who was head of a colored political faction that had decided to accept the new constitutional order as a Mephistophelian bargain, drove me past the ruins of the church his father had devoted his life to building. When the bulldozers came to knock it down after the neighborhood had been declared "white" under the notorious Group Areas Act, the elder Hendrickse went into a decline and soon died. Now only a chunk of the belfry remains standing to mark the site. What happened, Allan Hendrickse explained with grim satisfaction, was that this last portion of his father's church miraculously withstood the chain that had been wrapped around it and hitched to the bulldozer. And the chain had not broken after the bulldozer had been put into gear and driven to the end of its tether. Instead, the heavy machine stopped short, and its white operator went flying, broke his neck, and died. This was taken as a sign from God, and the bulldozer never returned to finish the job.

In Oudtshoorn, yet another town in the Cape that had been reordered on a racial basis under the Group Areas Act, a young colored official who had been detailed by his white superior to show me how well his people lived in their new township extended the tour to show me where they used to live before they were displaced. Every weekend, he said, you can see coloreds from Port Elizabeth or Cape Town or Johannesburg driving slowly through the old neighborhood in Oudtshoorn where they grew up. "And then the sorrows come," the young man said.

Apartheid is thus no longer a concept. It is there to see, or, rather, not see, for it is the screen that hides the vast reality of black South Africa from the vision of most whites. Hardly anywhere do whites now have to live near blacks—excepting those blacks, 120,000 in Johannesburg alone, whom they keep in their backyards to tend them as servants—and hardly anywhere is it ever necessary for them to see where blacks live, except occasionally at a distance from a passing car. On the screen of apartheid—this, it may be said, is its sinister beauty—whites can project any version of reality they please, including their own fantasies of life in a society where apartheid does not exist.

The South African state is still authoritarian for most of its people, but it can tolerate any amount of kinkiness. Of all known movements, only communism and black nationalism seem to be subject to intensive police quarantine. It is unclear whether the authorities have learned to draw sophisticated distinctions between words and deeds or are so preoccupied with deeds that speech has become relatively easy, at least when it is a matter of whites talking to whites or even blacks talking to whites. Seemingly liberal opinions sprout in the most unlikely ground, like succulent plants on the arid fringes of the veld: in slick magazines intended for the coffee tables of corporate executives who find it helps to be known to their foreign bankers as "equal opportunity employers" or even in the pro-government Afrikaans press. No longer does it make sense to talk of a white monolith; a little promiscuity in the realm of opinion is not a dangerous thing after all. It's good for the image, good for self-esteem. So the various white elites are constantly talking the country's future through a network of incestuous discussion groups that pride themselves on their openness and regularly solicit opinions from browns and blacks. These are drawn from a roster of 15 or 20 names among the 27 or 28 million, those mainly who can be counted on to be "responsible," plus a few who carry verbal whips and chains to satisfy an occasional white urge for flagellation.

Starting on the white side of the racial boundary, it took a while to learn that nonwhites are normally heavily outnumbered in such interracial encounter groups; that they tend to be invited mainly when whites want to show off to foreigners; and that the whites aren't all that interested in what they have to say. At one of the little symposia I attended, an establishment colored brooded silently for two hours as the whites ran through their usual clubby debate about the immediate future, then exploded: "I wonder if it worries you that I haven't heard a word you've said." When he stormed out moments later, the discussion missed a beat, then continued as if nothing had happened.

It took a while to realize, also, that the rules are entirely different when blacks talk to blacks. Here, too, something had slid loose, in that the danger of informers no longer stifles the expression of opinions in private conversation. But opportunities for public speech remain strictly limited. A black political figure needs no permit to go to an "international" restaurant in a "white area" to discuss the revolution with a foreign journalist. But if he tries to call an open meeting in the township to protest a rise in bus fares, it is almost sure to be banned as a potential "riotous assembly" under the Internal Security Act. At the same time that the authorities eased up on censorship, they enacted a law authorizing the police to forbid political pronouncements or songs at black funerals, which had become forums because the cemeteries were virtually the only places left where blacks could gather freely.

South Africa sates you with paradox. A black poet can say almost anything, it seems, as long as he is sparing in his use of proper nouns. Here is a passage from a poem called "Time has run out" by Mongane Wally Serote, a black writer living in exile, whose work sells openly in Johannesburg:

after these deaths
our staring silent eye
speaks of national revolution which we make...
we learned by losing children and dying terrible deaths
how to hold a gun and grenade
we know now
how to make fire fire fire
inside this hour
of intensely long and dragging movement...
this is our land
it bears our blood
it must bear our will

But Thabane Ntshiwa, a twenty-three-year-old diesel mechanic who scratched some slogans on a stainless steel mug that he used on lunch breaks at a factory near Johannesburg, not only had his mug confiscated but was himself arrested by the security police and charged under the Internal Security Act. "P. W.," one of the legends on the mug exclaimed, addressing the prime minister by his initials, "We want our land." Another said, "Release our leaders, release Nelson Mandela." The actual inscriptions were invisible from a distance of four feet and barely legible close up, but Ntshiwa had used proper nouns. I was allowed to handle the mug and talk to the prisoner in a small magistrate's court in Krugersdorp the morning he was sentenced. The magistrate noted that Ntshiwa had carried the mug on a daily basis into a canteen used by 135 other blacks whose passions might easily have been "whipped up." The sentence: eighteen months in jail, more than Ntshiwa had gotten on a previous conviction for culpable homicide.

The capriciousness of a system that can ban a mug and release a poem keeps its enemies constantly off balance while enticing potential collaborators, both at home and abroad. Western bankers and diplomats, Americans especially, who want to believe in a meliorative dynamic seldom make the fairly obvious calculation that blacks are left with less political freedom than they had thirty years ago.

If there is a mastermind behind all this, I remarked one day to Zwelakhe Sisulu, he must be a genius. Sisulu, a young black who might have an enormous following if he were allowed to lead, knew all about official capriciousness. In the three years since I had met him, he had been successively an editor and union leader; then, by official decree, a nonperson under a banning order that made it a crime for him to enter a newspaper or union office or be in a gathering of more than two persons; then, for nearly a year, a prisoner held incommunicado without charge; then a banned person again; and, finally, a union leader and journalist all over again, accredited to go to the Union Buildings in Pretoria and put pointed questions to the prime minister at a news conference. His mother in that same period had been banned, unbanned, banned again, and jailed. (His father, a former secretary-general of the outlawed African National Congress, had only been jailed, for he was serving a life sentence with Nelson Mandela.) Sisulu was prepared to agree that the system worked very effectively and that it was run by people who were certainly not stupid and probably quite shrewd. But he didn't think there were any geniuses among them. "A system like this can only evolve," he said, taking the long view—the only view available to blacks.

If whites took the long view, they would be in a panic. This is one reason that white reality and black reality can be regarded as so different that newspapers that editorialize regularly about the evil and futility of apartheid find it perfectly natural to make up different front pages for blacks and whites. In Johannesburg the black edition of the *Star* is called the Africa edition, underscoring the conviction of most whites that they are somewhere else. A Saturday morning's choice of front pages from the relatively liberal *Rand Daily Mail* nicely illustrates the assumptions made about the conflicting preoccupations of whites and blacks. On the white front page there is a large color picture of a little blond girl sitting on a bed, propping on her lap a book entitled *Best Loved Horses of the World*. The caption explains she is "making herself at home in the luxurious surroundings of one of the *Rand Daily Mail* Ideal Homes Exhibition showhouses." The headline on the paper's lead story warns:

SUMMER STORMS
ARE ON THE WAY

On the black front page the color picture shows a black nurse attending a black servant who survived a five-story fall from a fire escape. The main story concerns a magisterial order banning a series of political meetings by what is known as the Black Consciousness Movement:

ALL WEEKEND BC
MEETINGS BANNED

In Chinese the two characters used in the common term for "contradiction" separately represent a spear and a shield. Spear-shield is everyday South African reality, a feature of the land whites grudgingly share with blacks in their increasing millions. At one corner you see the world the way whites want to see it; at the next, the world as blacks experience it. The difference can be between an "international" hotel and a squalid rooftop barracks for black migrant workers that is periodically raided by the police. Or it can be between white bus stops conveniently located near the main shopping areas and black bus stops hidden away at the edge of town.

Spear-shield is visible in the Johannesburg skyline. The nondescript cement-block building near the railway yard where I once watched pass-law cases has been replaced with a fortresslike structure on reinforced concrete pillars, a gloomy monument to the system's survival and ruthlessness. Looking out a window in a corridor there, you can hold John Vorster Square and the Market Theater, two buildings that represent antithetical forces and endeavors, in a single mental snapshot. The one is the headquarters of the security police; looking at it, I would always count the floors till I picked out the notorious tenth, where many blacks and some whites have been tortured as a matter of routine. Two blocks away, in the city's old produce market, stands a complex of theaters and galleries where the country's racial conventions are ignored except as a subject for ridicule and condemnation, where torture frequently becomes a theme for moral inquiry. There is little that Athol Fugard or anyone else has ever thought to say on a stage about South Africa that has not been said there. Fugard's passion and pain; the triumphant mockery of *Woza Albert*, a black satire that later went to London and New York; or the comic revues of Pieter-Dirk Uys, a writer and female impersonator who wickedly takes off the Afrikaner establishment in drag ("Democracy is too good to share with just anyone," a favorite Uys character giggles, vamping her audience)—

they all get played in integrated theaters in the shadow of the security police.

For whites the contradictions can be taken as an expression of the country's undeniable vitality. For blacks they are only relatively less humiliating than the old, straightforward style of apartheid. Blacks are still ghettoized in their townships. Even if portions of these are being upgraded for a small, emergent middle class, they are nearly always set off by buffer zones—highways, railway yards, factories, mining dumps. South Africa never achieved the absurdity of segregated flights on its airline, but the trains and buses, the services the mass of blacks require, are still demarcated by race. Legitimate theaters, which blacks are unlikely to attend in large numbers, have been allowed to desegregate. But movie theaters outside the townships are still for whites only. Swimming pools at "international" hotels are supposed to be open to blacks and other nonwhites, but beaches remain segregated. Restaurants are a matter of guesswork. Where a "Right of Admission Reserved" sign is displayed, the guess is not difficult. Most are for whites only, but some allow whites to take blacks; a handful allow blacks to take themselves. It is this crazy-quilt pattern of deviousness, manipulation, and control that whites call progress. Some blacks allow themselves to share the illusion for minutes at a time, but most know it for what it is. They call it apartheid.

The least sign of black impatience vexes whites. Yet whites need blacks to validate their belief that apartheid has now ceased to matter—ceased, that is, to matter to them. Sun City, I was told, was ready to pay a black superstar, a Diana Ross or Sammy Davis, Jr., or Lena Horne, as much as the $1 million it supposedly showered on Sinatra to get that cachet. (The bait wasn't taken, but Shirley Bassey and George Benson, two black stars of lesser magnitude, came for less.) For much the same reason, I think, blacks have their place in the cosmopolitan fantasy that is constantly being marketed to whites. Ad agencies have different techniques for slipping them into promotions without denying outright the crude facts of South African life. Sometimes an interracial theme is presented as patriotic. An ad for British Petroleum shows a white and a black side by side in a coal mine. "Shoulder to shoulder in the search for energy," it says. Sometimes it is futuristic; a Johnnie Walker ad had a black couple drinking with a white couple in costumes out of *Star Trek* or the twenty-fifth century. "Good taste doesn't change with the times," it says.

An ad that grabbed my attention in the waiting room of Joshua Nkomo, the Zimbabwean political figure, was a two-page picture of a black South African model in what was described as a gold bouclé jacket. She also wore gold slacks, gold shoes, gold gloves, and a feathered gold beanie, and she was reclining on a parapet above El Greco's Toledo in order to display these garments from South Africa to the mainly white readers of *Fair Lady*.

"Lady in Spain," the article was called. "The Fair Lady team" had been flown to Madrid from Johannesburg, a caption said, by Iberia Airways.

I never succeeded in explaining to white South Africans why I found this remarkable. *Fair Lady*, the most successful magazine in the country, was published in English by the major Afrikaans press group, Nasionale Pers, which is intimately associated with the governing party. The prime minister was once on its board; its senior executives are reputed to be his confidants. Certainly Nasionale Pers would never show a black model recumbent on a parapet above Pretoria. Nor is the government it supports closely identified with the principle of free movement for blacks. I showed the article to Piet Cillié, then the board chairman of Nasionale Pers, and asked whether he didn't find it a little strange. He could not see what I was getting at. "It's an article on fashions," he said.

My point was extremely unsubtle. If I were the contentious sort, I might have made it more vivid by contrasting the model in Segovia to a black woman I had seen standing in the dock at the Commissioner's Court in a Cape Town black township called Langa, about six miles from his office. Her name was Virginia Nqanulyo, and her ensemble included a knitted white hat, a pale blue turtleneck jersey, and a baby wrapped in a yellow knitted blanket. The baby had been with her in Pollsmoor Prison, where she had been taken on a charge of having traveled illegally to Cape Town from a homeland called Transkei. The baby gurgled while the mother answered the questions of the white official on the bench; how she had lived for years in Cape Town, had met her husband in Cape Town long before Transkei achieved its bogus independence, had given birth to her children in Cape Town; how there was no livelihood for her in her "homeland." The commissioner gave her a suspended sentence of sixty days in jail on the condition that she leave Cape Town immediately. A few days earlier he had told another woman who said she would starve in Transkei, "We are starving in Cape Town. You can rather starve at home."

Lady in Langa, "Lady in Spain." Of course, they had nothing to do with each other. The one was a part of black reality in South Africa, the other a part of white fantasy. To do it justice, *Fair Lady* has a social conscience that periodically permits it to slip in an article about hunger in the black rural areas. But when it hands an Iberia ticket to a black model, it is imitating *Vogue*, showing its readers that *they* have risen above apartheid and joined a wider world. It's a characteristic South African disjunction.

The gap between black reality and white reality is huge and roughly quantifiable. The 4.5 million whites have more than 250,000 swimming pools and 800,000 servants; the per capita white income may be as much as fifteen times higher than that of blacks; the white 15 percent of the population has reserved more than two thirds of the land for its own use (leaving the other one third to the blacks, the browns, and the animals in the game parks). There are various ways of demonstrating that this gap is narrowing (or widening) as a result (or in spite) of a general rise in the wages of urban black workers. But I never knew how to calibrate the gap between white fantasy and black reality, or white fantasy and black fantasy, or to justify my impression that these were widening all the time. Whites insist this is a matter of "culture" and "civilization," as if these were static and immutable, when it is evident that for both themselves and the huge majority whose existence they all but deny, values and standards are churning crazily.

At one extreme there is the decadence epitomized by a magazine called *Style* that emulates, or sometimes seems to parody, the slick life-style magazines that litter American coffee tables with bulletins from the front lines of gluttony and display. "Nouveau riche is better than no riche at all," *Style* assures it readers. What it promotes is less a style than a syndrome that reeks of narcissism, aggression, and greed, equating insatiability with power. Thus this blurb for an article entitled "Still Married and Feeling a Little Passé?": *You're the sophisticated product of a fast-moving, permissive era. You live in an achievement-oriented society where anything that stays static soon begins to seem stagnant. No wonder your steady old marriage seems a little out of synch.*

In the South African montage, it should be pasted next to the following item from the *Star*:

> FINED FOR
> LIVING WITH
> HER HUSBAND

> A domestic worker, Mathilda Chikuye, was this week fined 30 Rands (or 15 days in jail) for illegally harboring her husband in her room at 20 Talbrager Avenue, Craighall Park....

Mrs. Chikuye does not live in an "achievement-oriented society." The insatiability of the whites and the craving for security of the blacks are in fundamental tension. While the up-market white magazines counsel their readers on how to have affairs, the advice-to-the-lovelorn columns in magazines directed at urban blacks dwell constantly on problems of infidelity, unwanted pregnancy, and the difficulty of achieving a stable married life in the overcrowded conditions of the townships. The black fantasy, it seems, is of something like the drab middle-class reality that can't seem to satisfy the appalling white hunger for more. This could be spear-shield with a vengeance.

The problem of segregating fantasies as well as people confronted the authorities when they initiated a television service for blacks. The theoretical justification for apartheid is essentially Jungian: that each of South Africa's racial, ethnic, and linguistic groups has its own collective unconscious that must not be disturbed. TV threatened to make them mutually permeable, forcing the whites to live in McLuhan's "global village" with everyone else. The state broadcasting monopoly sought to tame the monster by decreeing that all programs "targeted" at blacks had to be exclusively in one of five African languages—Zulu, Xhosa, Tswana, Sotho, or Venda—with none of the mixing of dialects or flights into English and Afrikaans that is common in real African speech. Thus there can never be a program in English directed at blacks, though they have used English as their political lingua franca for decades; programs in which whites and blacks talk to each other, as if they inhabited the same country, are also likely to be ruled out unless the whites are dubbed.

Black appearances on the channel aimed at whites have to be carefully rationed so as not to disturb viewers in their dream of a white South Africa. But the broadcasting monopoly's authority is not powerful enough to keep black fingers from straying a quarter of an inch to the white button on their sets. One evening we took our college-age daughters to visit their former nanny, Dinah Dibakoane, who was still living in the area outside Pretoria where we had deposited her in 1966. Now it was no longer a collection of tiny metal shacks in the veld; also, it was no longer supposed to be South Africa. The township had grown and obliterated the veld, and most of it had been gerrymandered into Bophuthatswana. The racial planners who had seemed so weirdly out of touch with reality had achieved their vision, except for one thing. Dinah, who like most urban Africans was competent in at least four languages, was watching Afrikaans rather than Tswana TV.

And that wasn't the worst of it. What she was seeing on her black-and-white screen was an old American sitcom, dubbed into Afrikaans, about a basketball team at a high school where there was at least one black teacher. She could also see the mystery series *Quincy* in Afrikaans, and even when she switched to the black channels, there was a fair chance that she would end up watching dubbed American shows there as well, *The Jeffersons* in Zulu or *Spiderman* in Xhosa.

In Pretoria a nondescript office building attached to a shopping mall seemed to me to house the Afrikaner antipodes. The Parkade Building it is called. I visited it to chat with Hendrik Verwoerd, Jr., the son of the martyred prime minister, in a crowded little office on the fifth floor.

Upstairs, Dominee Verwoerd, an ordained minister in the Dutch Reformed Church and former missionary, wrestles with what he takes to be the central dilemma facing his people: their continued dependence on black labor, which will ultimately force them, he fears, to concede political rights to blacks and relinquish their hard-won nationhood. The younger Verwoerd's solution is a strictly logical extension of his father's formulations, even if it appears to represent a retreat. The whites must carve out their own "homeland," an area of South Africa that will conform to the original Verwoerdian ideal: Not only will no blacks reside there on a permanent basis, but black labor will be largely excluded. The dominee, who manifests all the kindliness that visitors attributed to Verwoerd *père*, hastens to add that blacks will always be welcome as tourists or guests. The white homeland would not want to be isolated in Africa, he says. However, there are a couple of conspicuous obstacles to the realization of his scheme, Verwoerd concedes. One is that most whites are unused to doing menial tasks for themselves; another that there is no habitable region of the country where whites are in the majority.

To overcome these obstacles, he has organized a movement called the Oranjewerkers (Society of Orange Workers), which hopes to exert leverage on the Afrikaner government similar to that exerted on the Israeli government by Gush Emunim when it started to establish Jewish settlements on the West Bank of the Jordan River. The Oranjewerkers are still dismissed as a joke, Verwoerd acknowledges, but they are forming property and construction companies to amass the capital and work habits their scheme will require. All they ask of the authorities at this stage is the right to set up local enterprises employing only whites. At a later stage the Oranjewerkers intend to demand that their "white growth points" be proclaimed "white labor preference areas" so that no nonwhites can be hired in preference to a white for an occupation. Instead of building apartheid from the top down, as his father tried to do, Verwoerd wants to build it from the ground up, or halfway up, for he is not in favor of dismantling white power at the top any sooner than necessary. His aim is to create something that could endure, something that has never existed in South Africa: a self-sufficient white economy. In 1797 a prominent Dutch burgher named Van Ryneveld expressed the fear that it was already too late. "A peasant who has always been accustomed to have his work done by slaves and has therefore done nothing but superintend it will not always be brought to perform every kind of rural labor," he wrote. But if latter-day Zionists could attempt to build a true Jewish state after two millennia, Verwoerd reasons, maybe it is not too late for the Afrikaners after only three and a half centuries.

Of the 2.8 million Afrikaners, who represent 60 percent of the whites but only 8 percent of the overall population, 1,200 had joined the Oranjewerkers in three years. Had they all dispensed with black labor? I ask. "Not everybody immediately," the dominee concedes with a shy smile that lights up his honest blue eyes, "but everybody in the long run. They are all committed to the ideal." True to their principles, the Oranjewerkers seek to make use of no black services. It is not their fault that black cleaning women are used to scrub the corridors of the Parkade Building, but at least when they moved in, Dominee Verwoerd tells me proudly, all the furniture was carried by whites. It is also a point of pride that no black messenger is employed to carry the society's mail to the post office. The proof is before my eyes: Envelopes are piled high on Verwoerd's desk and nearby counters, waiting for white volunteers to show up and dispatch them; the mail has obviously not moved for days.

CHAPTER THREE

Blanc de Noir

When I met Johannes van der Linde in 1965, he did not seem to have even a nodding acquaintance with contradiction and moral ambiguity. He was a major then in the army's ready reserve force who devoted the nonmilitary portion of his life to increasing the size of his dairy herd and his farm in the Orange Free State. A hospitable, candid, thoroughly likable man, he patiently explained his theory of labor relations, using the paradigm of a father and his children: how, for instance, he had built a schoolhouse for the boys of his "boys," his black laborers of all ages, not because any outside authority had required it but because he thought it only right. "The white man won't get the benefits of doing right by the native if his only motive is self-preservation," he said.

On Sundays the school was made available to itinerant black preachers from the mission branch of his own church, one of whom, he was astonished to hear, started preaching "communism." It was his faithful "boss boy," Ou ("Old") Sam, who had called this to his attention. "It's very good to have black people like that," Major van der Linde said. "You meet white people who don't have the same quality. Of course, every now and then Sam will get cheeky or something."

I could not refrain from asking what happened when one of the "boys" got "cheeky." The major replied: "It's very like the way you treat your own children. You don't want to be too tough, but if you're not firm, you won't have your farm long. I have to clout one every now and then in the stable." Major van der Linde had heard that Afrikaners were often misunderstood in the world at large. For the first time a note of wariness crept into his voice. "Do you really think they'll believe this in New York?" he asked.

The interest of outsiders mystified him. "There's a lot of talk about these natives in the world today," he commented in a voice that expressed wonder and curiosity rather than the resentment other Afrikaners would have vented. "I ask myself why. Is it something in this century? It wasn't always so."

Before Hendrik Verwoerd, Afrikaners never theorized much about the status of blacks or dreamed of a white nation. The blacks and browns were simply there, part of the natural order: to be used, when there was a use for them; treated fairly, so long as that did not compromise the status of the poorest whites; possibly "uplifted" by regular readings from the Bible but never thought of as social and political equals, not before the kingdom of heaven anyhow.

The worst thing that could befall a white was to sink to the level of blacks, to become a "white kaffir." The worst kind of black was one who was *te wit* ("too white"). Academics argue now that the main theme of the Afrikaner's long tribal saga has been not racism but ethnocentricism, a preoccupation with preserving a cultural identity that must often have seemed fragile. Such interpretations tend to turn on brittle definitions of terms and away from history. The sense of an ordained racial hierarchy came very early, when the whites collectively amounted to less than a speck at the tip of the huge, unknown landmass; if it wasn't there from the start, the idea of hierarchy was certainly there long before the Afrikaners knew themselves as Afrikaners, a people of Africa, rather than as Europeans. And inside that idea the urge to dominance was always incubating, waiting to sprout.

Jan van Riebeeck, the Dutchman who established the first white settlement at the Cape of Good Hope to provide fresh vegetables and meat to ships of the Dutch East India Company as they turned east to Java, set the tone when he described the local inhabitants as "a dull, rude, lazy and stinking nation." He was referring to the brown-skinned people who came to be known as Hottentots or Khoisan. Pastoralists or hunters, these aboriginals did not leap at the opportunity to indenture themselves to the newcomers, so the company hauled in slaves and convict labor from Madagascar, India, Ceylon, Malaya, and Java. Van Riebeeck, the founder of "white civilization" in Africa, was evidently not tempted to settle; after nine years he left his torpid little way station and headed for the East Indies. By then miscegenation between whites and slaves, also slaves and aboriginals, was starting to produce the people now called coloreds who still mainly speak Afrikaans, which evolved from Dutch. In the early days a dark skin was not invariably a bar to white society, but the identification of color with class gradually hardened. Nevertheless, it took nearly two centuries before the idea of nationhood started to dawn on the whites, who were always small in number, scarcely 20,000 by the end of the eighteenth century. Latter-day nationalists traced the idea somewhat romantically to the decisive event in Afrikaner history, the Great Trek, when some 5,000 whites put the Cape behind them and journeyed into the interior in ox wagons.

But the trekkers never imagined they were getting away from blacks and browns. If their departure was a bid for self-sufficiency, it was self-sufficiency of a peculiarly South African kind, for they were all but out-numbered by the servants and former slaves they took along. They knew, too, that there were more blacks where they were going than where they were coming from, that they might have to bargain or even fight for their place in Africa. What they were fleeing was British colonial authority, which pressed first for the abolition of slavery in the colonies and then for the easing of other forms of coercive labor. Just as there is a connection by lineage between today's antiapartheid movements and the antislavery lobby that existed then, the resentments of interference that propelled the trekkers have had a century and a half to shape themselves into a cultural reflex. Their most specific grievance was over the imported idea that whites and nonwhites could sometimes be placed on an equal footing before the English courts. They called this "equalization," but it was really only a highly qualified legal concept, nothing more than the germ of an idea of equality, simply holding that there was an external authority that could, under certain circumstances, regulate the relations between master and servant. Even this, in their rough-and-ready view, was the antithesis of "justice" in the circumstances of Africa. It was a radical idea that, as one matriarch expressed it, obviously was "in conflict with the laws of God and the natural divisions of descent and faith."

Later, when they fought their two wars with the British to preserve their frontier republics, the Afrikaners relied on blacks to drive their wagons, tend their horses, dig their trenches, and scout enemy positions. They thought it immoral, however, for the British to put guns in black hands. Guns could make blacks a factor in political disputes, which could damage "the cause of civilization in Africa," said Jan Christiaan Smuts. In all this there was a consistent view of race relations that was succinctly put a century after the Great Trek by one of the founding spirits of Afrikaner nationalism, General J. B. M. Hertzog: "Whatever the rights of the native may be, they have no right to call on us to do anything that might jeopardize our supremacy."

Thus, at the heart of the struggle by the Afrikaners for their cherished "identity," there lurks an obvious and huge contradiction that has never been resolved: The freedom they sought for themselves from externally imposed laws meant, of necessity, the freedom to impose their laws on others. They even came to see it as a duty, one that defined their role, so the Afrikaners who fled British law took on the Mosaic mantle and pictured themselves as lawgivers. In fact, in a country that is 85 percent non-white, "white self-determination" is impossible without supremacy. And so a people who are widely credited with having fought Africa's first anticolonial struggles, who are native to the land and not colonists in any normal sense, have come to establish one of the world's most retrogressive colonial systems.

Earnest and sophisticated Afrikaners, of whom there are many, realize that it is necessary to avoid using or even thinking provocative words such as "supremacy," which have a tendency to backfire. But it is also necessary, they believe, to keep control of the country. For many white South Africans, control seems to be almost a physical sensation, habitually expressed in images of grip and stress. "You can't force them down all the time," an Afrikaner teacher in an industrial town called Benoni told me, explaining why he was supporting constitutional changes that would give browns, but not blacks, a token role in national government for the first time. The extremist opposition to this so-called reform adopted a slogan that was not just tactile but prehensile. "Don't let go," it urged. The raw reality of white power can be veiled from whites, but it cannot be hidden from blacks. There is nothing coy about the plainclothes white security cops who cruise around the major black townships in big Fords and Datsuns. Guns are usually conspicuous when these officers are outside their cars.

Elsewhere white power sometimes hides behind a black façade. A handful of blacks with doctorates in education work for the Ministry of Education and Training (alias Bantu Education), but they never are assigned to the headquarters in Pretoria. If blacks could have a hand in shaping the curriculum their children are reared on, in shaping their view of history, society, and Africa, in addressing the fundamental questions of citizenship and equality, then "white self-determination" would be on its way to extinction. Instead, "white self-determination" seeks to determine in an authoritarian manner what blacks may learn. Significantly, books by African authors such as the Nigerian novelist Chinua Achebe that are occasionally approved for white schools—presumably because they satirize black politics—are never used in black schools, where *Silas Marner*, that all-purpose universal set text, still is assigned. Serious writing by black South Africans is even less welcome.

There is no such thing, either, as a black official at the headquarters of the Ministry of Cooperation and Development. It would more accurately be known as the Ministry of Control, for that is its function in relation to black lives. Formerly called the Ministry of Plural Relations—and before that Bantu Affairs, and before that Native Affairs—it seems to require a new name every five or six years to sanitize and mask its real role, which is to regulate the movement of blacks and rationalize the pattern of black habitation in South Africa. It is this vast warren of white racial ideologues, constantly fine-tuning the huge corpus of apartheid law, that is responsible for telling millions of blacks whether, where, and when they can live with their families.

At this ministry's headquarters in Pretoria, black menials had a sign-in book where they were expected to put their X's next to their Christian names—Absalom, Samson, and John were the first three—in accord with the South African tradition that whites cannot be bothered to learn African names. At the Port Natal Administration Board, an arm of this bureaucracy that administers blacks who want to get a foothold in employment in Durban, I spied an organization chart for what was clearly labeled "The White Establishment" of one of its bureaus: The top 361 boxes all were color coded on a racial basis and plainly reserved for whites, down to the level of assistant typist; underneath were 168 boxes for black employees. As both graphics and social fact, the chart represented a white lid clamped on a black mass.

Again "white self-determination." How do the white elite groups express the need to exclude blacks when they are speaking among themselves? Do they continue to rely on euphemisms, or do they say, "Of course, we can't have any blacks"? At what point do they acknowledge that their aim is to keep power in white hands? Do they ever admit that they are preparing for an unambiguous racial struggle?

At times I would go around and around asking myself such questions. At times the answers seemed all too obvious. There was the morning in an amphitheater adjacent to the Voortrekker Monument, a lugubrious granite temple placed on a hilltop outside Pretoria on an angle that was precisely calculated so that every year, at noon on December 16, the Day of the Covenant, a ray of light would shine through the dome and fall on the inscription on a cenotaph: the symbolic resting place of Piet Retief, a trekker leader who became Afrikanerdom's first martyr when he was treacherously slain on the command of Dingane, a Zulu king. The temple, opened to the public on a segregated basis in 1949, was thematically conceived to portray the epic struggle between "civilization" and "barbarism." On a marble frieze inside its Hall of Heroes, civilization is always depicted as white, barbarism as black. But the gulf is not shown to be absolutely unbridgeable: Though attired in only a cape and a codpiece, a chief of the Barolong tribe is portrayed in honorable negotiations with one of the white chiefs by the sculptors, who, we are told, had a mandate to model their style on Verrocchio and Donatello and, simultaneously, "to guard against any un-Afrikaans elements creeping into the work." The Barolong chief, according to an early, unsanitized edition of the official guide to the monument, was exceptional. For the most part, "the Bantu was not amenable to reason. He respected one thing only and that was force."

And it was force that was now on display in the amphitheater, white force. The occasion was a military parade in honor of Prime Minister Botha, who had stepped down as defense minister after fourteen years. The Pretoria skyline shimmered in the distance with more monuments, pompous structures hastily erected up in the apartheid era by the descendants of the trekkers in tribute to their own power. There stood fortresslike government ministries turned inward on themselves in great slabs and hunks, as descriptive, in their own terms, of a mental outlook as the Stalinist monstrosities of Eastern Europe. Perhaps 2 or even 3 percent of the 10,000 or so troops who marched through the amphitheater had brown or black faces. But its location at the national shrine made this unmistakably an Afrikaner consecration. The New Testament selection read out by a chaplain resounded to the spirit of the surviving trekkers who had their revenge against Dingane at a site in Zululand that thereafter retained the sanguinary name Blood River. From Paul's Letter to the Ephesians he read: *Put on all the armor that God gives you that you may stand up against the devil's evil tricks. For we are not fighting against human beings but against the wicked spiritual forces in the heavenly world, the rulers, authorities, and cosmic powers of this dark age. So put on God's armor now!*

Mirage jets streaked low over the amphitheater, trailing stripes of colored vapor, then over the Palace of Justice in the center of Pretoria. About an hour later there, I watched as a white judge condemned three members of the underground African National Congress to the gallows for the parts they played in an attack on a rural police station where one black sergeant was slightly wounded.

In the courtroom an Afrikaner professor stood next to the dock with a stricken look as the judge swept from the bench in his red robes and the blacks in the public galleries defiantly thrust their fists in the air and joined the condemned men in singing *"Nkosi Sikelel' i-Afrika"* ("God Bless Africa"), a Methodist hymn that has long served as the black anthem. To Frans Maritz, a sociologist who had testified on behalf of the young blacks when the time had come to plead for mercy in sentencing, the clash of nationalisms seemed to have destroyed the middle ground where he had tried to take a reasoned stand. Just before the sentencing Professor Maritz had assured me that the three would be spared, that the court would have to take account of his testimony, based on interviews with them in their cells, that they were essentially passive young men who had been caught up in the wave of fury and despair that engulfed urban black communities at the time of the student protests of 1976 and 1977, when nearly 600 blacks lost their lives in confrontations with the police. In his view, they were victims of a sociological accident, neither hardened "terrorists" nor committed "freedom fighters."

Shortly after the trial, the professor's office at the University of South Africa was bombed by white extremists who thought he had committed racial treason by testifying for blacks. But by the time I visited him several months later, his sense of vulnerability had receded. The three young men had not yet been spared—-their sentences were later commuted as a result of international pressure, rather than the sociologist's arguments—but he had already recovered his optimism and sense of being in the mainstream. Now he could talk comfortably about how far the Afrikaners had come in their attitudes. In his view, they were pragmatically looking for solutions, inhibited only by their lamentable ignorance of the facts of the black man's situation in their country.

Blacks weren't really interested in freedom "and all that sort of thing," the professor said, but in economic advancement; if whites could help them gain that much, then violent pressures for changes in the legal structure might be deferred. The issue thus became how whites could overcome the passivity of blacks, which was inhibiting their advance. Professor Maritz was obviously a man of decency; of courage, too, considering his willingness to testify on behalf of three young "terrorists." He did not deserve to be glibly judged. But like many Afrikaner intellectuals of apparent goodwill, he seemed unable to hear how remote and patronizing he sounded when he talked about blacks. He could not seriously consider the possibility that black adaptation to free-market economics was strictly regulated in a system that placed severe legal restraints on the most ordinary forms of initiative such as the search for a job, setting up of a business, or purchase of property; or that, from a black perspective, the problem was the cultural attitudes of whites, which took for granted the proposition that black advance was possible only under white tutelage.

It is a favorite parlor game among Afrikaner elites, this search for some explanation of the black man's backwardness and supposed lack of initiative. In speculating about blacks, they reach for stereotypes that several generations of English writers and officials used, including some that were used to explain the quirky survival of Africa's white tribe.

As early as 1835 a British journal found the Dutch inhabitants of the Cape to be notable only for their cunning. "No people can trick or lie with more apparent sincerity," it said. In 1842 an English newspaper in the Cape commented on "the profound and rayless ignorance" of the Boers on the frontier. Lord Kitchener, the last British commander in that conflict, described them as "uncivilized Afrikander savages with a thin white veneer." Lord Randolph Churchill, shortly before he was unhinged by syphilis, portrayed the Afrikaner farmer as the personification of "useless idleness." His portrait of the Boer established a benchmark for sheer bigotry that no Afrikaner has surpassed:

> It may be asserted, generally with truth, that he never plants a tree, never digs a well, never makes a road, never grows a blade of corn. Rough and ready cultivation of the soil for mealies by the natives he to some extent permits, but agriculture and the agriculturalist he holds alike in great contempt. He passes his days doing absolutely nothing beyond smoking and drinking coffee. He is perfectly uneducated.... His simple ignorance is unfathomable, and this in stolid composure he shares with his wife, his sons, his daughters, being proud that his children should grow up as ignorant, as uncultivated, as hopelessly unprogressive as himself.

Few Afrikaners hear these echoes when they speak about blacks. The practice among them of intellectualizing about the black man as a racial type may have been initiated by Jan Smuts, the Boer War hero who came to be viewed as a turncoat by many in his tribe as a result of his later Anglophilia. It is striking that Smuts saved his weightiest theorizing about the black man and his destiny for elite audiences in Britain rather than Afrikaner audiences. What he had to say was seldom raw enough for them. "The negro and the negroid Bantu form a distinct human type," he said at Oxford in 1929. "It has largely remained a child type, with a child psychology and outlook." Of course, Smuts was eager to express his affection for blacks as a politician who wanted to be known as a *ware* ("true") Afrikaner would not have done in those days, or even now. "A child-like human," he told his English audience, "cannot be a bad human, for are we not in spiritual matters bidden to be like unto children?"

Gradually, as they became accustomed to power, other Afrikaners began to feel a need to be recognized as magnanimous and Christian in their attitude toward blacks. "As the parents of the black people of South Africa," the white minister of cooperation and development found it possible to tell a black assembly in one of the most wretched homelands, "we are aware of these peoples' aspirations and ideals and would like to help our children make their own way as adults."

It may be an advance that black backwardness can now be viewed as a problem, rather than predestination, but most white theorizing on the subject lacks integrity, for it departs from the self-regarding assumption that it is a problem only whites can solve. In other words, it departs, travels in a little circle, and returns to its premise. Verwoerd gave the Afrikaner a picture of his place in the world similar to the diagram of the heavens that the ancient astronomer Ptolemy provided: He was at the center. Present-day theorists bear comparison to the sixteenth-century astronomer Tycho Brahe, who recognized that the prevailing movements of the planets did not sustain the theory that they all were revolving around Earth and then, instead of questioning the central premise, recharted the movements. With a mighty expenditure of energy and ingenuity he thus managed to preserve the theory for a few decades by imagining that the paths of the planets followed a series of detours and curlicues known as epicycles. South Africa's new theorists even speak in terms of a "constellation" made up of the "homelands" and other black satrapies revolving in little epicycles around a white center of power. The Copernican view that it is all too complicated to be real, that sooner or later blacks will have to be at the center, remains heresy.

In search of concepts and jargon they can use to make their world make sense, the Ptolemaists regularly commit a kind of intellectual rape of the literature and journals of Western, mainly American, social science and economics.

There is a giddy enthusiasm, even innocence, about the strenuous efforts Afrikaner pedagogues make to translate old racial doctrines into cur-

rent academic jargon. They declare with patent sincerity that they are not
peddling apartheid. Far from it; they are only paying prudent heed to
findings in the *Journal of Negro Education* or a study done for the U.S.
Civil Rights Commission. A former rector of Pretoria University, C. H.
Rautenbach, cites the Reverend Jesse Jackson as his authority for the argument that school integration is an "antiquated concept." Daniel J. van
den Bergh, author of "A Pedagogical Study of the Black Man's Mathematical Ability," assured me that "very in-depth research" had clearly
demonstrated the need for separate technical education for blacks. For instance, he said, data collected by the Human Sciences Research Council in
Pretoria pointed to the conclusion that blacks and whites learn at different
optimal temperatures. Blacks, it appeared, needed classrooms that were
several degrees warmer.

There were many more reasons: Blacks come from a culture that is static
rather than dynamic; they are strongly oriented to group rather than individual effort; they are not given to detachment or objective thought; they
have a different concept of time. Eagerly, his eyes glowing with the excitement of his discoveries, Dr. van den Bergh expounded some of the
pedagogic consequences of these principles, assuring me that the "problem of Africa" was on its way to being solved.

The conversation was taking place in a $100 million technicon, estab-
lished to train blacks in civil and mechanical engineering, analytic chemistry, public health, and various other technical fields; a separate course,
including instruction in "speech and deportment," prepares black women
to function as secretaries. It is the Sun City of Bantu Education; you could
mistake it for a campus of the University of California—all exposed brick,
skylights, and hanging plants—unless you allowed your gaze to wander
beyond its perimeters to the squalid Pretoria township in which it is situated. In the harsh light of day, the technicon can then be seen as a monument to the conviction that a common society is unthinkable; not only
for whites but for blacks. This township is called Soshanguve, which is not
an African word but an acronym fashioned by white administrators for the
various black ethnic groups (*So*tho, *Sha*ngaan, *Ngu*ni, *Ve*nda) that are officially deemed to be foreign to an adjacent, virtually indistinguishable
township in the supposedly sovereign and independent Tswana homeland,
half a mile away. Whether Tswanas and Vendas can learn at the same temperature is never explained. Apartheid is profligate—only a country with
half the world's production of gold could afford to quadruplicate bureau-
cracies and facilities on racial lines—but the ideal of a separate technicon
for each black ethnic group is too expensive even for South Africa.

Education for blacks should go from the concrete to the abstract, so the
students are shown how to make things before they are taught the theory
behind them. They are encouraged to work in groups and even take tests
in groups, rather than pitted against one another. They may talk all they

want in class so long as they are talking about the subject. The school is geared for success; they have the time they need to learn. I comment that roughly such an approach was called progressive education in America about half a century ago. Is there any reason, I ask, why it wouldn't also be good for South African whites? It is a question that Dr. van den Bergh has apparently never considered. "There is no such thing as black education and white education," he replies, crisply nullifying everything he has been saying for an hour. "There is only good education."

But why then a black technicon in a place called Sotho-Shangaan-Nguni-Venda that must be conceived to be in another galaxy rather than where it really is, on the outskirts of Pretoria, scarcely fifteen miles from the prime minister's office? A small but important clue can be found in the elaborate arrangements that have been made to control political expression by the students. To be admitted to the technicon, I am told, a student has to be sponsored by a corporation. "If there is any disciplinary problem," an official says, "all we have to do is lift the phone." South Africa needs blacks with technical skills. But blacks with political aspirations as well as technical skills are emphatically not needed. That is the message.

In private conversation the minister of national education once expressed himself in simple terms for my benefit. Afrikaners were not racists, he said. They were simply revolted by the way some blacks sneeze and spit in public. When black manners improved, so would the willingness of whites to seek political accommodation. This was offered as a clinical judgment on both communities and as realistic political analysis. But I sensed that it reflected a mean little anxiety and primness in the minister as well, a physical tension left over from the days when the aim of Afrikaner politics was to keep poor whites from sinking to the level of even poorer blacks. "Togetherness" remains a frightening idea.

It is easy to lampoon official double-talk, but hidden here and there in the acres of verbiage are kernels of real meaning. Consider the minister of constitutional development. On home ground he once explained in a brief spasm of candor why there could be no place in the parliamentary structure for blacks even on the segregated basis of the new constitution, which gives coloreds and Indians a subordinate role in the national government. Blacks would outnumber whites, coloreds, and Indians, he said, by a ratio of 36:9:5:2; if only those classified as urban blacks were counted, the ratio would still be 16:9:5:2. "And what would remain of the principle of maintaining civilized standards then?" he asked. On another occasion he went so far as to explain how civilized standards have to be maintained. "It is in the long-term interests of South Africa," he said, "that the Afrikaner should always have the privilege of the leadership role." Not for just a day, not for just a year, but *always*.

That is the only premise on which orthodoxy is still demanded. An Afrikaner can go surprisingly far these days without reading himself out of the establishment. He can theorize on issues such as land reform or income distribution; he can draw constitutional models that look like chandeliers or DNA molecules; he can take his crayon to the map and find new borders for partition. He can even theorize about the likelihood of negotiation one day with the banned black movements. Those are all legitimate gambits in the intellectual game. What he cannot do is question the Afrikaner's "leadership role." He cannot appeal to values such as justice and equality. Only then does he become a renegade. It was "politically quite immoral" to appeal to justice and the "fairness factor," the newspaper *Die Transvaaler* retorted without any apologies or the smallest trace of irony, because that could only mean "surrender to black power." Justice might demand that the door be opened to black power, the newspaper was saying, but black power would be inherently evil. Therefore, justice was immoral.

Before long I came to find conversations with most middle-of-the-road, so-called enlightened Afrikaner thinkers anesthetizing. They seemed to last for hours and to float free above the land, beyond all gravitational pulls except those of career and influence. Most of all, I hated the sound of my own voice in these encounters, so calm, so neutral, so reasoned. I was not pretending to be detached as a journalistic stance. I really was.

Drifting along with the conversational current, I would reflect that these were not evil men, that they were victims, too, that the best of them were shackled to the obsession with power. Every now and then I would bump against a comment that would jar me out of my reverie. At Potchefstroom a political scientist described a day trip he had recently taken to Soweto with a fifty-year-old colleague who was setting foot in a black township for the first time. "I hope I see you tonight," the man said to his wife, nervously joking as he kissed her good-bye. My host chuckled condescendingly. He went on these excursions to Soweto twice a year as a pedagogic exercise. "We drink tea with them," he boasted. "No problem." He was saying, I realized, that the whites managed to drink from cups that blacks must have used, as they would never knowingly have done before.

We were sitting in a living room that was like many Afrikaner living rooms in which I had been entertained. An obvious thought that had eluded me before now registered. For a people obsessed with their cultural identity, Afrikaners have surprisingly few cultural artifacts they can call their own. Only the rich can now afford authentic pieces of Cape Dutch furniture, the best of which were bought up long ago by English-speaking businessmen and foreigners. Occasionally there is an old rifle of Boer War vintage, the head of a kudu, a family Bible, or a sentimental landscape of the Drakensberg Mountains. More often the Afrikaner shows himself to be a cultural hybrid, displaying cheap souvenirs from Europe and Africa;

porcelain figurines and pictures of windmills beside carvings of grizzled Africans or their daughters. My host's son walked through the room in army fatigues. Now and then we could hear the echoes from the artillery range on a nearby army base. Only about 10 percent of his students, the professor was saying, had been into the black townships nearest their homes. It was impossible to discuss contemporary issues without showing them a bit of their country. That was why he took these field trips to Soweto. It wasn't for his own benefit.

"What do I need to go to Soweto twice a year for?" he asked.

A full eighteen years had passed before I paid my second visit to the Van der Linde farm in the Free State. Johannes van der Linde was now a colonel, and—while he indicated that he harbored no grudge over the way he had been portrayed in print after my first visit—he was no longer naïve about what was believed in New York. In fact, he had just returned from New York, where he had stopped after a tour of the American Farm Belt, on which he was one of a group of South African farmers who had been guests of the Allis-Chalmers Corporation, the makers of the huge tractor that stood in a shed next to his Mercedes. The passage of years had turned his hair gray and thickened his gut. With the addition of more land, better cattle, and more black laborers, it had transformed him into an agri-businessman, and it had enriched his sense of humor. Broadly speaking, it had thus done for him everything it had done for Afrikanerdom as a whole.

As we rode out to inspect some nutritious rye grass on which he had managed to keep his dairy herd fat during the century's worst drought, he entertained me with tales of his American tour: the night he spent drinking in Milwaukee with a black accountant who asked whether blacks had rights in South Africa ("No," he said he replied, "but we're working on it"); the farmer from the Transvaal who somehow got separated from $1,500 at a bar called the Mardi Gras off Times Square in Manhattan; the Cabinet minister's son-in-law who exploded with loathing of American decadence in order, or so it seemed, to cover the tension and guilt he felt after an afternoon at a pornographic movie house. Colonel van der Linde himself had not felt undermined by New York but had liked it for good reasons: the mixture of people, the smart way they dressed, the verve, the pace of life.

Old Sam had died and been buried on the farm while the colonel was on active duty with his tank corps in Namibia. In 1965, he told me, he had four families that had been on his farm for more than twenty years and six that had been there for more than ten. Now there were twenty-five families in all, about 120 individuals, but fewer old hands. The old feudal relationship was less attractive to blacks. He gestured to the east to show me a cause of their increased mobility. There, like an extrusion of living substance, a dense human settlement could be seen extending over the nearest hillside. It hadn't been there eighteen years ago, or even five years ago, but it was already the biggest black settlement in the Orange Free State, with a population approaching a quarter of a million.

It had been named *Onverwacht*, which means "unexpected" in Afrikaans. Colonel van der Linde, at least, hadn't expected it, but it was now less than two miles, at its nearest point, from his land, occupying roughly the same amount of space he did. In between was a large dam, functioning as a kind of moat, and on that dam this Saturday morning young whites were windsurfing and speedboating in a segregated recreation area that was fenced off from the black settlement. No lens could quite capture the picture, but it was the image of South Africa: in the foreground, the rich white farm; at a middle distance, the water sports, also for whites; in the background, but clearly visible across the veld, the overcrowded black settlement in all its squalor. As one of the top officers in the reserve force in the Free State, my host must have been familiar with the contingency plans the military and police would have drawn up to keep Onverwacht within its designated perimeters; he did not appear to be worried. But he realized he would now have to be competitive in wages and living conditions to keep his laborers. There is a regulation that bars black farm workers from urban employment unless they can produce written approval by the white farmers' union in their area, but Colonel van der Linde was not going to rely on that. Already he had two brick houses built for his most valuable laborers, replacing the traditional mud shanties in which they had always been left to house themselves. It was just the start, he said.

The living conditions in his own house had changed more conspicuously than those of his workers. I dimly recalled being struck by the sparse furnishings of the brick farmhouse on that first visit, especially by the presence of a new refrigerator in the dining room as if it were a luxury to be shown off. Now there was a color TV, a videocassette recorder, an elaborate stereo system, an electric organ, and a liquor cabinet. The Van der Lindes had skipped several generations in taste. Their living room was smartly furnished with a sofa and matching chairs in brown velvet. On the walls, there were ceramic plates from Greece. But as her husband poured Boschendal blanc de noir, Mrs. van der Linde confided that she had not liked Greece. "It's so poor," she said. "So dirty." Later I asked whether she had ever been to the settlement next door. She grimaced and said no.

The colonel then told a story on himself, how he had lost his temper after being stopped by a black traffic cop for entering a black township without a permit. But as he told it, its point seemed to undergo a subtle change. Originally, I guessed, it had been a yarn about the "cheekiness" of a black officer and the way embarrassed white officials were then made to jump through hoops to placate an influential farmer. In defiance of the black officer's orders to halt, the colonel had roared away and then phoned "someone very high up," who assured him that blacks were not supposed to give summonses to whites, that they were expected to call a white officer if they thought there was a problem. But now, as he reached that point in his narrative, the colonel seemed a little uncertain about where to put his comic emphasis. Maybe he was thinking about how it would sound in New York. A small critical voice seemed to be warning him to tread carefully. Improvising a new punch line and laughing at himself, he conceded that he had probably been in the wrong. "The real fight," he said with unimpaired good humor, "is the one you have with yourself."

He sounded just as flexible when he reflected on the history of his people. "You can argue about history, whether the Great Trek was really necessary, or the Anglo-Boer War, or whether we were wrong in 1948, when we brought in apartheid," he said. "But you can't change it. That's reality. We must do what's right now." On its face it seemed a startling reflection for a farmer in the Free State, where blacks had never been permitted to own land since white authority was first established. But as I thought about it, it became less startling. It wasn't really so different from what he had said in 1965, that "the white man won't get the benefits of doing right by the native if his only motive is self-preservation." Basically it was a case of if at first you don't succeed: He had been doing right by his lights for a generation and he had certainly reaped the benefits, and what was new on the horizon was Onverwacht.

By road the entrance to the settlement was twenty-five miles from the Van der Linde homestead; in a straight line it was probably about eight. Since my previous visit to Onverwacht, the part that could be seen from the highway had received a Potemkinesque face-lift. There were bright new hoardings, metal sheds for what was said to be an industrial park, and rows of model houses. There was also a paved road with tall curved lighting fixtures lining it, but the paving and lights stopped abruptly almost as soon as the road wound out of sight from the highway. The biggest expanse of population was about six miles in, where there were rows on rows of little metal latrines awaiting the next influx. In the older sections, those that had been there for two or three years, cinder-block houses of a reasonable standard were regularly interspersed among the metal hovels and shanties; in the newer sections it was shanties all the way. It could have been a refugee camp in Pakistan, Honduras, Eritrea, or anywhere poor and "third world," a term white South Africans have come to use routinely to describe the black areas of their country. As a metaphor it beats "homelands" because it says they are not only in another country but in another world. South Africa can even be pictured as a "microcosm" of the whole North-South dichotomy, an image that provides several kinds of psychic balm: The whites can identify themselves then with the first world, which they tend to think of in racial terms; they can find support for the view that their country's problems are not susceptible to short-term resolution or even assert, as a Cabinet minister once did, that South Africa (meaning the mythical white country) was forking up more aid to the third world (meaning the majority of its people) than any other developed country.

It is only an argument meant to stifle other arguments, a debating point rather than an insight, but it can sound a little plausible until you drive into an Onverwacht. Many third world countries have irresponsible oligarchies that have as little conscience about their landless and unemployed as South Africa's white elites; sometimes, in truth, much less. But none of them, while preaching reform, creates refugee camps in the midst of prosperity as a matter of state policy. The people in the shanties I was passing were there not because they were poor but because they were black; no amount of money could legally purchase for them the right to move the thirty-five miles into Bloemfontein or a piece of land to till nearer at hand. I drove on until I could look back across the dam to the Van der Linde farm, where I had been sipping blanc de noir an hour before. It was mid-afternoon, but the light was failing rapidly as in an eclipse, and I could barely make it out. When I turned around, I saw that the northern sky had taken on a deep and ominous terra-cotta color. The drought had made the Free State vulnerable to dust storms, and valuable topsoil was now swirling up hundreds of yards into the sky in great, gritty clouds that were gusting toward Onverwacht and the Van der Linde farm without distinction.

A young couple I had seen walking hand in hand as I drove into the settlement were huddling against each other and walking backward into the wind as I drove out. Before I reached the highway, I had to turn on my headlights. I found myself thinking that the dust storm was exactly what the producer of a second-rate TV documentary might have seized on for his fade-out on such a day. But I had grown mistrustful of all South African metaphors. The thought of an inevitable catastrophe was frightening, but even more frightening was the thought that it could be indefinitely deferred, that the whites would go on windsurfing and trying to do right, the blacks would go on moving into squalid encampments, and the dust storms would just be dust storms.

CHAPTER FOUR

Rule of Law

It's time to talk law. Where other regimes have no difficulty tyrannizing their citizens under the cloak of constitutions guaranteeing universal human rights, South Africa's white rulers have been unusually conscientious about securing statutory authority for their abuses. When a right, even a birthright, such as citizenship, is to be annulled, it is always done with a law. Most whites are uncomprehending of the argument that law is brought into disrepute when it is used to destroy basic freedoms. Law is law. It's the principle of order and therefore civilization. Excessive liberty is what threatens civilization; law is what preserves it. The opposing view that law might preserve liberty is held to be a contradiction; in Africa, a promise of surrender. On this basis it has been possible to build apartheid as a comprehensive system of racial dominance. I thought I would get the feel of the basic statutes by holding them in my hands like an eggplant or a melon. Some laws, especially those reserving the best industrial jobs for whites, had been repealed. I wanted to feel, literally to weigh, what remained.

What remained weighed slightly more than ten pounds when I stepped on a scale with an up-to-date volume of all the laws in South Africa that relate specifically to blacks—laws, that is, that can normally be broken only by blacks (or by persons of other racial groups only when they interfere with the state's master plan for blacks). The figure of ten pounds had to be halved because the volume of 4,500 pages contained both the Afrikaans and English versions of sixty-four basic statutes that regulate the lives of blacks. These then amounted to about 2,250 closely printed pages, weighing about five pounds. But the statutes had given rise to some 2,000 regulations, adding two or three pounds. These, in turn, would have given rise to hundreds or maybe thousands of official circulars that were treated as law by the officials who regulate blacks. And there were the laws, regulations, and circulars relating to the administration of the Group Areas Act, the basic statute guaranteeing absolute residential segregation. In all, the basic corpus of South African racial law ran to more than 3,000 pages, and when all the regulations and circulars were added in, its dead weight was bound to be well over ten pounds.

Of course, the impact of apartheid cannot be measured in pounds. I could measure it only by trying to witness the system in operation, especially in the mazelike structure of courts and official bureaus it has established to channel black laborers in and out of areas of economic opportunity while minimizing their chances of establishing permanent residence with their families. If this structure were suddenly dismantled, there would still be wealthy suburbs, huge ranches, black townships, squalid rural areas, and migrant workers by the hundreds of thousands. But it would then be possible to think of the society as a whole and talk rationally about its needs. Apartheid ensures that the language for such a discussion hardly exists.

If South Africa were viewed as one country, it might be possible to recognize a glaring fact about its social geography: the existence of an almost continuous scimitar-shaped belt of black rural poverty, stretching for more than 1,000 miles from the northeastern Transvaal through the Swazi and

Zulu tribal areas and down into the two "homelands" for Xhosa-speaking blacks in the eastern Cape, a belt that is inhabited by about 7 million people, amounting to nearly 30 percent of the black population. Instead, in the layered, compartmentalized consciousness of apartheid, these blacks are dispersed in Venda, Gazankulu, Lebowa, KwaZulu, Transkei, and Ciskei: foreign places, another galaxy.

In apartheid's terms, it is revolutionary or at least eccentric to think of this band of poverty as South Africa's problem. It is the ultimate divide-and-rule strategy, dividing the land into racially designated areas and bogus homelands and the population into distinct racial castes and subcastes of which I can count at least eight: the whites, who are free to do anything except move into an area designated as nonwhite; the coloreds and Indians, who can move freely in the country but are barred from owning land in more than 95 percent of it; and the blacks, who are subdivided by law into six distinct impermeable or semipermeable categories.

Urban blacks come in two subcastes: the "insiders" and the "commuters." The insiders are conceded to have what amounts to a right of permanent residence in South Africa. The circumstances of the urban commuters appear to be exactly the same, except that the townships in which they reside are now deemed to fall within the boundaries of some homeland. Although they may be only a short bus ride from Pretoria, Durban, or East London, they are regarded by South African law as foreign or on their way to becoming foreign. But such commuters can still get "special" licenses of limited duration making them "authorized work seekers" in an urban area.

This means they are still far better off than a second group of commuters who must be regarded as a separate subcaste because they commute to the industrial centers from essentially rural homelands. These rural commuters are on a distinctly lower level of the hierarchy, but they are the most privileged of the four distinguishable subcastes of rural blacks. The rural commuters generally travel long distances to work, live in officially designated "closer settlements" without running water or electricity, and get their jobs through the state's network of labor bureaus. They generally work on annual contracts like migrant laborers, but at least they come home to their families at nights and on weekends.

The migrants, the next subcaste, live in urban townships or on the mines and sugar plantations in barrackslike single-sex hostels, usually for eleven months of every year.

Blacks who live in the white rural areas as farm laborers make up the next subcaste; by tradition they receive more of their compensation in kind—sacks of mealie (corn) meal usually—than in cash, but wages are gradually coming into vogue. And finally, there are the homeland blacks, who live their whole lives in the black rural areas. Overall, the former tribal reserves provide employment for fewer than 20 percent of the young blacks reared within their borders. The rest of the homeland blacks are mainly dependent on the wages of migrants, or scratch out a meager existence as subsistence cultivators on exhausted soil, or are unemployed and wholly destitute. The life-threatening protein deficiency known as kwashiorkor and the starvation condition known as marasmus are endemic among children in this group. In some black rural areas scarcely 50 percent of the children who are alive at birth survive past the age of five.

A lopsided social structure is not peculiar to South Africa. What is peculiar is the fact that it is legally mandated and rigorously imposed on the basis of race. It is impossible to change caste without an official appeals board ruling that you are a different color from what you were originally certified to be. These miraculous transformations are tabulated and announced on an annual basis. In my first year back in South Africa, 558 coloreds became whites, 15 whites became coloreds, 8 Chinese became whites, 7 whites became Chinese, 40 Indians became coloreds, 20 coloreds became Indians, 79 Africans became coloreds, and 8 coloreds became Africans. The spirit of this grotesque self-parody, which results from the deliberations of an official body known as the Race Classification Board, is obviously closer to Grand Guignol than the Nuremberg Laws; in other words, it's sadistic farce. "Look, man, it's all a game, it's all a big joke," I was assured once by a Cape Town colored who had managed to get himself reclassified as a white, a transformation sometimes described in Afrikaans by the term *verblankingsproses* ("whitening process").

The legal definitions of racial caste are vague, overlapping, and sometimes contradictory. A white is "any person who in appearance obviously is or who is generally accepted as a white person, other than a person who, although in appearance obviously a white person, is generally accepted as a colored person." In other words, a rose is a rose is maybe not a rose. "A colored person," this same statute holds, is "any person who is not a member of the white group or of the black group." (Unless, of course, he is an Indian, who may be the same color but is legally set apart on the basis of ethnicity, most of the time, anyhow.) But a colored can also be any woman "to whichever race, class or tribe she may belong" who marries a colored man, or a white man who marries a colored woman.

Mixed marriages have been illegal throughout the apartheid era—as they were, lest we forget, in a majority of American states within living memory. Mixed marriages between browns and blacks remained legal. It was only the white race that had to be preserved. Carel Boshoff, a theology professor at Pretoria University and son-in-law of Hendrik Verwoerd, informed me as if it were a matter of incontrovertible fact that a group could be diluted by 6 or 7 percent and still maintain its "identity." In fact, Afrikaner researchers in this esoteric field have concluded that 6.9 percent is the probable proportion of "colored blood" in their veins. Racism, it then may be deduced, is no more than 93.1 percent of their doctrine.

● ● ●

Viewed even on its own terms, South African racial law is not a body of law but a tangle of legalisms designed to maximize the power of official-dom and minimize the defenses of the individual. Thus blacks are either "qualified" or "disqualified" for residence in "prescribed" urban areas. Even if they are "qualified," they must have "authorized accommodation" in which only their "bona fide dependents" are eligible to live. Officials qualify, disqualify, authorize, and prescribe, and ultimately decide what all these terms mean.

The most privileged blacks have a limited, conditional immunity to arbitrary actions that all other blacks must endure. Even then, they can be removed if some official deems them to be "idle and undesirable." The law provides that "the onus of proof" that a black is legally in an urban area "shall be on the accused." It provides, too, that "a Black who is at any time found in any building under any circumstances giving rise to a reasonable suspicion that he resides in that building shall be deemed to reside there." That reasonable suspicion is enough to send him to jail if he fails to prove that his presence has been "authorized." The proof must be recorded in his reference book, the domestic passport all blacks over sixteen are required to carry when they are in "prescribed" areas. Failure to have the reference book, or failure to produce it, normally means jail.

In addition to his legal status, the reference book must spell out the circumstances of a black person's employment. "No person shall employ any Black if it appears from such Black's reference book," the law says, "that he entered into a contract of service with some other person and such other person has not recorded in such book . . . the fact that such contract has terminated." In effect, a black needs his employer's permission to quit; if he is not a "qualified person," his right to be in the "prescribed area" will end automatically with his job. Finally, a law called the National States Citizenship Act requires that all blacks be designated as citizens of one or the other black "national states," even if they have never lived in them or seen them. The implication of this provision was spelled out in 1978 by a Cabinet minister who looked forward to the day when all the black states would have accepted the ambiguous sovereignty South Africa offers and who pointed out that then "there will not be one black man with South African citizenship." Four of the ten black states are already held to be sovereign, and as a result, their supposed citizens—all but the youngest of whom were citizens of South Africa by birth and most of whom still reside in what is held to be South Africa—are vulnerable to deportation without right of appeal.

Those are some of the basics of South African racial law. There are plenty of wrinkles. Cynthia Freeman had white skin, blond hair, and blue eyes, but as the daughter of a white father and a colored mother, she was classified colored. When she moved to Johannesburg from Natal, she lived in a hostel for coloreds, then moved into a Hillbrow apartment, where she stayed for a time with a white man, who left her with a baby that also looked white. Her employers, a small construction company specializing in swimming pools, presumed her to be white. When she was charged under the Group Areas Act, she did not deny her racial classification but partly rested her defense on a loophole discovered by her lawyer, who contended that the definition of "colored" in the law under which she was charged was different from that of the classification system. As a person who was obviously white and generally accepted as white she met its racial standard, he said. She had a necessity to house herself and her child, he also maintained, and could not be convicted if no other housing was available.

In rebutting those arguments, the prosecutor had no choice but to expose the contempt and racism inherent in the system. His tone was derisive, inquisitorial, unapologetic. Why hadn't she moved back into the colored hostel? he wanted to know. "I can't stay in a hostel with a child," she testified, "and I've got the furniture. I need a home for my child." But there was a hotel in a colored area called Bosmont, the prosecutor persisted. Why hadn't she moved there?

"I never tried," she replied lamely. "There are so many people looking for a place, I'm sure it would be full."

The prosecutor then got her to concede that she had applied for official permission to stay in the white area and had been refused. "So even after the reply you still stayed in the flat," he continued.

"Yes, I had no option."

"You had an option, Miss Freeman. You had the hotel."

"I had the hotel," she acknowledged with a bitter laugh that sounded in the courtroom like a cry of pain.

That disposed of the argument of necessity. There was still the argument that she was obviously white. "Miss Freeman, as what do you classify yourself?" the prosecutor began.

"I classify myself as white, although I have been classified as colored officially."

"You classify yourself as white?"

"Yes, even my little boy."

But the prosecutor noted that coloreds and Indians had moved into her apartment building in the white area. Why, he asked, projecting his own racial feelings, would she allow her little boy to live in a building inhabited by coloreds and Indians if she really regarded him as white? "I have nowhere else to go," she answered. But if she were really white, why did she have colored friends? Surely by her choice of associates, the prosecutor implied, she was betraying her genes. Real whites, he seemed to be saying, associated only with whites.

"I am a Christian."

"I'm not talking about your Christianity now."

"I went because I am a Christian, and as far as Christianity is concerned, everybody is alike. So whoever I visited is immaterial to me."

"Are you aware of the laws of this country?" the prosecutor asked, rhetorically throwing a roundhouse swing that seemed to catch himself on the jaw.

Finally the case turned on the flatness of Miss Freeman's nose, the position of her cheekbones, and whether her hair was really blond.

A professor from Witwatersrand University testified that he could find no reference in the "anthropological literature" to high cheekbones as "a diagnostic criterion to indicate race" and that anyway, Cynthia Freeman's didn't strike him as particularly high.

Cynthia Freeman testified that her hair was naturally blond. Then why didn't she go to white hairdressers? the prosecutor wanted to know. Wasn't it really that she was afraid that they would recognize her as a colored and refuse to serve her?

Weighing up all these delicate points in a twelve-page opinion, the magistrate concluded that while the defendant's hair was probably natural, her nose was definitely flat and her cheekbones were high. "From the Court's observations," he declared, "it was obvious from the Accused's features that she was not obviously white." She was therefore guilty as charged and given a sentence of fifty days in jail, to be suspended on condition that she move out of her apartment and out of the white area.

Cynthia Freeman's judicial humiliation was one of apartheid's lesser atrocities, one of the gross titillations that are a recurring feature of South African life. Edward Crankshaw had a similar sort of excess in mind when he wrote that the "sheer frivolities" of the bureaucratic system in Russia contributed more ultimately to the undoing of the czar's autocracy than did its brutalities. Perhaps the same will one day be said of the apartheid regime, which repeatedly brings itself into disrepute with potential allies by arbitrarily victimizing individuals it might just as well have left alone.

The fairest way to view the streamlined apartheid system, to understand the meaning and limitations of the claims made for "reform," is to consider the circumstances and attitudes of its black beneficiaries, the industrial elite, which has not been freed from the racial caste system but promoted within it. Its members are able, finally, to join trade unions that have the same legal standing as the ones whites join. The law makes collective bargaining with black trade unions optional for employers, and more than 80 percent, perhaps 90 percent, of black industrial workers are without representation. Still, the system has allowed an identifiable black power base to come into existence and left it room to grow. Blacks are no longer barred by law from the best industrial jobs. And they can even purchase a leasehold on houses and land in their segregated townships.

The "reforms" that have been made enable the major South African industrial groups, such as Anglo American and Barlow Rand, to boast that they are "equal opportunity employers." It's an odd boast because all of them, the South African companies and the American and European multinationals, can appear to avoid discrimination on the basis of race only by practicing the most rigorous discrimination on the basis of racial caste. It is impossible to provide even the appearance of "equal opportunities" to the mass of migrants and "commuters," who are barred from taking advantage of the new housing opportunities. Hiring migrants would mar a carefully cultivated image. Therefore, the most progressive employers refuse to employ migrants.

From the perspective of white managers, the rate of social reform in industry is breathtaking. From the perspective of Timothy Zimu, a black, it is still the weight of apartheid that takes his breath away and leaves him almost speechless with anger. Only twenty-six when I met him, he had seen his wages triple in five years. His employer, the West German electrical giant Siemens, had given him special training and installed him in a supervisory position. The company hired no migrants, but Timothy Zimu's opportunities for advancement were far from exhausted. He had a color TV, a refrigerator, a stereo system, and a house full of new furniture. He was planning to buy the house and a new car. If he compared his lot to other South African blacks', he was near the pinnacle of the pyramid. But he compared himself to white industrial workers at Siemens, most of whom lived in a Pretoria suburb called East Lynne, which was built years ago on the site of a black township that was razed by bulldozers after it had been officially declared to be "badly situated." Timothy Zimu had spent part of his childhood in that township. He had seen what its destruction had done to his family, which had then been deposited by the state in Mamelodi, the segregated township that was now his home but also, as he experienced it, his prison. This old wound was rubbed daily, for the bus he took from Mamelodi to the Siemens plant and back again passed through East Lynne, where his supposed white peers lived in little ranch houses of a vaguely Southern California style that far outclassed his little brick township house. "If I want to live in East Lynne, I must live in East Lynne," Timothy Zimu said with sudden passion. "And I must get the same wages the people in East Lynne get."

Frank Bartos, an American who came to Johannesburg from Peoria, Illinois, as a representative of the Caterpillar Tractor Company and stayed to manage a major Barlow Rand subsidiary called Wrightech, realized that his most valued black workers might feel frustration even though they were now relatively well paid. He next did something few South African managers ever do: actually went to see how his workers lived in a township called Daveyton, which is to Johannesburg what Hammond, Indiana, is to Chicago. He thought the conditions "horrible." Being a doer, Bartos set out to make Wrightech's employees the best-housed black workers in the country. It wasn't only altruism or a recrudescence of Peoria values; he was trying to secure for his company a stable force of skilled black workers. So he put Wrightech solidly behind a development of 108 houses at the edge of Daveyton. Bartos assured me, "You'd be happy to live in the houses we're building."

All 108 houses were occupied when I went to visit them a couple of years later. To tell the truth, I would not have been happy to live in them. The little ranch houses were certainly decent; in South Africa as well as the United States it would not have been difficult to find white industrial workers in less appealing houses. And by comparison to the rest of Daveyton, with its rows of mass-produced township housing, these were palaces.

But there was a problem: Wrightech had inadvertently invented a new kind of apartheid within apartheid. Its workers now lived together and apart at the edge of the township in a tiny Levittown all their own. "Tycoons Village," one of the Wrightech householders told me, was the sobriquet with which the development had been tagged in Daveyton's shebeens. The Wrightech workers knew they had made a worthwhile investment, they wanted to believe they had done something important for their families, but they were also apologetic because they knew that their old neighbors were now uncomfortable with them. The feeling, as they sensed it, was that they had been bought, that they had somehow broken ranks and aligned themselves with white privilege. It was a feeling they could admit to sharing sometimes.

"The people here think of you as somebody pompous," one of the householders said in a voice that was more sorrowful than resentful. "You're identified with whites. You're identified as not pulling your weight. If you're here, you're confined here. All your friends are here. And it's true, you're less likely to take risks." While some barriers come down, others go up.

Doubly segregated, the Wrightech householders represented perhaps the tiniest of the proliferating subcastes. They were the elite of the black industrial elite, and on balance, it seemed, their experience confirmed the calculation that inspires South African businessmen and some Western investors: the possibility that black acquiescence in the status quo, if not active loyalty, may be bought or at least rented on a medium-term lease.

If you know the way, it is less than a half-hour drive from Daveyton to Vosloorus, another of these little apartheid islands that can be found beyond the mine dumps and railway yards in a seemingly illimitable sea of white suburbs. The men's hostel for black industrial workers there offers an instructive contrast with the tiny Wrightech enclave. Twenty or more men live in grubby little cubicles, where the walls are coated with grease from kerosene stoves and where some have to sleep on the floor because there are never enough beds. The point of this human contrast is that there is none. The men at Vosloorus and the men in the Daveyton enclave have essentially the same life histories, but they had different stamps in their reference books, certifying that they belonged to different legal subcastes. The mechanism of apartheid, designed to limit the number of urban blacks, makes the Daveyton men insiders and the Vosloorus men permanent outsiders.

Though they live their whole working lives in the same East Rand area, working at factories virtually next door to Wrightech or Siemens, the odds are overwhelming that they will never be hired by such supposedly progressive employers, never invited to take part in literacy or training programs, let alone fancy housing schemes. Yet they, too, are near the top of the pyramid of working blacks, beneficiaries despite the suffocating circumstances of their lives of the vaunted "new dispensation" for black labor. They have jobs in the white area, after all, are eligible to join unions, and their wages have risen dramatically. Yet the Vosloorus blacks don't see themselves as labor aristocrats. They are short, somehow, on gratitude. "We are still living on hungry stomachs," said Robert Mashile, a member of the black Metal and Allied Workers Union, whose wages had doubled in three years. He had a little more cash in his pocket, he admitted, but prices had risen steeply; his wife and five children were still in a homeland called Lebowa, and he himself was now in his sixteenth year in the Vosloorus men's hostel. That was his life; basically nothing would change.

Yet it was always possible for me to skitter around the base of the pyramid—whenever I thought I had reached the bottom, I came to the brink of a lower depth—and meet intelligent young men who felt for those in Robert Mashile's position the same envy, the same sense that they were standing on the far side of a social abyss, that he would feel for the Wrightech householders. In one of the poorest areas of one of the poorest homelands, a region called eastern Pondoland in Transkei, where there has been less development than there has been in many parts of Bangladesh, I encountered a former mine worker name Jalisi Mjoki walking along a rutted rural road in patched cord jeans and what was once the jacket of a track suit. He was twenty-nine and had lost his job at an Orange Free State gold mine because he had briefly gone AWOL to attend a family funeral. So he went to Durban, the nearest industrial center, where he was now technically a foreigner. Of course, he had no authorization to be there, let alone work there.

For five or six weeks he managed to survive, getting work illegally for a day or two a week on building sites. But his employers, mostly Indian businessmen, chased him away whenever the police were in the vicinity, and most of the time he had neither money nor a place to stay. Finally, out of fear and exhaustion, he returned home. An able-bodied, well-spoken young man looking for work in a rich land, he felt hunted. "I'm not used to running away," he said.

I asked if he ever thought about the reasons for his joblessness. "I've thought about this," he replied gravely, "and I think it's because whenever a person leaves a job, there are five or six waiting. I don't know how to solve it, but I think the problem lies with the people who are permanently employed. They should be made to give others a chance." In other words, he was blaming blacks, labor aristocrats like Robert Mashile and Timothy Zimu, rather than the whites who decreed his status in a lower subcaste. This was a tremendous plus for the system, I thought, one of the secrets of its remarkable durability. I don't regard myself as leftist or radical—that is, I generally deplore the consequences of revolutionary fervor as much as I do its causes. But at that instant I fervently wished that there existed an underground that really knew how to find young men like Jalisi Mjoki and raise their revolutionary consciousness. That night, when I drove out of eastern Pondoland, the sight of a fire burning across a ridge of dry winter grass made me think of the young Mao Zedong in Hunan, who wrote, "A single spark can start a prairie fire." I quoted that fragment of revolutionary history to the young black from Durban who had come along with me as an interpreter, then wisecracked, "It's a shame a single prairie fire can't start a spark."

If Jalisi Mjoki had been "authorized to seek work" in a white area, he would have been expected to confine his seeking to an official labor bureau, a kind of commodity exchange where black labor is traded on the basis of supply and demand. A prospective white employer fills in a form headed "Registration of Vacancy/Application for Labor." On a summer day at Park Rynie, a quiet retirement community on the Indian Ocean, I was permitted to leaf through the latest batch of these forms in an office that looked out through a protective wire screen on an open enclosure where the "work seekers" waited. This is some of what I found: the Sugarland Butchery offering $15.75 a week for a black who was "clean and bright"; a suburban homeowner bidding $42 a month for a "house boy" who "must be clean and not fat"; the Post Office in Durban requesting sixty men to dig trenches for telephone cables, a job that would last for six weeks and pay $3.60 a day.

"We are doing a lot of good," a white administrator named Hennie Venter said that day. He was wearing the summer uniform of his caste, a leisure suit with a short-sleeved tunic, in his case, pea green with little black checks. "The black is economical subsistence-oriented," he said. "Western man looks to the future; the black lives for the day."

The afternoon wound up in a large labor bureau called Prospecton, which is just down the road from the Toyota assembly plant in an industrial area south of Durban. There the pen where the "work seekers" waited was big enough to be turned into a skating rink. It was late afternoon, just before the close of business, and trading on the floor of the exchange had gone slack, but there were still 120 or 150 men sitting on benches, in case some work turned up. Normally, I was told, it was a black functionary who appeared at the window with the wire screen to select the candidate for a job.

What turned up on this afternoon behind the wire screen was my white face when I peered out from the inner office to take in the scene. Immediately there was a commotion among the "work seekers," men on their feet, arms waving, shouts of "Boss, please, boss." The white officials to whom I had just been introduced found comic relief, indeed hilarity, in the scene. "They all think you're an employer," shouted my escort, a good-natured old fellow on the verge of retirement after four decades in the apparatus of racial administration. "Tell them it's OK, you want someone to work in New York for you! Tell them it's OK!" I slunk away. Suddenly I needed to be by myself, as if I wouldn't be able to trust my breathing until I was out of the place.

On the other side of the subcontinent, near the Daniel F. Malan International Airport in Cape Town, the authorities have created an astonishing exposition of the racial caste system in operation. There in a space of about five square miles, roughly 200,000 browns and blacks have been distributed on a checkerboard of officially demarcated racial enclaves, each with the standards and regulations appropriate to the caste or subcaste licensed to inhabit it.

You can start at the privileged end by driving to Mitchell's Plain, a segregated township for coloreds that was built as an apartheid showcase. Tidy little town houses, landscaping, and floral beds near the main thoroughfares and shopping centers look as if they belong in the suburbs of San Diego. Then you can drive on to Nyanga, an established black township with unimproved matchbox houses and minimal facilities. Next to Nyanga is New Crossroads, a newer and much smaller subdivision for blacks that was meant to be a showcase but became frozen at an early stage of development when the authorities hatched a master plan for the 1990s that would involve rounding up all of Cape Town's blacks and depositing them in a new township called Khayalitsha ("new home") next to Mitchell's Plain. Meantime, there is still old Crossroads, a crowded warren of metal shanties that looks like a social disaster but is actually a triumph of black assertion, for it came into being without authorization and has been allowed to remain.

Next to Crossroads, but separated from it by a sandy no-man's-land of less than 100 yards, are the remnants of later struggles with the police, divided and subdivided into further tiny enclaves. Some have official permission to build shanties; others are required to live in tents.

Everyone understands that the tidal movement of black population has its origins in the absolute poverty that exists in black rural areas. The obstinate courage of the hunted people who stand their ground and refuse to be designated as "illegals" in their land can be very moving, but the truth is that heartlessness prevails. The people in Mitchell's Plain do not make common cause with the people in Nyanga. The people in Nyanga and New Crossroads do not help the people in old Crossroads, where some of them first gained a foothold. The people in the Crossroads camp are divided between those who are certified to be there and those who are seeking certification. The system designates all blacks in Cape Town as foreigners, even those it accepts as "legals"; then it compartmentalizes the "illegals" into as many small, vulnerable groups as possible. Sometimes it retreats, but always it dominates.

It dominates, and yet the word "indomitable" still must be applied to its victims. If I mention several of the individual "squatters" and "illegals" I met over two years in the area near the airport in Cape Town, you will understand why.

Goodwill Zisiwe was a handsome young man of twenty-two, short and wiry, with a mild expression that reflected none of the tension and defiance that were inherent in his situation. The defiance was in his very presence at the bush camp near Nyanga, for he had been arrested at the same spot a couple of weeks earlier and thrown into Pollsmoor Prison, where he shared with twenty-one others a cell from which he had just emerged. The tension came from his anxieties about his wife, Nofine. She had been in the final stages of pregnancy when she had been taken into custody. Some women who had been with her told him that she had later been transferred to the prison hospital to give birth, but he had been unable to get information on her condition, the delivery, or the sex of his child. In the meantime, he had lost his job at a lumberyard.

I met Goodwill Zisiwe again nearly two weeks later, when I visited the bush camp at midnight. Nofine and their healthy new son were out of prison, he told me proudly, staying for the night in a church basement. There were roughly 600 persons in the camp that night, living in pathetic little shelters, makeshift yurts created out of twigs, cardboard, and the sort of plastic sheeting that is used to make garbage bags. Small fires inside illuminated these flimsy shelters like Chinese lanterns, with long shadows flickering on their inflammable plastic surfaces as the huddled groups around the fires shifted positions.

"Dear little round house," a white woman who was there on a philanthropic errand cooed. "We very sorry," she said, speaking pidgin, or rather baby talk, to a self-possessed young black man, who sized her up with a long, cool stare.

"Why?" he asked.

"We sorry you not have house, permit, warm clothes like us. We *very* sorry."

It was an excruciating moment. The good woman had not really noticed anything about the man except his status as victim. For an instant it seemed to be touch-and-go whether he would respond to the decency of her sentiment or the condescension of her tone. He took a long drag on a cigarette, then split the difference, offering a neutral monosyllable. "Oh," he said mildly, a little dismissively but without apparent hostility. The white woman had now become the object of condescension, but she didn't seem to realize that, either.

Another man went by, carrying a roll of plastic sheeting. "One man, one room," he quipped. A group around a fire that included Goodwill Zisiwe broke into laughter.

There were inspirational speeches and hymns in Xhosa for those who stayed up, and Goodwill Zisiwe was one of the speakers, holding forth in a manner that commanded respect. Then the group sang a hymn. I asked what it meant. "God's spirit is with me like a bird," I was told.

They were worse off in some obvious ways than the sidewalk dwellers of Calcutta, and yet they were singing about divine providence. I found myself powerfully moved. About six hours later, just at dawn, the police stormed into the camp and burned it down again. I had no way of knowing whether Goodwill Zisiwe had been re-arrested, but it was bound to happen. If the police missed him in that sweep, they would get him in another. And still, it was clear, he would return.

Several months later I met Elsie Nyobole and Cynthia Balinyanga. Both had been deported as aliens to Transkei, a distance of 800 miles, and both had returned. In the process Elsie Nyobole had lost her husband and Cynthia Balinyanga had lost her child.

Elsie Nyobole had last seen her husband, Menge, two months earlier at Pollsmoor Prison, where they were put on separate buses for expulsion to Transkei. When she got to Umtata, the territory's capital, he was nowhere to be found. After waiting for a few days in a church, she wrapped her baby in a blanket and took a bus 120 miles to the town of Lady Frere, where Menge's sister lived. Failing to find him, she resolved to seek him in Cape Town. This entailed taking a bus to Graaff Reinet, where it ran into a police roadblock set up to intercept "illegals." She got off the bus and walked through the bush from midnight till dawn with her baby on her back and her possessions in a shopping bag. Arriving at a hamlet called Aberdeen, she boarded another bus that met another roadblock at Worcester, where, to avoid the police, she took a train to Paarl; where she caught a bus to Franschhoek; where she was able to get a place in an overcrowded taxi back to Nyanga, the place where she had been arrested originally. By then she had the equivalent of $1.10 left, and there was still no trace of Menge. So she moved with her baby into a two-room Crossroads shanty that already housed seven people. I met her the following week. When I asked if she was weary, she said she was weary. When I asked if she was sad, she said she was sad. Otherwise she did not display her emotions.

Cynthia Balinyanga's odyssey was nearly identical, except when her bus from Umtata hit a roadblock, the passengers scattered into the bush in the middle of the night. In the confusion and darkness, a woman kindly offered to carry Mrs. Balinyanga's four-month-old son. The two women then got separated on the other side of the roadblock and, in the darkness, boarded different buses. Mrs. Balinyanga didn't know when I met her whether Nonceba had ever made it to Cape Town or had been re-arrested and sent back with the baby on the via dolorosa to Umtata.

It may be said that these cases are exceptional. What is exceptional is the resistance these individuals muster to the almost irresistible pressure the law puts on black families to resign themselves to the separation and fragmentation synonymous with enforced migrant labor. Most rural blacks give up the expectation that families can be held together. Some who go on annual labor contracts start second families where they find themselves. Others squander their wages on prostitutes and drink. There are always some who fill the void in their lives with religion and a few who walk a narrow path of abstemiousness and frugality in order to overcome the odds and realize some dream, perhaps by winning an athletic trophy, starting a business in the homeland, buying a car, educating children. It is hard to generalize, for there are more than 800,000 black migrant laborers in South Africa, at least 250,000 of them in the industrial belt that has Johannesburg as its center—a foreign legion on its own soil.

I had seen where they worked. I had seen where they lived. I had seen the rural areas they left behind. What I had never done was travel with a migrant worker between his two worlds to see whether he was, in the words of a South African academic, not a man of two worlds but "a man of no worlds." So I asked two blacks whom I saw nearly every day in Johannesburg whether I could visit their homes, preferably in their company.

Napthali Ngcobo was the uniformed watchman and factotum in the lobby of the building where I installed my office. A chubby man in his mid-forties, he had the presence and instincts of a natural politician. On his corner in downtown Johannesburg he was a figure of some celebrity among blacks, chaffing the messengers, drivers, and cleaning women as they came and went, like a candidate getting down with the folks at a factory gate. I got the impression that he was a person of enterprise and convictions. Sometimes I saw him with a Bible; sometimes, a racing form. Various young women seemed to sit in his cubicle under the stairway as if it were a confessional. One evening on my way to the movies on the other side of town, I found him supervising the parking lot into which I had driven. Napthali, it emerged, was a fully fledged faith healer, a Zulu Oral Roberts, whose powers had been revealed in a series of remarkable dreams in which he was instructed by a tall and imposing Zulu in a white coat.

He was then living with his family in Zululand, having been laid off when the dairy company for which he had worked in Durban closed. During the one month a year he now spent with his family at home, his reputation for miracle cures still drew crowds. The rest of the year he could often be found preaching on Sunday mornings in Soweto at an independent black church called the New Swaziland Church in Zion. There he met a thirty-five-year-old cleaning woman called Winna, who now shared his bed in the cramped rooftop quarters where he lived with only a curtain to screen the couple from a young cousin who shared the same room. It was the same rooftop, as chance or fate would have it, that I had been watching on my first weekend back in South Africa when the police assaulted the inhabitants. Napthali would have been one of them had he not been in church.

Winna had twice traveled down to Zululand to stay with his wife. The New Swaziland Church in Zion did not object to this arrangement, which could be regarded as an adaptation of Zulu tradition to the circumstances decreed by apartheid. He was earning about $235 a month, and most of it still went home: $60 to keep an eighteen-year-old son, his hope for the future, in a boarding school; another $110 or so for his wife, who ran a household that still contained five of their eight children, plus his father. Napthali, it seemed, had successfully fitted the disparate pieces of his life together and achieved a measure of contentment, but in his own mind, in reality, too, this had been done in spite of the system, not thanks to it. "The whites don't care at all," he said. "They are the ones who make it impossible to live with your family. Even if you have money, they won't allow it."

Zalaowakho Mhlongo, known as Drum, relied on the products of South African breweries to ease his adjustment to Johannesburg. Apartments in Johannesburg all come with "flat cleaners" to do light housekeeping. Drum was attached to the apartment we took. When we discovered that he had a wife and children in Zululand and that the building gave him a rock-bottom wage of less than $110 a month, we felt compelled to add to it both cash and food. Drum understood some English and seemed to be under the impression himself that he spoke it, but the pleasant sounds that bubbled from him in response to our greetings were always unintelligible. Thus, although he spent an hour a day in our apartment over a period of many months, we never found out much about him.

I finally asked a black journalist and friend named Chris More to come over on a Saturday to help us get to know Drum by explaining us to him and interpreting what he said. The scene was not without comedy—the goody-goody foreigners asking the black servant to sit down for the first time in a living room he had been vacuuming daily, especially since Chris was late and we were finding it impossible to get the message across to

Drum that we weren't detaining him because he had done something wrong. The poor man looked miserable and tense until Chris showed up, but then a very pleasant transformation ensued. Invited to stay for lunch, he gradually relaxed. Given the opportunity, he was not at all inarticulate. "If you go around showing what you're feeling inside," he said, explaining the obvious, "you'll be out of a job." Soon he was responding to our questions about his life—his wife and seven children lived near Durban, where he was not, however, authorized to work—with questions about ours. "What are you doing in this place?" was the first. "Do you treat blacks in your country as badly as we're treated here?" was the second.

As it happened, Napthali and Drum got their annual leaves in different months, so it was arranged that Chris and I would drive to Zululand with Drum and then try to follow the directions Napthali gave us to his kraal, or homestead, on the Tugela River, where we would introduce ourselves to his family. Philemon, a nephew of Drum's who also worked as a flat cleaner in our building, was going on his first leave in fourteen months, so he came, too. Philemon was a striking young man, lithe and handsome, a jogger who was articulate in remarkably good English.

Riding in my Peugeot on the national road to Durban, he was a smooth and easy conversationalist. I had to ask only once for him to fall into the habit of calling me Joe instead of sir. He had never used the egregious "master." His daily runs in Johannesburg, about four miles each way, took him to another white suburb, where he apparently had a girl friend who lived in the backyard of a family she served as a maid. Now, returning to his three children and twenty-four-year-old wife, to whom he had written only once in fourteen months, he was wearing a track suit and carrying an Alitalia flight bag that contained a diploma testifying that he had finished 173d in the 1983 running of Johannesburg's major marathon, up from 307th in 1982.

If I had lived by any maxim as a reporter, it was that every person is an expert on the circumstances of his life. Black migrant laborers, it seemed to me, were the ultimate experts on black migrant labor. So the drive down to Durban turned into a rolling seminar, with me a student, on living and working conditions in the building where I had made my home for two and one half years. Our building was what is known in America as a co-op; as renters we were not privy to the deliberations of our owner-neighbors, whose standard of living was indicated by a census I took in the garage, where I counted: two Rolls-Royces (belonging to a husband and wife), seven Jaguars, eight Mercedeses, one Porsche, one BMW, and one Lancia, plus run-of-the-mill Cressidas and Rovers.

Philemon was one of the hustlers in the building who earned a little more by washing cars on a piecework basis. I asked how much. My neighbors who had their cars washed six out of every seven days paid a little more than $5.50 a month, less than a quarter a wash. What they paid in a month to these migrants—who had no opportunity because of their legal status to sell their labor at a higher price—was only slightly more than what I had been paying for a single car wash at the garage where I parked downtown. These few figures, for a neighborhood of English-speaking whites who vote overwhelmingly for the liberal opponents of the government's racial policies, pointed to the will to exploit as ingrained cultural reflexes. Of course, I was the only person in the car who found this surprising.

We reached Durban late in the afternoon and then drove up the Indian Ocean coast past the large sugar estates to an Indian community called Stanger, where we turned inland again. We had gone 475 miles by the time they showed me where to park, near a trading store at the foot of a hill, about ten miles from an obscure hamlet called Mapumulo.

The light was failing as we started up a steep, narrow trail. The generator used by a white family named Bignoux who had been running the trading store for forty years—the only whites within twenty-five miles in an area inhabited by tens of thousands of Zulus—made the only sound that competed with the raucous crickets. There were Zulu kraals made predominantly of round thatched beehive huts up and down the slopes that rose from the narrow valley. Yet the only visible light was the one shining from the trader's house. When we reached the farthest ridge, Philemon quietly informed me that we were now approaching Drum's kraal. A group of women were descending the trail. There was a soft exchange of murmured greetings. Their import came as a shock to Philemon, but this was not immediately apparent. The women had informed him, he told me after some moments, that his wife and children had gone to Newcastle, 175 miles away, to visit her mother.

By this time we were standing in the gathering dusk on a clearing in front of three huts. A few goats were tethered nearby in a pen made up of brambly branches. A couple of scrawny chickens darted along the edge of a small patch of sickly corn. This was Drum's domain, and now, snapping out of the hung-over haze in which he had seemed to be plunged during most of the drive, he squared his shoulders and took a lordly stance on the slope. A thickset woman bustled out of one of the huts, shot across the clearing, and disappeared into another, passing within two yards of Drum, who, his chin now thrusting at the heavens, hardly seemed to notice her. This was his wife, Thandekile, whom he had not seen in a year, on her way to inform his elderly mother that their Odysseus had returned. She zoomed back again to the first hut, apparently to ensure that it was in suitable order, then re-emerged to invite her husband to come inside and rest. The greetings between husband and wife and between Drum and his children were all in the eyes and murmured, brief civilities; there was no touching. This was the customary way in which a warrior returned to his kraal, I imagined, but I could not help thinking that it was also appropriate as a welcome to a husband and father who was a stranger, having spent no more than fourteen months at home over the previous fourteen years.

Inside, Drum sat against the wall on a straw mat. There were only four pieces of furniture: a table covered with oilcloth, two chairs that were reserved for Chris and me, and an armoire for clothes, which was supplemented by a cord fixed to the wall and weighed down with garments. The children were mostly shoeless; one, an undersized girl of eight who would have been considered small for five, was visibly ailing and malnourished. With their mother they sat against the wall opposite Drum. A candle, probably saved for just such a special occasion, flickered in between from a long-emptied brandy bottle that served as candlestick.

Drum ended the formal audience by going into the next hut with his wife. Philemon took Chris and me over the ridge to his father's kraal and the modern bungalow he had erected there for his family. On the wall the diploma from last year's marathon hung alongside a color snapshot of him at the finish line. He had met his wife, Sonto, in Durban, he told me, after he had already started as a migrant laborer. She had grown up in the Newcastle township and was only sixteen when they were wed. They had never spent more than a month together in nearly nine years of marriage. Sonto and the three children were supported by money he sent his parents; it was not sent directly to her.

I tried to imagine what it was like for a young woman from a township to live on this hillside, in a kraal, far from her relatives and friends, waiting for her dashing husband to return from *Egoli* ("the city of gold") in his track suit with another diploma. Waiting fourteen months. He had not written to say when he was coming, Philemon said, formally excusing her for her absence and, at the same time, covering his hurt and embarrassment. The obvious thought that Sonto's absence might be more than temporary crossed my mind; I could not tell whether it had crossed Philemon's. I told him that it would be possible for me to drive him most of the way to Newcastle a couple of days later. "Oh, that won't be necessary, Joe," he said. A slight tightness in his voice seemed to carry a hint that he felt it would be inappropriate for a Zulu husband to go chasing after his wife. He would pass his month at home keeping in shape by running and waiting for Sonto to return.

Except for a few stars and an occasional faint flash of headlights from a car or bus five or ten miles away, it was pitch-dark as we descended the hill. One of Drum's daughters clutched my hand all the way down. Drum led the way with a flashlight that he said we had given him. Several times in South Africa I had been told quite seriously by whites that blacks saw everything in two dimensions, that their brains conveyed no impression or concept of depth. Now, in the same conviction that skin color has everything to do with the way the world appears, one of the children asked a question in Zulu that made Chris laugh out loud. In a whisper he translated for my benefit. "How does the white man see in the dark?" the youngster wanted to know.

A couple of days later, along another dirt road through the Zulu hills, about eighty miles away, Chris and I found Napthali Ngcobo's wife. Our sudden appearance, she later told us, had given her a fright, for she assumed us to be police bearing bad news. "I had only time to pray," she said. "I thought, 'Has my husband passed away? Has my son died? Only you can help me, Lord.'"

Napthali's kraal, set on a hillside above the river, was an estate compared to Drum's. Pawpaw trees grew in the yard. The main house was made of the traditional mud and thatch, but it was handsomely trimmed in blue paint, and there were windows with real glass and curtains blowing gently in the breeze. It was adequately, though modestly, furnished. On his annual trips home, Napthali had brought kerosene lamps, a clock, a kerosene stove, a radio; and his wife, Martha, had tea to serve us, which Drum's wife had conspicuously lacked. With it came slabs of steamed bread, hot from the stove.

On a shelf near the table at which we were entertained, there was a framed color photo of Napthali in a guise in which I had never seen him. Instead of the brass-buttoned watchman's uniform he wore in the lobby, he was shown in a navy suit, a clerical collar, and a tunic of episcopal purple. One hand held a Bible; the other was gesturing, showing the way. What was riveting about this apotheosis for me was its setting, for I recognized the rooftop where he lives, the parapet where the cops had pummeled the blacks on the first Sunday after my return to South Africa, now more than three years in the past. Something moved me, or maybe more than one thing: the endearing half-comic image of the self-created holy man living a dream that whites could not batter, but also the notion that I had finally come full circle in South Africa. Whatever went into it, it was a feeling that could be enjoyed without heavy thought.

"Say hello to my husband," Mrs. Ngcobo said sweetly. "Please say hello to my husband."

CHAPTER FIVE

Forced Busing

Albino Carleo is also the son of a migrant laborer. He was still being carried in his mother's womb when his father, Gaetano, suddenly closed up his small butcher's shop in Cava de'Tirreni, outside Salerno and sailed for

Durban. In his first five years in South Africa, Gaetano drifted from job to job in the mines and on the railroad, overseeing black construction workers. When Albino first glimpsed his father at the age of five, it was the height of the Depression, and Gaetano had little to show for his efforts. After only a week back in Cava de'Tirreni, he headed for New York and opened a grocery in Brooklyn with his savings from Johannesburg. The South African climate, however, had spoiled him for North America. Back in Johannesburg in 1936, he bought a secondhand Ford bus and staked out a route from a black township called Alexandra to the center of town. He called the shoestring operation the Rapido Bus Company.

Albino's mother died without ever seeing South Africa. The son was already a young man when he followed his father's footsteps as a migrant and finally learned to know Gaetano by learning the bus business. Now in his eighties, Gaetano Carleo spends most of the year in his homeland at Cava de'Tirreni, while Albino oversees a corporate group with about 9,000 employees, twenty subsidiary companies, and a fleet of 3,500 buses from a headquarters of vaguely Neapolitan design in a quiet white suburb of Johannesburg.

The Rapido Bus Company changed its name to Rapid early on and then was absorbed into another small bus company, which gradually branched out into black "locations," the inhabitants of which found work in the white industrial belt, until finally the major private bus company, known as Putco, bought up all the Carleos' operation. The Carleos then turned around and purchased a controlling interest in Putco. Ownership of this franchise immediately threw them into a delicate relationship with the official managers of the apartheid system. The social engineers were busy looking for ways to limit the number of blacks who stayed overnight in the urban areas. Their aim was to build up a class of "commuters," blacks who could be allowed to work in South Africa so long as they shuttled back to their "homeland" every night. In its most elaborate and mature form, apartheid required buses, more buses every year as more blacks were flushed out of the white areas into vast rural slums known as "closer settlements." Putco thus grew with the elaboration of the system.

It had been enough for Gaetano Carleo to know buses. The maintenance manual Albino Carleo needed to study was written by Machiavelli, for he had to present an amiable face not only to his exclusively black public and the apartheid bureaucrats but also to the assorted tribal chieftains, headmen, flunkies, sellouts, and politicians who emerged as ministers in the new homeland states. Today Putco promotes itself as an "equal opportunity employer" and maintains a Putco Foundation to support black community charities. When I met him for coffee in his paneled office, Albino Carleo was surprisingly ready to expound on various subjects of social concern, including the "quality of life" in urban areas and the responsibilities of corporations. He also talked about getting along. "If there was a black government,'' he said, ''I would talk to them with the same sincerity of purpose that I have when I talk to the white government. But that's a thing of the future. If a small minority has de facto power, it is stupid to challenge them. What you can't get by force, you get by persuasion.''

A short man, slightly proboscidean, he spoke rapidly in a high-pitched voice, occasionally pacing the tiled floor. He was being generous rather than defensive, setting out a practical philosophy that had been learned in a hard school. ''People like to feel important, and if you display a sense of knowing they're important, they like you,'' he said. ''They like you and trust you because you represent a measure of their greatness.'' It was a philosophy he applied to whites and blacks impartially. He had just given a dinner in Pretoria, he said, offering an example, for the chief minister of a soon-to-be-independent homeland called KwaNdebele, a former truck driver named Simon Skhosana who was accompanied by the third of his five wives. KwaNdebele had been Putco's most important growth area for five years. In that time the population of this obscure tribal enclave had nearly doubled to 465,000. At the time of the 1970 census, before there was a KwaNdebele, only 32,000 people had lived in the area. ''He was very proud,'' said Albino Carleo, allowing himself a touch of condescension in order to display his social conscience. ''It is difficult to make people understand that the population explosion can destroy the world.''

But the population explosion in KwaNdebele, unlike the wider world, has little to do with breeding and practically everything to do with apartheid. In 1979 Putco started to run two buses a day from Pretoria to the resettlement camps of KwaNdebele, fifty-five miles distant. There were 263 a day in 1984, when the government was expected to pay Putco a subsidy of $26.5 million to keep its buses rolling to the homeland. That worked out to more than $1,000 for each ''commuter'' a year. It was the price the white government was willing to pay—and go on paying, year after year—to halt the normal process of urbanization. The KwaNdebele bus subsidy—the government's largest single expense in the development of this homeland—was higher than the KwaNdebele gross domestic product. This is basic apartheid economics.

The first time I saw KwaNdebele, two years earlier, it was a rash of ''closer settlements'' spotted over open veld that had previously provided grazing for some thirty white-owned farms. At a place called Kwaggafontein, I came upon the Nduli family, who had just been evicted from their kraal on a white farm near Middelburg, about fifty miles away. I found them with their paltry belongings on a plot white officials had staked out on a grassy hillside, which was fast being blighted by squalid shanties. Rose Nduli was literally sitting on the veld while her son, Kleinbooi, wearing a brown shoe on his right foot and on his left a black boot laced with copper wire, chipped away with a shovel at the dry stuccolike earth in order to prepare the ground for a shelter. When I asked who brought him there, Kleinbooi replied simply, "GG." The initials are the first two letters of the official license plates on the government trucks used to move blacks out of white areas. GG is as predictable as natural calamity. GG scoops you up when you least expect it and drops you somewhere you have never seen, leaving it to you to patch together the torn and ragged pattern of a life. And like natural calamity, it evokes depression and resignation, rather than resentment. "The law is the law," Rose Nduli said, "and we have nothing to say about it."

I heard only one angry voice at Kwaggafontein on that visit. It belonged to a man named Jim Masetlana, who started his working life as a tenant on a white farm and then was moved three times by GG in nineteen years. Without meaning to do so, I had uncapped his resentment by offering the cold comfort that he probably would not be harried anymore now that he was in a homeland. "This is no homeland," he said, waving his hand at the dreary refugee camp growing up around him. "It's just a township. Where I grew up was really a homeland. I had land. I could plow. Even the white farmers give you land to plow. This type of homeland I have never seen. They have no business taking us from the place of our birth."

This process—known euphemistically as resettlement—represented a final stage in a campaign to alienate blacks from their land that had already gone on in the Transvaal for 140 years. It was central to the government's plan to redefine the bulk of the black population as foreign. At first I had thought this was just an ideological word game, but the misery I had seen in out-of-the-way resettlement camps had long since cured me of that easy notion.

In 1960, 39.8 percent of the total black population was crammed into the former tribal reserves; by 1980 resettlement and gerrymandering had raised the proportion to 53.1 percent. In absolute terms, the number of blacks on the same 13 percent of the land had more than doubled in those 20 years, from 4.4 million to 11 million. And nearly half of these had already been stripped of their South African citizenship.

I thought I understood all that, but I was not prepared for what Kwaggafontein had become in two and a half years. It was no longer just a spot in a rash of "closer settlements." Now it was a part of a nearly continuous resettlement belt. You drove through the Pretoria suburbs and then through more than forty miles of rich farm country before you hit it; then you could drive another forty miles, and it was seldom out of sight: a serpentine stream of metal shanties and mud houses. I turned off the highway and followed a dirt road for five miles to see how far into the *bundu* the settlement now extended. This brought me to a place called Frisegewacht that seemed to be near the homeland's outer edge, for when I looked past the

last shanty to the next rise, all I could see was open grassland belonging to a white cattle farmer.

At Frisegewacht I met a man who worked at a munitions factory in Brits. He was earning $85 a week, an unusually high wage for a black industrial worker, but his job was in jeopardy. He was regularly late to work in Brits, which was on the other side of Pretoria, a distance of nearly a hundred miles by road from where he lived, because the first Putco bus often didn't reach Frisegewacht until 4:15 in the morning and his shift started at seven. His white supervisor—who lived, of course, in Brits—was not interested in excuses. To be on the safe side, what he really needed, he said, was a bus that would come at 3:30. As we chatted, a blue Putco bus came around the bend on a dirt track. Here we were, out in the veld, about seventy-five miles from Pretoria, more than five miles from the nearest highway. It would not have seemed much more incongruous to find a red London Transport double-decker there.

On a good day this "commuter" left at four in the morning and returned, seventeen hours later, at nine at night. Then, if he ate quickly and went straight to bed, he got five hours' sleep.

Frisegewacht was frightening in a different way from the more remote "closer settlements" I had visited where migrancy was the only possible answer to unemployment. The harsh condition and barrenness of such places seemed to portend a breakdown in the system. But Kwaggafontein and Frisegewacht were actually taking root. The black inhabitants, by their capacity for sheer endurance, were rescuing a seemingly harebrained scheme concocted by white ideologues and making it durable. There were little signs of commerce: shops selling groceries, meat, and even building materials, all trucked in from the white areas. Some shanties had been handsomely improved. GG no longer had to dump blacks here. Responding to heavy pressures and tiny incentives, they were coming from more remote areas on their own.

To catch the first Putco bus from the Wolverkraal depot in KwaNdebele, the photographer David Goldblatt and I calculated, we would have to leave the Bundu Inn no later than 1:30 in the morning. It is then that KwaNdebele's first "commuters" start to stir. Wolverkraal was even farther from Pretoria than Kwaggafontein or Frisegewacht. The black settlers of the new state who boarded the bus near there had to ride about ninety-five miles before transferring to local buses. That meant a minimum of one hundred and ninety miles, up to eight hours, every working day in buses designed with hard seats for short hauls on city streets.

The Putco depot was just a fenced-off clearing in the bush with a tiny shack for the dispatcher and nothing else. Rain during the night had cleansed the air, leaving a light breeze and a full moon to limn the hulks of the fifty-two buses.

It was about twenty past two when the lights inside the buses at the depot started to blink on one by one. Number 4174, which we boarded, had one bulb glowing dimly inside a red globe, another in a green globe, casting together an eerie light into a gloom made stygian, despite the clear night outside, by the coating of caked mud on the bus's windows. A sign near the cage in which the driver was encased declared that number 4174 was certified to carry 62 sitting passengers and twenty-nine standing.

At 2:40 in the morning, number 4174 left the depot and headed north and east, *away* from Pretoria, to pick up its first passengers at a place called Kameelrivier. The headlights showed six men and four women waiting patiently beside the dirt road, in what appeared to be the middle of nowhere, when the bus made its first stop, ten minutes late, at 2:50. At that place and that hour, the sight of a couple of whites on the bus was as much to be expected as that of a couple of commuting walruses. Momentarily it startled the passengers out of their drowsiness. Once our presence was explained, it became possible to ask a few questions as the bus rattled to its next stop.

John Masango, the first man to board, said he worked six days a week at a construction site near Benoni, an industrial town forty miles on the far side of Pretoria, taking three buses each way. The total bus fares he paid out in a week gobbled up one quarter of his wages. He was fifty-three years old, and he could get back to Kameelrivier by 8:30 at night. Only on Sundays did he ever see his home or his family in the light of day. Most nights, after washing, eating, and as he put it, "taking care of family matters," he was able to get to sleep by 10:00 or 10:15. While I was still thanking him for his patience, John Masango reached into a bag he was carrying and extracted a little rectangle of foam rubber about the size of a paperback book. He then pulled his blue knitted cap over his eyes and, leaning forward, pressed the foam rubber to the back of the seat in front of him; he rested his forehead against the foam rubber and dropped his hands to his lap. As far as I could tell, he was out like a light.

It was 3:20, and number 4174 had yet to reach the narrow ribbon of asphalt that connects KwaNdebele to Pretoria. But it had stopped by enough "closer settlements" to fill all its seats; anyone getting on beyond this point was bound to stand, not just this morning but every morning in the week. There were still nearly two and a half hours to go to Pretoria. Thus some people *stood* on the bus nearly twelve hours a week.

I looked around. Aside from the driver and one man who was smoking about four rows from the rear of the bus, David and I and a black Putco official appeared to be the only persons out of more than ninety who had not now dozed off. The center aisle was packed with bodies wound around themselves like anchovies in a can. A young woman's head slumped on the shoulder of the man seated next to her, who was too far gone to recognize his good fortune. Some of the heads lolled backward, but most of the forms

were bent forward like that of the man who carried the foam rubber. By 3:45 the bus had reached the highway, and the ride was now smoother.

The first streaks of dawn showed on the outskirts of Pretoria. It was October and splendid jacarandas were in full blossom, but seen from the vantage point of a black commuter bus the sight left me indifferent. It was only a few moments now until we turned into Marabastad, once a teeming black residential neighborhood at the very edge of Pretoria's downtown, at present a stretch of razed, overgrown real estate lying as a no-man's-land between the capital's commercial center and a tiny enclave of Indian-owned shops adjacent to the terminus where the buses from KwaNdebele disgorge their black passengers. Number 4174 ended its ride there at 5:40, exactly three hours after it had begun in the *bundu* at the Wolverkraal depot. Groggy KwaNdebele "commuters" staggered to waiting Putco buses that would carry them on the next stage of their journeys to work.

Since they spend more of their working week on buses than they do in their "closer settlements," the KwaNdebele "commuters" have little energy to spare for the study of the history of their nation-to-be. It was the bureaucrats in Pretoria, finally, who determined that there were ten black nations. They could just as easily have counted two, three, or twenty. Black nationalists, of course, count one.

Two or three would have meant the surrender of large amounts of white land and the creation of black power bases from which a successful challenge to white dominance might have been mounted. Twenty would have been unmanageable. Ten was an arbitrary compromise, a way of diffusing the demand for black political rights without being any more ridiculous than necessary.

In fact, scholars generally divide the black peoples of South Africa into two broad linguistic groupings: the Sotho and the Ngui. The dialects they spoke were mutually intelligible; their values and customs, broadly similar. There was no more in the way of ethnic differences in the nineteenth century between the people who came to be called Zulus and the people who came to be called Ndebeles than there was between the followers of rival Afrikaner leaders in the period of the Trek, such as Andries Pretorius and Andries Potgieter. All Afrikaners spoke the same language, but they ended up in two frontier republics, from which tiny tribal groups continued to splinter off in search of their own place in Africa.

Ndebeles married Sothos. They married Tswanas. They married Zulus. They lived side by side with Pedis, Tsongas, and Swazis. When they moved to the cities, all these various kinds of blacks tended to forget what they were. "A man sounded ridiculous," observed Can Themba, a black South African writer whose stories and early alcohol-induced death were reminiscent of Ring Lardner, "for boasting he was Mopedi or a Mosuto or a Xhosa or a Zulu—nobody seemed to care. You were an African *here*, and somewhere *there* was a white man; two different kinds of humans that impinged now and then—indeed often—and painfully.''

Then, in their will to create a fixed and stable order that had never existed, the white authorities started to draw the boundaries of ethnic "homelands," which closely approximated those of the old tribal reserves. Ethnic identities that had declined in importance suddenly had everything to do with what kind of third-class citizen a black was going to be. Some who regarded themselves as Ndebeles discovered they were living in a country called Bophuthatswana where Tswanas were supposed to have the upper hand. Apartheid revived old enmities among blacks and created new ones. This obviously did no harm to the actuarial prospects of the white regime, but once started, the process of division and alienation was hard to stop. When a motley assortment of Ndebele chiefs asked for a homeland of their own where they could have the fancy houses and cars that the Tswana chiefs were now getting, the white bureaucrats were put in a ticklish position. Apartheid was their idea, one Ndebele chief said, so it was up to them to "unscramble the egg" of black South Africa.

The white officials closest to the scene knew the impossibility of compartmentalizing blacks on an ethnic basis in the Transvaal; the truth was they were scattered and interspersed, had been for more than a century. Apartheid could no more create a pure Ndebele state than it could a pure Afrikaner state; it could only replicate itself, creating a tribal satrapy in which power was unequally distributed on an ethnic basis. The apartheid ideologues knew all this but were flattered by the Ndebele demand, which they embraced as an expression of Ndebele nationalism and therefore as proof that their theoretical ditherings had some validity. Oppression of Ndebeles by Tswanas vindicated their own oppressive policies, demonstrating what chaos there could be in South Africa if they weren't there to draw boundaries. So they compromised: There could be a homeland for southern Ndebeles but not for northern Ndebeles, who would continue to live in Lebowa.

Then it was realized that many in the soaring population of tiny, obscure KwaNdebele were not Ndebeles at all. Half belong to other black ethnic groups. They come, these Zulus and Shangaans and Swazis, to this most pathetic of homelands because it makes more sense to ride the buses than to wait in more remote homelands for jobs to come to them.

Buses. You always come back to buses. A survey by the Human Sciences Research Council in Pretoria found that 71.3 percent of the 534,000 black "commuters" had to travel more than two hours to work, and more than half were away from their homes at least fifteen hours of every working day. And always there was the reflection that the people on those buses, who theoretically come to South Africa only to work and then leave it nightly, are the lucky ones with jobs.

And there is still a whole other category of these resettlement camps—forgotten, forsaken places like Qudeni, another sixty miles down the dirt road from Nondweni in Natal—that are impossibly remote, beyond any social engineer's dream of a commuter route, where the only income is what migrants send home. All these came into existence as a result of the relentless pressure of the government while it was simultaneously seeking—and sometimes receiving—kudos at home and abroad for changing direction.

The contradiction has to be handled with some delicacy. Wherever possible, blacks have to be coaxed, wheedled, and conditioned to move "voluntarily." Instead of harassing black farm tenants and laborers to vacate their homesteads in white rural areas, the authorities bring white farmers around to the view that it is in their interest and a matter of patriotic duty to expel surplus blacks. When they decide to force the issue, the authorities pluck up small numbers at a time, with maximum stealth and speed. The blacks who man the GG trucks in these removals are never of the same ethnic group that is being moved. On the dirt road that runs to the resettlement sites outside Ladysmith, there is a small encampment of ·grant workers from far-off Venda who are employed to move Zulus. A ey-mour, a remote rural hamlet in the eastern part of the Cape that was a ʾ to be handed over to supposedly sovereign Ciskei, I watched one aftᴇ noon as Zulu workers erected rows of temporary metal shelters for Xhosa families that were about to be moved out of a white area fifty miles away. Some white official had selected the only soccer field in Seymour's black township as a convenient site for the coming resettlement. By midafter noon there was no soccer field left.

Ekuvukeni was a resettlement site, unadorned, out in the bush. "Here there's nothing, nothing, nothing," said a widow who had been there for three years. We were now on one of the many islands of the Zulu national state, the landlocked archipelago called KwaZulu. At dusk we ventured into a neighboring country called South Africa to visit Matiwaneskop, a "black spot" in which the authorities had signaled their intention to raze the community by painting numbers on every house and shanty they planned to take over by inexorable eminent domain.

On the way there we passed the ruins of a community called Steincoalspruit, where more than 11,000 blacks had lived on land first purchased by blacks in 1877. One hundred and one years later, nearly the entire community was moved twenty miles, across the homeland border to Ekuvukeni, by GG. Since my last drive down this road, I noticed, a subsidiary of Anglo Vaal, one of the South African mining houses, had started open-pit mining on the land of the displaced community. In Natal the "black spots" with coal usually seem to be expropriated first. But Matiwaneskop—one of 195 remaining "black spots" due to be rubbed out in Natal—was resisting.

What Matiwaneskop had to defend may look paltry, but virtually everything it had, including a new secondary school, it had built itself without support from a government intent on knocking it down. The people there—there were about 12,000—needed no lectures on community development or traditional values. In a letter their elders sent to the government to protest the threatened removal, they included on their list of "tribal achievements" the building of ten churches, sixteen schools, a library, and a mechanical workshop. They still had land for cultivation and grazing, they said, and had never known drought (unlike Ekuvukeni, where the water supply had dried up and water was then being trucked in). Yet they were only fifteen miles from Ladysmith, where many of them worked. And most important, the elders noted, "The graves of our forefathers, the traditional burial places of our chiefs, are the bonds that tie us inseparably with this place." The bureaucracy, which is tenderhearted about tribal traditions that serve its purposes, doesn't tolerate any heathen mumbo jumbo about forefathers' graves when a long-planned removal is in view. But the elders had become skilled diplomats in fending off white officials who came to lecture them about their duty to obey the laws. The last official visitor, it seemed, had nearly been undone by their generosity, reverence, and Christian compassion.

The scene, as it was described to us, was one I would have dearly loved to witness. Outside the community hall, an honor guard of young blacks formed a gauntlet that the commissioner from Ladysmith had to walk when he arrived to address a meeting he had requested. About 1,000 members of the community were waiting inside. Many white officials still like to be called "father" and "lord" in the old colonial style, and this commissioner, it seems, got the full treatment, including the gift of a sheep. Percy Hlope, the principal of the secondary school, explained why the community had decided to present a sheep. "I told him," Mr. Hlope said, smiling through a distinguished gray beard, "that he had chosen to work with black people, poor people, the most despised people in the land, and that therefore, he had identified himself with Jesus Christ. In seeing him before us, I said, we saw our Redeemer and therefore we thought it fitting to give him the only creature that can be identified with Jesus Christ."

The "Redeemer" was visibly moved, as well he might have been, by the moral superiority of the people who were supposed to be his wards. And when the time came for him to respond, he never got around to delivering the message that was presumably the point of the meeting: that Matiwaneskop's time was running out. Instead, Mr. Hlope said, he promised to report the community's sentiments to higher authority. The attitude of higher authority was indicated by a deputy minister with an unctuousness that was unusually sickening, even for a South African deputy minister.

"Every one of us," he wrote to a "black spot" community that was similarly threatened, "has to make sacrifices in some way or other to further peace and prosperity in this beautiful country of ours."

The South African official's wife put together a couple of bits of information and came up with a strange result that left her incredulous. "Is it true," she asked with friendly curiosity, "that you are actually writing a book on KwaNdebele?"

My wisecracking reply, delivered at a diplomatic party in Pretoria, struck me—but only me—as very funny. Its references were cross-cultural, yielding blinks, squints, and blank stares. "Yes," I said, "I'm calling it *The Boys on the Bus.*"

"Well, maybe you should see the other side," she said.

The other side proved to be a cattle ranch of more than 14,000 acres that two friends from her university days had been developing for twenty-four years. They had a herd of about 2,000 head plus three dozen or so prize studs for breeding. The reward for their life's work was a decision by their government to expropriate the land as the site of the new capital for KwaNdebele. Dirk van Deventer and his wife, Paula, had been informed that it was their patriotic duty to negotiate a good price for their holding and move on.

Tall and lean with craggy good looks and an uproarious, humorous manner that was nothing if not forthright, Dirk van Deventer was the South African Boer at his most appealing. His wife, who had earned an agriculture degree and held some of the cattle and land in her own name, seemed tentative in his long shadow. She had not pampered herself like the Pretoria wives—too much time outdoors on the veld had weathered her skin—but the mixed suggestions of vulnerability and strength in her look made her seem real, interesting, and appealing, too, in a way they could never be. The husband, whose right wrist was in a cast, made the *braai*, or barbecue, on a large boulder under an *enkeldoring* ("single thorn") tree, a kind of acacia that was prevalent enough on his land to have given its name to his farm. An ostrich, kept as a pet for nine-year-old Edward van Deventer, lumbered and scavenged nearby. It had recently swallowed his car keys, our host complained, mixing imprecations with a zestful laugh. As the steaks, chops, and *boerewors* (sausage) sizzled over the embers, he held forth in the same fashion on the injustice and lunacy of the pending expropriation, on the blight, erosion, and cattle thieving that had risen in the area with the rise of KwaNdebele. The nearest "closer settlement" was only four miles down the road, and some nights, Dirk said, he sat in a drainage pipe near his fence with a rifle, hoping to sight a poacher. "I'd kill him, too," he said, in a tone of boyish braggadocio rather than menace, "black or white."

Most of his neighbors had decided to be "realistic" and sell for the sake of South Africa and its future. "You voted for it, you do it," he said he told them. This was no closet liberal speaking. Dirk was what is known as a *bloedsap* (which is a political anagram describing a vanishing breed among Afrikaners—ultraconservatives reared in the South African party of Jan Christiaan Smuts and "SAP" by "blood"—still hostile to the governing nationalists). Although it was the white government that wanted to move the Van Deventers, he saw it as a surrender to "Africa" and "communism" and, synonymous in his mind with both those terms, which were synonymous with each other, as a surrender to ignorant and wasteful husbandry.

After lunch we drove into the veld to inspect the site of the new capital, or rather towheaded Edward did the driving, holding his head to the right of the steering wheel of the *bakkie* (pickup truck) since he was too short to see over it. His father shouted directions from the back in Afrikaans. "Drives a tractor as well as anyone on this farm," the father said in English. "Works all day."

As the little boy drove up an incline, his father pointed to a patch of red earth next to a stream at the bottom of the hill. "There's the independence stadium," he said with a sharp-edged laugh. "The secretariat buildings are up there," he said, pointing up the hill. "The civil servants live over there, I think." *Enkeldorings* were living there now; his cattle grazed among them.

Dirk hollered to Edward to stop the *bakkie*. He wanted to show us the veld, which had greened after long-delayed rains. After jumping down, he bent over to pick up some leaves, which he asked us to smell. They had a delicate, lemony fragrance. Then he pointed to a tree with bright yellow blossoms, which he identified as the *huilboom* ("cry tree"). Off in the distance a single cow stood transfixed on a ridge. Sensing a sadness in her stance, Dirk had Edward drive in that direction. His tender husbandman's intuition was borne out; a dead calf lay nearby.

We drove on past an old abandoned tin mine and the houses of some of his twenty-seven laborers. It was there that our host explained the cast on his wrist, which had fractured when his fist collided with the head of one of the twenty-seven. The man had begged off from work, saying he had to take his daughter to a doctor. Instead, he went off on a spree and got drunk. What was worse, the daughter really was in need of seeing the doctor, desperately so. When she had to be rushed to his office, Mrs. van Deventer discovered the father's neglect. But now she was afraid that her husband's manner of recounting the incident was leaving his American guests with a misleading impression. "You're not the kind that just beats them," she interrupted. "You hit them. Then you talk to them. Then you hit them again."

If he had to move, Dirk van Deventer said as we left, he might try ranching in northern Cape Province. But he was a Transvaaler at heart.

He would miss the trees. His brother-in-law thought he should move to America, a suggestion that comes up increasingly as a tease in Afrikaner conversation. I meant it as a tribute when I said he would fit in well in Texas.

The day at the Enkeldoring farm was supposed to show me the "other side." Other side of what? I wondered. It seemed to me to be the same side as Frankfort, a victory for the demented visions of the social engineers in Pretoria and maybe a handful of homeland ministers, for whom South Africa would now erect pretentious mansions on the Van Deventer farm, and a defeat for everyone else. But the failure of the homelands served a deeper need than mere social order. These black states or parodies of black states are bound to fail, bound to turn to the white government that created them. In their failure, they nicely confirm the white man's fixed idea of "Africa" and teach blacks a lesson about their fundamental irresponsibility and dependence; the turning back confirms the white's fixed idea of himself.

"You can live," an Afrikaner tycoon said to me once, "by having the feeling that at least you're indispensable."

Chapter Six

Generalissimo

"Some words," the novelist Jean Rhys wrote, "have a long thin neck that you would like to strangle." For any outsider who returns to South Africa after an absence of months or years, the word "change" is likeliest to provoke spasms of what might be called lexicide. "Do you see the changes?" was usually not a question, I discovered, but an assertion that they were all around and that if you didn't acknowledge them fast, your intellectual credentials would be open to question. "You had better learn," exploded an English-speaking lawyer whom I had unintentionally provoked, "that there is such a thing as barbarism!" There is such a thing as apoplexy, and he seemed to be on the verge of it.

So I got a little evasive. "Yes, it has changed," I would sometimes say, drawing the expected comparison to my first incarnation in the country, "but not as much as New York in the same period." That response was mildly provocative, interesting, and probably true without being open to challenge as a political declaration. Finally, after I had been back in the country for nearly a year and thought that I had my responses down pat, I was surprised to hear myself blurting out an answer I had never before tried. "Do you see the changes?" asked an Afrikaner businessman next to whom I was seated at a Cape Town lunch. The warning bells sounded faintly in my head, but I thought I was being flippant when I replied, "Yes, I never imagined they would be able to carry apartheid so far." Only when the words were out of my mouth did I realize that this was the answer that had gradually been taking shape in my mind all those months; to me, at least, it had the ring of cold truth.

Who could have imagined KwaNdebele? Or a resettlement program extending into the 1980s and beyond? Or black TV, where Zulu gangsters and Zulu detectives could fight it out in a Zulu city? Or the four independent homelands that were supposed to be striving in sad isolation from South Africa? It was only necessary to run your finger down the column of black population estimates published by the Central Statistical Services in Pretoria to see how far apartheid had gone. Despite a high birthrate, the number of blacks in South Africa regularly showed a decline. In 1976 there were 18.5 million blacks; by 1977, the official statistics claimed, there were only 15.7 million. Between 1973 and 1982, if you could believe what you read, there had been virtually no rise at all. Apartheid double bookkeeping, subtracting blacks every time there was an independence ceremony in a homeland, made this miracle possible. Who could have imagined that?

And who, I would ask myself, could have imagined a figure like Lieutenant General Xhanti Charles Sebe? Director of state security in "independent" Ciskei, a flamboyant black cop who sometimes wore a black Stetson with his smoked glasses and Christian Dior suits, this black generalissimo was as dedicated as any white to the system that produced him. Apartheid sent him to courses on intelligence gathering and bush warfare, put white colonels under his nominal command, and gave him a wedge of territory to secure in the many-sided struggle against "terrorism." It put a helicopter and a couple of planes at his disposal and also a fat-cat BMW sedan with frosted glass so that the assassins who were presumed to be lurking in wait for him could never know whether he was inside or where he was sitting. It gave him an armory of fancy weapons and listening devices, four small military bases, a prison system all his own, a chestful of medals, and a real security problem in an area that had long been the crucible of black resistance to white dominance. He was exactly what the system needed to generate for its own survival, a dependable black ally who believed, more or less, in its purposes. His power, which was turned effectively against his own people, was real, not symbolic, and this was how the system answered the demand for black power that had been inspired in the region only a few years earlier by Steve Biko, whom Charles Sebe, then a lowly sergeant in the South African security police, had been assigned to shadow.

When the black general fell after three brief years, his white handlers in the South African security apparatus did everything they could, short of bringing down the Tinkertoy government in the homeland they themselves had created, to get him back. Later, I imagined, they must have felt like the early space scientists after an accident with a rocket, telling themselves that since they had got one into orbit, they could do it again.

Charles Sebe could be viewed from a standpoint of liberal piety as a victim, too, of course, but I viewed him as a walking, breathing allegory of the whole racial conflict. If you considered what Ciskei really was—a sinkhole of despair and social misery into which the white authorities continued to pour surplus blacks from adjacent white areas—his enthusiasm for his mission had frightening implications. Of course, the white state had the capacity to put blacks on its payroll and set up homeland leaders in conditions of vassalage, but getting blacks actively engaged in the defense of this setup was something else. Yet what set Charles Sebe apart was how easy it always seemed to imagine the small twist of fate that might have landed him on the other side, where he would have had the same appetite for half-baked doctrines of guerrilla warfare that he now had for half-baked doctrines of counterinsurgency. He had sold out, it was true, but that was long before he could have imagined the rewards and power that would later be placed within his grasp. He had sold out because he wanted to be on the side of power and authority. Every culture, every society, produces such men. The ability of the South African racial system to perpetuate itself turned in part, it seemed to me, on its ability to recruit and reward blacks like Charles Sebe. That he could exist at all suggested to me that the racial system might be more durable than I had imagined.

So I made a point of getting to know him and found, before long, that this black militarist's dedication, energy, and power were being transmitted to a coterie of seemingly capable black aides, well-spoken, well-armed young men in expensive suits and cars who had found that they didn't have to join the underground to be where the action was in Ciskei. Created in his image, they showed Charles Sebe to be a leader. "My boys," he would purr, suddenly tender and avuncular, "I motivate my boys." Within a few months after I encountered them, they all were in one of General Sebe's jails, along with General Sebe. That surprising denouement put an ambiguous ending on my allegory, but there would be others to take their places.

I don't think Charles Sebe ever learned my name. When I phoned from Johannesburg and identified myself, there would be a pause on the other end, a palpable moment of uncertainty; then he would ask in a gravelly half whisper, "Is that my friend?"

"Yes," I ventured with considerable uncertainty myself the first time we had this exchange, figuring that anything less might cut it short.

All our subsequent phone conversations went the same way. "Oh, hello, my friend!" he would reply.

The truth was I liked him. I could not respect him for his commitment the way I respected the black trade union leaders in East London whom he harassed. But he never went in for the strained apologetics of the other homeland potentates who would tell you how they were using apartheid to fight apartheid from the inside. In Umtata, the capital of the nearby Transkei homeland, I met Tsepo Letlaka, who had jumped in several stages from being a leader in exile of the Pan-Africanist Congress, one of the banned nationalist movements, to being minister of justice in a black state that emulated South Africa by outlawing the movement in which he had once been active. He insisted that he had "grown up in the liberation movement" and his commitment was "completely unchanged." Transkei, he argued, was a fulfillment of Pan-Africanist principles, being black and independent. There was a more obvious explanation. Tsepo Letlaka had found a job and come home; whether he was a genuine nationalist or an agent in his exile phase, or a little of both, he was in from the cold.

Charles Sebe never had to squirm. A romantic who found it necessary to cast himself in a heroic role in a drama, he had been groomed by the security police for the part of a black anti-Communist crusader, and though he must occasionally have realized that he was acting in the theater of the absurd, he lived it. Even his victims found it hard sometimes not to share in the pleasure he derived from his role. The East London trade unionists all could do wonderful imitations of his slow pattern of speech, in which each syllable was milked for maximum effect. Constantly inventing his own recitative, Charles Sebe invented himself. "I think he belongs to the film stars," Thozamile Gqweta, the president of the black South African Allied Workers Union, said to me once. "He would make a very good movie. He's a bogus chap, but he's very good at what he does." By that time Thozamile Gqweta had lost count of how many times he had been in General Sebe's jails.

The first time I saw Charles Sebe he was standing at attention behind dark aviator glasses, a lean, almost feline figure, at the elbow of Ciskei's president, his own elder brother, Lennox L. Sebe. The brothers could scarcely have looked less alike. The president, a former school inspector and country preacher, was darker and heavier, ponderous in manner as well as physique. Charles Sebe was all coiled energy; he made me think of a sinister Tonton Macoute from Haiti. The president laboriously explained to an invited group of foreign journalists why he had decided to accept the dubious gift of sovereignty on South Africa's terms. The occasion was a preindependence referendum on that decision, in which all the levers of tribal loyalty and patronage had been used to turn out in his one-party backwater a popular response that could be held up as an endorsement. Gqweta and the other trade unionists who could have led an effective opposition were locked up for the duration of the campaign, but a panel of supposedly impartial foreign observers were flown from Pretoria to supervise the proceedings. They included John Sears, a Washington lawyer who had been sacked as Ronald Reagan's campaign manager earlier that year and now found himself on the sidelines in this improbably and pitifully destitute black Zion, having just negotiated a contract to represent South Africa as a lobbyist that was said to be worth half a million dollars a year to his law firm.

Charles Sebe was a brigadier that day, having just been promoted from colonel. He was a major general when, a year later, I had my first conversation with him. On a Sunday, I spent an afternoon with him in the heavily guarded compound where he made his home, surrounded by the homes of his most reliable lieutenants. The place was on a ridge only a couple of miles outside King William's Town, a small white trading center. The new blue-and-white Ciskeian flag was already flapping from a dozen flagstaffs at the prefabricated independence stadium that South Africa had hastily thrown up. But just as conspicuous that weekend were the banners of a competing black nationalism that had been on view at a mass funeral for a black lawyer who had represented Gqweta's union. His name was Griffiths Mxenge, and he had been brutally murdered—repeatedly and sadistically stabbed—in Durban. Fifteen thousand supposed Ciskeians had turned out at his funeral, the biggest funeral in the region since the one four years earlier for the martyred Biko, whose grave, in a black cemetery between the railway tracks and a gravel pit on the outskirts of King William's Town, was marked by a granite headstone that raised its own muted protest against the ceremonies that were about to be enacted in the stadium. "One Azania one nation," the headstone proclaimed, using the name that some black nationalists would like to attach to a black-ruled South Africa.

The general did not seek to play down the significance of the previous day's funeral. "It was," he said, squeezing off each syllable like a retaliatory shot, "*the re-vi-val of the Af-ri-can Na-tion-al Con-gress.*" Charles Sebe, it seemed to me, usually spoke in italics. The eastern Cape, South Africa's traditional cockpit, where blacks and whites first met and clashed, had a long lineage of black nationalist heroes stretching back decades before Biko and Gqweta. As early as 1930 a black trade union had briefly shut down East London with a general strike. What was a little new was a black general on the other side of the conflict.

"In South Africa, there is a ceiling for blacks, yes, there is a cciling," he remarked in a later conversation in his office. He was referring to the South African security police, in which he had never made officer's rank. Charles Sebe was now a lieutenant general and a world traveler with an office decorated with souvenirs from Israel and Taiwan. There was also a shredder and a Chubb safe containing a portion of his personal arsenal. The general was supposed to have command of all of Ciskei's burgeoning prisons, police, army, and intelligence service, but interrogation of suspected enemies remained a big part of his business. This gave a potentially sinister point to the otherwise quaint piety that was exhibited in a frame over his desk. "The most beautiful gift we can give each other is the truth," it proclaimed.

I was wondering how I might interpret that had I not come to his office on a voluntary basis as the general, slightly qualifying his loyalty to his previous employers, gently picked at what seemed to be the scab on an old wound. "Why is there no black man working in Pretoria as an officer of the security police?" he asked. "And why don't they sit around the table with blacks on a decision-making security matter in southern Africa?" In other words, if he was really a commander now in a sovereign state, why didn't he deal directly with his opposite number in Pretoria? Why did he still have to go through the chain of command, reporting to the white general's underlings in East London and Port Elizabeth? I volunteered no answers.

"It's a naïve type of an exercise," he concluded.

That was the closest I heard him come to expressing resentment of his former bosses. On another occasion he insisted that he had never experienced any racial slight in his twenty-five years in the South African police. "I was lucky for the whites to accept me for what I was," he said. "I never had conflict with them because I was dedicated to my job." He was what they wanted him to be, eager to please, and soon proved his worth by joining the African National Congress under an assumed name in Cape Town. In 1962 in Port Elizabeth, two years after the organization had been banned, he participated in the arrest of one of its key leaders, a black Communist named Govan Mbeki. Charles Sebe could remember having sympathy for the ANC "because," as he said, "I was a black man and it was they who were for the upliftment of blacks." But more important were the drama of undercover work and the approval, the personal upliftment, that came his way as a result of his dedication. If he felt any twinge of conscience, it was submerged in the idea that the fight against black nationalism was also a fight against "communism."

One of his last tasks as a South African cop had been to tail black nationalists drawn to King William's Town by Biko, who had been confined to his hometown by ministerial fiat in 1973. Biko's friends remember that they had only to look in their rearview mirrors to see Sergeant Sebe in his dark glasses, riding on their bumpers in an unmarked car. The general would always exercise his gift for dramatic narrative when he talked about those days. "Biko was nobody's fool," he said. "You know what Biko used to tell me? Biko used to say, 'Charles, look, one guy I like is yourself because you are very straight about your job. You don't compromise. And I am straight about my politics. I don't compromise. Now, if we overcome, I can never be ashamed to propose you as in charge of the security services.' ''

The recollection made him laugh, shake his head, and jackknife forward in his seat. "Really! That is what he said to me," he went on. "Then it was a big joke."

Biko's friends remember that Charles Sebe was often the butt of such jokes. They all were younger and better educated than he was—Biko himself was twelve years younger—and thought that he was a character, this eager black cop. They were laughing at him as well as with him, and he, of course, always knew it. Underneath the carapace of his new authority and rank, their contempt must still have rankled.

I pressed Charles Sebe for his feelings at the time of Biko's death in 1977. "I was very much involved in collecting intelligence about him, but he was a human being, *a hu-man be-ing.*" The general often repeated himself for emphasis. "He never had a gun to shoot at me, and I was on the other hand," he said. "If I was on the other hand, him having a gun to shoot at me, and then I shot first, I would be *very* pleased. But my answer is, he was a human being. I don't like scandal, my friend, I don't like *scan-dal.*"

I then asked him if he knew Pieter Goosen, the security police officer who oversaw Biko's interrogation and dispatched him in a comatose state in the back of a Land-Rover to Pretoria. "He's my friend!" Charles Sebe said. "I don't judge a person because that's not my work," he went on. "If he has got to answer to God, OK, he'll answer to God. It's not my interest."

"They are haunted by Biko," one of the dead man's closest friends said to me of the Sebes. But it was much easier to claim a tie to him when he was safely out of the way than it would have been were he alive to refute them. "He was a son of the soil. The circumstances of his death made the whole nation bitter."

Now he was re-inventing history for my benefit. By the "whole nation," he did not mean Biko's Azania but his own Ciskei, for which he would, if only he could, claim Biko as a hero. Lennox Sebe was now officially "President for Life," exalted by an Assembly in which elected representatives are permanently outnumbered by tribal chiefs who have been, in effect, mobilized into a political patronage machine run from the top. He had recently acquired a ten-seat executive jet and a Daimler limousine. He was about to move into his new presidential mansion in Bisho. Yet this onetime school inspector and country preacher, who had agreed to play politics by the white man's rules, was subject to fits of depression lasting sometimes for weeks, during which no decisions on matters of state could be taken in the homeland. What was haunting him was not just Biko—the proud, self-liberated black who had to be broken because he would not bend—but the unnerving suspicion that he himself was really an impostor.

The chiefs who supported Ciskeian independence were also rewarded with expensive sedans and houses. "Powerlessness breeds a race of beggars who smile at the enemy and swear at him in the sanctity of their toilets; who shout '*Baas*' willingly during the day and call the White man a dog in their buses as they go home." Those words were written by Steve Biko before he was silenced permanently several months before his thirty-first birthday. They cannot legally be printed in South Africa today, but Lennox Sebe from the sanctity of his position as putative leader of a putatively sovereign state can say anything that pops into his head about the evils of apartheid—"the oppressive yoke of political serfdom," he calls it—for unlike Biko, he makes no claim to equal rights in an undivided South Africa, although more than two thirds of his nominal Ciskeians who find any work at all spend most of their waking hours across the invisible border.

Meanwhile, it is South Africa that keeps his indigent state afloat, underwriting 80 percent of its budget, and it is South Africa that trains his army and police to face a common enemy, who are, as he himself said of Biko, sons of the soil.

"You can tell me about other things," Charles Sebe was saying, blissfully casting himself in the role of spymaster, "and I won't differ with you. But security, intelligence, military, it's my trade, and the strategy is in my bloodstream. I like it."

He was a happy man, possibly the only truly happy man in the whole of Ciskei, for he was living his fantasy. He had given speeches on "terrorism" in southern Africa in Jerusalem and Taipei. Now he had confirmation of his status from a citadel of learning that was geographically much closer but, in the South African context, light-years and even eons away. Charles Sebe, a former black constable who had gotten his secondary school certificate in a correspondence course, had been invited to lecture on "The Communistic Guerrilla Onslaught" to Afrikaner students at the University of the Orange Free State. That meant more to Xhanti Charles Sebe than being invited to lecture at Cambridge or Oxford could have meant to Jan Christiaan Smuts.

"I would like you to be there," he said, "because I have highlighted quite a number of things in this paper."

When he rose to speak after a benediction and introduction in Afrikaans, the general solemnly gave his undergraduate audience a rigid salute. Few of these young Afrikaners would ever have had occasion before in their lives to sit and listen to a black man delivering a speech, so Charles Sebe's presence in their midst was nearly as surprising to them as it was to him. Then, as they got their first earful, it became even more surprising, practically stupefying at times. Some, who were unused to spoken English, may have imagined they were having a hard time following the speaker because of language. But the general's exaggerated articulation made every word comprehensible; it was the connections between the words and the sentences they formed that became bewildering. This was only partly because his prepared text was lacking in coherence. General Sebe frequently wearied of reading and recharged himself every few minutes by speaking extemporaneously so that his remarks droned like a high-altitude plane that unpredictably dives down for strafing runs, then sails up again into the blue yonder. When he was flying on his own, the general's hands rose and fell, catching fistfuls of air, and his voice teased out sounds that pleased his ears, rolling *r*'s and long diphthongs to which he added an extra beat and inflection. The roller-coaster effect suited the evangelist's role he was now playing as he depicted a struggle between forces of darkness, black "terrorists" manipulated by the "*dra-gon of comm-u-nism*," and the forces of light, represented by the allied republics of South Africa and Ciskei.

"The subject is quite a complexed one," he said in his hoarse, throaty way. "Some of you might have nightmares tonight because of the big threat that I will talk about."

From their earliest days these Afrikaner students had been force-fed on Manichaean interpretations of an impending struggle, but to hear a black man assert that he had come to "psychologically awaken" them must have disturbed the order of priorities and categories on which they had been reared. After all, if there was any awakening to be done, it was supposed to be by white missionaries who concerned themselves with blacks. What business could a black have meddling with white souls? What was hardest to understand or accept was his easy assumption of authority. "I read about communism, I am still reading about communism *the-o-ret-i-cal-ly*," he boasted, trilling the last word, "but I am also working communism *prac-ti-cal-ly*."

And communism, of course, was everywhere. It was in South Africa's churches, its student organizations, and, above all, its black political movements. Black theology and white liberalism were equally infected. "I don't know what that is," he said, taking off from his text, "but in my context a liberal is a Communist." I turned in my seat and looked around the hall to see if anyone had blinked at that; as far as I could make out, General Sebe was getting an increasingly respectful hearing. He made little mistakes—he was off by a factor of 100 when he said there were 3 million Cubans in Angola—but these were not the sorts of slips his audience was prepared to catch. Nearer to home, I wondered if anyone in the room besides me knew that it was in this same city of Bloemfontein that the African National Congress, which the general was now lambasting for its "atrocious activities" on behalf of the Kremlin, first came into existence. That was in 1912, when the czar was still in St. Petersburg, and Lenin in Zurich, and it started off with the unbelievably moderate aim of providing the white government of the two-year-old Union of South Africa with a "direct and independent channel of informing itself as to the things uppermost in the natives' mind from time to time." It wanted then only to make known their grievances, not to share in power.

Only two or three persons in the hall abstained from the enthusiastic applause that greeted that conclusion. Charles Sebe had earned it by offering himself as proof to these young Afrikaners that their system of partition and exclusion had black support. Now, he fielded questions. Did he really mean to say, a skeptical questioner asked, that there was no social conflict in South Africa between blacks and whites, that all black demands were manipulated by Communists? "That is my case," he replied firmly.

Was Ciskei ready to send its troops to do "border duty" against the Communists in Namibia? the next questioner demanded. "That is in process," he promised, to hand-stinging claps. Finally he brought down the house with his answer to a young man who wanted to know how he could support "separate development" and denounce apartheid: What, after all, was the difference?

"I've got to educate you," he began. "It's a matter of ignorance. You are white; I am black. I'm having my own traditions; I'm having my own norms. I live the way I live." Blacks wanted to own what whites owned and live in cities. "But not," he went on, "*in-ter-mar-riage*. What will you get from *in-ter-mar-riage*? You get a colored." The word was pronounced with contempt. "You don't get a white person, you don't get a black person, but a frustrated child, which does not belong anywhere." Charles Sebe had not spent half his life in white government offices without learning how to pander to white risibilities on the subject of race. He was talking in terms of black pride, but he neglected to answer the question about what was wrong with apartheid.

Afterward in the social hall, where wine and cheese were served, I accosted one young man with thinning blond hair and a little mustache and asked what he made of the visitor. The response was ethnological. "Sotho people are very different," he said. "We have Sotho people on our farm."

As far as I could make out, he was saying that Ciskei might be able to produce a Sebe but that was no reason to change the social order where he lived. What would he have thought, I wondered, if he'd ever heard the likes of Steve Biko?

And then one day Xhanti Charles Sebe vanished. Like a rank-and-file member of a black trade union, he had been thrown into one of his own jails on the orders of his brother. Another brother, the transport minister, was also jailed. "Sebe Runs Out of Brothers," cracked a headline in *City Press*, a newspaper in Johannesburg aimed at blacks.

The feud, I learned from South African officials who made it their business to know, had its origins in a question of whether the president was actually the son of the late Mr. Sebe. Two other sons thought that only they were legitimate. Since Lennox Sebe supported his own dubious claims to chieftainship through his lineage, someone might have suggested that Charles, the next eldest, was the real chief. Made paranoid by the family tensions, the president decided to strip his brother of all his positions of command, leaving him only the intelligence service as a fig leaf to conceal his disgrace.

It was at this point that the president took up the narrative, which was as entertaining for him as it was for me. He stretched out his legs and studied the surface of his ostrich leather shoes. In this posture his chin rested on his chest, which compressed his jowls to something like a pudding. Often his choice of words recalled his days in the pulpit. "I could clearly see him leaving the light and going into the road of perpetual darkness," he intoned mournfully, describing Charles's reluctance to accept the "decision of the nation," by which he meant his own decision to put the general in his place. The president said he had been "rudely shocked" by the discovery of Charles's usurpation of power and administrative shortcomings. When he revealed the "decision of the nation" to the chiefs and headmen who composed his party's caucus, the fears and resentments that had accumulated as the general built his miniature police state finally were voiced. "They dared to tell me things that hurt me," the president said. Now he was playing Lear, suffering *lèse-majesté* at the hands of his own.

These events had occurred as Lennox Sebe was to leave for Israel. A few Israelis had discovered they could do profitable business in Ciskei by feeding the president's illusions that he had foreign relations extending farther than Pretoria. First they had persuaded him to purchase his jet, which then couldn't be landed on the grass runway that was Ciskei's only excuse for an airport, and now they were promising to introduce him to members of the Israeli government. But before leaving, he said, he took the precaution of inducing one of his brother's aides to keep him informed by phone of the general's activities. The plot thickened rapidly: The aide found Charles Sebe drafting a memorandum to General Johan Coetzee, the commissioner of police in South Africa, on his brother's unpredictable conduct. Lennox Sebe got wind of the letter and resolved to fly home. On his return to Zwelitsha, he discovered that his own foreign minister's residence had been machine-gunned the night before, but he saw through the ruse: The argument was to have been made that "terrorists" were on the loose and, therefore, the general had to be restored to his positions of command for the safety of a state under siege.

"I was in Israel, but I make bold to say," he now declaimed, reenacting for my benefit what he then said to the Cabinet, "that the whole trick comes from the department of State Security. I'm saying it in front of the general, 'Forget about terrorism.'"

He then ordered his brother disarmed and started arresting the general's aides one by one. Charles Sebe pleaded his innocence, maintaining as he had so often in my hearing that he was a professional. "Well, well, well," the president said, chortling triumphantly as he contemplated the pitiable vanity of that boast. "It didn't click to him that the game was up. A word to the wise is sufficient, but an advice to fools makes them go quickly to their *self-appointed snares*." The president, who also spoke in italics, was saying the general had to be locked up, too.

The self-satisfied gurglings that were coming from the presidential chair by the end of this two-hour monologue would have alarmed me considerably if I had been worried about the future of the South African homeland system. I wasn't, and they didn't. Solemnly I asked whether there was any chance for a reconciliation. Only Sir Ralph Richardson, in a role like that of Sir Anthony Absolute in *The Rivals*, might have soared to the level of sanctimonious hokum that the "President for Life" now reached as he expressed his astonishment over his discovery, only after the arrest, of the personal luxuries on which the general had squandered state funds. A rural development project for a hundred people, he exclaimed dolefully, could have been started with the money that went to furnishing his brother's farm. "How can you trust such a man to speak about the cancer of communism when in the same breath he is plowing the ground for it and cultivating it?" he asked.

I refrained from inquiring about the source of the investment that was being poured into his own farm or the cost of his new Daimler.

White officials had hoped to promote a restoration, but when I asked about that possibility, a South African shook his head and sighed resignedly. "There's no hope," he said. (In fact, not quite a year later, Charles Sebe was convicted and sentenced to twelve years in jail on a charge of incitement. The accusation was that he had tried to break into one of the jails he had administered in order to free his former deputy, who had been arrested on orders from the "President for Life." The conditions and location of Charles Sebe's imprisonment, I am informed, are not known.)

The whites now blamed themselves for having made Charles Sebe vulnerable by concentrating too much authority in his hands. Of course, that aroused jealousy. Of course, *they* would fight among themselves. *They* always do. It is in *their* culture. This was what outsiders could never be made to understand about *them*. It was a mistake to rush history, a mistake to expect too much in Africa, although as one of his closest white colleagues was eager to affirm, "Charles Sebe was a good friend of South Africa." Not a good South African, mind you, since he was black, but a good friend nonetheless.

Having based their homeland system on the most retrograde tendencies in African tribal life, the whites could derive their usual solace from the results: At least they knew they were indispensable. But what did that say about the durability of the system? Could they ever find dependable black surrogates? "I used to think this was the only way," said a white who had worked closely with the Sebes. "Now I think we're creating a monster."

I would have given a lot to know what lessons Charles Sebe drew as he did push-ups and sit-ups in his cell in order to keep fit. Would he have expected the whites to intercede successfully on his behalf? Would their failure to do so make him re-examine his loyalties? Or would the fact that he had been jailed by blacks in a black state make him nostalgic for the days when he worked directly for whites?

The month the general was cashiered, I met handsome 18-year-old Bay-anda Majole at an impoverished settlement in the Transkei. He wanted to join the police; not Transkei's homeland police, he specified, but the South African police. Pressed for reasons, he was not at all inarticulate. "I'm a strict person, and I believe in enforcing rules," he said. "I also want to be able to protect myself."

Growing up in Transkei had disillusioned him with the whole idea of black rule. When there were fights between rival factions in the area where he lived, the Transkei police never wanted to know about them. The only black government he knew was corrupt and predatory. It would be better for blacks, he felt sure, if whites ruled the whole of South Africa.

The hillside on which we were standing offered a startling visual example of the deprivation that the South African system seeks to legitimize. On the South African side of a sluggish stream called the Umthavuna, you could see a homestead and a few farm buildings, many trees, extensive pastures, and terraced cabbage plots, which were irrigated by water pumped from the river. On the black side there were several hundred houses, hardly any trees, hardly any grass, erosion out of control, no water pumps, and not even a single tap. This contrast made Bayanda Majole angry at his own people, rather than at the few on the other side of the Umthavuna.

Bayanda wasn't interested in ambiguous outcomes, in making the best of a bad situation. As he saw it, you sided with either the blacks or the whites, and life in independent Transkei had settled that question for him. He was proud, consciously hurt in his pride, but inoculated, it seemed, against slogans about "black pride." And so he would enlist in the South African police if the South African Defense Force wouldn't take him.

It was not my place to argue with this young man, and I didn't feel inclined to do so. Bayanda Majole had helped explain Lieutenant General Xhanti Charles Sebe to me. He seemed to be a logical outcome of the homeland system, an example, therefore, of what could be described as its success. This outcome was what the homelands were all about, showing that, properly channeled, black anger could be turned against black anger.

CHAPTER SEVEN

Controlled Strength

Black anger isn't a problem only for the authorities to divert into storage tanks—homelands, hostels, and jails. It's a problem as well for anyone who wonders why there isn't more of it. The ordinary white conditions himself not to think about this, the way Californians try not to think about earthquakes, but inevitably there comes a moment when he confronts the question of why blacks with all their numbers endure what he would find unendurable. Even whites who reject stereotypes (the most common being the one about blacks as guileless children of nature) regularly lapse into wondering what it is that explains the long wait for black anger to make itself felt. Often then they resort to pseudo-Marxist speculation about the conditions in which "prerevolutionary" societies rise or to convoluted cultural and sociological theories. One I heard had to do with messianic cults that mix African beliefs in spirits with the promise of Christianity, the argument being that messianism as a cultural reflex helped sublimate black anger.

Such speculation made me uneasy, mainly because I regarded it as a distraction from my task of looking at the reality of South Africa as it is. Theorizing about the future, I thought, was often a device for evading or excusing the present. Yet it sometimes seemed necessary to ask what mixture of black complicity, resignation, or hope kept the system working. So one afternoon I tried out the messianism theory on Buti Tlhagale at his Soweto church. Father Buti, a young Roman Catholic priest with training in Rome, a background in the Black Consciousness Movement, and a fine, speculative mind that could be ironic as well as ardent, usually picked up an argument as if it were an artifact, examining it from various angles before taking it apart. This one he just swept aside.

"That's not how it is," he objected. "The students you see here aren't waiting for any messiah. They just get cut down so fast. A student leader lasts for three to six months. They go to jail, or they go to exile. Or they wear out—they come home and they just sit. You'd expect them to be angry and resentful, but you never hear anything out of them. It's the pressure. They've just had too much."

There was courage and resentment among blacks, Father Buti was saying, but it was no match yet for the fear the security apparatus could inspire. The gentle young priest fully grasped the implications of his argument, both for himself as a preacher of the gospel and for his people.

"We must hate just a little bit more," he said.

I had already lived through one of the short cycles of repression he was describing. Young blacks I met when I first came back to South Africa had been grabbed from their homes by the security police, subjected to months of solitary confinement, beaten and tortured and interrogated, then released under various forms of legal restriction and extralegal intimidation. The contrast between the optimistic, spirited young men I had met early on and the taut, somber veterans they had become provided one measure of the widening gulf between black and white. These transformations had been accomplished in only a year or a year and a half. I had been wandering around southern Africa, a professional tourist, a taster at a buffet, while they were being humiliated and broken down. I had been collecting impressions of a conflict that only occasionally breaks into the open; they had been at the front.

"But you shall be free one day," promised a poster in the offices of the South African Allied Workers Union on my first visit to East London. Stuck on the wall near the poster, for all to see, was a copy of the Freedom Charter, a populist manifesto advanced as a platform by the African National Congress and its affiliates when they were legal organizations. "South Africa belongs to all its people, black and white," the Freedom Charter promised. If anything, that was conspicuously less true then than it had been in 1955, the year the document was drafted, but the promise had not dimmed.

The union's offices were crowded that Saturday morning with black workers: young men and women who worked at East London factories. By joining the new union, they were asking for trouble. Many of them would be out of a job and blacklisted in East London long before the town, let alone the country, belonged to all its people. Thozamile Gqweta, the union's president, had been in one of General Sebe's new jails in the homeland at that point for two months, and there was no telling when he would be released. All the signs pointed to confrontation and conflict, yet 100 or so young workers were backed up into the corridors, patiently waiting to pay their dues and receive membership cards; in six months a handful of black organizers with no previous trade union experience had signed up 15,000 workers. The atmosphere was that of a revival: Hope could surmount any barrier; salvation was assured, if not exactly imminent. The leadership—at least the portion of it not detained with Gqweta—seemed to share this headiness. In this setting I met Frank Tongo.

The regional secretary for the union had a shaved head and a goatee and a bright, slightly caustic manner. He had been working for eight years in a clerical position at the Hoover Company, the American appliances maker. He wore a necktie to work but had emerged as the union leader when SAAWU, the acronym by which the movement was known, burst on the scene. The company's local managers, all white South Africans, wanted to break the union, he was convinced, but the top man was under pressure from the American home office, which had subscribed to a set of principles for American multinationals working within the apartheid system that had been drafted by a Baptist minister from Philadelphia, the Reverend Leon Sullivan. One of the principles promised collective bargaining with freely chosen union representatives, and Frank Tongo was confident that the enthusiasm and steadfastness of the workers would be enough to drive home this wedge.

Eric Mntonga, who also wore a necktie to work, carried confidence nearly to euphoria. A laboratory assistant at the Wilson Rowntree candy factory, he had just led his first stoppage, winning a minor skirmish with management in an early test of strength. "We've been longing, we've been looking for a union," he said, "and now we have it. They begged us to come back, and already things are changing. The managing director said that if anything doesn't satisfy us, I don't have to go to the personnel director; I can speak directly to him."

Before I left the SAAWU office that afternoon, I was assured that the power of the new black unions would ultimately put an end to the pass laws, the migrant labor system, and the Group Areas Act. I flew on to Port Elizabeth, where I met the leaders of a new black union in the motor industry, the Motor Assembly and Component Workers Union of South Africa. And they, too, were ready to declare openly that the freedom they sought was not limited to their factories or township. This meant, they realized, that they were bound to clash with the authorities.

On subsequent trips to East London and Port Elizabeth, I saw how the reality of white power in South Africa made itself felt. Scarcely half a year after my first visit to East London, I found that 2,000 members of the new union had lost their jobs. They included Eric Mntonga and 470 others who had been fired at the chocolate factory. Mntonga had just spent eighty-one days in one of General Sebe's jails. The British-owned candy company insisted that the union had provoked a showdown. Its case was half persuasive until a security police memorandum on union busting was leaked to some sympathizers of the union; the candy company had followed the instructions point by point. On that visit I finally met Gqweta, a former salesman with the lean good looks of a trained athlete. In the year that he had been the union's president, he had been arrested repeatedly without ever facing a charge. A few hours after we talked, he was again detained, this time by the South Africans instead of Sebe's men.

Back in Port Elizabeth that same month, I found that one of the union leaders I had met there was in detention and the others were no longer wearing neckties. The Ford Motor Company had taken the stand, reasonable enough in normal labor relations, that a blue-collar union could not be led from desks in its front office; the leaders, given the choice of leaving the union or returning to production jobs, were back on the assembly line. The grease on their overalls wasn't the only sign of the changes they had experienced. The accumulated strains of those months had different origins—the watchfulness of the police, shop floor confrontations with white supervisors, disputes over tactics within the new black labor movement, formal negotiations with the company's skilled negotiators, the militant hopes still welling within the black community—and it was normally impossible to respond to one of these pressures without intensifying others. All this showed in their faces and their voices, which sometimes now turned sardonic and bitter. They weren't less committed, but they seemed less hopeful, as if they were doing what they had to do, whatever the consequences.

What they had to do the last evening I was in Port Elizabeth was call off a strike at Ford and General Motors that they had started to put pressure on a third company, Firestone, which had dismissed some black strikers. The sympathy strike tactic was bleeding the community and the union, which had dreamed of becoming in Port Elizabeth what Solidarity was then proving to be in Gdansk. I went to a mass meeting at which the facts were faced. It was dusk and the light was failing as 2,500 black workers stood in orderly ranks in a hall to consider a tactical retreat. The somber light, the somber mood, made for a moving chiaroscuro study in blacks and browns. There was little or no dissension; the gathering felt its own righteousness and strength, yet it recognized that these were still far from enough.

Months passed before it became possible to ask about what happened to the black trade union men who had started to disappear. I heard Frank Tongo's story first. The security police had let me find out the day before I saw him again that they had been following me, so we drove around through deserted streets near the beach area and then stopped, when it seemed we were unobserved, in a parking lot adjacent to a segregated white beach. Frank Tongo had been through something harrowing, and he definitely did not want to go through it again. The police had told him they would kill him, he said, if he talked about what had happened to him in jail. He didn't really believe they meant it, but he had become an insomniac since his release, and the threat was with him every night.

Yet, even before agreeing to talk to me, he had defied them by filing a lawsuit against the minister of law and order, contending that he had sustained "serious bodily injuries" and injuries to his "dignity and self-esteem." A young black man from Port Elizabeth named Sipho Mtimkulu, who had filed a similar suit against the minister of law and order, had recently vanished and was presumed by his friends and relatives to have been murdered. It was not hard to imagine the thoughts that kept Frank Tongo awake.

The white officers who worked him over appeared to put in a normal working day. He was taken from his cell in an ordinary jail at about seven in the morning and transported to Cambridge, the security police headquarters in East London. At half past four in the afternoon, he was cleaned up and sent back. The time in between he spent stripped to his underpants in handcuffs and leg irons, periodically contorted into a human doughnut with his wrists manacled to his ankles. This made it possible for his interrogators to dangle him by a chain from a heavy board they had rigged between two desks so that his body was just off the ground. He could then be spun on the chain and beaten with sticks, a procedure that was followed daily to persuade him to acknowledge that the leadership of his union was operating on instructions from the African National Congress. When he denied it, a soft rubber hood was placed over his head, expanding like a balloon when he breathed out but sticking to his face when he inhaled in a manner that made him feel he was suffocating.

The humiliation and helplessness were worse than anything he could have imagined. On the fifth day he collapsed and couldn't for a time be wakened. By then he was bleeding from not only the nose and the mouth but the ears; also, he found that he could no longer urinate.

Gauging how much abuse a given human organism can sustain must not be an easy task for the interrogators. They had made a mistake with Biko and had been under heavy pressure from the politicians ever since not to make any more. They may have feared that they had gone too far with Frank Tongo. In any case, someone bungled and took him to a doctor who had the courage and sense of professional ethics to determine how the injuries had been sustained and then to insist on hospitalizing his patient.

Three months after his release, Frank Tongo was fired by Hoover, which still claimed to be upholding the Sullivan principles. Frank Tongo said that he had been doing the same job for seven years and that he had been told he would be promoted if he gave up his position in the union. The managing director, a South African named Ted Ashdown, acknowledged that he had taken advantage of a slowdown at the plant to weaken the union by dismissing some of its organizers. I asked whether he had happened to notice the bruises on Frank's face when he returned to work. "I noticed them, but I don't recall that they were too bad. If they had really been bad," he explained, "I know we'd have asked him to stay home a little longer—for the sake of the secretaries."

"Listen, Mr. Lelyveld," Ted Ashdown said to me in a confidential tone, "you've been in this country long enough to understand how things are." We were now speaking man to man, white to white. What followed was a twenty-year-old horror story involving a black worker who had given a friend change for a pack of cigarettes on the understanding that he would get the money back on payday. Payday came, and the borrower played dumb, denying there was any debt, whereupon the lender picked up an iron bar and cracked him across the skull, doing permanent damage.

The old story was offered as a parable. That, I suppose, was why Frank Tongo couldn't urinate after five days in the custody of the security police, why he had to be dangled almost naked from a chain, beaten with sticks, and made to feel he was being suffocated by a rubber hood. It was because blacks were so violent.

In a second city I renewed my acquaintance with another black trade unionist who had just come out of detention. This was the first of several stories about interrogation and torture I was to hear from brave and committed men who had to acknowledge that they had cracked under pressure. It was especially appalling because, as the man told it, all the admissions he made to satisfy his interrogators were false. First he had been questioned in the security police offices in the Sanlam Building in Port Elizabeth, notorious as the site of the interrogations in which Biko sustained his fatal injuries. The union leader was made to stand in his Jockey shorts on two bricks for two days and two nights; during all that time, he said, he was denied toilet facilities. Periodically he was slugged from behind on the right ear, always the right ear. Electric shocks followed. Then finally one night he was removed from his cell and taken, with a canvas bag over his head, to a location outside the city.

There the union leader was handcuffed to a pole and made to stand in his bare feet on something that felt like a soggy rag. A wire was attached to a toe, and the shocks started again. "I felt like I was being dissected or dismantled," he said. "Everything inside me just felt loose. Once they take you there, you'll have to prepare many yeses."

Now his interrogators were telling him the answers he was going to give them and drilling him to make certain he had them right. Soon he found himself admitting, he said, that he had gone to Lesotho to take instructions on trade union tactics from representatives of the underground, that he had met secretly with Bishop Desmond Tutu, a black Anglican whose prestige the security police were then bent on damaging. "And I've never been to Lesotho. Never—ever, ever," the man insisted. "Before my detention I never, ever met Bishop Tutu. But I had to admit it. They have it in writing. Later I went to the bishop and apologized. He just laughed and said, 'You're not the first.'"

The Biko inquest found that no one was criminally liable for his death: Thozamile Gqweta was another who said that, four years later, he had that verdict flaunted in his face by white security policemen who wanted to convince him that he was entirely at their mercy. "They said that if I didn't speak the truth, I would go in the same manner that Steve went," he said. "They told me I must not be fooled by what was said in the press, that everyone knows exactly what happened to Steve."

The sense that Gqweta was Biko's natural successor was widespread in the eastern Cape. The police seemed to share it. In one room in which the young union president was interrogated, a poster showing Biko breaking his chains hung on the wall as a mocking reminder of what could happen.

"We are going to assault you each and every day of your stay here," Gqweta said he was told at the start of what proved to be three months of detention in 1981. Over three years he was arrested eight times by South Africa and Ciskei without ever being brought to trial, but it was only in South Africa, he said, that he was assaulted or even questioned.

At each session, he said, he would be ordered to take off his clothes. "Up the wall!" his interrogators would then command when his answers failed to satisfy. This was the signal for him to stand on a trunk so that he could be handcuffed to the bars on a window, with his face to the wall. Then the trunk would be removed, leaving him dangling. In that position, he would be swung like a pendulum and beaten, not once "but approximately every day" for three months.

The next detention was more than twice as long and harder to bear, although he was never again assaulted. In the month before it began, there had been a succession of violent deaths involving persons close to him. His mother and the man she lived with died in a fire; at their funeral a girl friend was killed by a supposedly stray bullet fired by one of General Sebe's men; then Mxenge, the union's lawyer, was slain in Durban. In solitary confinement Thozamile Gqweta came close to a breakdown, suffering blinding migraines that continued to recur months after his release. At first, when he got out of jail, the sound of a human voice speaking at normal conversational levels caused him unbearable pain.

The rationalization that South Africa is menaced by "terrorists" makes it possible for most whites to condone any form of counterterrorism, including torture, assassination, and bombings. It all can be denied and simultaneously defended; the price of liberty is high, the outsider is reminded. In the interrogation rooms the opposing sides in the conflict see each other without illusions, sometimes even with begrudged respect. The closer the interrogator comes to torture, the closer he comes to exposing himself and the system that employs him. To the degree the prisoner breaks down, he is exposed, too, in his human frailties. A relationship of intimacy and candor is thus established. "We are fighting for our cause," Thozamile Gqweta said he was told in between beatings, "just as you are fighting for yours." Obviously this was both a wheedling compliment and a threat, an indication of how determined his interrogators felt themselves to be. Could it also have been a plea for absolution?

Possibly the strangest feature of the South African system is the interplay between arbitrary police power and traditional judicial forms. The security police are given effective carte blanche, then are regularly made to answer for their use of it in open court; this usually requires lying on a colossal scale. Once the political detainee is charged, released, brought into court as a witness, his interrogators can be extensively and even mercilessly cross-examined by one of the small fraternity of South African lawyers that has continued the battle for civil liberties.

This has happened so routinely that the white public and press have become inured to torture stories. The broad question of whether the system could survive without systematic use of torture is rarely raised. Instead, the issue has been narrowed to the legal contest in the courtroom, to whether torture can be shown on the basis of probabilities to have been used in a particular case. If so, the system can be seen to be denouncing torture; if not, it has been unjustly accused. Either way it is vindicated. Thus it was not front-page news when the following fragments of testimony became a matter of public record in South Africa:

> *When I arrived in the interrogation room, the three interrogators ordered me to strip, which I did. Des attached a pair of pliers to my penis. While I stood there, my interrogators laughed at me and Des told me that I was going to die that day. Des, with the assistance of Venter and the other interrogator, then blindfolded me. They then put cloth around my wrists. I was then handcuffed with the bracelets of the handcuffs placed on the cloth. My arms were forced over my knees and an object which felt like a metal bar was placed over my armpits and under my knees restricting me to a crouching position. The metal bar holding me in the crouched position was then balanced on two ironing boards so that I was suspended. During this time, they kept laughing and taunting me and saying I was going to die. They then started applying electric shocks to my knee....*

> *He handcuffed me from the back. I then felt some electric wires which were being placed on my back and they were being cellotaped onto me. When he was questioning me, they then started shocking me with the electric wire. They were two, Van Wyk and Trollip. The one was busy shocking me, the other was saying,* Praat, praat, praat *["Talk, talk, talk"]. They continued like that, asking me about certain people, until they decided to stop shocking me and then Trollip grabbed hold of my private parts and started shocking them and I, as a result of the pain, screamed again....*

None of this testimony was found to have been credible by the courts. On occasion it does happen that the former detainee is believed. Cedric Mayson, a onetime Methodist minister, testified in Pretoria that he had been kept standing naked for two days, during which he was mocked and assaulted. Thirteen security policemen corroborated one another's evidence that nothing of the sort ever happened. The judge accepted Mayson's evidence, but the thirteen returned to their assignments without anything being said about disciplinary proceedings.

● ● ●

"I wish this were a police state," General Coetzee remarked to me with smooth good humor and affected modesty when he agreed to see me. "Then I would have more influence." If he had that influence, he indi- cated, he would use it to bolster the defenses of the government and, spe- cifically, its security forces in the psychological war that he felt was being waged against them. The fight against terrorism was a fight for the rule of law, he argued glibly, and, secondly, for the possibility that democratic processes can be developed in South Africa in an orderly manner; there- fore, for democracy's sake, he said, "Let the experts fight it out with the terrorists in the shadows."

The shadows, presumably, meant the interrogation rooms. A judicial commission headed by an Afrikaner jurist who was later rewarded with the position of chief justice on the highest court in the land found that de- tention without trial was indispensable for the security of the state. The commission never looked at the question of how the information was ob- tained; it did not soil its judicial robes by acknowledging that threats, hu- miliation, beatings, and torture are an essential part of the process. Two days after the commission's report was handed to the white Parliament, there was another death in detention, followed by another embarrassing inquest. The minister of law and order then found it necessary to publish explicit directions to the police to safeguard political detainees. "A detai- nee," his order declared, "shall at all times be treated in a humane manner with proper regard to the rules of decency and shall not in any way be as- saulted or otherwise ill-treated or subjected to any form of torture or in- human or degrading treatment."

Few other authoritarian regimes have sufficient conscience to formulate such a rule; few other authoritarian regimes are so hypocritical. The police were being told to do what the government had said they had been doing all along, but no court was given the power to enforce the directive. The interrogation rooms would be kept in the shadows. "If there is no tor- ture," the redoubtable Helen Suzman asked in Parliament, "why can they not just keep quiet?"

The presumption of guilt is written into South African security laws; on some terrorism charges the onus is on the accused to prove his innocence. For those who have been detained but not charged, the possibility of in- nocence does not arise. This was explained in memorable terms by a no- torious figure in the security police, Major Arthur Cronwright, at the inquest into the death of Neil Aggett, a young white doctor who had been serving as an official of a mainly black trade union. The detainee had been found hanging in his cell, an apparent suicide, after ten weeks in the cus- tody of the security police. Major Cronwright, who had supervised Ag- gett's interrogators, explained that the authorities had information that he belonged to a cell of the African National Congress. Why was there no reference to that allegation in the statement Aggett had made before his death? asked the lawyer for the dead man's family in cross-examination. Probably, Major Cronwright said, he had failed to confirm the information the police had; in that case his answers would not have been recorded because, the witness explained, "They were in the negative, and the Commissioner of Police isn't interested in negative answers."

The commissioner of police is *not interested.* It is described as a condition, a state of mind, and as such it becomes a functional definition of fanaticism. Wrapped up in their racial holy war, the security police can only assimilate reality when it feeds their fantasies.

Among the government's white supporters, Aggett's suicide was immediately taken as confirmation of the worst suspicions of the police. "He died for his cause," I was told a few days after Aggett's death by F. W. deKlerk, one of the Cabinet's younger members. I asked the minister, who acknowledged that he had never heard of Aggett before his death, to try to recall his immediate reaction upon hearing the news that another detainee had died in police custody.

"Anger," he replied instantly.

"Why anger?"

"I knew how it would be used against us," he said.

An outsider cannot fail to become aware of unfocused anger as a by-product of South African life or the patterns of aggression and casual violence to which it gives rise among both blacks and whites. Apartheid ensures that the victims of most black violence are black and the victims of most white violence whites. That is one of its virtues, its supporters would contend.

Very occasionally a close reader of South African newspapers will come upon archetypal stories of the white madam who has been raped by a black servant or the white farmer accused of murdering a black woman after she became pregnant with his child. Occasionally, too, there are stories of casual or random gunfire: For being too "noisy," a fourteen-year-old black caddie in a town called Alexandria is shot in the head; two whites shoot up a black railway carriage near Pietersburg, killing three and wounding two ("I hate everything that is black," one of the accused then tells the magistrate); five white soldiers on furlough in the western Transvaal take a couple of potshots at two black schoolboys, one of whom dies.

Self-destructive violence is far more typical. In the township of Soweto, where the number of cases of murder and manslaughter in a year is more than double what it is in the whole of Great Britain, a knife is the weapon in at least 85 percent of the cases. Poverty, overcrowding, broken families—all are part of the etiology that is usually outlined in explaining ghetto violence; so, too, in the case of Soweto, is the almost complete absence of preventive action by the police, who are preoccupied with protecting white neighborhoods and with surveillance of black politics.

Among whites, the gun is usually the weapon, and the victims are typically relatives or friends. Often, as headlines regularly recount, it is a child who has come upon a loaded weapon a parent has kept at hand against the more remote danger of dusky intruders:

BOY DIES IN
SHOOTING ACCIDENT

BOY'S "GAME"
WITH PISTOL
ENDS IN DEATH

BOY, 6,
SHOT BY
BROTHER

Guns are always at hand, too, in white neighborhoods to settle marital disputes:

WIFE SHOT HUSBAND
7 TIMES, COURT TOLD

"DEVASTATED" DAD SLAYS TOTS
THEN TURNS GUN ON HIMSELF

WOMAN SHOT HUSBAND IN BED, COURT TOLD

In the last case, since the husband had a black woman next to him in the bed, there was no penalty at all. "In these circumstances, she was justified in shooting the scoundrel," Justice Human of the Rand Supreme Court declared. Normally the South African legal principle of diminished responsibility makes for light sentences when the surviving spouse can show that the deceased was unfaithful or otherwise responsible for raising the level of emotional stress. A Nelspruit magistrate levied a fine equivalent to $1,200 on a man who shot his wife in the head at point-blank range. "You were provoked by your wife's hitting and swearing at you," he told the man, "but you had no right to pull out a pistol and shoot her."

If this was what happened when whites killed their nearest and dearest, it seemed hardly any wonder that white interrogators fared well in South African courts when one of their prisoners died. Nor was it necessary, in such a violent country—when the total of political detainees known to have died in police custody averaged out to fewer than three a year over twenty years, almost exactly the same as the number of persons killed in "terrorist" attacks in the same period—to draw comparisons to El Salvador or Iran in order to demonstrate that the security police are subject to constraints. In fact, it is their boast that the rate of deaths among ordinary criminals is higher than it is among political prisoners.

● ● ●

Whites complain with some reason of the world's "double standards" in judging the South African variety of repression more harshly than that of more murderous regimes, then pirouette on the spot and leap into a breathtaking display of double standards. When the first accounts of torture started emerging from black-ruled Zimbabwe, where the government of Robert Mugabe was experimenting with laws and methods of control inherited from white-ruled Rhodesia, few South African whites were prepared to draw the trite lesson that violence begets violence. Zimbabwean torture was an outrage. It also, by some roundabout but inexorable logic, served to vindicate South Africa.

To go to Zimbabwe in this period was, in this respect at least, to see mirror images. In Harare, I had asked Emmerson Munangagwa, a Cabinet minister, about the reports of torture. He responded elliptically, avoiding a categorical answer but seeking to impress on me his own sense of revulsion, which was rooted in his experiences as a "freedom fighter," over any use of torture. The first thing he did when he took over his department was to revisit a room in a police station where he had been tortured by white officers who hung him upside down by leg irons from butcher's hooks that ran along a track on the ceiling. This enabled his interrogators to bat his suspended body back and forth on the track from one end of the room to the other, as if he were a hockey puck. The game continued until he lost consciousness. The day after the independence ceremonies, the butcher's hooks were still on the ceiling, and astonishingly, his former interrogators were now on his staff, as was another official who acknowledged having once sent him a letter bomb. They told him they had just been doing their jobs; he then promised they could start in independent Zimbabwe with a "clean slate." Some had later proved to be South African agents, but others still appeared to be loyal officers, the minister said. In the beginning he had no choice but to trust them, he explained. Zimbabwe could not have been expected to dismantle its only security agency.

As for the possibility that there were now black torturers, Munangagwa could only say that he deplored it. "People like myself and the prime minister who suffered in the past don't like to see people detained," he said. "We always said that if we ever got power, we won't allow those things to happen in Zimbabwe." Nevertheless, within a few months there were at least three times as many persons in detention without charge in Zimbabwe as there were in South Africa.

CHAPTER EIGHT

Part of Us

It's an obscure but striking historical curiosity that the first white woman to die and be buried in the Transvaal, the region that was to become the country's economic and political heartland, wasn't an Afrikaner but an American. Jane Wilson was the wife of a minister in the first tiny group of missionaries dispatched to South Africa by the interdenominational American Board of Commissioners for Foreign Missions. Her death in 1836 at what is now a rail siding known as Sendelingspos—or "missionary's post"—outside the western Transvaal town of Zeerust came a little more than a year before the earliest trekkers established their first settlement on the far side of the Vaal River. The Americans, who had been in South Africa for a year and a half, had come to Sendelingspos in hopes of taming the heathen heart and saving the soul of Mzilikazi, the renegade Zulu chieftain who broke away to establish the Ndebele nation. They found this South African Genghis surprisingly gracious and hospitable, but then, before they were fluent enough in his language to start proclaiming the gospel, they were struck down one after the other by a fever, and once they were diseased, they were shunned. The result was that Jane Wilson's grave was all the Americans had to show for their year among the Ndebeles, when they made a melancholy choice that can be seen as a harbinger of the political choices successive American administrations now face when they try to straddle the South African question. Put crudely, it boiled down to a choice between black and white.

The Ndebeles and Afrikaners had been moving into the same territory simultaneously, and after a couple of skirmishes, the trekkers decided that Mzilikazi had to be taught a lesson. The attacking Afrikaners then rode through the mission station, trampling its crops and shooting down Ndebeles who thought they might find refuge there. The Americans, fearing that Mzilikazi might imprison or kill them, agonized over whether they should take flight with the attackers. It is evident that they were afraid to be the only whites left in the vicinity after the trekkers had withdrawn to their base on the other side of the Vaal. Daniel Lindley of Ten Mile Creek, Pennsylvania, summed up the rationalizations that led the missionaries to desert the Ndebele chief and "the wicked people for whom we felt the deepest pity" in a report to his sponsors in Philadelphia:

> We did not like the idea of leaving him so abruptly and with a company of men who had shed the blood of so many of his people, lest our doing so might put an insuperable barrier in the way of other missionaries who might possibly wish hereafter to approach him for the

purposes of giving instruction. Yet we thought the possibility of our doing mischief in this way very small for the time of his overthrow, we fully believed, had come.

Mzilikazi was deeply wounded by the decamping of the whites, who had kept none of the promises made on their arrival to impart great truths and useful skills. Re-establishing his nation in what is now Zimbabwe, Mzilikazi survived for more than three decades, displaying thereafter a healthy skepticism toward missionaries.

Daniel Lindley was another survivor. In a remarkable career that did not finally end in South Africa until 1873, he went on in the American way, pursuing his own ends on both sides of the racial divide. He left his faint but discernible mark on the main forces that are now in conflict: the Afrikaners, who had formally adopted him as their *predikant*, or parson, and had named after him a town in the Orange Free State as well as a Transvaal hamlet, Lindleyspoort (Lindley's gate), and John Dube, a Zulu pastor of a church he founded, who became the first president of the African National Congress.

The American subtheme in South Africa's turbulent history underscores the proclivity for earnest but inconsistent dabbling that now gets dignified every four to eight years under the rubric "policy." In recent years we have seen the United States groping under Gerald Ford toward a policy of joint covert operations with the white regime in Pretoria; then, within twenty-four months, proclaiming under Jimmy Carter its wish to see the speedy termination of that regime; then promising Ronald Reagan's "constructive engagement." It is thesis and antithesis, never synthesis, and it is prefigured by the pious Presbyterian figure of Daniel Lindley cantering across the subcontinent after his flight from Mzilikazi to reestablish himself on the Indian Ocean coast on the outskirts of what was not yet Durban.

When I first went to Africa, contradiction and ambivalence continued to be the main themes of the American involvement in South Africa. The realization that this was the case dawned on me slowly. It seemed fantastic to me to suggest that my country had any real complicity in apartheid but not fantastic to speculate that American power might one day make a difference on the side of the disenfranchised. Puny Rhodesia had not yet gotten away with its defiance of a Labour party government in Britain; the first of the several Nigerian coups and its aftermath in Biafra had yet to occur; "terrorism" was a phenomenon of the nineteenth century; and the term "third world" had yet to set off in self-satisfied Western minds a rush of images of physical ruin and moral chaos, nor had anyone yet dismissed the United Nations as a "theater of the absurd." In other words, the lib-

eral idea that Americans were on the same side as the world's poor still had some life.

It was an American ambassador in what was still called the Belgian Congo who revealed with a dry quip a fundamental element in the situation. G. McMurtrie Godley was no mannequin in pinstripes pretending to be a strategist. He chomped cigars, had trouble keeping his shirttail in his trousers, and spoke English as if he knew it to be a living language. When I remarked that a crisis seemed to be in the making in southern Africa, with the issues of Rhodesian independence and South Africa's illegal occupation of the territory now known as Namibia possibly coming to a boil at the same time, he blew a cloud of smoke at the ceiling and then dismissed the idea that American power might be brought to bear against the white regimes. "The day has not yet come," Mac Godley said, "when white men will fight white men in Africa for the sake of black men."

Naturally it was a point that could not have been lost on planners in Pretoria. They must have known that wherever American warships ventured—into the Gulf of Tonkin, the eastern Mediterranean, or the Persian Gulf—they would never blockade South African ports in order to uphold a United Nations resolution.

Another lesson in the ambiguity of the American position on South Africa came after the election of President Reagan, which South Africa's state broadcasting monopoly hailed as a defeat for "pseudoliberalism, permissiveness, state intervention, appeasement, and antipatriotism." There was hope now, the commentary proclaimed, for "Western Christian culture."

The hope turned out to be an American political scientist from Georgetown by way of Johns Hopkins and the Nixon White House, who possessed an American political scientist's faith in the "modernizing" aptitudes of military elites. Chester Crocker, the new assistant secretary of state for Africa, described the leaders of the South African armed forces as a "lobby of modernizing patriots." In America his name was known mainly to specialists and lobbyists; with a precisely trimmed mustache and a banker's caution with words, he was guarded, remote, resolutely nontelegenic. But in South Africa his name was dropped into conversation as if he, rather than Kissinger, had turned out to be the new Metternich. One of the best-informed operatives Washington had ever fielded in the region, Crocker was ready to see South African military power used to impose an American agenda on the region. Through support of insurgencies and covert sabotage operations across its borders, Pretoria managed to force neighboring black states to recognize its hegemony, acknowledge their economic dependence, and act against South African black exiles. Washington occasionally moralized over the means, but it warmly applauded the results, accepting the taming of black nationalism inside and outside South Africa as an advance toward regional stability and a setback to So-

viet influence. It was Chester Crocker, in fact, who coined the term "constructive engagement."

"It is not our task to choose between black and white," he said. The American task was to defend Western interests, which he listed as "economic, strategic, moral, and political," in that order. The ordering of priorities was more rigorously accurate as an expression of real relationships, but the change, once again, was mainly verbal. Crocker had resurrected the premise of a secret policy memorandum of the Nixon years: "The whites are here to stay and the only way that constructive change can come about is through them. There is no hope for the blacks to gain the political rights they seek through violence, which will only lead to chaos and increased opportunities for the communists." Even though the regimes of Mozambique, Angola, and Rhodesia all had fallen, it seemed more plausible than ever as a description of the situation in South Africa. And Crocker found a way to say it openly by balancing two axioms: The United States would not let South Africa be "destabilized," and it would not align itself with apartheid.

It would depend on the whites who were still busy elaborating the apartheid system to bring about constructive change. The evident contradictions in this stance could be resolved only by a willfully blind acceptance of the assurances of reform that are offered to visitors like Chester Crocker in the offices of white generals, Cabinet ministers, and corporation executives. Winnie Mandela put it perfectly. "Constructive engagement," she said, meant telling blacks to call off their struggle because "the bosses are working it out."

Some Americans set themselves up as arbiters of the South African conflict; others take sides. And all the while, seeking to preserve their system, South Africans hold up a mirror to America so that Americans are struck, however ambivalently, by a weird family resemblance. It would be excessive to speak of the Americanization of apartheid, but a little imitation makes it possible for the envoys of American venture capital and enterprise to feel increasingly comfortable and optimistic in the environment apartheid shapes. If what is taken for normal in San Diego or Houston can be made to seem not abnormal in Durban or Johannesburg, then the problem can be presumed to be on its way to resolution. The discovery that a black is sitting at the next table in a restaurant or holding down a skilled job at a decent wage—that the whole of South Africa is not necessarily a penal colony for all blacks all the time—flashes a message of hope to the American mind.

I experienced these small epiphanies myself, usually as a result of a glimpse of middle-class life, something everyday that left me momentarily absorbed in the South African dream that the racial conflict might quietly fade away. Early one morning, walking downtown to my office, for instance, I saw a new Toyota pull to the curb with a well-dressed black couple inside; the woman got out and walked briskly away, presumably to her job, and then the man drove off, presumably to his. That was enough to cause me to reflect that most people in the world would find it hard to regard them as victims. Then, carried away, I was seized by the hope that maybe, somehow, it all would work out. The fleeting evidence that racial hierarchy could be dispelled for a moment put the grinding issues of South African life into a soft, blurry focus as for an ad for a new shampoo. Apartheid, too, could be milder, gentler, making the country easier to manage. But the dream of its fading away was like the Marxist vision of the withering away of the state, and no black could sustain it for long.

Americans were seldom there for long, and the idea that blacks might want more than piecemeal change involving a selective lowering of barriers for selected segments of their population was surprisingly easy to overlook. A false analogy was at work: We saw Jim Crow go away, so why can't apartheid? The reason is apparent to South African whites. It is because legal equality for blacks would lead swiftly and inevitably to the loss of white power and the destruction of the whole apartheid edifice. Reasoning from American analogies, Americans talk about human rights and living standards while fuzzing the central issue of power. This makes it easy to suppose that whites who talk about "reform" and "change" are talking about an end to white dominance when often they are really searching for ways to make it more tolerable so it can endure.

Mike Rosholt, the chairman of Barlow Rand, South Africa's second-biggest conglomerate, went to the trouble of making a pilgrimage to the Reverend Leon Sullivan in Philadelphia to consult him on how to draw up a code of fair employment practices. It was not just for show. Rosholt demonstrated that he was in earnest about being an equal opportunity employer, monitoring his managers on their performance in upgrading the status of black workers and investing more heavily in training programs than the multinationals in South Africa. But Mike Rosholt had to try three times when I asked my question about whether there didn't have to be an outcome to the South African conflict before he could come up with an answer that he thought would sound right in New York.

"Look," he began, "no one really wants to face an ultimate . . .

"I don't believe that any white person here really . . .

"Very few liberals want to face a situation where there's an immediate equality," he said finally, his voice pitched very low, "and I don't believe it is necessary. I'm a great believer in evolutionary stages. But there's got to be movement."

Obviously the American multinationals wouldn't want to say that "immediate equality" isn't necessary. That would be regarded as uncouth at home. Yet what they do say sometimes amounts to the same thing. Mobil devotes a two-page color ad in South African magazines to the importance of upgrading what it calls not the education of blacks, but "Black Education." The apartheid pattern is at least implied. The advertising focuses instead on what it takes to be larger issues:

> If the Free Enterprise system is to prevail and grow, we need quality people and Whites alone cannot fill the additional 220,000 management and skilled or semi-skilled posts which must be created each year between now and the end of the century.
>
> Merely educating and training a greater number of people is not the answer—the quality of Black Education and its end product must be improved.... South Africa's future and yours depends on it.

The advertisement shows a black and a colored leaning disconsolately against a wall in a ghetto setting. Scrawled on the wall, over their shoulders, is graffiti. "Black education needn't be a dead end street." Let things go on as they are going, the outside world is advised, and there will be hundreds of thousands of educated blacks, maybe millions, and perhaps then apartheid can be further eased. The political issue of who controls "Black Education" is evaded in the ad. Still, if it is saying anything to blacks as well as whites, Mobil is saying, "Apartheid needn't be a dead-end street."

"Historically," Chester Crocker once wrote, "South Africa is by its nature a part of us."

Crocker was talking about how we see it, leaving aside the question of how the majority of South Africans would see it. We have principles and interests that we have to try to reconcile, he was saying. Therefore, we must be simultaneously for stability and change, if that is possible, and maybe even if it is not. But then Inanda "by its nature" must also be a part of us, if any place in South Africa is. Inanda is the black area near Durban where Daniel Lindley started to save black souls and John Dube, ANC founder, passed most of a long life.

John Dube acquired land in Inanda, less than a mile from the spot where Mohandas Gandhi, inspired by Tolstoy, established a kind of rural commune so that whites and Indians could live in interracial harmony. Gandhi published a paper called *Indian Opinion* from his Phoenix Settlement starting in 1904, the same year that Dube founded a Zulu paper called *Ilanga*. When I first visited the Phoenix Settlement in 1965, it was still set in the midst of sugarcane fields and rural small holdings of both Zulus and Indians who had been living peacefully together since the days of Dube and Gandhi. When I went there seventeen years later, most of the vacant space had been filled in by black and Indian refugees from Durban neighborhoods that apartheid had leveled. A new Phoenix had risen from the ashes of Gandhi's dream, a segregated Indian township—the very antithesis of what he had hoped to build. Phoenix, the township, now spilled over one hill; Inanda, the black area, extended over the others. Gandhi's tiny Phoenix lay squeezed in the apartheid vise, a landmark to a South Africa that never was.

Where blacks were still living on Indian-owned land, the authorities were busy getting them expelled. Inanda had been dropped into a legal limbo. It was no longer a part of South Africa exactly, but not yet a part of the Zulu homeland, so neither was responsible for building a proper water supply system when the area's population soared by 153 percent in the 1970s with black refugees from the white areas. Outbreaks of typhoid and cholera followed. All this was going on while Chester Crocker was writing about the prospect of "purposeful change."

And of course, it was purposeful. But then, to confuse my parable, the kind of change Crocker meant came to Inanda. First, the army mobilized an emergency supply of clean water for the stricken area. Then the business community, lobbying through the Urban Foundation, its privately endowed department of good works, demanded a proper water supply system and a plan for housing whereby employees of the foundations' corporate sponsors might own their homes. The result was a model "self-help" scheme in which building sites, along with piped water, decent roads, and various community facilities, were provided to families that also got the credit, building materials, and technical advice they needed to put up houses. When I visited the place, about seventy houses had been rising every month for two years, and Inanda now had a small corps of private black building contractors.

Obviously it was a showpiece. Still, it was a grass-roots project that would be acclaimed anywhere in the world, proof of a wealthy land's capacity to tackle the problems of human wretchedness it had largely invented and legislated for itself. And it brought to my mind a contrast that was full of poignancy and ambiguity. Several weeks earlier I had visited the barrios, the crowded shanty areas that ring the Mozambican capital of Maputo farther up the Indian Ocean coast. Here a radical political movement had been mobilizing the masses for nearly a decade, but on the afternoon of my tour that meant mobilizing them to stand on line for water rations; equality had come to mean equality of need. In South Africa, meantime, a system that went about producing refugees, occasional epidemics, and gross inequalities, could incidentally, as an experimental digression from its usual pursuits, start to house and feed some of its people as the political leadership in Maputo had earnestly wanted to do all along.

If I had seen a development like the Inanda project attributed to Frelimo, the revolutionary party in Mozambique, rather than to a foundation backed by an oligopoly, I would certainly have been impressed. It seemed only reasonable to be impressed in South Africa as well, even though the authorities were busily trying to purge Inanda of tens of thousands of "illegals.'' In the name of "self-help," apartheid was thus spinning off yet another subcaste in Inanda.

Just the opposite had happened in Maputo at the time of "liberation" from Portugal, when the *cidade di cimento* (the modern "cement city") had been thrown open to the black masses with the nationalization of all housing that wasn't actually occupied by its owners. It spurred a cataclysmic flight of the entrepreneurial and managerial Portuguese classes, leading, with a further push from South African–backed insurgents, to the conditions of economic collapse I had glimpsed. And now socialist Mozambique was busy evicting unemployed blacks from the center of Maputo faster than the white authorities in Durban were evicting them from Inanda. Moreover, those same socialists were looking to hated white South Africa to come to the rescue with investment and skills. That black Mozambican officials might one day visit Inanda to draw pointers from the housing scheme there for the barrios of Maputo was no longer unimaginable. These twists, inversions, and reversals left me feeling a little dizzy. White South Africa seemed able to say to its own blacks and its black neighbors, *Do it our way or not at all. On your own you'll only make a mess of it. We'll make sure of that.* A neologism that had once popped into my mind was there again. You could call this whitemail, I thought.

Inanda was part of us, presumably, because a section of it had finally benefited from the free-enterprise system. But its inhabitants would not be able to purchase freehold title to their land, as John Dube had done before the passage of the Native Lands Act in 1913, not at least until Inanda had been formally merged into a homeland, which the Zulu leadership had so far firmly rejected.

On the other hand, if "liberation" would do to Durban what it had now done to Maputo, would it be worth it in the eyes of Inanda's residents? My opinion, which didn't matter, was that it would be worth it, even then, but the issues blurred. If, by some miracle, democracy could suddenly come into existence in a society as skewed economically and socially as South Africa, how could its leaders fail to respond to pressure for radical change in the name of equality? And how could such changes, given the near monopoly of managerial and entrepreneurial skills by a racial caste, fail to bring about economic collapse? With such prospects and probabilities, how could a prudent black government run the risk of political democracy? Would it, too, not be tempted to go on in a state of "permanent transition" in order to preserve a multiracial, mainly white, oligarchy that kept the mines, farms, and factories producing? I had always believed that my country should be on the side of political and social democracy in South Africa. Standing in Inanda and thinking of Maputo, I was left wondering whether such a side could really exist or, rather, since I knew that it existed, that it was imperishable in the sentiments of many black and some white South Africans, whether it could ever make its mark on the land apartheid had shaped.

I cut short my visit to Inanda because I was due at the national championship of a ballroom dancing competition for blacks and browns in which the contestants, responding on some level to the idea that they were part of us, would be graded on their ability to do it our way. Hundreds of them had been drawn from all over the country to the Durban Light Infantry's regimental hall, which had been rented for the occasion from the South African Defense Force by the makers of a cheap white wine, the sponsors of the event. In both New York and Johannesburg, I had seen Athol Fugard's *Master Harold . . . and the Boys*, in which two black waiters in a teahouse prepare for such a contest in the township. The hall of the Durban Light Infantry was where they would have dreamed of arriving.

A small combo listlessly banged and blew its way through a succession of tunes that were played, it seemed to me, at high school dances in the Bronx thirty years earlier. In no sense was this the music or rhythm of the townships, which were Motown and disco, imported and Africanized. The dress was formal, resplendent in the case of the adults in the advanced categories, where the men wore white tie and tails and the women gowns of gauze and taffeta in lime green or raspberry, lemon or shocking pink, with sequins on the skirts and sparkle in their hair to catch the light. A single white troopie in fatigues, with an Uzi submachine gun slung under his arm, stood transfixed and astonished at the door, where he was supposed to be on guard to protect the army's property. The judges were whites, including a couple that had recently danced off, I was told, with "the gold cup for whites" in their separate, reputedly more advanced league.

The man, a platinum blond who wore elevator shoes, was named Trevor. His partner, whose frozen smiles had a way of melting into expressions of boredom and disdain, was Mandy. When the juvenile, novice, and intermediate championships all had been settled, the lights dimmed, and the combo took a break so that Trevor and Mandy, dancing not to the colored combo but to strings on a cassette recording they had brought, could offer a "demonstration." No connoisseur of the art, I found their sudden chin thrusts and sideways stares comical. But there were "oohs" and "ahs" from a group of Zululand nurses and teachers with whom I was standing. "Thank you," said Trevor, taking the microphone and gently patting his perfectly unmussed hair, "I know that you people enjoy the tango from the applause you give your own couples when they dance." You people, your own couples. In white ties and tails and sequined gowns, they still didn't come close to making it in his eyes, the distant blue eyes of a colonial subaltern.

It was past two in the morning when the last of the big trophies had been handed out to the new black ballroom dancing champions. The troopie at the door had locked away his weapon and changed into his street clothes so that he could split as soon as the hall was empty. And Mandy had long since left in a taxi when Trevor next took the microphone to offer a final critique of the performances he had been judging. "I would like to say the standard has improved tremendously," he said, pronouncing his verdict from on high. "Just keep working on your basics, and I hope to see another improvement next year."

This was the tone of a man who had done his duty. There was no hint that he might have enjoyed himself for a moment. But Steward Dephoko, a machine operator from Sasolburg who had just taken the prize in advanced Latin dancing with his partner, Alinhal Mareletsa, didn't hear the condescension. His own performance had been full of fun and verve and daring gymnastics; I thought he could teach Trevor. But the new champion had danced in a multiracial competition at the Carlton Hotel in Johannesburg, where he had come in only fourth. "I was no match for the white guy," he acknowledged. So he was not offended by what Trevor had said or the way he had said it. "If he tells me to work on the basics," Steward Dephoko said, "that's exactly what I'm going to do."

So Trevor's way is Steward Dephoko's. One day, with violins playing and soft lights casting beguiling shadows, they may appear in their patent leather dancing shoes, each immaculately attired, at the same ballroom dancing contest and dance as equals. It is the dream of a happy ending to apartheid. And South Africa, as the credits roll up on the screen to all the strategists and officials and industrialists who never lost faith, will still be a part of us.

CHAPTER NINE

Pilgrims

South Africa's inviting climate limits the ability of the state to monitor conversation. Anyone who is sufficiently paranoid to fear that miniaturized listening devices may be lurking in a phone has only to step outside into the golden sunshine to converse with greater ease. So serious political conversations tend to take place not in basements or garrets but in gardens, as if revolution were a neglected branch of horticulture involving plants that germinate only slowly. On a mild but overcast winter's afternoon in a Cape Town garden, a political figure of radical views made the point that sometimes the plants never flower. The world might imagine that a revolution in South Africa was long overdue and inevitable, he said, but that would be a dangerous delusion. The state's enemies had to recognize that it had available to it a strategy to prevent revolution: gradually deracialize the hierarchy of oppression so that substantial numbers of nonwhites benefited from it. In other words, make collaboration respectable. At this stage it was the greed and inbred racism of the whites, rather than the uncompromising demand of an aroused people for full equality, that made the failure of this strategy seem likely. "But," this serious-minded horticulturalist observed, "revolutions sometimes fail."

He was talking about not only the struggle for power but what happened afterward. There was no single answer to the question of what "liberation" in South Africa might mean. Did it entail Africanizing the country or Westernizing its majority? Would freedom from racial oppression mean a different form of regimentation? Could it be, as Gandhi, Mao, and Frantz Fanon had preached in different ways, that revolution came only when some critical mass of the oppressed had liberated itself from its sense of impotence and inferiority?

I mistrusted political mysticism and the religious instinct in politics, and yet as I traveled the country, I had a series of encounters with religiously inspired blacks, browns, and whites who couldn't wait for liberation to be liberated. They had an instinct that could be undervalued as romantic or utopian, but I learned to regard them as South Africa's glory, if not its hope; its moral, if not its political, center. They were members of the smallest minority in the country, for they defined themselves as South African before they mentioned a color, tribe, or ethnic group. I mention these free South Africans because their positive moral energies keep alive a sense of a South Africa that could be: not an inevitable South Africa being brought into existence by unseen forces of historical necessity, but not entirely a mirage either, for it exists in tiny outcroppings—in these lives, in lives like these, in the lives that they, and those like them, touch.

Joe Seremane was sent into internal exile and arbitrarily transmogrified there from a black South African into a Bophuthatswanan. As a black man who had once dared to take a political stance, he was expected to learn the lesson that his fate was controlled by invisible and anonymous officials, that destiny was what they said it was. But Joe Seremane had a sense of humor as well as a sense of the absurd. His personality was simply too expansive to stay bottled up in a dusty Transvaal township called Montshiwa, where he had been dumped.

An alert reader of the letters columns in the English-language newspapers of Johannesburg or nearer-to-hand *Mafeking* (after an orthographic reform, *Mafikeng*) *Mail* might have noticed a few years ago that Montshiwa had suddenly become the unlikely platform for a whole chorus of unintimidated, sometimes mocking black voices. There were Pax Patria and Domus Vero, Justice Lover, and Black Savage, not to mention an urbane and chatty jazz critic named Monty Simon and a certain Wetsho-O-tsile

Seremane, who playfully ended one of his many letters by declaring, "Pens such as Domus Vero, Justice Lover, Pax Patria, and Black Savage have said it all for me." That was as close as Joe Seremane ever came to acknowledging that he was all of the above.

The editors of the letters columns were slow to catch on. On one glorious morning, two of Joe's epistolary alter egos managed to make themselves heard in the *Rand Daily Mail*. Addressing whites under his various aliases, Joe Seremane could be caustic, tender, and uplifting, all at once. Addressing the white hope South African pugilism was offering to heavyweight boxing, Gerrie Coetzee, Justice Lover explained his reasons for rooting for his black American opponent. "Gerrie, you and I and all of us are caught up in a nasty historical trap!" his open letter began. He then drew Coetzee's attention to a decision to desegregate the Pretoria stadium where the fight was to be held. What had the local authorities been trying to avoid? "My black body," answered Justice Lover, "totally disregarding my beautiful, tolerant and patient soul." How could he root for a white South African boxer while he himself was not accepted as a South African? "No, Gerrie," he concluded, "I'll back you the day that you and I are Azanians in a unitary non-racial and non-discriminatory state."

"My beautiful, tolerant and patient soul." There was a touch of self-mockery in the words perhaps, but they should have melted the hardest white heart. Pax Patria could also spread the balm of black compassion for whites, assuring his "white brothers" that blacks were not reared to hate, even those who "have suffered terrible pains which we would never want to recount—because it hurts—in the police cells and prisons." The casual reader could take this as a rhetorical device, but the testimony was autobiographical. "I'll keep trying to forgive," Justice Lover was writing in his next published effort a couple of weeks later, "but for how long?"

Forgiveness was soon strained by a letter signed simply "Anglican" from a white suburb called Berea. Anglican had warned blacks against "being taken for a ride" by Communists, who would exploit their grievances under apartheid, "then push you into a farm, together with a hundred others, and make you work for nothing." "Anglican brother," Justice Lover replied, "we have already been 'pushed into farms' right here in South Africa—forced to be citizens of homelands. I also know what it is to work for nothing—the experience I gathered right here under your system of government." At about the same time, Jack Senwamadi got a little note of congratulations for having won five rands, in those days nearly eight dollars, for "a best Extra-Forum letter" in the *Rand Daily Mail*. Then the *Mail* became noticeably less receptive to the letters; the voice of Montshiwa, it seems, had become too recognizable or perhaps too insistent.

By the time I met him, Joe Seremane and his entire cast had been virtually frozen out of the Johannesburg letters columns. Now he was speaking mainly to blacks, especially blacks who were learning to think of themselves as Bophuthatswanans. When even the *Mafikeng Mail* showed signs that it might have heard enough from Domus Vero, Kubu Segathlhe stepped into the breach and started to run off his own home-typed newsletters for circulation in the townships. The man would not be turned off or silenced. "The Rustic's Viewpoint" these latest screeds were called.

Some rustic. Joe didn't grow up in the bush but in a township near Johannesburg. He had traveled through South Africa; his restless and inquiring mind had traveled the world. Yet cast adrift in a homeland, he became haunted by the perception that the homeland blacks—the biggest, fastest-growing segment of black South Africa, after all—were being written off by blacks in the "struggle" as completely as they were being written off by whites. If the struggle were to be saved from a possibly fatal compromise, orthodox black nationalists seemed to imagine, Bophuthatswana could not be seen to exist. It thus followed that there could be no alliance with anyone involved in opposition politics in the homeland. Yet someone, Joe saw, had to keep a spirit of debate and quest alive in these homeland regimes, someone like Domus Vero.

It all boiled down to a refusal to be satisfied with white paternalism, and it all was pouring forth in a steady flow from a little study this self-liberated black man had built for himself in the backyard of his township house in a homeland. The first time I visited there, he showed me the scrapbook in which he had compiled his missives. "Mightier than the sword," he had written on the cover. I knew Joe then only as a field worker of the South African Council of Churches, but he overflowed that role. The letters he dashed off only hinted at the energy, wit, and amplitude of his conversation, in which his whole body seemed engaged, his long fingers eloquently playing to the rhythm of the words and his long face catching and reflecting every shading of humor.

He also had one of those South African laughs that are not merely rich and full-throated but become a kind of statement, a small triumph of personality, the response of strong individuals to the ridiculousness of having to pass a whole life trapped in someone else's dream. The blacks I knew who had suffered most seemed to laugh best. Winnie Mandela laughed when she spoke about her visits to her husband, with whom she had not had a truly private moment in twenty-one years; how on her last visit he had upended himself on the other side of the Plexiglas window in the prison visiting room in order to show her a toe that had required an operation because of an ill-fitting shoe. "I saw the foot for the first time in twenty-one years," she said, laughing. This woman was a heroine worthy of Tolstoy. Joe Seremane's laugh had that heroic quality, too.

Justice Lover, Pax Patria, and Domus Vero had first felt the urge to preach to whites in 1976 in an interrogation room in Pietermaritzburg. There Joe was subjected to what is sometimes known as the helicopter, the torture in which the naked detainee has his wrists handcuffed to his ankles and then is suspended from an iron bar. "My reaction, my physical response, I'm unable to say to the closest person in my life, even my wife," he said. But his emotional reaction was a revulsion that expressed itself as a kind of pity for his interrogators.

Joe, who was then nearly forty, hadn't waited that long to discover that he was as good as whites. His father was a stern, self-disciplined Shona from what was then Rhodesia who worked as a clerk on a gold mine near the town of Randfontein; his mother's origins were Tswana, but she would smack her children for referring to a playmate as an Ndebele or a Xhosa. "Those are your people," she would say. So he had only thought of himself as an African. The sharp cutting edge of apartheid was just beginning to slice into the land, and he was of the last generation of urban black children who sometimes played with whites. "The mine dumps were the no-man's-land where we played," he told me. "It was maybe there that we gauged ourselves against our master and thought that we had no right to feel inferior."

His first taste of political struggle came at the same time, during what was known as the Defiance Campaign in the early fifties when the congress movement, adopting the Gandhian tactic of civil disobedience, dispatched its supporters into segregated "whites only" facilities. The congress was operating on a timetable that placed it well ahead of the civil rights movement in the United States. Joe Seremane and his teenage friends in Randfontein were never recruited or trained for civil disobedience, but as soon as they heard about it they headed straight to the post office to shout, "This is our country!" and other slogans on the white side of the barrier, until a police van arrived and they were hauled off to the station for a caning. The police were less indulgent when they picked him up, a decade later, for agitation on behalf of the banned Pan-Africanist Congress. In 1963 he was sent to prison on Robben Island in Cape Town's Table Bay with the most stalwart blacks of his generation to break rocks and carry night soil for six years.

In that lot Joe included his best friend from the Randfontein mine dumps, the number two accused in the trial in which he was number one, who found his way, in an incredible odyssey, from the island to business school in Muncie, Indiana, and then a trainee job on Park Avenue in New York with a banking multinational. The Robben Island man then lived on Roosevelt Island in the East River until, his odyssey still not complete, his bank assigned him to Johannesburg, where he now resided in a new custom-built house in Soweto's Prestige Park. It was not that Joe regarded multinational banking and Prestige Park as a happier ending than welfare work and Montshiwa, to which he was restricted after he left the island. What mattered to him was the striving, the insistence on self-definition. It sent some people into exile to write or to undergo military training or end-

lessly to wait, some into the church, and others, who never found a way
out of the townships, on binges of acquisitiveness as if a black man, finally, could prove his worth only the way whites seemed to do it, by the
car he drove or the house he built. A black man of Joe's generation could
be dazed when he contemplated the various destinations reached by his
contemporaries, all of whom had started out with a confident expectation
that they would live to be free men in their country. The dispersal of energies and commitment testified to the power of the system, but a single man,
Joe Seremane believed, could still show the limitations on that power
through clear thinking and plain speaking. So, when his peregrinations
through the country as a cigarette company salesman led the authorities
to suspect that this Robben Island alumnus might be traveling to forge
clandestine links between the rebellious Soweto students and the underground, he found himself preaching about the problem of bitterness to an
officer of the security police.

He had not meant to end up a Christian. On Robben Island he went to
church only because Robert Sobukwe, the Pan-Africanist leader, was being
detained in a cottage near the chapel and it was sometimes possible to
glimpse him and even show him a clenched fist as a gesture of support on
the way to worship. Even now he wonders about the Christian patience and
forgiveness of his people. "If it's such a good thing," he asked, "why don't
they see it?" But it's not the old story of what whites fail to see that goads
him, living in a homeland, but the parody that these little black despot-
isms make of the Pan-Africanist dream he carried to prison; it's the spectacle of other blacks' accepting as a kind of fulfillment this sham
democracy, the spectacle, too, of township drunkenness. In his letters Domus Vero rails against "the evil and action-killing shebeens," against filth
and squalor, the absence of public hygiene and social vision. He finds
"moral decadence" in the black public service and "social degradation"
in the people. "Everywhere that the people are gathered you feel that uneasy silence on things that matter, and the shallow semblance of approval," he writes. "Is it treason to reason?" he asks.

His jeremiads go unheeded. He is the village scold. Some of his old co-
horts may even feel that by staying in Bophuthatswana, he has opted out
of the struggle. But he is his own liberation struggle, and at least he has
liberated himself. On my last afternoon with him, we drove through Mmabatho, the showcase capital. Black gardeners were working in the gardens
of high officials as they do in Pretoria; only here many of the officials were
black. Joe Seremane was recalling with pride a jazz combo in which he
played on Robben Island.

"Where did you get the instruments?" I asked in astonishment.

"There were no instruments," he replied. "We were bop scatting; we
did it by voice. Each guy played two or three instruments. There were guys
there with fantastic musical memories. We had the cream."

The Robben Island memory regenerates and re-energizes, just as he said. There wasn't the slightest suggestion that he now felt left out in Mmabatho, but he could be driven almost frantic by his sense that such an idea was catching on. "The most painful thing is that people don't know it's working," Joe Seremane said. Apartheid was working, he meant. "They have to get in here and fight it."

There are not all that many stories of Afrikaner apostasy, but it is impossible to dismiss them as aberrant and inconsequential. If there are still Afrikaners interested in writing their own history sixty or eighty years from now, I imagine that they will find their heroes from this period among those who turned their backs on the dream of an enduring racial order, that they will then find meaning in the short life of Frikkie Conradie.

Frikkie, who was brought up on a farm in the western Transvaal, never in his youth heard anyone question the divinely ordained right of whites to rule over blacks. Ruling on his father's farm was a physical thing. He could remember the children in the family screaming in fear when his father applied his boot to the head of a prostrate laborer, or chased black trespassers across the veld in his *bakkie* as if they were game.

It's not an easy country, he was taught. It requires discipline, imposed by one generation on the next, accepted, and passed on in the usually unspoken assumption that discipline and morality are one; that indiscipline—a breaking of ranks, a doubt too persistently or openly expressed—is immorality, which can only lead in South Africa to a breakdown of social order. In Frikkie Conradie's case, this ethos coexisted without conscious strain with the abstract, intellectualized lessons in ethics and theology he received on his way to becoming a dominee, until it cracked and disintegrated in a single night. That was his first night in Holland, where he had gone for graduate studies in theology, and all it took was an encounter in Afrikaans with a fellow South African who was there for the same purpose. The fellow South African was not white. His name was Allan Boesak, and he went on to become the leader of a movement of dissident ministers in the nonwhite branches of the Dutch Reformed Church, probably the most eloquent voice of protest that had ever come from the colored community. On that night of their first meeting, Allan Boesak simply asked Frikkie what he thought of apartheid and then, after getting a guarded, conventional answer, proceeded to recount his own family's experiences in a series of forced removals under the Group Areas Act from homes in Cape Province. "I met Allan, and that's where the whole story starts," Frikkie told me. "Blacks succeed in getting through to us, and then we begin to understand what is happening."

Once Frikkie learned to listen the way he listened that night, he never stopped. Back in South Africa, he refused the ordination for which he had been trained in the white branch of his church and instead became the first white minister to take this step in the black branch. Then he went to serve a black congregation in a dilapidated township called Alexandra, receiving the salary a black minister would get without the subsidy normally made available to white missionaries. He did not regard himself as a missionary bringing the light but as one who was receiving it from the people he served. "They take you as a racist and a paternalist," he said, "and they make you into a human being."

A lean man, pale and bearded, was speaking sorrowfully yet passionately about family when he said this. His whole life had been shaped by the stunning discovery he had made, and now, like some poet who has suddenly found his voice, he spoke with quiet confidence, mixing urgency with humor. He still didn't know much about Christianity, Frikkie said, but he understood what Jesus meant when he asked who is his real mother, his real brother. That much he had experienced, for he had more fathers and brothers and sisters in the real sense among blacks than he had blood brothers and sisters. His defection had caused his mother and father great suffering, had led his brother and sister to shun him. He could only feel sorry for them. Afrikaners worry so much about what they stand for, about their precious identity, that they never experience life. "We ban people," he said, speaking softly, "and in the same process we also ban life out of our lives."

His words sat in my notebook for a week. I didn't fully understand what they meant or how I might use them. Then, at age thirty-five, Frikkie took a curve too fast on the way to the western Transvaal to visit his father's farm, and died barely twelve hours before his wife gave birth to their first child. Simultaneously a widow and mother, she immediately came under intense family pressure to have the funeral in the church Frikkie had left, for the sake of his aging parents. A mutual friend asked whether there was anything that might guide her in this extremity in my interview with him. I got out my notebook and typed up my notes, including the sentence "I have more fathers and brothers and sisters in the real sense of the word among blacks than I have blood brothers and sisters."

The funeral service was at the church in Alexandra, followed by burial in the black cemetery, where Frikkie, once again, crossed a barrier no other white had crossed. His old family was there in the small black church, and so was his new family, which overflowed in the hundreds into the church-yard. The eulogies became prayers for freedom and reconciliation. I found it hard to tear my eyes away from Frikkie's white relatives, who were having to share their grief with Bishop Tutu and others who were notorious in the Afrikaans newspapers as agents or dupes of Soviet subversion. Then a brother got up to speak on behalf of the family. A large middle-aged man, he spoke in Afrikaans with careful courtesy, saying he trusted the people of Alexandra would always remember the message his brother had brought them. Frikkie Conradie, of course, would have instantly reacted to the condescension; he would have said that this was getting the meaning of his life exactly wrong.

Allan Boesak, who was there when the whole story began, came much closer. "Frikkie Conradie," he said of his friend, "lived and died a free man."

For a self-liberated black the question is not how to take sides or surmount isolation. It is how to make a commitment that will be more than a gesture, more than a sacrifice. It is easy enough to flash and vanish like a shooting star, achieving the status of victim. The authorities stand ready to provide a quick, dirty lesson on power to any young black. It is harder to choose exile, but what appears, at first, to be heroic can fade into a callow compromise, in the lengthening retrospect of a lifetime passed in dusty refugee camps and alien cities. What is obviously hardest is to stay and remain effective, staying not just to keep faith but to advance the cause of equality.

Malusi Mpumlwana, a political lieutenant and heir to Steve Biko, started to struggle with the question of commitment—of whether there was something required beyond courage and astuteness—shortly before his friend died. Malusi was then in the same Pietermaritzburg prison in which Joe Seremane had been interrogated and tortured. In Malusi's case the treatment generally known as the helicopter was introduced as the horse. Sometimes, when his contorted body was dangling from the bar, his interrogators would break for tea, leaving him alone with his pain. Sometimes they would cane him on his bare feet, which burned with each cut, then loosen his manacles and insist that he stand—and go on standing for hours—on his flayed soles and heels. The heaviest interrogation lasted about three weeks; for long stretches he was not allowed to sleep or use the toilet. "The methods they used were tough methods," he said, "but I expected worse things. So from day to day I told myself, 'This is not the worst yet.' I was able to keep my cool because I always said, 'It's not over yet. The real bad things are still to come.' And then it was a surprise when it was all over."

The main reason I found his account of interrogation more chilling than others I had heard had to do with Malusi himself. I could think of very few people I had known whose demeanor so perfectly reflected character and intelligence. Malusi Mpumlwana spoke softly, with a natural reserve, yet had a ready and wholehearted laugh. He was modest to the point of selflessness, yet he conveyed confidence and authority. He was alert without seeming wary, direct without seeming assertive. I was obviously biased, but I thought he walked in a special light; it was as if you could see it in his eyes, which took on a vaguely Oriental cast from his high cheekbones and wispy mandarin beard. Any interrogator, it seemed to me, who wasn't already stupefied by hate, violence, or drink would have to view him with respect. A system that could attempt to humiliate and break a young man like this, I thought, showed that it was fundamentally resigned to its own moral rancidness.

I had known Malusi Mpumlwana for three years before I heard his experiences of detention in any detail. While his story was by no means the worst I heard, it moved me most. There are those in what is called "the movement" who might say that Malusi lost his political bearings in jail in Pietermaritzburg. When he emerged he seemed full of a mystical—and therefore politically suspect—insight; even more than tactics, he now felt an urgent need to discuss basic theological issues of good and evil and what it meant in the South African situation to be doing God's will.

Late one evening, after a long conversation, he summarized his reflections for my benefit: "What happened is I said, 'Exactly what is going on? What does God believe in? Look, we are very honest men, and we are committed to something that is very important. It *should* be done! Somebody has got to do it! And I believe that no self-respecting, loving God can fight against this or allow this stupid nonsense to happen.' And this happened to me, and I said to myself, 'Perhaps what is happening is that I plan and expect God to bless. I don't say I am on God's side; I say God is on my side or should be on my side.' And I began to sit back and reflect, 'If God wills good to happen, and I also will good to happen, where is our difference?' And then I thought that perhaps I should take more trouble to align myself with what might be God's wisdom. And since I have done that, I have become more than ever convinced that there is no greater foundation for a struggle for change and emancipation in this land than a conviction that it is God's will.

"But then, of course, you don't coopt God into your will." Here Malusi laughed, a deep laugh from his chest. "You participate in His will and make your little contribution. Not only should this be the case, but I think you've got to know that *all* these people are God's people. Good and bad alike. He loves them but hates the evil that they do. And therefore, you can smash evil with all the power you can muster, but you've got to save every last soul of them."

Again Malusi laughed, not self-consciously but as if he had been caught unawares by the immensity of this demand. And once again, I have to acknowledge that the meaning of his words was and is beyond me. I knew they were not a summons to pietistic quietism or fatalism, nor did they represent a renunciation of the struggle in which he had been engaged. In a mundane sense, I imagine, they meant that those who sought to lead had to involve themselves more deeply than they had done so far in the lives and sufferings of the people, that their sense of urgency should express itself more in the intensity of that involvement than in their pronouncement of political demands and timetables. But that vague formulation is nothing more than one skeptic's attempt to put into words the commitment Malusi was trying to put into his life.

Biko and his friends had discovered in the movement they called Black Consciousness that each individual had the capacity to liberate himself. "It let us be free," Malusi said. "Very, very liberated, to the extent that even if you went into a town like Bloemfontein where you would have cringed in the past, suddenly you felt like you could challenge the whole white commando. Biko's thrust was that political emancipation would not make sense without psychological emancipation because even if you had a change of government with people who felt inferior, what country could you run? So his view was that 'Black man, you're probably the greatest contributor to your own oppression,' that 'The white man has only to set the machine and leave it on automatic and you run it yourself.'"

The theological questions that preoccupied Malusi in detention eventually carried this self-liberated activist to a new kind of concern for those left behind. "The measure of your freedom," Malusi said, "is to what extent you are able to recognize the unfreedom of others and battle to undo it. And then, while you're doing that, you get unfree again." Here he laughed at a paradox Black Consciousness had not foreseen.

Only two brief weeks intervened between his release from detention in July 1977 and Steve Biko's last arrest. There was time for only one long and speculative conversation. Malusi tried to impart his sense of urgency about the need to consider the "role of God in this situation." Biko, a believer, was troubled by the theological problem of evil. Africa knew God, he felt, but God somehow overlooked Africa's suffering. The conversation reached no conclusion, and then Biko left on the trip from which he never returned.

It would be hard to exaggerate this irony: two close friends—one who had just been tortured, the other about to be tortured to death on behalf of what is supposed to be Christian civilization in South Africa—and in the little time left to them, they talk about the "role of God in this situation." The news of Biko's death came fewer than forty-eight hours after Malusi had learned about the death of his own father. With no time to mourn either of the two most important men in his life, he had to make arrangements for two funerals on successive days. The second, Biko's, had to succeed as a political statement, an expression at once of outrage and renewal. There were 20,000 mourners that afternoon in King William's Town, several hundred of them whites, the rest blacks. As the casket was lowered into the grave in the segregated cemetery next to the railway track, their protest seemed to reverberate throughout the country. The authorities reacted with mass arrests, bannings of organizations, bannings of individuals. Malusi Mpumlwana went back to jail. Biko's killers went free, while his friends and followers went to jail.

Released finally under a banning order that made him a political non-person, he found the movement he had helped build effectively obliterated. Many of its adherents had fled the country. Attempting to align himself with God's will, Malusi resolved to stay.

His decision to become a priest in the black branch of the Anglican Church, which his father and grandfather had served as ministers, was not easily made. It had not yet been taken when I met him, three years after Biko's death, at the time of Ciskei's hokey referendum on its hokey independence. Malusi by then had the status of an apostle because of his relation to the martyred Biko, but he was supporting his wife and children by working as a furniture salesman.

We drove to a tannery near the town of Alice that had been part of the community programs Biko's movement had fostered as an initiative in black self-reliance. All that was left was the cement foundation; the authorities had razed the building, demolishing the Biko legacy. They had done their work well. Malusi did not pretend that the vision of Black Consciousness was still smoldering in the hearts of the soon-to-be-Ciskeians. In the cemetery, Biko's grave had the largest headstone but did not appear to be better tended than any of the others. It had not become a place of pilgrimage.

He recognized reality, but he didn't speak that evening as if the movement had failed or lost its way; in his view, Black Consciousness had been another chapter in the long saga of black resistance. He was then just thirty, still banned and under surveillance. Although he had been through more than most men experience in a lifetime, he was in the position of having to make a new beginning. I was struck by his quiet confidence, the light-heartedness that seemed to coexist with earnestness, not uneasily but as if they were somehow part of the same impulse.

That evening, as we were being seated in a steak house with "international" status, Malusi excused himself and went up to the bar to greet a white man, who seemed less than overjoyed to see him. Stiffly, the man introduced his black acquaintance to the blonde with whom he was drinking. Returning to our table, Malusi explained that the man was an officer in the security police who had once been his shadow. In that role he had displayed an exceptional lack of subtlety and often managed inadvertently to tip the black activists off about police tactics and intelligence. That made him a favorite, and Malusi had developed a protective instinct for him, not wanting to see him replaced by someone more efficient.

"I don't think I've deliberately not hated," he remarked later when I told him how astonished I had been. "It's not part of my nature to be hateful, I think, but I can be quite indignant, and I detest evil. I can see the security police as individuals because I've come to know that you can get chaps working themselves up to be very bad. But I also see them as part of a culture, part of a system, which makes them very dangerous animals to be let loose.''

On another of my visits following the homeland's independence, he managed to laugh when he showed me a formal letter he had just received from the Ministry of Internal Affairs in Pretoria, informing him that he would henceforth need a visa to visit the Republic of South Africa. "Should you arrive at a South African port of entry without a visa," the letter said, "you will not be permitted to enter."

By then he was in his first year of divinity studies near Pietermaritzburg, where he had once been detained; the letter therefore meant he needed a visa to continue in theology, Greek, and church history. The more we worked out the implications of the predicament the more uproarious our laughter became. Technically, it seemed, he needed a visa to apply for a visa because the South African Embassy to Ciskei was still in white King William's Town. If he wanted to continue his studies, he could go into exile overseas, which would mean applying for a South African visa to reach a port of exit, or apply for a visa to stay home. Malusi had decided to apply because there was no purpose that could be served by his rotting in the township. "I'm not an alien, I can't possibly be an alien, but they've made me acknowledge that I'm a foreigner," he said. "They've succeeded beyond their wildest dreams."

Eventually this black South African living in South Africa got his visa to South Africa, and it was only then, five years after Steve Biko's death, that he made the decision to become a priest.

"Do you believe the churches can actually bring this regime down?" I asked incredulously.

"No, not the church as an institution," he replied, "but Christian conviction, which is my mainstay." As I understood him, he was talking about a conviction that grew not merely from a will to overcome the personal humiliation of apartheid but from a deeper sense of how it distorts the lives and increases the suffering of the masses of poor blacks. "It is very important to understand how people live, so that becomes the driving force behind you," he said. "I identify in every way with an intention to liberate oneself from the self-perpetuation of oppression, but at the same time, I don't think that for me it means that you must be married to a particular political ideology. What's important is a burning decision to change the situation in every way possible."

Having just started parish work in the poorest of Durban's townships, Biko's heir said he didn't side with any one of the political sects fighting apartheid but with all of them. "I recognize all good as my pursuit," he explained, laughing again from the chest, "not just so-and-so's good." For that very reason there were some who now counted him as lost to "the movement."

• • •

In the same week that he had his last serious conversation with his friend Malusi Mpumlwana, Steve Biko had another long conversation with a white pastor whose spiritual and political pilgrimage had been perhaps the most remarkable any South African had taken. The Reverend Christiaan Frederick Beyers Naudé, who was then in his seventh decade and only a few months away from being silenced by a banning order, had talked politics rather than theology. Near the end of an arduous quest, he had come to believe that for a white South African, especially an Afrikaner, doing God's will meant supporting black political initiatives. Specifically Beyers Naudé was preoccupied then by the question of what could be done to harness the fractious black movements into something like a unified force.

The trajectory he had traveled to reach this point, where he was beyond any doubt a traitor and heretic in the eyes of most Afrikaners, had carried Beyers Naudé from one end of the South African political firmament to the other. Naudé's apostasy was especially galling because it had occurred at the very heart of a power elite. Once he had been the most highly regarded Afrikaner clergyman of his generation; now, or so the top security officials contended, he was an agent of the underground. Contained within that charge was a germ of plausibility, for Beyers Naudé had unquestionably aligned himself with a cause most Afrikaners viewed as revolutionary. He had crossed the invisible line that separates liberals from radicals in the eyes of most whites: He had sided with blacks.

Yet the man was more remarkable than the story of his life. It wasn't only the distance he had traveled but his readiness at every stage to go on traveling, to find some new injunction in any new set of circumstances, that set him apart. His principles only began the process of his detachment from his Afrikaner patriarchy. What did him in was his openness to experience, his readiness to step across the racial barrier and see for himself what it was really like over there.

Initially he could tailor principles, like most preachers, but he could not deny facts. Starting in late middle age, he taught himself to embrace them. The urgency came from this openness; the more he knew, the more he felt was demanded of him. Even after he had been placed under a banning order and confined to a single district, he managed to travel deeper into the heart of South Africa than practically any other white. Ostracized by Afrikaners, he sought a wider community, and yet, even after leaving his church so he could worship with blacks, he never ceased to be an Afrikaner dominee in his unfailing courtesy and pastoral manner, even in his grooming. The safari suits he wore in summer always looked freshly pressed; his hair was always neatly combed and never, it seemed, in need of cutting. His days were crammed with appointments, but he never allowed himself to seem rushed or distracted.

Beyers Naudé doesn't mention his father, a severe and distant figure in the patriarchal mode, as a model for the life he has led. But it is hard not to notice a rough symmetry between the journeys of father and son, although they traveled in opposite directions politically. Jozua François Naudé was one of only six out of sixty delegates at the peace conference that ended the Boer War who refused to sign a treaty that gave the losing side peace under the British crown. In the face of certain defeat, he would have preferred to go on fighting. He then became a dominee but still wasn't resigned to the loss of Afrikaner sovereignty when, thirteen years later, in 1915, the fourth of his eight children and second son was born and named after another uncompromising Afrikaner. General C. F. Beyers, a Boer War hero, had died the year before in a brief rebellion provoked by the decision of some of his old comrades, who now held authority in Pretoria, to take South Africa into the World War on Britain's side. In the same period Jozua Naudé became one of the half dozen founders of a secret society that swore an oath to advance the cause of Afrikaner nationhood and dominance in all spheres of South African life. This was the Broederbond, which slowly amassed influence and power over the next three decades in what outsiders, including many Afrikaners, came to see as a sinister conspiracy. When Beyers Naudé, a half century after the founding of the Broederbond, broke with it to found an organization called the Christian Institute, his initial idea was that an elite group of idealistic Afrikaner clergymen could gradually change the outlook of their people through mutual consultation in private on the issues they faced. The Broederbond was quick to condemn the institute, and eventually it was banned. But different as his aims and methods would become, the son's instinct in searching for a way to return his people to the path of righteousness may have been nearer to that of his father at the outset than he or orthodox Afrikaners would have imagined.

So much for symmetry. What is striking about Beyers Naudé's formative years is his complete insulation from the business of race. The issue grazed his consciousness at the University of Stellenbosch, where he excelled in Hendrik Verwoerd's social science course, but it never preoccupied him. There came another slight flutter of doubt when he started visiting a German mission station in the Cape called Genadendal after becoming engaged to a daughter of one of the missionaries. There coloreds and whites met in one another's homes on the basis of equality, the first such contacts across the color line he had experienced. He was left with the guilty knowledge that it could be done, that there was a contradiction that probably needed some rationalizing between the kind of Christianity on which he had been reared and the kind practiced by his prospective in-laws, but it was nothing he allowed to burden his conscience.

To do so would have been to throw a shadow over his future, which seemed so tidily arranged. At the age of twenty-five, when he was serving his first congregation, he was approached in private by some of the elders and invited to join the Broederbond. Twenty-five was the minimum age for membership; the founder's son was right on course as one of the elect. The all-male monthly meetings of his "circle," or cell, became the main source of intellectual stimulation and fellowship in his life outside the church; here, too, he felt himself to be engaged in a sacred enterprise. Then, at thirty, he was called to a congregation near Pretoria, which meant moving to the Transvaal from the Cape, where the numerically predominant coloreds had seemed to blend into the landscape. In the Transvaal it was impossible not to notice that there was a huge black community physically present in the white heartland. For the first time, he acknowledged that there was a problem. It was something to think about, he thought—something to think about later.

The year 1948 comes, and Beyers Naudé votes for the National party and feels, when it squeaks into power on its apartheid platform, a deep sense of fulfillment tinged only by a filial regret that his dominee father, who died a few months before the election, had not lived to see this realization of his dreams. In the new government's first year, he becomes a minister in the Pretoria congregation that most of the Cabinet members attend. The vigor and obvious sincerity of his preaching win him a growing reputation, and he moves in social circles that include the most powerful figures in the Afrikaner church and state. He is nearly forty before this picture starts to change significantly. Then, as a result of a half-year tour of Europe and North America as an emissary for the Dutch Reformed Church, he wakes up to the fact that his knowledge of what goes on in his own country is riddled with blanks. In Holland and England, Canada and the United States, churchmen ask him about the Defiance Campaign, which the congress movement has been waging. He has heard of it only vaguely and ignored what he has heard, so it is as remote to him as a report of a clash in Sumatra. Names of black leaders such as Albert Lutuli and Z. K. Matthews are mentioned in his presence; he avoids acknowledging that he has never heard of them. He is asked what he thought of Alan Paton's *Cry, the Beloved Country*; he confesses that he has heard of neither the author nor his book.

The trip teaches him a lesson about his own insularity; it also provokes him to undertake a private study of the biblical, theological, and historical justification his church has advanced for the South African system. The result is devastating. None of the justifications can be defended. Now, in his early forties, he finds himself burdened with an incubus of doubt.

"I was afraid," he said. "I just couldn't face it." Then in a period of five years, which brings him to the age of forty-eight and his first experiences as a pariah, reality rapidly catches up with him. As Beyers Naudé seeks to reconcile his secular and religious faiths, apartheid gets steadily harsher and more aggressive ideologically as a result of the ascent to power of his old teacher Verwoerd. The consequences for those who stumble or break ranks on racial issues become clearer and more severe. His reputa-

tion for integrity and his high position in the church—he has become acting moderator of his synod—make him a sounding board for the private
anxieties of three white pastors who have been meeting rising resistance to
their missionary efforts in black communities as a result of the sufferings
imposed by Afrikanerdom's quasi-theocracy. At this point he makes his
first misstep on the slippery slope of Christian action. Saying he knows
there are problems but cannot imagine that conditions are really so bad,
he resolves to do the one thing that a shrewder, more self-protective man
would avoid at all costs: to go and see for himself. In middle age, for the
first time in his life, he enters black townships and the hostels reserved for
migrant laborers. For the first time he allows himself to speak to blacks
about what it is like to be black in white South Africa. These are not outspoken political people but the deferential, pathetically moderate elders of
Dutch Reformed mission churches. Yet once he knows the circumstances
of their lives, the weight of his doubt becomes almost too heavy to bear.

At this point his personal history starts to converge with the history of
his times, for he is chosen as one of the representatives from his synod to
an ecumenical conference on apartheid that brings the major denomina-
tions in South Africa together under the auspices of the World Council of
Churches. Partly as the result of his efforts, the delegation from the Dutch
Reformed Church manages to find common ground there on racial issues
with the English-speaking churches, but that common ground is a retreat
from apartheid and an affirmation that members of all racial groups have
an equal right to share the "responsibilities, rewards and privileges" of
citizenship. First Verwoerd and then the synods of Naudé's church repu-
diate the key resolutions. But when the time comes for him to recant, as
the other delegates from his synod have done, Beyers Naudé refuses.

He has shown that he is a potential dissident, but he is not yet ostracized. In fact, he remains the senior minister of the most prestigious Dutch
Reformed congregation in Johannesburg for two and one half years and
a member of the Broederbond. He begins publication of a journal called
Pro Veritate that addresses itself to the church's role in society and the
questions it has evaded and finally gives up his pulpit to found his Christian Institute as an ecumenical movement aimed primarily at influencing
the white churches. His own church condemns the institute, before it has
had time to do anything, and subsequently proscribes it formally as an
heretical organization.

Yet at this point, having overturned his life, he has merely broken ranks.
He still has never talked politics with a black nationalist, still knows next
to nothing of the history of black politics. In fact, he has not even had English-speaking friends or gone to dinner in a non-Afrikaans home. Nevertheless, by the age of fifty Beyers Naudé has been condemned as a traitor
and almost wholly isolated within Afrikanerdom. In his family his motives and conduct are a source of bewilderment. Two sisters stop speaking

to him, one permanently. Suddenly he has to learn to speak to his wife, his three sons, and his young daughter in a new way, not as the patriarch whose judgment on moral issues is final but as an equal trying to explain and persuade. Family love survives because he learns to accept debate, but that means accepting the reality that his elder sons will not follow him politically; only his wife, finally, manages to make that adjustment and go on making it as he blazes a new trail.

In this period, when his journey was still beginning, I encountered Beyers Naudé. It was 1965, and he was on the verge of liberalism. He still believed that initiatives for change would have to come from enlightened whites, that the Afrikaner people would not be able to go on negating the "voice of conscience." If the church moved, the people would follow, he said. Implicitly he was saying that the churches could be the vehicle for clearing up what was basically a misunderstanding. He claimed that there were about 120 dominees in the Dutch Reformed Church who were silently sympathetic with his position. Soon it was only their silence, not their sympathy, that he experienced.

But he was now launched and reaching out to black and colored churchmen, and this introduced him to a basic law of South African social dynamics: The more a movement for change seeks the serious involvement of blacks, the less it appeals to whites. It took only a few years for him to hurtle across the political spectrum, moving from critical Nationalist and reluctant dissident to active white supporter of black initiatives.

When Biko and other black students flaunted the banner of Black Consciousness, the Christian Institute was the one white-led organization that wasn't offended. On the contrary, it rushed to offer organizational support and to introduce this new black leadership to potential financial backers in Western churches. Beyers Naudé, like an explorer on uncharted seas, pressed ahead with such high-voltage questions as civil disobedience, conscientious objection, boycotts, and economic sanctions. Inevitably, its white membership dwindled, liberal white businessmen stopped writing checks, and the authorities stepped up their pressure, seizing Naudé's passport and declaring the Christian Institute an "affected organization"—in effect, subversive.

And still this was not the end of his journey. In 1976 the Christian Institute expressed its support for the aims of the "liberation" movements so long as these did not conflict with the gospel. A month after that, Naudé spent a night in jail for refusing to testify to an official commission that had advised the authorities to act against the Christian Institute on grounds that it promoted black dominance and socialism. What churchmen describe as his prophetic ministry had now carried him to an unabashedly radical stance, but he expressed himself in terms of moral urgency, not political jargon:

If you truly love your country, then decide now—once and for all—
what kind of country you wish to give yourself to and then commit
yourself to see to it that you have a share in the way such a country
is being created and built—even if it eventually has to be built from
the ashes of a society which has destroyed itself through its own
blindness, its avarice and its fear. For whatever is going to happen in
between, one thing I know: A new South Africa is being born—a
South Africa in which I wish to live . . . a South Africa in which I wish
to give of myself to all the people of our land.

The next year, in the aftermath of Steve Biko's death, it became a criminal
offense to print those words: The Christian Institute was banned as an organization, and Naudé was banned as an individual; that meant it was illegal for him to travel in the country, enter black areas, attend meetings,
or be quoted in any publication.

And still that was not the end. Despite his restriction, which wasn't lifted
until 1984, Beyers Naudé stayed in circulation, still maintaining, it seemed,
a wider circle of contacts among black churchmen and activists than any
other white in the country. His political effectiveness was hard to assess
and easy to belittle, but there was really no way of calculating how many
lives he might have touched. For blacks he remained, Desmond Tutu wrote,
"the most resplendent sign of hope in South Africa today." The authorities seemed to endorse this tribute, for they paid Beyers Naudé the unusual homage of declaring him to be, under their security laws, a "listed"
as well as a "banned" person. At the age of sixty-eight, he was still regarded as dangerous; had his "listing" remained in force, it would have
been illegal to quote his words even if he died. Scarcely a month later a
political movement called the United Democratic Front came into existence, resurrecting the slogans and themes of the outlawed African National
Congress. The new front named Christiaan Frederick Beyers Naudé as one
of its patrons, along with the imprisoned Nelson Mandela.

It was easier to understand why blacks chose to honor Beyers Naudé than
it was to see why the security police persisted in regarding him as a threat.
Was their need to proscribe him explained simply by the old bitterness over
his treason to the Broederbond? Or was there a touch here of ethnic pride,
a sense that a little Afrikaner backbone was what the forces of resistance
required to become really threatening? Why couldn't his voice be heard?
Whom would it move? It wasn't as if thousands of black youths were going
to follow a near-septuagenarian Afrikaner dominee over the barricades.

This mystery was partly dispelled for me when, toward the end of my
stay in South Africa, I finally heard Beyers Naudé preach. One afternoon
I learned that he was due to show up at a vigil on the issue of resettlement
in the homeland that was being conducted by the Black Sash, an organization of white women that seeks to serve blacks caught in the coils of

apartheid. His name was not on the printed program, but I was told he would deliver what amounted to a sneak sermon. I raced to get there in time and looked around the whitewashed chapel in which the vigil was being held. There were fewer than fifty persons, maybe thirty of them whites. There was also a press table, but it emptied before Beyers Naudé rose to speak; he still could not be quoted. The organizers of the vigil had been recording the talks of all the other speakers, but now, as Naudé covered the short distance from his seat in the front row to the lectern in a few loping strides, his back bent slightly as if he were walking uphill, the tape recorder was switched off.

His text was I Kings 21, the story of Ahab, king of Samaria, who coveted the vineyard of Naboth the Jezreelite. Standing under a simple wooden cross, he read from his Bible only once, near the end of his narrative, which he related with the simplicity and immediacy of a fresh, cleanly told news report: how Ahab offered Naboth the choice of money for his vineyard or a better vineyard somewhere else; how Naboth replied that he couldn't surrender his patrimony; how Ahab then returned to his palace and sulked until his wife, Jezebel, promised to find a way to separate Naboth from his land; and how Jezebel then made illicit use of the royal seals to send an order to the elders of Jezreel so that Naboth would be hauled up on fabricated charges of blasphemy.

There was no straining after comparisons, but Naudé let the story tell itself. His voice had a bright resonance, which carried through to the one passage that he read, in which the Lord—taking note of the penance of Ahab, who tears his clothes, puts on sackcloth, and goes on a fast—tells Elijah the Tishbite, "I will not bring the evil in his days: but in his son's days will I bring the evil upon his house."

The voice softened when the time came to reflect on the portion's meaning. The words "South Africa" and "resettlement" had yet to be spoken; there was no need to speak them now. There are many parallels in our land, Naudé said, but there are also differences. There it was just a case of Ahab and Jezebel's getting overcome by a greedy wish to own a particular vineyard; here it is a matter of state policy. In the same spare terms in which he had recounted the stoning of Naboth, he now described the agony and weeping of those who lost their land. As an Afrikaner, he continued, he was painfully aware that his people were largely responsible. How does this happen to a people? He spoke briefly of the power of ideology to stifle reason and compassion and then of a concept of self-interest—which he said Scripture and history both refute—that safety lies in grabbing and keeping.

"Why does God allow it?" he asked, putting the question speculatively, then restating it directly: "Why, God, do you allow it?" Naudé didn't wait for an answer or pretend that he had one already. "I don't know," he said, sounding briskly conversational, "but I know that sooner or later the Supreme Being that we call God ordains there must be justice. Is that day of judgment approaching in our land? I don't know, but we must pray and strive for liberation, and in the meantime, we all have our responsibilities and duties." He then ended by praying for migrant laborers, their families, those who make the policies that control their lives, those who carry them out, those who don't understand, and those who do understand but whose lives are ruled by fear.

It was very nearly a perfect homiletic exercise, I thought. It was also, I imagined, what Christians call a witness. There was nothing in the sermon that could be described as incitement, scarcely anything that could be called political. Its preoccupation was with scriptural themes from start to finish; the sense of urgency had come from Beyers Naudé's exposition and example. "We all have our responsibilities and duties," this Christian had said. I was neither Christian nor South African, but I thought, if I were South African, the experience of hearing that sermon could have changed my life. In what amounted to a moral Rorschach test, he had left it to his listeners to supply content to the words "responsibilities" and "duties." Their answers would come from themselves, not him. I could not imagine what this tiny audience, made up largely of middle-aged white women, might be thinking. But in that brief instant, it occurred to me that younger and darker South Africans might come up with an answer that was neither explicit nor implicit in Beyers Naudé's presentation. It occurred to me that they might think of guns.

CHAPTER TEN

W-A-R?

It is possible to pinpoint an hour in which the Bastille might have been stormed in South Africa and wasn't: That prospect was raised, and extinguished, on March 30, 1960, a day that saw the most impressive assertion of disciplined black political will in this century. On that morning, a procession of at least 15,000 and possibly 30,00 blacks marched in ranks down a highway from the nearest of the black townships to the heart of the city. The route brought most of the marchers to within three blocks of the Parliament Building. By the time the vanguard got that far, a distance of eight miles, an air force helicopter was hovering overhead and armored cars with police and army units were massing in the side streets. White troops with fixed bayonets arrayed themselves in front of Parliament, and machine-gun emplacements were established on its grounds. Only nine days earlier but 900 miles away, a confrontation between a crowd of unarmed

Africans and nervous white policemen in an obscure black township called Sharpeville had ended with the deaths of 68 blacks. No one could calculate the possible repercussions of another Sharpeville at the portal of white power.

It proved to be an episode that radical and liberal white academics have regarded as a "revolutionary moment" squandered. Still the march is generally acknowledged to have represented a turning point, the moment at which black leaders were finally forced to see the inadequacy of non-violent tactics in the South African context.

Yet white power has never been quite as unsure of itself as it was for a few moments at midday on March 30, 1960. I first set foot in South Africa five years after the event, but I came eventually to sense that what happened contained essential clues to a whole epoch of racial struggle. What first set me thinking about it was a conversation in Cape Town with a young colored woman who described the feeling of awe that gripped her when, as a schoolgirl, she watched from a sidewalk as the marchers made their way into the city. Nothing in their demeanor was menacing; they were not yelling threats or brandishing fists. Yet to her young eyes the black marchers looked as unthwartable and dangerous as destiny itself. School had been dismissed early on account of the presumed menace that the marchers represented, and she had rushed home. "I had only one more street to cross," she said, "but that was the street the kaffirs were marching down. I was afraid to cross. I stood inside one of the shops and prayed to God that no one would say something that would make them mad. The next morning in school, some of the boys said they hoped the kaffirs burned the whole of Cape Town down, just to show the whites. I told them not to talk like that."

Where did the feelings of inevitability that the marchers obviously felt and inspired come from? And more to the point, where did they go? The answers turn, in part, on the relationship between that huge throng and its leader. Philip Kgosana was slightly built, twenty-three years old, and only six years out of primary school. For a period that can be measured in minutes rather than hours, he appears to have held the fate of his country in his hand as no other black man has before or since. There can be no doubt that if he had ordered the crowd to march the final few blocks to Parliament, it would have marched, whatever the consequences. Was that, I wondered, a possibility he considered at the time?

It took me several months after leaving South Africa at the end of my last tour there to locate Kgosana in Sri Lanka, where he had been living for three years. Finally, one morning, a call came through in London from Philip Kgosana in Colombo. I was not heading for Asia, and he was not due to visit Europe, so we agreed to communicate by mail and phone. I sent a long list of questions; some weeks later I opened my mailbox to find a cassette recording with Philip Kgosana's answers in the form of a meditation on the events of March 30, 1960. By then, I calculated, he had passed half his life in exile.

Listening to the somber, sad cadences of the exile jarred my imagination. I had never fully appreciated just how extraordinary young Kgosana's leadership actually was. Not only was he a youth, but he was practically brand-new to politics—and he was of the wrong ethnic background. Of the black men who marched in that column behind him, 98 or 99 percent were Xhosas. Philip Kgosana, who had come to Cape Town on scholarship to study economics at the university there, hailed from the other end of the country, from a hamlet northeast of Pretoria.

Then there was the matter of his short pants. Practically every onlooker who later recorded his impressions was struck by the fact that the leader of the rough-hewn masculine crowd was dressed like a schoolboy. The movement in which Kgosana had enlisted, the Pan-Africanist Congress, had launched the nationwide protest against the pass laws, producing within five hours the Sharpeville confrontation and the national crisis. Arrests in Cape Town had left young Philip Kgosana the ranking leader there. His appearance at the head of the march, he said on the cassette, had to be carefully timed. "I was evading arrest and therefore would not present myself openly like that except on a strategic move. I wanted to make sure there was no confusion in case the people hit against the police."

Whatever the reason for his late appearance, his short pants had another, more important meaning, which went part of the way to Philip Kgosana's standing with the migrants who followed him. He had come to the University of Cape Town bringing little more than the clothes on his back, and those garments had come to him as charity. The son of a poor rural pastor in the Church of Christ, he was past seventeen when he started high school in a segregated township of Pretoria called Lady Selborne. He thought he would become a pharmacist, only to discover that blacks were barred from that field. Instead of absorbing rejection fatalistically, he carried his grievance to a black patriarch, who referred him to an agency of white philanthropy. There his assertiveness and obvious intelligence made such an impression that arrangements were made for him to go to the University of Cape Town, South Africa's Cambridge, on a scholarship. Just before he left Pretoria, Kgosana went to a midnight meeting in an unlit church in Lady Selborne, where he heard Robert Sobukwe, who was then, after a break with the African National Congress, about to launch his as yet unnamed Pan-Africanist movement. "I had instant admiration of the man," he said. A year later, when Sobukwe came to Cape Town to lay the groundwork for his campaign, the undergraduate from Pretoria was there to offer his services.

Sitting in Colombo, across the gulf of miles and years, he could still respond to my question about the short pants by recalling the provenance of virtually every garment he wore on the day of the march. The jacket had been a gift from the headmaster of his high school. So were his shoes; he wore no socks, for he had none. His sweater and shirt were hand-me-downs from an older Pan-Africanist leader. "There was no magic about the shorts," Kgosana said, "except that they tell an untold story that at that time I did not have many clothes to wear."

There was no magic about the shorts, but they point to this student's extreme indigence, which was as severe as that of the masses he led, so severe that he had moved into the barracks for migrant laborers in Langa township when he arrived in Cape Town. One of the questions on my list was whether he had moved in with the migrant laborers to organize them. "It was simple deprivation that took me there," Kgosana replied. "But as things turned out, I found myself among my own people and had to lead them when the critical moment came."

Sobukwe's antipass campaign touched a nerve in Cape Town, drawing a quicker, deeper response from the black masses there than any agitation had elicited in South Africa until then. The African National Congress had experimented with nonviolent tactics over the previous decade. The authorities replied by banning and jailing its leaders. Sobukwe's reading of the lessons of the fifties was that the ANC had not dared enough. His idea was that Africans would stop carrying passes, present themselves for mass arrests, fill the jails, and deny their labor to the system until the pass laws—their foremost grievance—were abolished. Stop carrying them not merely as a gesture but as the beginning of the end of the system. That, he promised, would be the first step to an early triumph for black nationalism.

An intellectual, Sobukwe was true to his conviction that a leader should not ask the people to do anything he would not do himself. So he offered himself for arrest at the police station in what is now Soweto, effectively ending his political career. Nine years were to pass before he was released from detention, and never again, tragically, was he free to speak in public before his death in 1978. The immediate effect of the leader's arrest was that he was not available when, just five hours later, the shooting started at Sharpeville. Yet what happened in Cape Town went far to justify Sobukwe's belief that there was a bedrock militancy in the black masses that was only waiting to be mined.

Kgosana carried Sobukwe's banner in Cape Town, where most Pan-Africanist activists were laborers. For eleven crucial days he was the link between the intellectual who led—then vanished behind bars—and the masses in whom the leader believed. Every African, he told a mass meeting in Langa the day before the campaign started, had to promise himself that he would never again carry a pass. About half that speech was made up of Sobukwe's final instructions. It was the last time the leader's words could legally be read in public in South Africa, and those words became the basis for Sobukwe's eventual conviction for incitement. Yet what Sobukwe promised was "a never-ending stream" of nonviolent campaigns until a goal he defined as "independence" had been reached. "We are not leading corpses to a new Africa," he vowed.

I looked again at the Langa speech; the explanation for the astonishing denouement of the march eleven days later was all there. Interpreting Sobukwe's instructions, Kgosana twice made it explicit that "absolute non-violence" meant that civil disobedience extended only to not carrying passes and staying away from work; it did not extend to disobeying a lawful order from the authorities to disperse and go home.

Sobukwe's tactical error was to underestimate both the weapon of non-violent resistance and the ruthlessness of the state. He was not, in fact, a Gandhian; he did not believe in forcing the regime to show its violent face to itself and the world. So he hoped for a miracle and took himself out of action, leaving instructions that were mute on the question of what to do if the authorities failed to follow his script.

Once the campaign was launched, the authorities were shrewd enough to stop making arrests for violation of the pass laws in Cape Town. "Absolute nonviolence" broke down briefly on the first evening, when the police fired on a crowd, killing two and triggering a riot. Only on the fourth day did the PAC manage to get a hundred of its volunteers arrested, but then, instead of filling the jails, the police released the same hundred in response to the next day's demonstration, at which Kgosana himself was picked up.

By the morning of March 30, no one was in jail for pass-law offenses in Cape Town, it seems, but the strike Sobukwe had promised had now paralyzed the port and those industrial sectors that were dependent on black labor. Across the nation the spirit of resistance among blacks still seemed to be on the rise. On March 28 a bill was introduced in the white Parliament to give the government arbitrary power to ban other black congresses. At the same time plans were drawn up to proclaim a state of emergency under existing laws, which meant that the police would be able to use preventive detention. In fact, the first wave of mass arrests of black, brown, and white activists had occurred in the early hours of the thirtieth, before the proclamation had been made public. Shortly before daybreak, the police descended on Langa and Nyanga, another of Cape Town's ghettos, in an effort to break the black strike by beating the migrants out of their rooms and onto buses that would carry them back to work. The mass arrests and beatings were the immediate provocation of the great march that morning, which thus occurred on the spur of the moment, in a context that would more properly be described as counterrevolutionary than revolutionary.

At first it was assumed that this march would go to police headquarters, the destination of two smaller marches in the preceding week, but Kgosana decided that would be fruitless. "It was my own decision that we should march to Parliament in order to highlight the seriousness of our concern," he said on the cassette. But then he learned that troops were drawn up in front of Parliament, so, acting on his own, he decided to go to police headquarters after all. "I thought it was not wise to force my way to a Parliament surrounded by troops because otherwise an opportunity would have been presented to the racists to shoot and that was not my purpose," he said, speaking into the recorder in Colombo twenty-four years after the fact.

Remembering Sobukwe's instructions, he found himself negotiating with the same Afrikaner police commander who had released him five days earlier. The twenty-three-year-old black youth in short pants demanded to see the white minister of justice in order to make his demands. A journalist who was within earshot recalls that he was told, "The minister is at lunch."

On the spot, Philip Kgosana had to ask himself how long he could maintain his authority over a crowd of 15,000 or 30,000. He also had to wonder what his followers would do and what would happen to them if the police arrested him then and there. And he was obliged to take account of Sobukwe's order "that you peacefully disperse without making any noise or interjections." The Afrikaner commander promised that Kgosana would see the minister if he sent his people home. He was speaking, the journalist recalls, of a "gentlemen's agreement." Kgosana debated with himself and bargained with the commander for twenty minutes. Cape Town seemed to be holding its breath. Eventually he agreed.

"Mr. Kgosana called for silence and the murmuring of thousands of voices stopped," the *Cape Times* reported the next morning. Then, as he later testified, "When I ordered them to go back quietly, they went back quietly." A police van led the way.

Philip Kgosana was arrested at 4:45 that afternoon, when he returned with four other members of the Pan-Africanist Congress for his appointment with the minister. Emergency regulations forbade publication of that fact, so as far as his followers and newspaper readers were concerned, he simply vanished. Later, when charges of betrayal and bad faith were aired, it was revealed that Kgosana had been briefly visited in his cell by a civil servant who was acting as a surrogate for the minister. Calvinist consciences did not have to be troubled; there had been no betrayal, for he got his meeting and had never been promised, after all, that he would not be arrested. The policeman who made the promise was subsequently reported to have been denied promotion to brigadier for having presumed to negotiate with a black.

The emergency was proclaimed on the afternoon of Kgosana's arrest, and the Unlawful Organizations Act, which would be used shortly to ban the Pan-Africanist and African National congresses, was rushed through its second reading in Parliament. Langa and Nyanga townships were cordoned off by police, army, and even naval units. Water and electricity were cut off, and the troops were sent in to break the strike by force. "It took the police four days of continuous brutality to break the strike," Tom Lodge, a leading scholar on the period, has written. On the eighth day after Kgosana's detention, arrests under the pass laws were resumed in Cape Town. They have continued relentlessly, year after year, ever since. And, of course, the Pan-Africanist and African National congresses remain unlawful organizations.

What happened on March 30, 1960, was not that the blacks lost faith in nonviolent resistance. What happened was that the authorities used the full power of the state to stifle nonviolent resistance for a generation. Why has the march not been repeated? The simple answer is that the security police have effectively orchestrated black politics, mainly through repression but also through a selective lifting of the throttles and stops, so that the remarkable sense of opportunity and hope that existed on the eleventh day of Sobukwe's antipass campaign has not recurred. Frustration and anger, they have found, are easier to contain than hope.

South Africa was anything but an open society in March 1960, but it was not yet fully fledged as a police state; the formidable arsenal of arbitrary powers on which the white authorities have since relied was largely assembled in the five years following the emergency. In March 1960 the white authorities used complicated legal proceedings and trials; thereafter the emergency powers were incorporated into the structure of criminal law and regularly expanded. In effect, the emergency became permanent, making it possible to lock up political suspects first and worry later, if at all, about framing charges.

The effect of repression has been to rob black nationalists who try to operate within the system of any legitimacy. For a generation blacks who are serious about politics have been conditioned to think that their real leaders are outside the country, or in jail. Today a more sophisticated Afrikaner leadership could not strike a durable bargain without the movements the government outlawed in 1960, in particular, the African National Congress, which may be one of the world's least effective "liberation movements." Nevertheless, because of its heritage of more than seventy years and its ability to wage "armed struggle"—however desultory and feeble—it has kept its grip on black loyalties. Compromised by its readiness to condone repression anywhere in the Soviet sphere—in exchange for training and arms—it remains the broad, true church of politics. And the ANC today is revolutionary in a sense it was only accused of being in 1960.

That year, toward the end of a four-year trial of ANC leaders on trumped-up charges of treason, Nelson Mandela envisioned the course of negotiations with the white government. Under cross-examination the alleged and future revolutionary dreamed aloud about a process of give-and-take after the government agreed to talk with the real leaders of the people:

> I would say, "Yes, let us talk" and the government would say, "We think the Europeans at present are not ready for the type of government where there might be domination by non-Europeans. We think we should give you 60 seats, the African population to elect 60 Africans to represent them in Parliament. We will leave the matter over for five years and we will review at the end of five years." In my view, that would be a victory.... I'd say we should accept it but, of course, I would not abandon the demands of the extension of the universal suffrage to all Africans. That's how I see it, my lords. Then at the end of the five-year period we will have discussions and the Government says, "We will give you again 40 more seats," I might say, "That is quite sufficient, let's accept it," and still demand that the franchise would be extended, but for the agreed period we should suspend civil disobedience.

Instead, it was the authorities who suspended civil disobedience; they suspended the African National Congress, too, and Nelson Mandela finally went underground, then slipped out of the country and traveled to Algeria to take a course in revolutionary tactics.

On August 5, 1962, only sixteen days after his reinfiltration into South Africa, Nelson Mandela was arrested and ultimately convicted of high treason in the second of two trials, then sentenced to life imprisonment. Now having spent more than half his adult life, nearly a quarter of a century, behind bars, he has become the living symbol of his movement and the personification of the bondage of his people, most of whom have never seen or heard him. Mandela's 1960 dream of compromise sounds like a lesson in civics from another era, not only because of the regime's intransigence but because a gradualist settlement would not be easy to sell to the exiles in Angola, Zambia, and Tanzania who have dedicated their lives to revolutionary struggle. The effect repression has had is to make the revolutionary stance and a revolutionary settlement the only stance and only settlement that most politically active blacks can imagine supporting.

Yet, for better or worse, most politically alert blacks are not revolutionaries. Repression has introduced a drastic split in black politics between the acceptable political style and the available means. The fear of compromising with apartheid nullifies most black political efforts inside the country, making them seem either futile or fraudulent. Only the new black trade unions have a chance to build real organizational strength, and even there the most militant leaders have to be ready to fend off the accusation that they are working within the system, as, of course, they must every time they negotiate a contract, confront the police, or contemplate legal action to secure the rights of their members.

The black literary imagination strains to find a believable connection between the contradictory certainties of ultimate victory and present failure. So it finds the link in themes of betrayal, which help explain why heroic sacrifice is so often futile. There is an ambiguous note of fatalism, perhaps because there can be little expectation of early success. The African National Congress has little to celebrate beyond its survival. A revolutionary movement that finds itself in exile on its seventieth anniversary has to dig deep into its reserves of faith. "Seventy years," mused Mamphela Ramphele, Steve Biko's comrade, the last time I visited her clinic in the northern Transvaal. "We should hang our heads in shame rather than celebrate it."

The exile leaders stress the need to develop "secure areas" within the townships and homelands so training and organization can take place at the grass roots as well as in bush camps pushed back into Central Africa by the constant threat of retaliation by the South African military. Skillfully adapting tactics the Israelis pioneered in Lebanon, Pretoria sponsored insurgencies against neighboring black states to make border areas unsafe for its own rebels and the cost of backing them prohibitive for black governments. As soon as rebels link up to an established political network within South Africa, they run a high risk of stumbling across an informer's trip wire; that risk exists even if they keep to themselves because the resistance movement is also heavily infiltrated on its exile side by black and white agents.

A high proportion of the young men who infiltrate South Africa on sabotage missions after having been trained as soldiers in the "struggle" wind up in the hands of the security police, who squeeze them for information, select those who seem to have potential as double agents, and run the rest through the constantly grinding mill of political trials. The testimony in those trials then furnish a record of the slow, painful development of a revolutionary culture among young blacks. Here is Simon Mogoerane, a young man who grew up in a dingy township called Vosloorus near Boksburg, explaining what it meant to come of age there to an Afrikaner judge in Pretoria who has just found him guilty of treason:

We have hostels in the township where migrant laborers stay, people who stay away from their families for a very long time and are quite inclined to become a nuisance in the township, committing rapes, fights and such things. Another thing is, we stay in very small houses and . . . even if one has a girlfriend, he has just nowhere to take her to. There is just no comfort in the township whatsoever.

His formal plea for mercy comes across as the cry of a frustrated lover and consumer. He is talking about inconvenience and "comfort" rather than liberty, equality, fraternity. The migrants are not his abused brothers, or the sons and brothers of the marchers Philip Kgosana led, but "a nuisance in the township." Very simply, the courtroom spectator infers, he believes that blacks should have what whites have, that he, specifically, should have it. On this basis a political consciousness is gradually formed, and when the 1976 disturbances broke out in Soweto, he now testifies, "I thought at that time that the war had started and that freedom was near. . . . I thought I had to take part as an oppressed person."

The Afrikaner judge cannot believe he has heard right. "I'm sorry," he intervenes, "did you say you thought the war was near? W-A-R?"

The young man has been testifying in Sesotho, so the question and response have to be filtered through an interpreter. "Yes," he tells the red-robed judge, he meant war. "This was because of the riots."

The judge still doesn't get it. "What war?" he asks.

"What I mean is, immediately the uprisings had started, I thought this was the war which would eventually lead to freedom and I, as one of the oppressed people, also had to take part."

"I was just wondering whether the word 'war' was used." The judge persists. "W-A-R?"

"Yes."

"Is the word 'war' the correct word to use?"

"I mean a fight between groups of people. I do not know how one defines a war."

The young man is saying that he wanted to fight for his country. The judge, who conceives of it as *his* country even as he finds the young man guilty of treason, appears to consider the concept ridiculously overblown for a black from Vosloorus. Marcus Motaung, another defendant in the trial, simplifies it when it is his turn to plead in mitigation. "In South Africa," he testifies, "I was so hardened that I decided that all whites should be killed." He then left the country to get military training, but before sending him back to attack a series of police stations, the resistance movement refined his political understanding. "I was taught that the whites and the blacks in South Africa have got to live together. That was the greatest thing I received in the ANC teachings," he tells the court. His lawyer then asks what he conceived his role to be when he returned to his country. "I took myself to be a soldier, a freedom fighter," he says.

The judge took him to be a criminal. On June 9, 1983, Simon Mogoerane and Marcus Motaung both were hanged, H-A-N-G-E-D, in Pretoria along with a third member of the African National Congress named Jerry Mosoloi. In explaining its reasons for lengthening the roll of black martyrs, the government noted that four policemen, all blacks, had been killed in the raids in which they took part.

"We take them as mere militants," as ANC official in Lusaka later explained, "and we turn them into revolutionaries." The "mere militants" come out with a political consciousness that has been shaped on the wheel of apartheid; in many cases, of which Marcus Motaung's was one, this amounts to nothing more theoretical than an urge to reclaim the land by killing whites. Later, when they make their way back to South Africa as "revolutionaries," they often wind up killing blacks—informers, policemen, but also bystanders—or risking their lives to put bombs in empty government buildings, or missing their assigned targets altogether as a result of being betrayed by comrades who broke under interrogation or turned out to have been agents. The level of mishap and misadventure seems grotesquely high. In the first ANC trial I went to in Pretoria, two of the accused had been arrested at a secret rendezvous with an underground contact who led sixty policemen to the meeting. Two others, having been instructed to make their way back to Mozambique if anything went wrong, abandoned their unfired rockets in the veld after the first misfired in an attack on a gasoline depot, then were caught stealing a car. The final two, including one supposedly given advanced training in East Germany, drank too much, had their Russian-made weapon stolen, and, in a desperate effort to recover it, announced that they were on an important mission for the underground.

Blacks, it usually seemed, reacted with more pity than contempt for those who let down their cause under heavy pressure; with the whites, or so I guessed, it was normally the other way around. But why, after so many years of preparing, theorizing, plotting, and training, were so many young men sent into the country on underground missions found to be so woefully ill-prepared for the dangers they would confront? I could only speculate because the exile movement's suspicion of outsiders prevented any conversations with its young fighters.

So I was left with my own intuitions, reflections, and questions. The blacks were obviously outclassed in technology and firepower; they were also, it seemed, insufficiently ruthless. Why? Certainly I do not believe that whites are meaner or smarter than blacks, but starting from a base of power enables them to imagine that they are. An army or police unit patrolling the eastern Transvaal has radio contact with a headquarters or camp; if it stumbles on trouble, it knows it can summon helicopters or armored troop carriers. A few insurgents trying to swim like Mao's fish in the boundless sea of black South Africa have only their wits and the camouflage of their skins; if they stumble on trouble, they are on their own. By the time they have drawn close to their target, they are now several hundred miles distant from their base. These "freedom fighters" may be trained as soldiers, but they are called on to perform as saboteurs and espionage agents. They must make their lonely way. The worst thing they can do is to succumb to the temptation to seek out sympathizers or friends, who are likely to be under surveillance already.

So they are home, among their own people for the first time in four or five years, hearing their own language but knowing they will be at risk every time they use it. Maybe they notice that the standard of living has improved, that it is much higher than what they have seen in the Angolan bush. Suddenly the townships look inviting: If only they could call a halt....

Slowly, painstakingly, the movement attempts to build an internal network that could be capable of providing some cover to at least some of its operatives; and it waits for opportunities, for the kind of luck that a world war represented for Lenin, or a Japanese invasion for Mao, or the collapse of a regime in Lisbon represented to the insurgents in Mozambique, Angola, and, eventually, Zimbabwe. What that could be in the context of South Africa no one seems to know. The smart guys in the Western think tanks seem sure it doesn't exist. Guerrillas can never be more than a "serious nuisance" in South Africa, according to Lewis Gann and Peter Duignan, two unsentimental analysts from the Hoover Institution at Stanford. It is "military fantasy" and a "political fable" to imagine that the regime can be brought down by the forces of resistance. Its police and army are not subject to "revolutionary infiltration." White control will last, apparently indefinitely. The regime's opponents live in a "dream world."

Yet even if the experts at the Hoover Institution could demonstrate scientifically that it is hopeless, the struggle would not terminate itself. And the old debates about the movement, which has failed so far to pose any kind of insurgent threat to the regime, would still go on. Nearly a quarter of a century of exile has failed to produce a South African *What Is to Be Done?* or *The Wretched of the Earth*. If the African National Congress has had a fresh thought about the social order for which it is fighting, it has studiously kept it to itself. Meanwhile, the major theoretical contribution of the exiled Pan-Africanist Congress has been the suggestion of a new name for the country. Azania is a historical and cultural misnomer, but now that it has been chiseled into Steve Biko's tombstone, it has taken on an undeniable authenticity for a generation of South African blacks. The term is a Hellenized version of an Arabic designation for East Africa. There is no evidence that it was ever applied to South Africa before the early 1960s, when an exiled member of the Pan-Africanist Congress, which was then casting around for a new name that could be used to forge a sense of national identity among blacks, was inspired to write from Algiers to Evelyn Waugh in Somerset to inquire where he got the name he used for the African kingdom in his novel *Black Mischief*. If Waugh had known that he was assisting in the christening of a post-revolutionary black-ruled South Africa, he would have recognized an irony equal to any he had imagined for his Azania. But Waugh did write back. With only a touch of his customary churlishness, he replied, "As you should know, it is the name of an ancient East African Kingdom."

Henceforth, for the Pan-Africanist Congress and many other black South Africans, the promised land became Azania. Shortly before I left the country, the political grouping that traces its lineage to Sobukwe and Biko attempted to articulate its vision of an Azanian People's Republic. Liberation couldn't be allowed to mean merely the integration of the brown and black middle classes into the white oligarchy, one of the theorists suggested. It wouldn't come and shouldn't come, he insisted, until it represented the hopes of the black masses. And if it was to do that, it had to junk all the old racial and ethnic appellations that the whites used to divide and rule—all, that is, except those of black and white.

In other words, whites need not apply to become Azanians until after the revolution. It was the old debate of the 1940s, as replayed in the 1950s, as replayed in the 1970s (having been largely suppressed in the 1960s), and it seemed to have no greater appeal now to the black working classes than it had in the past.

The truth, it seemed to me, was that most blacks were ready to embrace any movement or ideology that promised results. At any given moment the movement that dared most, sacrificed most, and compromised least was the one that had the strongest claim to legitimacy in their eyes. Most blacks were able to applaud both sides of the argument about whether whites might belong to their revolution—that is, they believed with the Freedom Charter that "South Africa belongs to all who live in it, black and white," and they believed with Sobukwe and Biko that the struggle was for the restoration of African land to a self-reliant African people.

In between, the debate over revolutionary tactics, values, and participation was occasionally settled with fists and clubs. At a segregated medical college in Natal, a follower of the Black Consciousness tendency was kicked and battered by other young blacks until he agreed to repeat a five-word invocation: "Nelson Mandela is my leader." Aggrey Klaaste, a black columnist who could be sharply independent on political issues without ever falling into the trap of sounding "moderate" to whites, wrote of the incident in a mood of despair. "It is going to be a long haul," he concluded, "and there are some among us who even have the dare to say that come Uhuru, we will be on the first planes out of Azania!"

As night was falling, I took a stroll on the piebald grassy expanse that stretched along the seafront near my Colombo hotel. When I returned,

Philip Kgosana was just parking his Datsun. It wasn't hard to recognize him: an African in Colombo is nearly as rare as a Sri Lankan in Pretoria. My first reporting assignment after South Africa had carried me to India. Colombo was then, all of a sudden, too close to bypass.

He drove me to one of the newest tourist hotels on the seafront, where we settled into a corner of a cocktail lounge that was otherwise populated by American and French tourists. Feeling my way conversationally, I checked out small random points that hadn't been clear to me when I listened to the cassette with his narration of the events of March 1960. The headmaster who gave him the jacket was black, not white as I had assumed. (These days, he had heard, the man was lecturing at a homeland university.) On the night before the great march, Kgosana had stayed in a house in the township, not in his room in the hostel; that, finally, was the explanation for the short pants—there hadn't been time to run back for trousers.

The voice that furnished these responses was lighter, younger-seeming than the heavy, meditative voice on the cassette, still ardent for the lost land but not adjusted in pitch for history's echo chambers. I wanted narrative, and he let me have it, first in conversation and then, at the end of a long evening, in the form of a 111-page autobiography he had written several years earlier.

He had written it for his children. In a real sense, they were foreigners, for they had been born and reared in exile, never once setting foot in the land he claimed for them. "Can it be," he said, "that we have never explained to our children the situation in South Africa or why we're here?" So he wrote about Sobukwe and the march into Cape Town and his own arrest that afternoon, which he said he had anticipated. About how, nine months later, he was let out on bail by an Afrikaner prosecutor who had seemed not unfriendly, perhaps sensing in Philip Kgosana strengths he would have admired in a young white. And then how he was persuaded by his older brother to cross the border while he could. Once in Swaziland, then still a British protectorate, the young Pan-Africanist sent a telegram to Julius Nyerere in what was still Tanganyika, asking for help to enable him to go farther. Philip Kgosana simply assumed his name would count for something in Dar-es-Salaam, and it did.

His extraction from southern Africa was a celluloid adventure story, with narrow escapes, car chases, even a love angle. Nyerere's lieutenants arranged to send a plane to pick him up, but the charter pilots advised they would have an easier time landing in Basutoland, later Lesotho, so arrangements had to be made for him to be airlifted back across South Africa into that landlocked state. Then, just as the plane from Dar was finally due, Basutoland was suddenly aswarm with South African agents hunting the fugitive. Kgosana, hidden in a house near the one landing strip, could see Nyerere's charter plane circle and land, but he could also see a security cop he recognized from Cape Town parked on the runway. That night he was spirited back into South Africa by friends and driven at breakneck speed through the Orange Free State and Transvaal to what's now Botswana, where he finally made his connection with Nyerere's pilot. Basutoland still proved to be the most important station on his roundabout dash into exile, for in the house where he was hiding he met a slender student nurse named Alice Moruri with a radiant, unforgettable smile, who, a full six years later, followed him all the way to the Horn of Africa to become his wife.

Nyerere saw him his first evening in Dar-es-Salaam. Then Kwame Nkrumah received and lectured him in Accra. Kgosana's celebrity ruffled the exile leadership of the Pan-Africanist Congress, and there was a falling-out. Subsequently, having been flown to Ethiopia as a state guest, he was ushered into the presence of the King of Kings, Elect of God, His Most Puissant Majesty Haile Selassie, who mumbled an edict to his attentive minister of the pen, which led to Kgosana's being enrolled in the military academy at Harar, in a class of future officers who would figure prominently in the Ethiopian revolution. He graduated after three years with a paracommando's wings. Promised a job as a training officer by Holden Roberto, the leader of one of Angola's three rebel movements, he next moved with his new family to Lubumbashi in Zaire.

In effect, he became a black mercenary. I asked if he thought that by joining Roberto he was contributing to a revolutionary upsurge in southern Africa. No, he said, he just wanted the experience of military command because that was something a black man in his country could never have. But Roberto's army proved to be a half-starved, disorganized rabble. This was not his cause, and Zaire was definitely not his country. The young Pan-Africanist, who had once embraced Nkrumah's vision of a United States of Africa, wanted out within half a year.

Resuming his exile's odyssey, he then moved unwittingly into an even more sinister heart of darkness. He had completed his undergraduate studies in economics and statistics in Addis Ababa; now he thought he would pursue public administration at the university in Kampala. So he arrived in Uganda shortly after Idi Amin's coup, in time to live through the entire nine-year terror, which pulverized what remained of the Pan-Africanist dream. The nightmare to which his white countrymen clung as a justification for their system and their lives—as if Amin, the black psychotic, had been sent to them as a divine sign—furnished the context of his daily existence. He knew more about it than any living South African, and in his mind it justified nothing. He still wanted to be free in his land.

At the end of the terrible decade that had started for him in Zaire and ended in Uganda, Philip Kgosana was acting head of whatever remained of the UNICEF operation in Kampala, an international civil servant entitled to "home leave." This took him back to Botswana and Swaziland, where his aged parents, closely monitored all these years by the South African security police, could be brought to meet him, the wife they had seen only once, and the grandchildren they had never met. So it happened that in a Swazi resort area known as Happy Valley, he found himself soaking one afternoon in a hot mineral spring with two white undergraduates from Pretoria University who were speaking Afrikaans. He had not used the language for two decades, but he could still follow it. Introducing himself as a Kenyan, he asked them in English what they were speaking. Then, having struck up a conversation, he baited them with assumed innocence, asking how they could allow themselves to soak with him in a hot pool but insist on living apart from their countrymen. The young Afrikaners, he was amazed to discover, were only too eager to unburden themselves to a Kenyan. "Don't you think it oppresses us, too?" one of them asked. Kgosana still refrained from introducing himself properly, but he was moved.

On my last evening in Colombo, I sat with Philip and Alice Kgosana on their veranda, looking out on their garden, which was graced by a spreading frangipani tree. Inside, Ugandan-born Motlotlegi, now eleven, was taking a recorder lesson. As a tropical port, I remarked, Colombo was slightly reminiscent of Durban. They didn't know, the two exiles said sadly; they had never seen Durban. I then described the showcase homeland capitals, where those who made their compromise lived on their own little islands of privilege. I spoke about their servants and cars, their rationalizations and frustrated anger. Philip Kgosana shook his head from side to side, seeming to acknowledge, in that instant, that from the vantage point of his twenty-three-year exile he could see the temptation as well as the deceit. Alice Kgosana's reaction was less complicated, mixed only in the sense that it mixed anger and disgust. "It's not their things we want," she said, her eyes blazing with feeling, "it's our freedom. They can never understand that. Oh, no, they can't. Living their life, that's not freedom. They don't know what freedom means."

Disillusioned by exile politics and Africa as well, Philip had ceased to believe that this freedom could be brought to South Africa from outside. It would have to have its own spontaneous growth there, he now said. Being outside himself, he could only watch and wait. At forty-seven, he sometimes had a thought that would have been unthinkable ten or twenty years earlier—that he might have to wait for the rest of his days.

When the conversation came around to this point, I asked one last time whether he had ever regretted his decision on March 30, 1960, to divert the Langa marchers from Parliament. "They would mow you down," he said, reliving that moment again, which meant acknowledging the fact of white power, then and now. "And they would walk on your blood. And the world would scream, it would scream its protests. And then Verwoerd would emerge with bullets in his head, and he would say, 'This is survival. We are fighting for our survival.' "

CHAPTER ELEVEN

Prologue to Azania

It is just barely possible that the gold-bearing reefs of the Witwatersrand will be exhausted before South Africa finally runs out of solutions designed by whites to get around, meet halfway, or vent off black demands. Inventing incomprehensible constitutional models and reinventing the map of South Africa are industrial operations in their own right, with their own rules of supply and demand. After a spasm of black resistance, culminating in acts of official gruesomeness such as the shooting of nonviolent protesters at Sharpeville in 1960 or of students in Soweto in 1976, the output of blueprints and maps suddenly soars. For a little while, significant elements in the white power elite seem to be steeling themselves to address the central issue of black political rights. But then, like a high-board diver who suddenly loses his nerve, they substitute a simple jackknife for the triple back somersault that would require. Not now but later, they say; maybe in another generation. "I sympathize entirely with the Native races of South Africa," Jan Christiaan Smuts claimed in 1906, "but I don't believe in politics for them." Smuts was several generations ahead of his fellow "Afrikanders," as he was still calling them, for at least he acknowledged that there was a problem. "When I consider the future of the Natives in South Africa, I must say that I look into shadows and darkness," he admitted, "and then I feel inclined to shift the intolerable burden of solving that sphinx problem to the ampler shoulders and stronger brains of the future."

And that is where it remains. Here again we find that Jan Smuts has returned, more than thirty years after his rejection by white voters and his death, as the presiding, though unacknowledged, genius of an epoch that is presumably, but by no means surely, the last for white South Africa as a ruling caste. It is a position he gains by default. There is a vague awareness that his posturings as a philosopher and international statesman have not worn well. But those posturings provide clues to the present, for they represent a willful obtuseness and indifference to contradiction, which is what white South Africa is left with now that it has backed off from the absolutist racial ideology of Verwoerd.

South African whites have worked their way back to 1948, the year they spurned Smuts for apartheid. Once again coloreds have the vote, and there is talk of allowing blacks to elect a toothless national council, an exercise in diversionary tactics that Smuts promoted nearly half a century ago. He did not assert the principle of white supremacy; he merely practiced it. Smuts played down the old Afrikaans-English antagonism among whites; justified white rule on grounds that it was necessary for economic development; allied himself with business interests, even when that meant antagonizing the white working classes; and fobbed off black political aspirations by changing the subject, changing the time scale, waxing philosophic, or promising "practical social policy away from politics." In a nutshell, that became the policy of P. W. Botha, who back in 1948 had been a young Nationalist firebrand for whom Jan Smuts and all his works were anathema. Thirty-five years later, when he introduced a new constitution giving browns but not blacks a subordinate role in a multicolored government, Botha successfully resurrected the platform on which Smuts went down to defeat. The Botha way, white voters were told, was the middle way between extremes of left and right. "No generation," Botha said when I interviewed him, "can say that the next generation won't take further steps. A country and its people are living organisms, and while there is life there must be movement."

Movement in a circle: The intolerable burden of the "sphinx problem" was still being shifted to the ampler shoulders and stronger brains of the future. It will remain there until the sphinx imposes its own answer in Xhosa or Zulu. However long that takes, the white elite's would-be "modernizers" will continue to turn out blueprints and updated partition plans, as if their failure to evoke black consent has resulted from a failure of ingenuity that perseverance and time can overcome. The consent of black leaders with plans of their own cannot be sought, the white planners know, because it cannot be gained without conceding on most of the major points in dispute: common citizenship, open schools, an end to resettlement and the pass laws, the scrapping of all racial statutes. Conceding on these points would mean relinquishing dominance, the feeling of control, that whites know as their way of life.

Under the various schemes that have been floated as academic trial balloons, the transition to what is called consensus comes in two stages or six stages, resulting in a government or governments with three, four, or six tiers. The country can be divided into two, three, five, six, ten, twelve, thirteen, or eighteen parts. These parts can be left separate, or they can be knitted together again in a federation or confederation, a constellation or common market, a commonwealth or condominium; or, possibly, a confederation between a white-dominated federal state and a black federation; or any other combination of the above.

The problem of Johannesburg—how to divide, share out, or set it apart—eventually defeats most of the mapmakers who try to devise a solution based on partition. It is the unholy Jerusalem that no one can relinquish, not because of its history or its saints but because of its wealth. Already blacks account for more than 60 percent of the 2.8 million persons in metropolitan Johannesburg. Holding the black share of the population down to that level requires more than 120,000 arrests a year under the pass laws within forty miles of the city center—120,000 arrests so that whites, who account for less than one third of the metropolitan area's population, can have the continued comfort of imagining that they live in a "white area." Those whites are more than 20 percent of *all* South African whites; in fact, about 40 percent of all white South Africans live within sixty miles of Johannesburg, in the industrial belt that has the city as its core. Rather than contemplate abandoning them in a radical partition, most planners look for devices to make the present racial checkerboard more acceptable to most blacks without spreading panic among most whites. In their schemes, what are called "gray areas," or multiracial zones, are interspersed among black ghettos and segregated white areas. In the segregated areas different groups would have "communal autonomy." Local government could then be segregated outside the open areas but multiracial at the regional level. Planning thus seeks to achieve a situation similar to that produced by civil war in Belfast or Beirut. If there weren't too many bombings along the way, that could be construed as progress in South Africa.

I asked a thoughtful member of the governing party in the white chamber of Parliament how long it would take to establish a regime that most whites and most blacks could accept. "Four, five, or six decades," the politician replied. He was giving essentially the same answer that Jan Smuts gave in 1906; he was saying, in effect, "Not in my lifetime." According to demographers, the black population could be as high as 55 million by the earliest of these dates. By 2053 it will be anywhere between 60 million and 100 million; the number of whites will not be much more than 7 million.

These projections explain the efforts being made by Afrikaners especially to forge alliances with coloreds (most of whom at least speak Afrikaans) and Indians (traditionally viewed by Afrikaners as foreigners). The idea is to shift the racial boundary from white versus nonwhite to black versus "nonblack." But it is hard to see how the citadel of power can survive under the weight of such numbers.

It is commonplace now for white Cabinet ministers to run through a litany of the drastic demographic changes the country will see in the coming decades—the swelling black numbers, the rising demand for jobs, the pace of urbanization—as an argument for the perpetuation of white dominance. The proof of black inadequacy to govern is in the rest of Africa or

nearer to hand in the homelands. Ergo, as the transport minister, an amiable bigot named Hendrik Schoeman, tactlessly put it, "in this country four
million whites must think and plan for twenty-five million people. It is a
question of the protection of the minority with whom the brain power lies."
South Africa can reform, but reform must come from the top and only on
the initiative of those with brainpower. The whites represent order; the
blacks, chaos.

"The revolutionary movement was being born," Edward Crankshaw
notes in his narrative of the decline and fall of czarist autocracy in Russia,
"at the very moment that devoted reformers were making an impact on
the system."

Can this have any meaning for South Africa today? The analogy to
nineteenth-century Russia is appealing: The paradoxical mixture of contempt for the West and slavish imitation that marked the aristocracy there
is characteristic also of the racial oligarchy; the forms of revolutionary
idealism and violence, of literary expression and penitential self-sacrifice
by the children of the elite—all have their conspicuous parallels. But there
are obvious limitations to the analogy. The racial and ethnic hostility is
deeper than any cleavage of classes, which helps explain why the czar's
ministers were more determined reformers than Afrikaner power wielders
of today. Nevertheless, at the very moment that devoted reformers were
trying to make an impact on the South African system, I found myself in
Potchefstroom in the Transvaal, the seat of an Afrikaans university that
still forbids social dancing. On campus *Drie Susters* (Three Sisters) by "A.
Tsjechof" had just completed a run. Others, it seemed, were groping for
analogies.

My visit happened to coincide with the referendum for white voters on
the Botha constitutional plan to give South Africa its first nonblack government that wouldn't be exclusively white. In Potchefstroom the political
struggle had been an all-Afrikaans affair, a *broedertwis* ("fight among
brothers") between those who supported the prime minister and those who
assailed him and his plan for opening the door to "mixed government."
The governing party's organizers tried with only limited success to intercept voters outside the Potchefstroom town hall. Their opponents were exuberant, sometimes raucous; they knew they would probably lose, but
bucking the machine, they could still say out loud what most Afrikaners
had been reared to believe. At a safe distance, across the street, blacks in
small groups of three or four stood watching, exchanging nods and occasional remarks in Tswana; every now and then they laughed. The brown
nonblacks, the coloreds and Indians who were the supposed beneficiaries
of the supposed reform, seemed to be keeping far out of sight.

There were four Potchefstrooms. I left the white town and went to look
for the other three. I found them by following a black bus to the edge of

the white town, past the outskirts of a small industrial area dominated by a fertilizer plant. Beyond was a wire-mesh fence and a stucco structure that looked like a toll booth or a factory gate. This was the entrance to Ikageng, the black township.

Having no permit to enter, I drove along the perimeter, following a road that wound around a huge slime dam where the water from the fertilizer plant rose as a physical barrier between the black township and the remaining two Potchefstrooms, one Indian and the other colored. A pond lay between these two segregated townships, preventing brown nonblacks from undue mixing with other brown nonblacks. At a fork in the road, I turned left to Mohadin, the tiny Indian enclave, which was distinguished by its mosque and a half dozen large homes for the extended families of wealthy merchants, overshadowing the typical township matchboxes on tiny plots. Promosa, the colored township to which I then circled back before crossing the several racial borders again on my return to white Potchefstroom and the polling station, was a little larger and a little poorer, more of an encampment; the sterile result of white racial planning, a sorry sight.

This short, superficial tour served to restore perspective. I wondered what proportion of the white nonblack voters had ever driven around the slime dam and actually glimpsed Mohadin and Promosa. It seemed a reasonable guess that more than 80 percent of the voters had never seen the enclaves where their supposed new allies would wait to hear their verdict. The brown nonblacks might be invited to align themselves with the white nonblacks, but they would continue to reside out of sight, apart from each other and everyone else, on the wrong side of the slime dam.

So what were the whites fighting about? Only the timing of the white retreat, it seemed. The right-wingers, who struck me as more forthright and slightly less calculating than the prime minister's backers, thought he was breaking up the *laager* (circle of wagons) sooner than necessary. His supporters accepted the explanation that he was only trying to enlarge it.

As I nipped from side to side in the Potchefstroom *broedertwis*, I became the recipient of successive innuendos about the loyalty of the players in the opposing camps. For the first time, I was hearing Afrikaners talk openly about emigration. It was not a new impulse, I knew. Some trekkers made it to the highlands of Angola in the nineteenth century; one doughty pioneer went as far as Cairo in hopes of finding a Zion where his people would not have to battle dusky trespassers. After their Boer War defeat, another lot took off for Patagonia. Their latest Zions seemed to be Paraguay or Ronald Reagan's America. "Some of the people who are leading the campaign for a no vote are already buying property," a Botha supporter said, "so they will have a place to go when their policies land us all in a mess."

Another Afrikaner, a young lecturer, privately acknowledged that black rule might be the only solution for South Africa but said he saw no way for it to be achieved peacefully. He thought rural America might be a safe and congenial place to rear his children. "I also liked Seattle," he said. Yet another faculty member confided that some of his relatives were talking of leaving. "They say, 'Our calling is over,'" he said.

"We can hold it for another ten years," said a man at a *braaivleis* (barbecue) held that night on the lawn of the town hall for the Conservative party, the right-wing faction.

"We can be like the Israelis," said a businessman. "We can tell the world to get stuffed. *Fuck the world!*" His voice rose several decibels to add these sentiments to the general conviviality. A few appreciative chortles came back in echo.

Annette Jacobs, the vivacious wife of a law professor, said her grandfather had spent six months in jail after the 1914 rebellion. "I'll fight if there's a yes," she promised. It felt like Texas; this was Alamo talk, I thought.

Then Ben van den Bergh, a local party figure who taught German at the university, interrupted this flow of pleasantries and social chitchat with a terse, pointed question. "What do *you* think is really going to happen?" he asked me.

I smothered my reply in platitudes and qualifications about how hard it was for anyone, especially a foreigner, to read the future. Then I offered it up in three words. "Plenty of conflict," I said sagely.

"It has to come," he answered, turning away.

And then, years later, the future becomes the past, as has now happened in Zimbabwe. "We said we'd leave this country the way we found it in 1890," Cornelius Hoffman, known as Kas, told me the first time I visited him at his farm outside of Enkeldoorn, the only predominantly Afrikaans-speaking community in the old Rhodesia that had just vanished forever. The promise of a scorched-earth retreat across the high veld to the Limpopo was a slight embarrassment now for those who, like Kas, had stayed on and still intended to remain. "*Ach*," he said with a helpless shrug and a laugh, "we're Zimbabweans now, but what's in a name? We thought it would kill us to become Zimbabweans."

Cornelius Hoffman was a hulking, larger-than-life anachronism, not just in black-ruled Zimbabwe but in the whole region. In appearance as well as in thinking, he could have been reasonably presented as the last surviving *voortrekker*, for he wore the full, untrimmed beard of the Afrikaner pioneers from whom he was directly descended. His great-grandfather, Josias Hoffman, had been the first president of the Orange Free State when it proclaimed its republican sovereignty in the mid-nineteenth century. His father had trekked to Central Africa in response to a newspaper advertisement placed by Cecil Rhodes, who rewarded him with 6,000 acres at Enkeldoorn. In 1947, when King George VI visited the self-governing colony of Rhodesia, the old Boer was summoned into the royal presence to show off the medal he had received for his role in the suppression of the 1896 rebellion in Mashonaland. He lived on until 1954 and was buried in a small family plot across the road from his homestead.

The image of the old Boer showing off his medal to his sovereign helped to explain the time warp in which the son had grown up. The father had escaped the Boer War, the son its sour heritage, and that gave the white tribal feeling he expressed its fixed, primordial quality—a seeming innocence, not without sweetness, which helped explain also how more worldly and cynical English-speaking colonists fell into the habit of calling Afrikaners childlike. It was at the Hoffman homestead that I heard the story of Dingane and Piet Retief told as living history, the way Paul Kruger might have told it. Moments after we first introduced ourselves, Kas Hoffman grabbed me by the arm and hauled me to a screened veranda that doubled as a gallery for a framed sequence of now yellowing prints illustrating *Die Moord von Piet Retief* (The Murder of Piet Retief). The leap from that saga to that of the war just ended in Zimbabwe—or, to his mind, the one that was just getting under way in South Africa—was no leap at all. The events were separated by a century and a half, but the conflict was one and ineluctable.

I mean to portray Kas Hoffman respectfully as a primitive—in the sense of authentic or uncorrupted—Afrikaner and also as a reasonably unambiguous symbol of hope. For as the behavior-modeling psychologists are always eager to explain, individuals find it easier to adapt their conduct than their opinions. This individual Afrikaner had experienced no epiphany, no blinding conversion or remorse, but he had adapted to Robert Mugabe's Zimbabwe, drawing on the same inheritance of perseverance and values that had put him at the extreme right of the white Rhodesian political spectrum. Black rule had become the surprising reality that, even more surprising, he found he could accept. This was not entirely a happy ending, but it suggested that the ending in South Africa did not have to be apocalyptic; that if there were to be an Azania, there would be untold thousands of white Afrikaans-speaking Azanians who would manage to find ways of their own to reinterpret and thus to preserve a heritage that had always held death to be a kinder fate.

Robert Mugabe was hard to swallow but less so than the thought of parting with land that his family had farmed for nearly nine decades. He was never in any real doubt that he wanted to stay or that South Africa was simply not his country, but he needed a new set of words to explain that feeling to himself and others. These he got from his dominee, a young

South African from Natal named Johan Wasserman who responded to the sense of bewilderment and abandonment that had settled on Enkeldoorn's Afrikaner remnant, which felt, for the first time really, that its prayers had been rejected. Even the omnipotent God might have had difficulty answering those prayers, he pointed out, for they contained an absolute contradiction. On the one hand, they had prayed for peace; on the other, they had implored the Lord to see to the defeat of Robert Mugabe. Yet defeat of the guerrilla factions at the polls was likely to lead to renewed war. They had been praying for peace for years; they had been praying for Mugabe's defeat for only five or six months. Therefore, God had weighed their prayers and had fulfilled their deepest, longest-standing need after all: He had blessed them with peace.

Kas Hoffman was then able to take the argument a step further. Black government, he reasoned, had to be acknowledged as the will of God. "I respect it as such," he said. It was a stunning discovery, and it made him wonder what else might lie in store. He still could not believe that it was divine will that he should live under "communism." Perhaps, after all, God would give him a sign to leave as a penniless refugee. "My whole life is in his hands," he said, "but at the moment there has been no sign at all. I only pray that the spirit will come down and work on these leaders and turn them away from communism and make Christians of them."

Until that had manifestly happened, he went on, adapting the traditional view of his people's history to his new conditions, how could Afrikaners feel that they had completed the mission for which they had been called to Africa? Tradition could be adapted even further, for if God now preferred black government for his people, wasn't it obvious that he was punishing them for their willfulness? And if that was the case, who was more likely to be punished now than the whites of South Africa? "They are so independent," Kas said, speaking with a sharpness I could not have anticipated, "they no longer rely on God almighty. Everything is their own creation. They're not concerned about their next-door neighbor. I don't think I could fit in there. I just don't feel at home."

Besides, if God still intended to punish white South Africa for its pride, it would be crazy for Cornelius and his wife, Cornelia, to join the exodus as if they thought it to be the promised land. He said as much to a nephew who had come to gather up his mother, Kas's own sister, and take her to what he assumed to be safe refuge across the Limpopo. "You people are sitting on top of a time bomb," he told him. "When that thing explodes, you won't know what hit you." Most things hadn't changed. There was still the everlasting problem of the blacks. The "boys" on his farm were still "boys," capable of carrying out a fairly complicated task but only one at a time, not two in sequence, and only if he oversaw them with a strong hand. Then Cornelius Hoffman recounted a disconcerting experience in the new Zimbabwe that he had not yet fully digested.

A well-spoken black man, dressed with casual stylishness, had driven up to the farm and introduced himself as Comrade Noshonga, the local representative of Mugabe's party, known as ZANU. The man's manner couldn't have been more polite, but he made a request that Cornelius Hoffman had to regard as appalling and indecent: He said he would like to meet with the laborers on the farm. "You can see how I felt about that," Kas said, dropping his voice and speaking gravely. "If there are any problems on this farm, I can sort them out myself. I don't need any help. We've never stood for outsiders interfering with our boys."

"What did you do?" I asked.

"Well, he was from the party," Kas replied, his voice dropping lower. "What could I do? I let him speak to them."

That was not to be the end of his humiliation. A few days later, while he was having his tank filled at the gas station in Enkeldoorn, the ZANU man drove up. He recognized Farmer Hoffman with his voortrekker beard, recognized him with pleasure, it seemed, as a progressive Afrikaner who had readily accepted the full implications of the Mugabe policy of "reconciliation" in the new Zimbabwe. Now, to his astonishment, Kas saw something he had never seen or dreamed of seeing in his first fifty-three years in Enkeldoorn: His new friend from ZANU, this black man, was advancing on him with a wide smile and an outstretched hand.

"You know, I never shook a black man's hand," Kas said. "We don't mix with them at all."

"What did you do?" I asked again.

His eyes were downcast and his voice was practically a whisper when he made his confession. "I shook it," he said.

I saw Cornelius Hoffman twice in the following year. The first time I bumped into him in South Africa, at the airport in Port Elizabeth. He was there for the funeral of a brother. In the sterile new terminal at the Hendrik F. Verwoerd Airport, this white Zimbabwean was an apparition, an African Rip Van Winkle stepping out of some grade-school storybook. Heads spun, eyes darted; outwardly, at least, he was more foreign in those surroundings than I was.

The next time I saw him he was back on his farm. He and his wife Cornelia seemed more at ease in Zimbabwe. There was little of the contempt and resentment that seemed almost to choke many English-speaking whites. The Hoffmans sounded genial and indulgent, as if there weren't anything surprising about the adjustments whites were having to make, given the unchangeable fact of black rule. Kas himself didn't feel threatened, but voiced sympathy for widows and pensioners. "It's hard to be an old Af-

rikaner woman,'' he said. This was in the second year of Zimbabwe's independence.

The third year was just running out when I stopped by the farm for the
last time. Enkeldoorn had gone the way of Salisbury by then, changing its
name to Chivu. Cornelius and Cornelia said they had found it hard at first
to think of themselves as members of the Nederduitse Gereformeerde Kerk
(Dutch Reformed Church) of Chivu, but they were now able to mix Afrikaans and Shona in this way without wincing, almost without self-
consciousness. Kas had now found that the result of the ZANU man's single visit to the farm had been to bolster the ruling party's organization at
the grass roots without diminishing, as yet, the authority that he had cus-
tomarily regarded as God-given. Now he had a workers' committee, linked
to the party organization, that had to give its approval before he could apply to the authorities to discharge an employee for cause. But the system
worked smoothly and to his advantage, he assured me, pulling out a thick
file as he got down to cases.

The first chairman of the committee had been Mambo Muchireripi, the
storekeeper at the little shop the Hoffmans ran on their farm, where they
reclaimed most of the cash wages they paid out. When Comrade Mambo
was caught in a profit-sharing scheme of his own devising, Kas Hoffman
summoned the workers' committee, which readily authorized the farmer
to apply to the Ministry of Labor and Social Services for permission to
discharge him. The deputy chairman, Comrade Kefas, who was in charge
of the work gang at the piggery, had then taken Comrade Mambo's place
at the helm of the committee.

"He was the next to go," Farmer Hoffman said with great good humor.
The pigs had been neglected, and the committee had blamed its chairman.
Now it was on its third chairman, and the farmer, far from grumbling about
Marxist interference, as other whites were then doing, showed every sign
of deriving a sportsman's satisfaction from his ability to play by the new
rules.

There had been some wild shooting in the neighborhood one day, when
200 soldiers gave chase to a couple of ''dissidents,'' black deserters from
the new national army who were ethnically and politically at a disadvantage in the new order. ''Didn't I tell you that the Matabeles would never
submit to the Mashonas?'' Kas asked. He had indeed; practically every
white I had met in Zimbabwe in the months after independence had predicted a tribal showdown, and Robert Mugabe had not disappointed them.
Kas was unsurprised but not given to sounding snide. If anything, there
was a new source of relief in the discovery that as a white, he was no longer
involved in the country's political conflicts.

"It's sad what's going on between the Mashonas and the Matabeles,"
the last voortrekker said, ''but this is still a darn good country to live in.

Let them fight it out, if they have to, as long as we don't come into the crossfire.'' He no longer felt responsible for history, in either Zimbabwe or South Africa. ''We've had our war,'' he said.

A copper plaque on the wall of the Hoffmans' living room, around the corner from *Die Moord von Piet Retief* expressed Kas Hoffman's revised and more humble sense of his place in Africa in the form of a prayer:

Grant me the serenity
To accept the things I cannot change,
Courage to change the things I can
And wisdom to know the difference.

Afterward I noticed that the plaque seemed to be a staple in the souvenir shops of Salisbury and Bulawayo. Then, it seemed to me, I started seeing it almost anywhere I went in southern Africa. North of the Limpopo the prayer was usually in the homes of those who had supported the fallen white regime; south of the border it popped up in the offices and homes of those who opposed the existing racial order. It was, I learned, a version of what is called ''The Serenity Prayer,'' which Reinhold Niebuhr, the American theologian, wrote during World War II for a service in a small Congregational church in the Berkshires. I found it hanging in one of Soweto's most popular shebeens, within sight of the Protea police station, where some of the nastiest interrogations have taken place. I found it in Cape Town, in the residence of an Afrikaner clergyman who had joined the colored church and participated in a march on Parliament on behalf of black squatters; and in an obscure township called Lenyenye, I found it in the independent clinic that had been opened by Dr. Mamphela Ramphele, the mother of Steve Biko's child, who was also the keeper of his legacy.

''The Serenity Prayer'' didn't suggest that anyone was caving in or that there was a middle way of compromise that blacks and whites were yearning to take. But remembering where I had first seen it, in the home of an Afrikaner Zimbabwean, I got a tiny charge of hope every time I came on it again. It was a reminder that most individuals, white and black, were basically sane, that they could rise above their inheritance or, at least, adapt it when left with no other choice.

That helped make life bearable on a day-to-day basis in South Africa, but it was not much comfort in the long run, for I also accepted the truism about violence and what it begets. The question, it seemed to me, was not whether there would be violence in South Africa but whether there would ever be an end to it. There are lots of ugly possibilities of what could happen along the way to make self-fulfilling the whites' prophecies of disaster after power slips from their hands. There could be an Argentine-style junta, possibly with a brown or black front man, to bid for Western support.

Eventually the whole society could implode on itself as in Northern Ireland or Lebanon. Or, worst of all for the present ruling minority, blacks could govern according to the values that whites have displayed. It is also possible to fantasize a reasonably open and stable society that begins to fulfill the country's enormous promise as a model for Africa and the world. Those who now hold power have been hearing about that dreamy possibility from blacks, wayward whites, and interfering do-gooders from outside for decades, and occasionally now, to flatter the outsiders and themselves, they pretend to believe in it. But they don't, not for a moment. That is why apartheid existed in the first place and why it still survives.

Beyond all the fatuous theorizing and scenarios, there is the reality of what actually happens, day after day. Those I admired most, blacks and whites, were those who really looked, those who managed to shed their armor and arguments and take in the larger truth.

The two kinds of looking were displayed on the single worst morning I passed in southern Africa, at the end of the single worst week. The sequence of events started for me at a dinner in Cape Town at which all the other guests, besides my wife and myself, were supporters of the governing party. Inevitably the discussion came around to Zimbabwe, which had been independent for less than a year, and how in black hands it was rapidly regressing into an era of tribal warfare. Of the eight persons at the table, I was the only one who had set foot in the country since the end of white rule. Without meaning to be provocative, I mentioned that I had recently made several visits there after an absence of fifteen years and that my strongest impression of the new Zimbabwe was that it very much resembled the old Rhodesia. I suggested they might be surprised if they looked for themselves. One of the guests, a lawyer, let loose with a furious barrage at point-blank range across the table. "There will be a bloodbath in Zimbabwe," the lawyer promised, "within six months."

He was too cautious. Within forty-eight hours I was back in Zimbabwe, looking at the results of a bloodbath big enough to silence me for a while. I drove into an army camp at a place called Connemara where 50 men from one tribal group had been massacred by members of another group only because they believed they would be slaughtered themselves if they didn't act first. Altogether more than 300 were dead in the senseless killing, and the rival guerrilla factions were still confronting each other with mortars and automatic weapons in the most densely populated townships of Bulawayo. Perhaps unfairly, I imagined I could hear the lawyer and most of white South Africa cackling over the Zimbabwean dead.

On the Sunday morning of that week, I forced myself to go to the railyard in Bulawayo, where the authorities had established a makeshift mortuary in three refrigerated freight cars so that families could search for missing brothers and sons in the aftermath of the fighting. A white army physician on duty in the railyard pursued me in the self-appointed role of Greek chorus, speaking on behalf of the subcontinent's whites. "The irony is," he said, "that the European in this country was *right*! And the European in this country has been branded as a racialist by the whole world!"

I knew the answering argument, but my ardor for disputation was still at a low level. So I didn't point out that there had been no guerrilla armies in the country when 250,000 whites asserted their sovereignty over more than twenty times as many blacks in 1965, that this harvest had been sown then. I didn't say anything.

I walked away. The relatives were now filing through the first of the refrigerator cars. The black bodies inside were lightly coated with frost, but the stench of death was no figure of speech. "This is our independence," said a merchant who had failed to find a brother and a cousin in the first refrigerator car and was now waiting for his turn to enter the second. "It's ridiculous, our independence. It's pathetic."

At just that point I saw a scene that left me choking on the accumulated horrors of those days. It was the sight of a white man leading two white adolescent boys into the first car on the siding. The man was dressed in his casual Sunday best, in powder blue shorts and matching knee socks. With blond hair slicked back and pomaded, he fitted the caricature of a white African. He looked stony and determined, the kids looked scared. At a glance I thought I read the meaning of this little tableau. The man was providing a racial lesson, showing the boys what blacks do to each other, cultivating their sense that black means death, negation, ruin. Why, I wondered, couldn't the lunatic do that at home?

A little while later, I looked up and saw the man walking in my direction. He had a pleasant face, and although I had already convicted him of first-degree racism, I returned his lopsided half smile and fell into conversation. Piet Marais worked for Zimbabwe Railways. He was there with his sons, Paul and Darin, ages thirteen and fifteen. "Kids is cruel, kids is cruel really," he said when I asked what had possessed him to bring his boys to the railyard. They had heard about the killings at school, and full of high spirits, they had come home every evening with wisecracks and crude jokes.

"To them it's just a lot of dead kaffirs," Piet Marais said. "I bring my sons here to see firsthand what they are speaking. I don't want them to speak secondhand."

And now that they had seen it, I asked, what did he expect them to say?

"I hope they say nothing really," the railway man replied. "I just want themselves to feel, 'Hell, this is terrible.' I want them to stop talking about it really."

If I understood him right, Piet Marais was speaking about letting live. He was also speaking about common humanity and peace. Maybe he had seen too much war. He said that morning that he didn't know whether he would stay in Zimbabwe. He thought all governments were basically the same and wanted to remain, he said, but felt he might have to leave if the events of that week kept being repeated. I learned nothing about his politics, never saw him again, and don't know what he finally did. But I hope he found serenity, for he had, I thought, the wisdom that knows the difference, that could make the difference if anything can.

WILLIAM WISER

THE CRAZY YEARS

Paris in the Twenties

WILLIAM WISER

THE CRAZY
YEARS

Paris in the Twenties

They called it "the great good place"—the city where everyone went, where everything was happening, where life was lived at its peak. Paris in the 1920s was cheap, unfettered, exhilarating, a haven for geniuses and crackpots, a seedbed of artistic accomplishment. Never before or since has so much creative energy erupted in one place at one time.

The Crazy Years tells the story of that madcap period when writers and painters, musicians and dancers, the new and old rich, the exiles from Communist Russia and Prohibition America all converged at a unique moment in history upon an exciting and irreverent city. Paris in the 1920s was where you found Joyce, Picasso and Stravinsky, Diaghilev's Ballets Russes and Sylvia Beach's Shakespeare and Company, Josephine Baker and Isadora Duncan. It was here that Lindbergh landed and Hemingway took off. Packed with information on the people and places of this beguiling city, The Crazy Years nevertheless wears its learning lightly and engagingly.

CHAPTER ONE

The Twenties might well have begun on a section of railroad track outside Montargis.

In the early-morning hours of May 24, 1920, a platelayer named André Radeau was walking the crossties through the Bois de Leveau along the Paris-Lyon-Marseille line, 113 kilometers from Paris, when he was accosted by a barefoot individual, clad only in pajamas, moving toward him in the dim light.

"You won't believe this!" called out the apparition. "I know it must sound incredible, but I am the President of France!"

The gentleman in pajamas was scratched and bruised. He claimed to have fallen from the presidential train en route to Roanne. André Radeau escorted the distraught fellow to the gatekeeper's lodge at the next crossing. There, in a one-room cottage, the gatekeeper, Dariot, and his wife were as perplexed to receive this unexpected guest as Radeau had been to encounter him on the PLM tracks.

The stranger introduced himself as Paul Deschanel, the President of France. He then asked Dariot to notify the *sous-préfet* at Montargis of his accident. The gatekeeper assured the gentleman he would do as he wished, but made no move. Instead, he joined his wife and the platelayer, who were whispering together in a corner.

"Madame," intoned the visitor, "I can see that your husband does not believe I am President of the Republic. Have you ever seen a photograph of Paul Deschanel?"

The gatekeeper's wife had taken shrewd notice of the gentleman's attire. The pajamas were of impeccable quality; his feet—except for a trace of cinders from the roadbed—were pink and clean, with well-trimmed toenails. If he was a lunatic, he was a distinguished one.

"Yes," replied the good woman, "I have a photograph of him on the mantelpiece." This was a picture of President Deschanel clipped from *Le Petit Journal* and set in a cheap frame, flanked by blurred likenesses of Joffre and Clemenceau. The man did have the same white mustache and haunted look about the eyes as Paul Deschanel, but in all honesty she was obliged to reply, "I'm afraid you are not much like him."

"True, I am in pajamas. But that does not prevent me from being President of France."

His protests continued even as she sat him down upon the bed; then—while he insisted her husband call the *sous-préfecture*—she washed his skinned knees and elbows. As if dealing with a recalcitrant child, she put him in her own as-yet-unmade bed, still warm from the bodies of her husband and herself. Meanwhile, the platelayer went in search of the nearest doctor.

When Dr. Guillaumont arrived, he was accompanied by a gendarme. From the doctor's examination it was apparent that the stranger had, as he insisted, fallen from a train. Dr. Guillaumont applied antiseptic to the superficial injuries and administered an anti-tetanus injection. By now it seemed reasonable that the gendarme inform the *sous-préfet* of the gentleman in pajamas at the gatekeeper's lodge who claimed to be the President of France.

It was Monday of Pentecost, an official holiday. Monsieur Leseur, the *sous-préfet*, decided to investigate this curious incident in person—but there were no taxis. Also (not unusual) the phone was out of order.

From the station in Montargis, Monsieur Leseur sent a telegram to Roanne inquiring about the presidential train. Was or was not the President aboard? The first reply was that the train had arrived in Roanne but that President Deschanel had left word with his valet not to disturb him before 8:00 A.M. Meanwhile, the *sous-préfet* had engaged a local pharmacist to drive him to the humble cottage in the Bois de Leveau. Upon hearing that the object of their efforts was a man clad only in pajamas, the pharmacist had the foresight to bring along a spare suit of clothes. A second reply from Roanne made their errand all the more urgent: President Deschanel was indeed missing from his compartment on the train.

By now a great many observers were assembled in the single room of the gatekeeper's lodge, gathered around the bed where the gentleman in pajamas—who may or may not have been the President of the Republic—sat propped against a collection of pillows, holding court, trying to remember how he had got onto the railroad tracks at Montargis.

Members of the presidential staff arrived that afternoon to confirm that the disoriented stranger installed in the gatekeeper's bed at Bois de Leveau was Paul Deschanel, the French President. From Paris came the President's wife, along with Alexandre Millerand, leader of the National Assembly and next in line for the Presidency. These two delegations arranged to collect the President like some parcel gone astray. They dressed him in the pharmacist's spare suit, put a pair of white socks on his feet; he wore slippers borrowed from Dariot, the gatekeeper. The President complained of *un trou dans le mémoire*, but in spite of a hole in his memory, he was aware of the odd misadventure and would in no case return to Paris by train. He was driven back to the Palais de l'Elysée in a convoy of several motorcars.

The story given out to the press by Millerand was that President Deschanel had retired early in preparation for a day of speechmaking in Roanne; the presidential train was traveling at no more than twenty-five miles per hour to ensure the President a good night's sleep—thus, when he fell from the train, he was not more seriously injured. It seemed he had opened the window to his compartment and leaned out, seeking a breath of air. The window was of faulty design, the President leaned too far. Newspapers printed the dispatch, but conjecture crept into the editorials: somehow the official explanation lacked substance.

Elected in January 1920, the new President was already showing signs of an erratic and unstable mind. A cabal of ministers and senators promoted Paul Deschanel over Clemenceau in a political maneuver to keep "The Tiger" from being elected to the highest office in the land. The obscure Deschanel was duly elected President but could never quite recover from his unexpected triumph over the formidable French hero Clemenceau. Deschanel's remarks and behavior at public receptions became increasingly bizarre. At the British Embassy, he set forth such extravagant proposals that the diplomats thought he might be drunk. After a speech, a group of schoolgirls presented him with a bouquet; he then tossed the flowers, one by one, back at them. On one disturbing occasion he wandered away from an official delegation to embrace a tree beside the path.

Following the episode of the presidential train, Deschanel went to the Château de Rambouillet to escape the capital and the pressures of office at the Elysée. One morning he walked away from the dreary order of business at a state meeting—a natural enough impulse—in the direction of the tempting lakeside, and from there continued his stroll into the lake, fully clothed. His valet saw him striding through the water and plunged in after him.

By autumn, Deschanel's brief term of office came to an end at Malmaison, an institution on the outskirts of Paris for the treatment of nervous disorders. On September 23, Millerand became the new President of the Republic.

During Deschanel's manic-depressive term of office, two playful but serious revolutionaries of art—Francis Picabia and Tristan Tzara—came to Paris from Zurich, where they had founded a new movement destined to sow anarchy in the established patterns of French culture. The movement was called Dada, the first word the founders had come across in *Le Petit Larousse*, a nursery term for rocking horse. According to the tenets of the new faith, visiting Montargis in one's pajamas, wandering into a lake in a business suit, falling in love with a tree, was evidence of the essential Dadaist in us all and precisely the example the President of France should set.

Surely Deschanel was the harbinger of the age. In those early months of 1920 may have come the first suggestion of the Twenties as *les années folles*, the crazy years.

The first time a flimsy, cratelike Gotha aircraft flew over the rue St-Honoré, an antique dealer wearing a spiked helmet from the Franco-Prussian War fired his hunting rifle at the interloper. Impossible that Paris could ever become a military outpost and enemy target. During the 1918 bombardment, one million Parisians fled to the relative safety of the countryside: as the ghostly zeppelins drifted above the Seine, bearing a deadly cargo of explosives, those who had not fled the city took shelter in wine cellars or along the underground quays of the Métro. Gertrude Stein and Alice Toklas went into the concierge's lodge so as to have six stories above their heads: it was true, said Alice, that one's knees really did knock together as described in poetry and prose.

German gun emplacements ranged within ninety miles of the capital, close enough for Big Bertha to blast at the very heart of Paris. After the klaxons sounded All Clear, the city became a vacuum, eerily silent. The streets were empty after dark except for roving patrols of *hirondelles*, the police who bicycled along the boulevards, the pointed ends of their capes swept backward like the wings of swallows. At dusk the city took on the pale color of absinthe—nine out of ten street lamps were extinguished under wartime restriction. Nightlife had all but ceased except for the *caf'-conc'* on the rue de la Gaité, kept open for soldiers on leave. The remaining street prostitutes around the gare Saint-Lazare ducked into shadow when the *hirondelles* cycled by.

Children and the aged were evacuated as much to escape the penury of wartime winters as from danger of zeppelin raids. Coal was rare, shipped from England or brought in from the Cévennes mountains south of Lyon now that the rich coal-mining region of the northeast was occupied or under fire. Parisians waited in everlasting queues for a ration of *boulets* made of coal dust, peat, and straw. The intervention of a cabinet minister was necessary to obtain a cartload of coal for the sculptor Rodin, dying of pulmonary congestion. The Japanese painter Foujita was so impressed when a girl named Fernande broke up a Louis XV chair to make a fire for his visit that he proposed marriage to her. Between the stately lines of chestnut trees in the Luxembourg Gardens were patches of beans and carrots; even the fashionable Parc de la Muette in Passy had been sown with potatoes.

There were, as ever, Americans in Paris—but few. The unconventional daughter of a clergyman, Sylvia Beach, traveled between Paris and Belgrade (where she distributed pajamas to Serbian troops) during the war and in Paris witnessed a direct hit from *Grosse Berthe* on the church of Saint-Gervais when the cathedral was filled with worshipers: ninety-one were killed outright, another eighty-six gravely injured. Ernest Hemingway was standing near the Madeleine when the façade of that church was blasted, his first wartime experience. Another volunteer for ambulance duty, John Dos Passos, saw one shell explode harmlessly in the Seine: immediately fishermen went out in boats or used nets at the quayside to scoop in the stunned fish.

Paris, said Malcolm Cowley, was all the lovelier under the threat of death. For many Americans the rite of passage to the European conflict was a tour of duty in the overseas ambulance corps; several of these "gentleman volunteers" were writers, or would-be writers. They were a handful of friendly visitors—Malcolm Cowley, E. E. Cummings, John Dos Passos, Dashiell Hammett, Ernest Hemingway—with no personal share in the larger event taking place, but whose senses, Cowley noted, were sharpened by the thought of dying the next day. A passion for Paris often developed during this indoctrination tour in the besieged city, an ambulance driver's love at first sight would persist as a lifetime affair of the heart. The Great War was the largest adventure on the horizon, and Paris, its reconnaissance post, was the most beautiful city in the world.

The banker J. P. Morgan's erratic nephew Harry Crosby enlisted in the Norton-Harjes Ambulance Corps, his first flirtation with the danger and risk of death he craved, and an episode in his life that would wed him forever to Paris. Ernest Hemingway caught only a glimpse of Paris before he went on to serve with the Red Cross in Italy. E. E. Cummings and John Dos Passos went to the north-eastern front in separate units of the Norton-Harjes Ambulance Corps in France. The Paris of World War I was a brief but central experience in their young lives, a wartime interlude that would affect the sensibility of their formative years and color the literary work to come.

E. E. Cummings arrived in Paris a virgin at twenty-two. "They carried us to a foreign country," explained Malcolm Cowley, "the first that most of us had seen; they taught us to make love, stammer love, in a foreign language." "La Ville Immense," Cummings called the city—"la femme superbe et subtile." The association of Paris to Woman was inevitable for the Boston-bred young man whose father was a Unitarian minister and an official of the Watch and Ward Society. Paris, empty of men, but everywhere provided with "the finest girls God ever allowed to pasture in the air of this fresh earth," made it hard for a young poet to resist the "Tu viens?" whispered from all sides. Deliberately or by chance he did not locate his unit headquarters for five truant weeks, during which he wandered Paris at will. Women were everywhere, openly available, hovering in his path. "Tu viens?" This extended idyll all but obliterated thoughts of Boston; the young man's puritan upbringing was no defense against falling in love with a prostitute.

He met Marie-Louise at Sultana Cherque's restaurant, the Oasis, on the rue du Faubourg-Montmartre. When Marie-Louise completed her classic tour of the territory between République and the Madeleine, she and Cummings would sit among the pimps and street girls of the Oasis until dawn. In college French the poet stammered his love to this foreign delight. The affair was no wartime transaction between Montmartre tart and doughboy on the loose: Cummings was genuinely enamored of her, and she, to all appearances, was attracted to him.

Contrary to every tradition of the professional *fille de joie*, Marie-Louise invited the young man home with her to a tiny flat on the rue Dupetit-Thouars and into her bed—although they did not consummate their love in the way that would seem most natural to Marie-Louise. Nevertheless, the two slept together through the late mornings in the most innocent of intimacies. Five weeks were hardly enough for Boston's blue-eyed boy to wriggle free of Watch and Ward. Impossible to imagine the French girl's reaction to this persistent chastity—but Marie-Louise continued the relationship with her American naïf right up until Cummings, a virgin still, reported for duty.

At the front, ambulance driver Cummings became involved in a Kafkaesque affair that colored his remaining time in France and provided the material for his first book. In defense of a friend who had written an indiscreet letter about the low morale of French troops (the letter, naturally, was intercepted by the censor), Cummings, along with his friend, was accused of sympathy with the enemy. The two American volunteers were interned at La Ferté Macé, a concentration camp for military misfits.

It took all the political pressure the Reverend Cummings could summon, via a series of letters to President Wilson, to secure his son's release. When Cummings was finally allowed to leave La Ferté Macé, he was to report directly to the U.S. Embassy, where he would be notified of transport home. He had three days in Paris before his ship sailed.

At the Hôtel des Saints-Pères in the heart of the Latin Quarter he washed away the dirt and vermin of prison life. Ambulance duty, and the grim reality of La Ferté Macé, had altered certain New England concepts of morality. The young poet stepped out into the rue des Saints-Pères alive to every sensation, excited by every possibility. As he went in search of his particular love along the streets she was known to frequent, Cummings fell in love with Paris all over again.

It was time to dispense with a virginity he could no longer tolerate, in the city where such a loss or gain so conveniently transpires. But prostitutes are the night's most impermanent creatures. For all the substance he could find of his evanescent butterfly, Cummings might have imagined the girl. She had left the flat on rue Dupetit-Thouars. He retraced the erratic path of her working nights from République to the Madeleine; he lingered at curbsides and *coins de rues*, where her solicitations would most likely take place. Again and again he returned to the Oasis where they had so often met and talked away the small hours before dawn. But the poet was never to recapture his first love except in verse. This was the last year of the Great War. So many had passed through Paris, had fled, had died, had disappeared.

The final night in Paris, Cummings was overcome with the desire to end his troublesome innocence: he had become a man in every way but one. Late, at the Oasis, the pretty waitress Berthe shared a table with him, and a bottle of champagne. Before the city stirred to life again at dawn and he was due to take the boat train to Le Havre, Cummings accompanied the sweet and compliant waitress to her *chambre de bonne*. Berthe became the last-minute substitute for Marie-Louise, love partner by proxy, a bittersweet farewell to Paris.

For Dos Passos the wartime adventure had taken place "on the fringes of the great butchery." Ambulance duty was almost as rearguard and tame as it was for Jean Cocteau. (Cocteau served as an "officer" in Misia Sert's private ambulance corps, costumed in a stage-military uniform designed by Coco Chanel.) Whatever guilt, disappointment and frustration Dos Passos felt about his passive involvement removed from the battlefront, he sublimated in Paris after the Armistice. There he wrote his first successful novel, *Three Soldiers*, a fictional version of the war. His own oasis in Paris was Madame LeCompte's hotel-restaurant Le Rendezvous des Mariniers, on the quai d'Anjou.

From this sanctuary on the medieval Ile St. Louis, Dos Passos circled outward along the stone quaysides and through the incredible tangle of streets on both sides of the pont Marie to explore the city he found more intense and satisfying than military life had turned out to be. On at least one extended promenade, Dos Passos was accompanied by Fernand Léger, who had just been mustered out of the French army where he had served as stretcher-bearer at Verdun and been gassed at the Aisne. (Of his military experience, Léger said: "Three years without touching a brush, but contact with reality at its most violent, its most crude . . . the war made me mature, I'm not afraid to say so.") Dos Passos had no wartime adventure to match the painter's "contact with reality," but a walk with the older man was a revelation: a way of looking at smokestacks seen from the Montmartre funiculaire; the flat planes of a river barge as mass, a sill of geraniums as detail. Léger was in the process of adapting his Cubist techniques to a particular vision of the machine age. In Paris, where the several branches of art meet so familiarly, Dos Passos was invited to share the painter's perceptions.

While Dos Passos was involved in the excitement and stimulus of postwar Paris, E. E. Cummings wrote him of his boredom and unhappiness at home. His outraged father was planning to sue the French government for the false incarceration of his son. As an affidavit for the case, he encouraged Cummings to record his prison experiences—although the young man nourished no special grudge against the French. On the contrary, Cummings was as rabid a Francophile as ever: his hapless arrest and military detention only reinforced a growing resentment of all bureaucracy and authority. But the poet began to put down his impressions of La Ferté Macé episode to satisfy his father's scheme: the affidavit, however, grew beyond any such legal intent to become that classic document of World War I, *The Enormous Room*.

The little ladies of Paris had fascinated Cummings and Dos Passos from the first. Dos Passos referred to his excursions in search of architecture and *les petites femmes* ("alas, the remorseful prophylaxis after"), while Cummings would recall Frenchwomen of his own in the lines:

> little ladies more
> than dead exactly dance
> in my head, precisely
> dance where danced la guerre

Demobilization brought home an army of women as well as men. The little ladies were streaming back from the front, where professionals had operated clandestinely as canteen girls or openly in the "red lanterns" for enlisted men and "blue lanterns" for officers.

A new recruiting drive was on for prostitutes to serve in the brothels of the capital. Known as *maisons closes*, the houses of prostitution had not altogether languished during the war—with the troops of three Allied nations passing through Paris—but air raids, police restrictions, and the military patrols in search of deserters disturbed the tranquil flow of business. As an influx of foreign visitors joined the returning *poilus*, seeking the classic pleasures associated with Paris, new and exigent tastes required the famous houses like the One-Two-Two (behind the Galeries Lafayette) and the historic Chabanais (beside the Bibliothèque Nationale) to seek fresh recruits from the chorus lines of the Folies-Bergère and the Casino de Paris. Girls from the provinces took the familiar road to the bordels of the big city, pimps awaited them at the gare de Lyon and the gare Saint-Lazare.

The flourishing upturn in the flesh trade during the Twenties encouraged Marthe Lemestre to establish a three-star house of rendezvous, Le Sphinx, the first important *maison close* on the Left Bank. "Martoune" obtained the backing of four respected investors (one of them a bank) for her palace of unrivaled opulence. Set in the somber neighborhood of the Montparnasse Cemetery, the house was easily distinguished by its stucco Sphinx added to the façade of 31 boulevard Edgar Quintet.

Martoune inaugurated the establishment modestly enough with a staff of fifteen *filles de joie*—but girls of reputedly superior gifts. Eventually as

Some of Marthe Lemestre's charming 'filles de joie' relaxing at Le Sphinx. With its magnificent Art Deco interior it was the first important maison close on the Left Bank.

many as sixty charming hostesses entertained hundreds of clients nightly, not only as bed partners but often simply as graceful tablemates with whom one discussed art and the issues of the day over a bottle of Taittinger. With complete confidence fathers brought their adolescent sons to Le Sphinx for a traditional initiation into the carnal mysteries.

The wine list at Le Sphinx was as extensive as the choice from the cellar at Maxim's, an understandable investment for the house, since a considerable part of Maxim's clientele were familiars at Le Sphinx. Of the three important houses (Le Sphinx, the Chabanais, the One-Two-Two), Martoune's Le Sphinx was the most avant-garde, with Art Déco interiors in Egyptian motif instead of the gold leaf and drapery, candelabra, and canopied beds traditional to the older houses.

Sexual tolerance is a given of Parisian attitudes, including the freedom to be homosexual. Inevitably, a colony of the third sex, uninhibited by legal or social pressures, became an accepted component of the mixed milieu.

France was a convenient channel crossing from England, Paris the destination of social outlaws of whatever sexual inclination, even for a single permissive weekend. At the end of World War I, Vita Sackville-West—author, intimate of the Bloomsbury circle—embarked on a passionate escapade in Paris with Violet Trefusis. Violet had only just married Denys Trefusis, an officer recently returned from the front, but her liaison with Vita predated the nuptial ceremony and was a more compelling commitment, Paris a more tempting idyll, than a tame honeymoon in London. Vita darkened her face with dye and wore a stained bandage around her head—bandages in postwar Paris being a common enough sight—to dress as a sailor. Violet called her "Julian."

In her diary Vita wrote of the heady sense of freedom she felt as she strolled the boulevards of Paris with Violet beside her: "I never appreciated anything so much as living like that with my tongue perpetually in my cheek, and in defiance of every policeman I passed." It is doubtful whether a French policeman cared if she dressed as a boy. Even as the two husbands converged on their errant wives, Vita went on: "There was no abatement . . . in my passion for the freedom of that life."

This was 1920: freedom was in the air, in Paris, at the beginning of the decade.

During Vita Sackville-West's fling with Violet Trefusis, Vita's husband, the diplomat Harold Nicolson, was attending the 1920 Peace Conference at Versailles. The end of the War to End All Wars had brought the Big Four to the Hôtel Crillon, on the place de la Concorde, to squabble over questionable promises and secret treaties while Europe was being carved into a new design. Under the elegant chandeliers of the Crillon, presidents and prime ministers dismantled two empires, deposed four kings, and brought forth three new republics. The press corps gathered under the arcades on the north side of the *place*: Paris had become the focus of international news.

Censorship had ended with the Armistice. French newspapers extended their daily editions beyond the single page imposed as a wartime measure to save paper. The journals could flaunt their political affiliation once more with editorials on German reparations and annexation of the Saar. Wire services and foreign-language dailies opened agencies as close to the Champs Elysées or l'Opéra as possible. For those who were already Over There and wanted to stay on in the favorite city of the postwar world there was a scramble for appointments to Hoover's American Relief Administration, but legions of young hopefuls jostled for posts as stringer journalists covering the Peace Conference.

Rookie newsmen moved from the U.S. Army publication *Stars and Stripes* into the Paris agencies of Reuters, the United Press, and the Associated Press. John Dos Passos and Vincent Sheean became roving foreign correspondents, with Paris as a frequent stopover or convenient headquarters. Dorothy Thompson covered the Peace Conference from the *Philadelphia Ledger*'s Paris office. Captain Walter Lippmann had served as propaganda officer with General Pershing, then became press attaché to President Wilson, with the prospect of elucidating Wilson's Fourteen Points to Anglo-American readers.

A midwestern journalist, James Thurber, had been inducted into the army in the final months of the war. He was trained as a code clerk, received sailing orders, and arrived in France two days after the Armistice was signed. When Thurber reported for duty at the Hôtel Crillon, his commanding officer informed him with undisguised sarcasm, "I requisitioned a code *book*, not a code clerk." Thurber was the tenth such mistake in as many weeks. Nevertheless, in the confused laissez-faire operations of those postwar months, Thurber was allowed to linger, or malinger, with nine other redundant code clerks at the chancellery of the U.S. Embassy, 5 rue de Chaillot. The wide-eyed Ohioan had stumbled into the ideal sinecure.

"Finie la Guerre" was the street song of the moment. "Girls snatched caps and tunic buttons from American soldiers, paying for them in hugs and kisses, and even warmer coin." Eventually Thurber was to collect warmer coin of his own when he took what he called "the first step aside." The girl was a dancer, Ninette, from the Folies-Bergère. After a long separation, Thurber, like Cummings, attempted to search out his first love—but Ninette had married another doughboy, been to the American Midwest and back to Paris. Meanwhile, Thurber, too, had married; the meeting with Ninette had been inspired by guilt and curiosity: *finie l'affaire*, but not the affair with Paris.

Colonel McCormick of the *Chicago Tribune* could not resist the challenge of launching a Paris edition of the *Tribune* to compete with his arch-rival James Gordon Bennett, who had long cornered the English-language news market with his Paris *Herald*. McCormick appointed David Darrah to run the *Chicago Tribune*'s Paris edition, and Darrah sought out such journalists as George Seldes and Vincent Sheean to work for the new daily. The third U.S. journal to open a bureau in Paris was the *Brooklyn Eagle*, edited by Guy Hickok.

The news desk of the Paris *Herald* was known for its staff of literary hopefuls with unfinished novels in their suitcases: on his second trip to Paris, a civilian now, Thurber also carried with him the inevitable first draft of a novel. He was unable to get a job in the Paris *Herald* newsroom—there was a long waiting list of apprentice newsmen hoping for jobs on the English-language dailies—and it looked as if Thurber and his new bride would have to return to the United States when finally Thurber convinced David Darrah that he was not a poet. Darrah had been besieged by what he considered literary types looking for a job on the *Tribune*, and what he needed was somebody who had experience writing headlines. Thurber had been a reporter for the *Columbus Dispatch*: he was hired, to begin work the next night—the pay was $12 per week.

Thurber found himself working alongside another aspiring novelist, William Shirer. Later Shirer confessed that once he had met the expatriate writers Hemingway, Fitzgerald, and James Joyce, he had abandoned all hope of writing fiction. Thurber also concluded that he was no novelist: he threw away his half-completed manuscript to concentrate on the short humorous pieces for which he became known.

The newspaper mogul James Gordon Bennett boasted, even to his employees, "I can buy all the brains I need for $25 a week." To take revenge for the meager salary—a marginally living wage only because of the favorable exchange rate—reporters treated the news as something of a joke, extending the most trivial items into extravagant features or inventing unverifiable dispatches out of whole cloth. Paris was the newsman's playground; work and pleasure were meant to overlap. After the paper was put to bed, journalists from the foreign dailies met at Le Chien Qui Fume in

Ernest Hemingway, recovering from a war wound in Italy, where he fell in love with his nurse, Agnes von Kurowsky. He would later celebrate this bittersweet affair in his second novel, A Farewell to Arms.

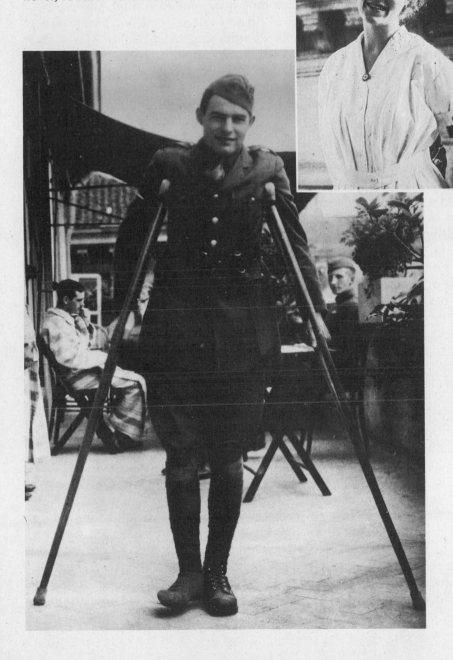

Les Halles, still alive and bustling with fruit and vegetable vendors under the arc lamps of the market sheds. In this hectic atmosphere, the reporters swapped notes and anecdotes, ate onion soup, and drank with the prostitutes and market loaders while the rest of Paris slept.

The publishers who were quick to seize on the growing American presence in France, and to extend the hometown news to editions in Paris, unintentionally provided a conduit of literary talent by way of their overseas operations. Correspondents James Thurber and Janet Flanner served their apprenticeship as journalists in Paris, then scaled their work to the higher demands of the fledgling *New Yorker* (Janet Flanner as the magazine's Paris correspondent "Genêt"); the working style of newspaper prose helped sharpen the novelistic technique of John Dos Passos and Ernest Hemingway. When William Bird first came to Paris, he directed the Consolidated Press office on rue d'Antin, but left the agency to become an expatriate publisher of the Three Mountains Press in a cellar printshop on the quai d'Anjou. In this way, many of the reporters and editors of Paris-based journals would move on from the newsroom to produce what Ezra Pound defined as literature: news that stays news.

When Sherwood Anderson brought the news of Paris to a group of young writers in Chicago, Ernest Hemingway had just turned 21. Hemingway was editing a house organ, the *Cooperative Commonwealth*, to earn money so that he might marry his fiancée, Hadley Richardson. The young journalist had worked briefly on the *Kansas City Star* and had contributed features and articles to the *Toronto Star* at a penny a word. Hemingway nurtured an outsized ambition to write prose fiction; newspaper work was his first tentative approach toward a literary career. Editing the *Cooperative Commonwealth* was a dullish stopgap job until he could take Hadley to Europe on their honeymoon: he was already changing his salary into Italian lire in anticipation of the trip.

The great adventure in Hemingway's life until that time was ambulance duty during the recent war. He had narrowly escaped being blown apart on the Italian front during the Austrian offensive at the Piave in 1918. For the remainder of his life he would bear the psychic as well as physical scars of that wartime episode. He likened the trauma to the sensation of having for an instant met death—the soul slipped from his body like a silken handkerchief drawn from a pocket—and in the next instant he was restored to life. His wounds were treated at the Ospedale Rossa in Milan, where he fell in love with his nurse, Agnes von Kurowsky. Theirs was the supremely romantic affair Hemingway would celebrate in his second novel, *A Farewell to Arms*. In that story the heroine dies in childbirth, but the unhappy truth was that Hemingway's first love threw him over to marry an Italian officer.

Despite whatever intrusions reality made in the Hemingway remembrance of things past, he remained a romantic where his own past was concerned. The original excitement of that adolescent love affair overcame any bitter aftertaste of the ending to romance. Ernest convinced Hadley that they should spend their honeymoon in Italy. Meanwhile, Sherwood Anderson was delivering his rapturous report on Paris as a literary paradise, the ideal place for a young writer to launch his career. Hadley became as excited about the prospect of Paris as Ernest: the Italian plan was abandoned.

Anderson provided the couple with letters of introduction to Gertrude Stein, Ezra Pound, and Sylvia Beach—Americans all, three important sources of influence and advancement in a writer's apprenticeship. The last night in Chicago Hemingway showed the attractive side of his character: Anderson heard a knock at his door and opened to the shy, grinning giant-of-a-man. Attempting to repay a debt in his own way, Hemingway presented the older writer with a rucksack of canned goods, making a gift of the last food stores he had hoarded for the stint in Chicago.

Ernest Hemingway and his new bride took the converted troopship *Leopoldina* on its rough winter crossing to France. He carried with him the letters from Sherwood Anderson: "I am writing this note to make you acquainted with my friend Ernest Hemingway, who with Mrs. Hemingway is going to Paris to live, and will ask him to drop it into the mails when he arrives there...."

CHAPTER FOUR

Newcomers to Paris were unaware that prices had quadrupled since the beginning of the war. Some items had increased ten times over: tobacco was 100 per cent higher, soap 500 per cent. Unemployment was naturally severe after demobilization of the largest army France had ever assembled; pensions for the aged were on the way to becoming worthless. But the incoming horde took little notice of the price of bread, officially raised from fifty to ninety centimes. The downward spiral of the French franc was only another inducement that lured the first wave of Americans to Paris. The same day newspapers announced the bread increase, January 1, 1920, the dollar stood at 26.76 francs—a single American greenback could purchase a month's supply of bread.

The former zones of industrialization in northeastern France were devastated—not only the French, but most European economies were ruined by the war—while the United States had flourished during 1914-18 and at the beginning of the Twenties was the world's leading industrial power.

But the outward aspect of Paris was unchanged: the city smiled beguilingly at its visitors, although a poverty of means and spirit lay just behind the façade. Those with money—gold, or currency redeemable in gold— were the new pilgrims. Following the 1924-26 financial crisis in France, the dollar would rise to a record high of fifty francs. A lopsided economic balance opened the way for a dollar-rich invasion of expatriates to France. As little as $80 purchased tourist-class passage across the Atlantic. A modest allowance from home would subsidize an American in Paris for what appeared to be forever.

In 1919 F. Scott Fitzgerald earned a mere $800 from his writing; in 1920 his income soared to $18,000. He had just married the southern belle Zelda Sayre (who had turned him down as a poor prospect in his $800 year), and by Valentine's Day Zelda was pregnant. The newlyweds were anxious to make lavish use of the first profits from Fitzgerald's best-selling *This Side of Paradise*: Paris seemed the very paradise in which to spend the big money. The glamorous Fitzgeralds were a symbol of carefree high living, ambassadors of the Jazz Age, and—since a pregnant flapper would have little status in Manhattan—Scott and Zelda decided to bring the Jazz Age to France.

That summer, the Fitzgeralds sailed on the *Aquitania*. Maxwell Perkins, Fitzgerald's editor at Scribner's, had supplied letters of introduction to French and English authors: at this stage of his career Fitzgerald was in adolescent awe of established literary figures abroad and had every intention of using the Perkins-Scribner's connections as a passe-partout from the New World into the Old. In Paris, Scott and Zelda camped on the doorstep of Anatole France but did not meet the illustrious Frenchman. They did meet the Irishman James Joyce. On that occasion Fitzgerald declared his everlasting obeisance to Joyce's genius and threatened to jump from a window to demonstrate his sincerity. Joyce persuaded him not to. ("That young man must be mad.")

Scott and Zelda went to the Folies-Bergère, where the presence of so many American doughboys—returned from the trench warfare Scott missed—may have dulled the flesh-and-feathered spectacle. They trekked with indifference through the galleries of the Louvre, and with a hangover each, toured the halls of the Palais de Versailles. Against the current belief of Americans that "they do things better in France," Fitzgerald concluded that Europe was of antiquarian interest only.

Frenchmen demonstrate a great love for Americans—immediately after a war—but Scott and Zelda were from that other America France cannot tolerate. Their hotel manager did not see the humor when Zelda fastened the elevator cage with a length of rope to be sure of having the elevator at their constant disposal. Scott was not gifted in languages and made no attempt to come to know his French hosts. Like so many touring Americans, the Fitzgeralds were only happy in the company of fellow Americans. The

French either ignored the golden couple of the Jazz Age or deplored them. Champagne lacked the kick of bathtub gin, Paris was a bore. It was as if Scott and Zelda had come to the wrong party, too early, and could only recall with overwhelming regret the wild party they had just left.

So the Fitzgeralds sailed home to Manhattan. When the real party got under way, they would be back. Paris in the mid-Twenties—crowded, excessive, frenetic—was exactly the fete they were seeking all along.

"Is it not extraordinary," wrote James Joyce, "the way I enter a city barefoot and end up in a luxurious flat?"

The first flat to house the Joyce family was a rent-free "matchbox" lent by Madame Savitsky, Joyce's translator in Paris, on the rue de l'Assomption. At the urging of Ezra Pound, James Joyce came to Paris early in 1920 for a two-week visit: he would stay twenty years. After a journey of "silence, exile, and cunning" by way of Trieste and Zurich, Paris seemed the next logical stopping place. Joyce had got the message in Zurich from Ezra Pound—who had it from Jean Cocteau and Francis Picabia—that Paris, eternally susceptible to the miracle of rejuvenation, was entering a new golden age. In Zurich Joyce had exhausted funds and friends: a quixotic lawsuit launched against an employee of the British Embassy further reduced his resources and welcome. After the wartime ordeal of living on English lessons and a poet's wages, Paris was indeed a return to Eden for Joyce.

Ezra Pound had already quit the London scene where he and Wyndham Lewis were at the vortex of the Vorticist movement. He diagnosed London as moribund, afraid he might "wake up one morning with web feet" after having fled the United States for the same reason.

Pound introduced Joyce to his own patron, the American lawyer John Quinn, who became interested in Joyce's nearly completed novel *Ulysses* and offered to contribute $1,600 toward its publication. The indefatigable Pound was assembling a coterie of Joyceans—admirers and possible supporters—in Paris. Pound's tag line after each discussion of the Irishman's dilemma was "You must help Joyce." Ezra Pound could be endlessly resourceful and completely selfless in his efforts to help another artist in whom he believed.

The two writers, James Joyce and Ezra Pound, were remarkably different in appearance and manner. Joyce, with his neat haircut and rimless glasses, dressed as conservatively (even in hand-me-downs) as his means allowed. Next to him, Pound cast an almost satanic image: he affected poet's garb of loose collar and careless *cravate*, often a cape, worn with a sinister wide-brimmed Spanish hat. Gentlemanly James Joyce was the most retiring of men, with a ritual of elaborate courtesy meant to keep society at bay. Joyce was stiff and uneasy with newfound acquaintances, while

Pound was at his voluble best, opinionated and direct, meeting and knowing everyone, astir in every intellectual stew.

Despite his reticence, Joyce allowed himself to be fed to the lion hunters by Pound. In his poverty, Joyce naturally gravitated toward the solvent. Through Pound, he was invited to the Natalie Barney salon where he first met Madame Savitsky, who not only agreed to translate *A Portrait of the Artist as a Young Man* into French, but generously provided the destitute author with her rue de l'Assomption apartment.

Pound suggested to Jenny Serruys, the literary agent, that she might be able to help Joyce. James Joyce then fell into the habit of appearing at Miss Serruys's office to announce he needed a bed for his borrowed flat or to ask where he might obtain a table to write on. Miss Serruys looked after the writer's day-to-day needs, lent him money, and even introduced her fiancé into the league of friends who helped Joyce: Joyce was very happy to accept a discarded army overcoat from the young man—the best coat, Joyce emphatically declared, he had ever worn.

Three days after his arrival in Paris Joyce was presented to the proprietor of Shakespeare and Company, Sylvia Beach.

"Is this the great James Joyce?" asked Miss Beach.

"James Joyce," replied Joyce, shifting his ash-plant walking stick to shake the hand of the diminutive figure.

Sylvia Beach, with her gentle sensitivity to literary genius and superhuman patience with literary temperament, was to be an even larger force than Ezra Pound in the advancement of Joyce's career. Very soon Joyce asked her if she would send any stray students of English his way; he had made a bare livelihood teaching English in Trieste, and he was prepared to do the same in Paris.

Ezra Pound could not resist the opportunity to bring together the two great men of modern letters, T. S. Eliot and James Joyce. While Pound was briefly in London, he learned that Eliot would be visiting the continent and contrived for Eliot to deliver a parcel to Joyce when he passed through Paris. The two men had very little to say to one another, perhaps because Joyce performed—as he invariably did in such circumstances—an off-putting show of courtly protocol. Wyndham Lewis accompanied Eliot throughout the visit, for which Joyce (flush for a change, in borrowed funds) played generous host. Joyce paid for every round of drinks, then invited Eliot and Lewis to an expensive meal at his favorite restaurant, Les Trianons. It was impossible for either visitor to pay for as much as a coffee. Eliot privately complained to Lewis of Joyce's excessive politesse and insistent largesse. Eventually the parcel from Ezra Pound was opened and found to contain secondhand clothing and a worn pair of brown shoes— the shoes, no doubt, meant to replace the dirty tennis shoes Joyce habitually wore that first year in Paris.

James Joyce shortly after his arrival in Paris in 1920.

Since the loan of Madame Savitsky's flat, Joyce had moved his family of four twice—but thoughtfully returned the items he had borrowed from Jenny Serruys when one of the flats turned out to be fully furnished. By the end of the year Joyce discovered the apartment of his dreams at 5 boulevard Raspail. Boulevard Raspail is a long, somber residential avenue running from the Latin Quarter into the heart of Montparnasse: its rows of respectable but indifferent façades probably suited Joyce's idea of sanctuary—or he may have been pleased to live on a boulevard that honored Balzac at the junction of place Vavin. The apartment rental was far more than the writer could ever hope to acquire, but once again his Paris friends decided they "must help Joyce" and agreed to subsidize the cost of housing the Joyce family. As to furnishings, Joyce was indifferent—except that he demanded a table with square edges to write upon, while Nora Barnacle (who would not become Joyce's legal wife until the end of the Twenties) converted each of their temporary living quarters into a passable replica of a flat in Dublin. It was on the boulevard Raspail, and soon after in an apartment lent by Valery Larbaud at 71 rue Cardinal Lemoine, that Joyce completed his masterwork *Ulysses*, ending with the most resonant affirmative in literary history, Molly Bloom's classic "yes."

Chapter Five

"Yes," lamented Gertrude Stein, "the old crowd has disappeared." But even as she said it, an active contingent of the old crowd, her crowd, was moving back to its prewar premises. The Germans had twice failed to break through at the Marne for an invasion of Paris, but now a peacetime invasion was taking place. Great colonies of the uprooted—Russian émigrés, in force—joined the returning soldiers swarming into the capital.

At war's end the artillery post on the roof of the Hôtel de Ville had been dismantled and the Cocteau-inspired cabaret, Le Boeuf sur le Toit (the Ox on the Roof), established. Kiosks were plastered over with ads for the new comedy *Phi-Phi* or Paul Colin posters of Mistinguett (singing "Mon Homme") at the Casino de Paris. Except for a token force on occupation duty, the French army had demobilized. The survivors of Ypres and Verdun formed queues at their local city halls to marry wartime sweethearts and crowded around the Havas ads, looking for employment. Zeppelin damage and Big Bertha scars were still visible; signs in the Métro requested patrons to relinquish their seats to *mutilés de la guerre*. The same taxis and couturier vans that had relayed troops to the Battle of the Marne were back on the boulevards in a familiar traffic tangle and cacophony of horns.

Of the old crowd Gertrude Stein knew best, Matisse had abandoned Paris for the Riviera, but Braque was back from the trenches, where he had suffered a head wound that required trepanning. Wearing a turban of bandages, he experimented with sand and plaster applied to canvas, working at his old studio on the rue Caulaincourt in Montmartre. But few of the Cubists went back to Montmartre: studios had become expensive in the burgeoning nightlife district—a rural outpost before the war, its vineyards and terraced garden plots had by now been filled in by apartment blocks.

The Bateau Lavoir—so named by the poet Max Jacob because the ramshackle wooden structure resembled the laundry boats tied up along the Seine—where the Cubists had lived and worked in picturesque misery (Picasso's tea froze in the pot overnight and was reheated for *le petit déjeuner* next winter's morn) was abandoned. One of the first to evacuate was Jacob himself. During the war he had converted from Jew to Catholic, taken the baptismal name Cyprien, and now shuttled between Paris and the contemplative life at a monastery in the village of St-Benoit-sur-Loire. Picasso took pains to avoid meeting Max Jacob (Cyprien) and André Derain: they only reminded him of the days of frozen tea in the leaky Bateau Lavoir. In a period of new attachments and shifting allegiances, the painters of the prewar Ecole de Paris had scattered to other arrondissements, principally to Montparnasse. But Georges Braque and the poet André Breton remained loyal to Montmartre. The war had only interrupted Braque's interest in the Cubist concepts he had discovered alongside Picasso; Breton was brooding over the beginning dreams of Surrealism.

The Parisian world of art could not long support a postwar vacuum of ideas: even a statement of anti-art would serve until a substantial movement should coalesce. Marcel Duchamp had managed for a time to shock bourgeois sensibilities by a reverse art of "ready-mades," exhibiting a shovel, a wine rack, and a toilet seat as gallery pieces. This spirit animated the background to the first *dernier cri* of the decade. Dada was born in Zurich during the war (February 8, 1916) when Tristan Tzara delivered the first Dadaist manifesto at the Café Terrasse, accompanied by Hans Arp with a brioche dangling from his left nostril.

The advent of peace negotiations in the Paris of 1920 brought two uninvited delegates to the capital—Tristan Tzara and Francis Picabia—determined to declare a new war in the art world. Revolution, not reconciliation, was the principal item on their agenda.

Early in the campaign, Picabia escorted his friend Tzara to 27 rue de Fleurus to announce to Gertrude Stein that Dada had arrived in Paris. Miss Stein was fond of Picabia, but she was neither interested nor amused by his proclamation. In her original and inventive way, Gertrude Stein might be thought of as a Dadaist unaware, but she was not likely to become part of a movement she had not discovered for herself. (Her own work had been ridiculed too often for her to offer her name to a group devoted to ridicule.) The Steins, Gertrude and her brother Leo, had purchased and pronounced upon the works produced under the various labels of Impressionism, Postimpressionism, Fauvism, Futurism (an Italian movement which caused more stir in Paris than in Rome), and above all Cubism—but Dada was not to receive the Stein imprimatur. Never mind. "The true Dadaists," declared Tzara, "are against Dada."

The first public Dada manifestation took place at the Palais des Fêtes on January 23, 1920. A stunned audience sat through a preliminary literary discussion passively enough but with visible discomfort; however, when Tristan Tzara read as a poem an insignificant newspaper item chosen at random, accompanied by castanets, cowbells, and rattles, the first major battle was joined. The whistling, hissing outburst of insult was exactly the reaction the Dadaists had hoped for.

At the Salon des Indépendants the very next month, the Dadaists gave out the false report that Charlie Chaplin was the latest convert to Dada and would be present on stage. This announcement naturally attracted an overflow audience—Chaplin, of course, did not appear. As the Dadaists read aloud their poems and manifestos, the outraged crowd hurled vegetables at the rostrum. The lights had to be switched off in order to evacuate the auditorium. By the time Tzara's *Vaseline Symphony* was presented at the Salle Gaveau that May, a contingent of gendarmes patrolled the aisles to deal with the riot that had become traditional.

Cubism had been equally revolutionary before the war, but by 1920 the movement had plunged beyond its breakthrough years. Although Braque was still experimenting in the Cubist manner and Léger had adapted Cubist techniques to an interpretation of the industrial age, only Juan Gris would continue to paint Cubist pictures until his death in 1927. Even though Picasso was one of its originators, Cubism was no longer part of his quicksilver interests. When the Salon des Indépendants held its 1920 exhibit reuniting all the Cubists of the prewar years, Picasso refused to show. He had quarreled, then broken with Derain and Braque in his denunciation of Cubism. "I took Braque and Derain to the station," said Picasso of his friends who went off to war. "I never found them again."

In Rome Picasso had fallen in love with auburn-haired Olga Khoklova, a dancer with the Ballets Russes. She was the daughter of an officer in the czar's army and appeared to be of an upper-class background that made her all the more desirable in Picasso's eyes. She was not one of his easy conquests: a member of the Diaghilev troupe overheard Picasso at Olga's bedroom door asking to be allowed to see her and her reply, "No, no, Monsieur Picasso. I'm not going to let you in." No intrigue in his company escaped Sergei Diaghilev, and he warned Picasso, "With Russian girls, you have to marry them."

They were married at the Russian Orthodox Church on rue Daru, the honeymoon took place at the Hôtel Lutétia, whose wedding-cake façade dominates boulevard Raspail at the Sèvres-Babylone intersection. Marriage to Olga brought a complete change in Picasso's outlook and style of life. Olga created a household of upper-middle-class respectability in the heart of the Right Bank bourgeoisie. Since the name Picasso could now open doors to the highest circles of Parisian society, Olga intended to leave her precarious dance career far behind and enter the ranks of the Tout-Paris. The Picassos received and were received. The high point for Olga in the social ascent was an invitation to the rue Masseran town house of Count Etienne de Beaumont.

The painter, who had worn the stained corduroys of Montmartre, simple fisherman's garb, or the "monkey-suit" of overalls when he worked, now purchased his first dinner jacket. With it he wore the Spanish *faixa*, a cummerbund of red or black with fringed edges (an item he had formerly worn beneath his overalls to protect his kidneys against the damp cold of the Bateau Lavoir). The bohemian chaos Picasso brought with him from la Butte was confined to the painter's studio one flight above the smart flat on rue La Boétie.

With Olga as the model for a series of serene Greco-Roman figures of heroic proportions—airily dancing on Mediterranean beaches or seated, solid as statuary—Picasso entered his period of Neoclassicism. Olga became pregnant; life was ordered, almost predictable. Picasso sought his way out of Cubism and beyond by studiously contemplating the antique past.

What next? was a question that also vexed the impresario Sergei Diaghilev, who culled for his ballet productions only the most advanced ideas of the avant-garde. At this threshold of new beginnings—the Ballets Russes had been badly disrupted by the war, the company in desperate need of a renascence—Diaghilev had the happy inspiration to bring Picasso together with the composer Igor Stravinsky for a ballet project based on a theme by Pergolesi. Stravinsky and Picasso were alike in several ways: short of stature, with intense and animated expressions heightened by the fierce eyes of buccaneers. ("When Picasso looked at a drawing or a print," said Leo Stein, "I was surprised that anything was left on the paper—so absorbing was his gaze.") Both men were inordinately proud of their small feet and hands; both were health conscious to the point of hypochondria. They shared with Diaghilev a superstitious dread of death. In 1920 these three temperamental moderns set to work on the ballet *Pulcinella*.

The first set designs Picasso conceived—in the style of the *commedia dell'arte* (the painter had always been fascinated by Harlequin) but updating the period to nineteenth-century Offenbach—were altogether inappropriate to Diaghilev's conception of the project. In an argument over side-whiskers instead of masks, Diaghilev suddenly tore the sketches to pieces, then ground the torn bits underfoot. Ordinarily this outburst would have led to an irrevocable break between the two men. Picasso's Spanish pride and Diaghilev's stubborn will could not accommodate opposition, yet Picasso—perhaps conditioned to Slavic turbulence by Olga's temper tantrums—managed to dominate his rage. As suddenly as he had exploded, Diaghilev became, as he could, all charm and persuasion. In a miracle of reconciliation Picasso designed new costumes, then altered the set. *Pulcinella* was the success Diaghilev needed to bring the Ballets Russes into the Twenties, a reassessment of the classic past filtered through the perceptions of a painter and a composer of genius.

At the time of the Armistice, Gertrude Stein remarked that Apollinaire's death had changed Paris. Guillaume Apollinaire had been the leading exponent of the avant-garde during the Belle Epoque: poet, critic, impresario of Cubism. He died not of his wartime injuries—a head wound that required trepanning like Braque's—but of Spanish influenza, the second great scourge of the infant century. (Influenza slaughtered an estimated ten million, a number equal to all the deaths attributed to World War I.) The story Gertrude Stein embellished and passed on was this: as Apollinaire lay dying, he heard cries from the street, "A bas Guillaume!" which in his delirium he thought were meant for himself instead of Kaiser Wilhelm. But Guillaume Apollinaire died three days before the Armistice, so he would not have heard the victory cry from his deathbed. Gertrude Stein loved a story that was a story.

Although she did mourn the passing of Apollinaire and the finale to the era he represented, Miss Stein was not one to languish long. In a sense, the disappearance of Apollinaire as the ambassador of Art left that post vacant for Gertrude Stein.

For Miss Stein, a way of marking the end of the war and the beginning of the Twenties was to replace the unwieldy Ford ambulance she had driven all through the war (her "second-class hearse") with a pert two-seater she named Godiva because the new motorcar arrived from Detroit in its natural state, stripped of accessories and trim. (A chain-smoker, she installed her own ashtray.) She was writing again, often from the lofty driver's seat of Godiva as she waited out a garage repair or sat parked at a Parisian curbside.

At one of the garages where Godiva was being serviced, Miss Stein heard a French mechanic—a conscientious older man—refer to his hopeless apprentice as one of *une génération perdue*. Men, he explained, become civilized between the ages of 18 and 30, but the war generation missed the civilizing period. Miss Stein later applied the term to those twenty-year-olds like Ernest Hemingway whose characters were altered and whose outlook was shadowed when the natural order of their lives was interrupted by war. The writer Matthew Josephson was present when Miss Stein labeled his generation "lost," but he remembered the French phrase as *une généra-*

Pablo Picasso at his studio on the rue la Boétie shortly after his marriage to the tempestuous Russian ballerina, Olga Khoklova (inset).

tion fichue, which means "ruined"—thus the famous label may have been
largely romanticized in the translation.

A grapevine of news and gossip, a network of introductions or a chance
meeting, began to link one outpost of the new age to the other.

Sylvia Beach had started Shakespeare and Company, her lending library
of books in English, and mail-drop service—a kind of Left Bank American Express—first on the rue Dupuytren, then at 8 (later 12) rue de
l'Odéon, across the street from Adrienne Monnier's La Maison des Amis
des Livres. Sylvia Beach and Adrienne Monnier met when Sylvia's wide-
brimmed hat blew off and Adrienne, in her long peasant skirt, went chasing the hat down the rue de l'Odéon. Les Amis des Livres performed the
same literary services for French intellectuals as Shakespeare and Company did for the English-speaking community. Miss Monnier and Miss
Beach remained friends—a rare accomplishment in the competitive atmosphere of the Quarter—thus the French and Anglo-American circles that
frequented the rue de l'Odéon were sometimes concentric.

The two bookstores were, in a way, salons as well as *librairies*. At
Shakespeare and Company, Gertrude Stein made contact with a number
of new writers passing through or newly installed in Paris since the war.
She could find reading matter in English and was delighted that her own
privately printed *Tender Buttons* was among the books in the lending library. For Gertrude, bookstore browsing and gallery openings were social
occasions as well as intellectual stimulation—the new writers and painters
she met were invited to her studio-salon at 27 rue de Fleurus. At a Left
Bank gallery Picasso, with whom Gertrude Stein had quarreled, came up
to her and said, "Hell, let's be friends"—so they shook hands, and she
invited him to her studio. The studio on rue de Fleurus became a meeting
place in the heart of Montparnasse for everybody who was anybody (or
soon to become somebody), along with the idly curious or the curiously
idle, any passing eccentric or new face in Paris willing to reply to the question Miss Stein's companion Alice Toklas asked at the door: "De la part
de qui venez-vous?"

Guests might turn up by no one's explicit instruction, or they might have
been invited by the forgetful Miss Stein herself. Not that the "de la part"
mattered as much as Gertrude Stein's keenness for new people, her swift,
instinctive summary of character, or her early discernment of originality
in the most unlikely visitor. Her prejudices were legion, but they worked
as often in the guest's favor as not.

Gertrude Stein and Sherwood Anderson—whom she immediately liked
for his large Italianate eyes—met at Shakespeare and Company. Again
through Sylvia Beach, Miss Stein met Ezra Pound, whom she was not sure
about. Pound had known Yeats in Ireland and Eliot in England and now
Joyce in Paris. Since James Joyce also frequented Shakespeare and Com-

pany, Miss Stein almost met him there, but, in her words, not quite. Pound was a generous friend to writers and painters and musicians, as well as an influential force in the arts. (It was the influence that made Miss Stein unsure of Pound.) Through his editorship or association with "little" magazines, he managed to help his gifted contemporaries publish their work, and he genuinely wanted to help Miss Stein. Gertrude Stein was practically unpublished at this time except for self-publication at her own expense, even though she was recognized throughout the literary underground of the day as an important new voice and guiding spirit to other writers. As anxious as she was to publish (her dream was to appear in the *Atlantic Monthly*), she was wary of Pound as a counterinfluence with the young and as a formidable rival. Nevertheless, the two important arbiters of art met at Shakespeare and Company.

Pound was invited to visit the famous studio on rue de Fleurus, where the walls were hung with paintings by Matisse, Derain, Gris, Braque, and most of the Fauves and Cubists who were unknown before Gertrude and Leo Stein began buying their work. Miss Stein sat slumped heavily beneath the portrait Picasso had painted of her. (She complained the painting did not resemble her. "It will," said Picasso—and it did.)

During Pound's debut at the Stein salon he spoke at great length and with his customary enthusiasm. Gertrude Stein was not in the habit of being outtalked. In Pound's enthusiasm he fell out of Miss Stein's favorite chair, or broke it, according to a revised version of the incident. After the first visit, there were no others.

After the Ezra Pound fiasco, Sylvia Beach—the quiet diplomat of the Quarter and self-effacing go-between—was wary of introducing Gertrude Stein to a writer as reputable as James Joyce. Joyce and Stein, the two commanding presences of Montparnasse, neither met nor acknowledged one another's existence. Like Sylvia Beach, Ernest Hemingway came to know both: he discovered that one did not mention the name of one great "general" to the other. At Gertrude Stein's salon, "If you brought up Joyce twice, you would not be invited back."

Yet the lines of communication were open: new cliques came into being as the older circles enlarged or faded from the scene. The Parisian network was extensive: vital connections were made by those asking what next? at the same moment.

The Hemingways arrived in Paris on the boat train from Le Havre in a jostling compartment filled with soldiers. They checked into the inexpensive Hôtel Jacob and discovered a restaurant, the Pré aux Clercs—dinner for two from twelve to fourteen francs, Pinard wine at sixty centimes—at the corner of rue Jacob and rue Bonaparte. Rue Bonaparte reminded Hemingway of François Villon's Paris, when wolves would slink into the city under the public gallows at Montfaucon. In letters home he wrote of the priceless time they were having "walking the streets day and night, arm through arm, peering into courts and stopping in front of little shop windows." Their hotel room resembled a grog shop, he boasted to cronies in Prohibition Chicago. Rhum St. James was fourteen francs a bottle. "It is the genuwind 7 year old rum as smooth as a kitten's chin." The franc, in 1921, was "fourteen to a paper one."

Hemingway had an instinct for finding cheap lodgings in unlikely neighborhoods. Their first home was a small flat in a marginal quarter off the rue Mouffetard. The place de la Contrescarpe attracted a floating colony of hard-drinking *clochards* who bought liters of raw wine or, for a few centimes more, drank rum at the Café des Amateurs on the square. The Hemingways lived around the corner at 74 rue Cardinal Lemoine (across the street from one of James Joyce's borrowed residences, at 71). Their acceptance of Paris on the sordid level, as well as the sublime, made it possible for the newlyweds to adjust to the rude surroundings and settle into the neighborhood as would any French couple in the same circumstances.

When Janet Flanner visited the Hemingway flat, she climbed the fetid spiral staircase with water spigot and crude *pissoir* on every landing. The few rooms of the apartment were of indeterminate shape, all angles and unexpected corners, the furnishings heavy and ugly. The bathroom was no more than a recessed closet with water pitcher and bowl, no plumbing, only a slop jar. The slop jars were emptied out at the landings, garbage carried four flights down to the courtyard.

"You can live on less and less" was Hemingway's motto at the time. Ernest and Hadley offered Miss Flanner an egg for lunch the day she visited. There were boiled potatoes and *vin ordinaire*—the Bois-Charbon-Vin shop was just across the street. From the Mouffetard open market Hadley bought the cheapest legumes; a favorite was *poireaux* (leeks), which she prepared French fashion: boiled, then served cold with oil and vinegar. A goatherd brought his *troupeau* along the place Contrescarpe in the early morning, playing a shrill tune on his pipes to alert customers. At night the *vidangeurs* passed with their horse-drawn pump to drain the foul septic tanks in the quarter.

In order to write undisturbed, the young author rented a room at 39 rue Descartes, where Verlaine was said to have died, thus paying indirect homage to the French literary past. True homage was paid to Flaubert, whose dedication to *le mot juste* was a driving inspiration to the beginning writer struggling to find exact words of his own.

With the chill rain of late autumn the walls stained with damp. Hemingway would look out across a gray panorama of rooftops from his attic window: an incredible complication of chimneypots, *bombé* sheet-metal roofing, church towers, and twisted drainpipes from the Sorbonne to the vast esplanade of les Invalides. If the smoke from neighboring chimneys blew in an unobstructed line, he knew his own chimney would draw: it might be worth the investment of a bundle of firewood from the Bois-Charbon-Vin merchant.

By midwinter Hemingway was forced to seek the warmth of "a good café on the place St. Michel" to set down in blue French lycée notebooks the beginnings of those first stories of a remembered Michigan. When the sky lowered in winter and the city was a study in slate, the principal escape from gelid hotel rooms and unheated ateliers were the terraces of the big cafés, glass-enclosed, warmed by charcoal braziers. A single glass of wine or a *café filtre* entitled a client to sit for as long as he cared to. The tales Hemingway wrote by hand in the blue lycée notebooks he later typed on a Corona portable typewriter Hadley had given him for his birthday.

At first he hesitated to use Sherwood Anderson's generous letters of introduction to Ezra Pound, Gertrude Stein, and Sylvia Beach. Hemingway discovered Shakespeare and Company on his own and introduced himself to Miss Beach. The bookshop was warm and well stocked with books Hemingway was too poor to buy but happy to learn he could borrow. He called Sylvia Beach "Madame Shakespeare" and wrote to her at 12 rue de l'Odéon in that name. Sherwood Anderson's photograph was among those in Miss Beach's private gallery of literary friends, but Hemingway did not inform Sylvia Beach of his friendship with Anderson or produce the letter Anderson had written until, shyly, he presented his introduction to her long after he had become Shakespeare and Company's "best customer."

He then began to call on Gertrude Stein and wrote to Anderson: "Gertrude Stein and me are just like brothers." He was both impressed and amused by his discovery of Ezra Pound, who at that time was learning to play the bassoon and made his own crude but serviceable furniture out of crate wood. "Pound took six of my poems . . . he thinks I'm a swell poet." He boxed and played tennis with Pound and sat at the feet of Miss Stein— then absorbed in the way of a perfect student the lessons he could best apply to his own lonely pursuit. As a student he accepted advice and criticism from both these original sources—at least during the initial literary kinships "when the flowers of friendship bloomed," uncomplicated by the blood feuds of the late Twenties—but wisely the young writer kept his two instructors in the arts well apart.

To relieve the hard discipline of sustained literary endeavor, the young Hemingway boxed or attended the spectator sports at Auteuil and the Vé- lodrome de Paris. Another escape from creative pressures was walking. Hemingway discovered parts of Paris that devotees of the Dôme, the Cou- pole, and the Rotonde would never quit their wicker chairs to visit: the outdoor boxing rings of Ménilmontant and the riverside restaurant Chez Robinson, with tables set in perches in the trees along the upper reaches of the Seine. During his expeditions through the city, the writer collected those moments, public and private, he could draw from: an inventory of telling detail to give dimension to his fiction. He made casual friends of seven-day bicycle racers and grizzled fishermen on the quays of the Ile de la Cité, dependent on the tiny *goujons* they caught to supplement pensions reduced drastically by the falling franc. He was a sparring partner of professional boxers, friend to café waiters, confidant of prostitutes. Along the open boulevards and down strange culs-de-sac the young heavyweight prowled the city he loved best, his personal domain.

If Hemingway truly intended to be a writer, Gertrude Stein told him, he would have to give up journalism. "If you keep on doing newspaper work you will never see things, you will only see words and that will not do...."

Although Hemingway was at first dependent on overseas assignments from the *Toronto Star* for a bare livelihood, he saw the truth in Miss Stein's warning. Journalism had contributed considerably to the stripped-down Hemingway style—bits of newspaper dispatches, experiences, and obser- vations he had picked up as a correspondent would emerge as the hard- edged, concentrated literary vignettes of his first effort, *In Our Time*—but his newspaper prose would have had a trivializing and finally destructive effect on his fiction. Hemingway trusted Gertrude Stein's judgment in lit- erary matters; he submitted his manuscripts to both Gertrude Stein and Ezra Pound, separately. "Ezra was right half the time and when he was wrong he was so wrong you were never in doubt about it. Gertrude was always right."

While covering the 1922 Lausanne Conference for the *Toronto Star*, Hemingway had met the correspondent Lincoln Steffens. Steffens was greatly impressed with Hemingway's short story "My Old Man" and asked if he might personally send it off to his friend Ray Long, at *Cosmopolitan* in New York. It was the season of autumn rains in Paris, so Ernest con- trived for Hadley to meet him in Lausanne for a quasi-vacation for them both. When Hadley arrived, she was so tearful and distraught that her husband was unable to piece together what had happened. Hadley had thought Ernest might want to work at his own writing during the Swiss so- journ and as a surprise had brought along his manuscripts. A valise containing the sum of Hemingway's first year's work in Paris had been stolen at the gare de Lyon.

Hemingway hurried back to Paris to confirm the full extent of the disaster: worse, every carbon copy had accompanied its original in the missing suitcase. Only two stories survived: "Up in Michigan," which had been tucked away in a drawer after Gertrude Stein had declared it too sexually explicit, and "My Old Man," which had been returned with a rejection from *Cosmopolitan*.

At 27 rue de Fleurus the crushed young writer received considerable sympathy, and an excellent lunch, from Alice Toklas and Gertrude Stein. Miss Stein thought some good must come out of the tragedy since Hemingway would be obliged to reconsider his youthful oeuvre from point zero. But Hemingway was badly shaken. No loss in his life had been as traumatic since the time Agnes von Kurowsky wrote announcing her engagement to another man.

When Hadley became pregnant, Hemingway went again to Gertrude Stein to announce in the tone of defeat and self-pity he sometimes affected: "I'm too young to be a father." In the childless world of the Stein-Toklas household he had a sympathetic audience: Gertrude Stein had never been interested in wives or mothers or the customary domestic arrangements. The reluctant father-to-be was offered a glass of eau-de-vie.

The Hemingways returned to the United States for the birth of the baby, a boy they nicknamed Bumby. Ernest was now obliged to consider his enlarged responsibilities as a family man, so he accepted a salaried job with the *Toronto Star*. Being a paid hireling on the newspaper for which he had worked as a free-lance reporter in Europe was a depressing comedown, Toronto an impossible city after Paris. He soon clashed with his iron-willed editor, thus ending the brief period of middle-class respectability in Canada. The Hemingways returned to Paris, this time to a flat at 113 Notre-Dame-des-Champs, close to the separate establishments of Hemingway's two tutelary saints, Ezra Pound and Gertrude Stein. Miss Stein and Alice Toklas became the unlikely godparents to Bumby, Alice to provide suitable garments in wool and needlework for their infant godson. Ezra Pound continued to instruct the new father in literary craftsmanship, while in turn receiving lessons in the art of boxing.

The whine from the buzz saw in the courtyard sawmill drove the young writer once again to the isolation and quiet of a good café in which to work. His new sanctuary was the nearest bistro in the quarter, the Closerie de Lilas, where poets and artists had met since the time of Baudelaire. From the café table where he worked he could look out upon the equestrian statue of one of his favorite military figures, Marshal Ney. (Hemingway was unusually superstitious and thought the coincidence of having the gallant marshal nearby brought him luck.)

Feeling "belly-empty hollow-hungry" after a morning's work, Hemingway took a promenade through the Luxembourg Gardens: his goal, the Palais du Luxembourg, where Impressionist and Postimpressionist paintings were housed, awaiting official recognition by the Louvre. It was at the Palais du Luxembourg that Hemingway made his curious attempt to understand how painters like Cézanne created landscape so that he might learn to do the same with words. On the return trip home the hungry young author occasionally lingered in the park near the Medici Fountain, just before the guard closed the gates for the night, to kill a stray pigeon with a homemade slingshot. He would carry the dead bird home for supper, tucked inside his jacket.

In other matters of economy, Gertrude Stein offered her advice. She taught Ernest to cut his wife's hair. Miss Stein's idea of saving was that Hadley buy clothes for comfort and durability—like the heavy, shapeless garments she herself wore—so that the money could be invested, as hers was, in paintings.

After Bumby was born, the Hemingways could be seen trudging through the Luxembourg Gardens, Ernest in baggy suit with elbow patches carrying Bumby on his hip, Hadley in makeshift dress following silently like an Indian squaw.

During this period of marginal living at free-lance writing—a rare check from the German magazine *Der Querschnitt*, an occasional win at the Auteuil racetrack—Hemingway met Harold Loeb. An editor of *Broom*, a magazine of the arts edited in New York and Paris and printed in Berlin, Loeb had published a novel, *Doodab*, in New York and had been a boxer in college—two dangerously competitive accomplishments to bring to a friendship with Ernest Hemingway. Furthermore, Loeb represented the ease and affluence of the Loeb-Guggenheim families at a time when the Hemingways were struggling to survive on "next to nothing a year." (Loeb's cousin was the art collector Peggy Guggenheim.) Nevertheless, Hemingway did become friendly with Harold Loeb. In the beginning the two men were the closest of café companions, fellow writers and boxing partners.

Through Loeb's mistress, the dancer Kitty Cannell, the Hemingways came to know Pauline Pfeiffer, a fashion editor on the Paris staff of *Vogue*. Pauline Pfeiffer was to play an important role in the life of the Hemingways, but a role altogether inconsistent with her first impression of the young couple. It was Hadley she liked. She thought Ernest a disagreeable boor. She knew the Hemingways had little money, but her ideas concerning a woman's wardrobe were the reverse of Gertrude Stein's: she considered Ernest a brute not to allow Hadley to dress well. Pauline took it upon herself to give the neglected wife advice on the new fashions that made Paris the style capital of the world.

Before the war Gabrielle (Coco) Chanel was shared by two wealthy lovers in a ménage-à-trois that shifted from Arthur Capel's country estate and hunting lodge to Paris, where Chanel was installed in a ground floor apartment of her own in Etienne Balsan's *hôtel particulier*. For the Frenchman Balsan, Coco was the charming partner he could display at Maxim's and Delmonico's. The Englishman "Boy" Capel saw her as more than a casual cocotte. The slim, dark-haired Auvergnate dressed simply, yet exquisitely, in a way that belied her humble origins. No one would have believed what Chanel all her life took such pains to obscure: she had grown up in rural poverty; she had made her way to Paris on the music-hall circuit, then into the *beau monde* with the help of lovers like Balsan and Capel.

Chanel had a flair for design and the ambition to go into business, so Capel set her up in a millinery boutique near the Hôtel Ritz. Her hats were successful: Chanel proved to be in her element among the discriminating buyers of the place Vendôme. Her aspirations extended beyond the millinery trade: Coco Chanel intended to become dressmaker to society. While still designing hats for her boutique, she observed one evening a theater audience of women as elaborately costumed as the Molière characters on stage and murmured a prophecy and a promise to Capel: "That can't last. I'm going to dress them simply, and in black."

The Ballets Russes had set the style for the previous age with its exotic display of orientalism beginning with the startling production of *Sheherazade*. The sets and costumes by Leon Bakst were an important influence on the leading fashion designer of the prewar years, Paul Poiret, when he introduced the vibrant theatrical colors of Bakst: Persian blues and greens, the hard, flat orange known as tango. Poiret also introduced the harem-inspired *jupes-culottes*, turbans, ropes of pearl—to be accompanied by sensuous perfumes of his own manufacture.

But high fashion was completely disrupted by the great European conflict. The textile industry had collapsed in the devastated north; demand for original creations had so diminished in wartime Paris that leading couturiers simply closed their doors and donated their delivery vans to Misia Sert's private ambulance service. Immediately after the Armistice in 1918, Parisian designers were busy again: the woolen mills in the north were rebuilt by state priority; the silk factories near Lyon were back in production—silk competing now with a new artificial fabric that would revolutionize the stocking industry, rayon.

Women of society turned first to Poiret, Worth, and Molyneux for the lavish wardrobes denied to them during the four years of austerity in dress.

The *Gazette du Bon Ton* offered advice to women attending functions at military hospitals: "We must make ourselves as beautiful as we can for the wounded." Again, Paul Poiret was the most sought-after couturier: the instant revival of his prewar harem wear coincided with the revival of interest in the Ballets Russes. But as Chanel pointed out, such costume exotica could not last.

At the beginning of the Twenties American suffragettes had just won their voting rights (Frenchwomen had already gained the vote in 1919), and fashion would reflect the spirit of liberation. Before the war Poiret had succeeded in banishing the antique whalebone corset—but he had then made women into awkward geishas by putting them into long ankle-clinging hobble skirts. Freedom of movement became an essential consideration in designing for the new woman. Shop girls wore silk stockings for the first time and experimented with Ambre perfume and Fleur de Pêche, skin cream of crushed almonds. Women smoked openly, extending long ivory cigarette holders or dangling a *mégot* between lacquered fingernails.

By 1922 there were eighty feminist societies with some 60,000 members throughout France. The new heroines were social outlaws like Lady Duff Twysden and Nancy Cunard of the lean and hungry look, or Zelda Fitzgerald, the I-don't-care girl of the Jazz Age. These were the models for characters in novels and models for the way women in the Twenties wanted to look and dress. No one saw more clearly than Coco Chanel that women had emerged from the foyer into the larger world of independence and possibility—she had done so herself.

At first Capel may have backed Chanel's millinery enterprise as a way of indulging his attractive mistress with a gift of money he could as well afford to offer as a trinket from Cartier's. It was soon evident that Chanel was not only a gifted originator of design but a businesswoman of insight and inspiration: if she wanted to establish her own *maison de couture—pourquoi pas?* The shrewd peasant side of her character, and her worldly dealings with men, gave Coco Chanel an outsized respect for the power of money. Capel's investment in her was a means of making a beginning; after that, she would create a name and fortune of her own.

Just before the war Coco established the House of Chanel on rue Cambon, where it would remain a landmark throughout the Twenties and beyond. From her headquarters in the heart of the *quartier d'élégance* she set out to challenge the reigning prince of fashion, Paul Poiret. In the wake of Cubism, Chanel created cubes and rectangles out of a bare meter of fabric; she did away with the curved trace of bosom and buttocks, lifted hemlines, eliminated showy detail. The Chanel line was austere but graceful, and if not as lushly feminine as the Poiret costume, her clothes appealed to the modern, independent, and—like herself—career-minded woman. In the severity of her design, Chanel pursued what she called *le luxe dans la simplicité.* Poiret sighed and saw the world of Chanel as linear and flat, her direction a deluxe impoverishment: "Until now, women were beautiful and architectural, like the prow of a ship. Now they all resemble undernourished telephone operators." Slowly, but with devastating effectiveness, Chanel began to encroach upon Poiret terrain by designing for defectors from his exclusive clientele, le Tout-Paris.

But just as Coco Chanel's business venture began to show enormous promise, her personal life collapsed. Hard edged as she was in the daggers-drawn fashion world, her shrewd gift of assessment failed her in affairs of the heart. Against every indication, she made up her mind that Boy Capel intended to marry her. Instead, the British aristocrat became engaged to Diana Lister, an Englishwoman of his own rank and background. In the thoughtless manner of the rich, Boy suggested to Coco that he might introduce her to his fiancée—so that his mistress might bestow her blessing on the match.

No sooner had Chanel recovered from the shock of Boy's engagement than she was plunged into grief over news of his death. In December 1919 Boy Capel was killed in a driving accident near St. Raphaël. Chanel had become half reconciled to Boy's marriage, but his death—the loss of the only man she had ever loved—was a blow from which she could not recover. Coco Chanel lapsed into lethargy and black depression: even her bedroom was draped in black, the color she had made fashionable. Boy Capel had left her a legacy of £40,000. She would never be without money again; she was wealthy, and alone.

An intimate friend, Misia Sert, one of the most influential figures of the prewar social and cultural scene, offered her high-spirited company. Misia lured Coco out of her shadowy, cloistered life into the light. Her husband, the painter José-Maria Sert, took charge of redecorating Chanel's town house at 29 rue du faubourg St. Honoré: he changed the color scheme of the somber bedroom to pink. Misia's example as patron of the arts and social hostess to le Tout-Paris inspired Chanel to open her own salon to that variegated parade of artists, poets, princes, and the publicity minded.

Jean Cocteau became a regular at 29 rue du faubourg St. Honoré: a talented poet-painter-cinéaste and gregarious wit who could be wickedly diverting after a stressful day of fittings in the rue Cambon. Twice Chanel saw Cocteau—financially and supportively—through disintoxication cures for his addiction to opium. She also saw him through the great loss of his life (just as Misia had done for her) when his young protégé Raymond Radiguet, author of *Devil in the Flesh*, died at the age of twenty in 1923. By this time Chanel had become involved with the poet Pierre Reverdy, who had been cofounder with Apollinaire of the arts journal *Nord-Sud* and was one of the emerging Surrealists. As both lover and patron to Reverdy, Chanel sponsored the publication of a volume of his poetry, with watercolor illustrations by Pablo Picasso.

This was Picasso's period of following the lead of Jean Cocteau as social butterfly—Picasso's "unreliable period," in the words of Gertrude Stein. Chanel's salon was a favorite visiting place for the painter, who was being courted by wealthy collectors and entertained by the lion hunters of the nouveau riche.

Another member of the Chanel circle was Picasso's friend Max Jacob, who had once been appointed Superstitions Consultant to Paul Poiret (to advise on which colors brought *bonheur* or *malheur* to the wearer). A religious mystic since his conversion to Christianity, Jacob suggested to Chanel that she should trim her hair in the manner of Jesus Christ, then launch the new coiffure in her own persuasive way.

Chanel did in fact wear her hair clipped short in advance of the rage for bobbed hair and the even more boyish shingle cut. To accommodate the new fashions in millinery—the bell-shaped cloche hat that fit the head like a helmet, cloth or jeweled bandeaux across the forehead, turbans and matador caps—shorter hair styles for women were inevitable. Cropped hair had already enjoyed a brief success in France just before the war when Antoine the hairdresser convinced Eve Lavallière to appear on stage with her hair cut daringly short. Even the dancer Caryathis preceded Chanel in shedding the crowning glory of the previous age when she clipped her long tresses and left them, as a reproach, on the pillow of an indifferent lover. The ultimate in shorn hair marked Genica Athanasiou's appearance as Antigone in the 1922 Jean Cocteau production: Cocteau had persuaded her to shave her head bald and pluck her eyebrows to conform to his conception of the Greek heroine.

Antigone was a landmark theatrical event in other ways: the music was composed by Arthur Honneger, the sets designed by Picasso, and the costumes were by Chanel. "I asked Mlle. Chanel for the costumes," Cocteau announced, "because she is the greatest designer of our day and I cannot imagine the daughter of Oedipus badly dressed." Little attention was given to Cocteau's play at the minuscule experimental theater l'Atelier, but Chanel received considerable publicity from her first venture in costume design. Man Ray took photographs of the costumes, Georges Lepage did a series of drawings of the Chanel designs for the French *Vogue*, and a review of the play was headed, "Chanel Goes Greek."

Chanel had passed through her Russian phase the year before at a time when Russians and all things Russian were à la mode. She engaged ruined countesses, Russian saleswomen, and fine-boned Slavic models to launch her exclusively Russian line. This was a temporary aberration, a move away from the classic Chanel pattern: the blouses were loose fitting in the muzhik-peasant style, ornamentation and embroidery reappeared—excess she had ruthlessly eliminated with her simplified Cubist line. The Baltic period at 31 rue Cambon lasted not much longer than Chanel's interest in the exiled Russian, Grand Duke Dimitri Pavlovich.

Coco met Dimitri at a party given by Marthe Davelli. At twenty-nine the Grand Duke was eleven years younger than the great lady of fashion, but in the tradition of penniless aristocrats in exile, he made obvious his interest in the older woman of means. Marthe Davelli observed the rapprochement and took Coco aside to reveal what must have been obvious to Chanel, that Dimitri was her lover. Dimitri's taste for champagne and Charvet neckties was getting to be more than Marthe Davelli could afford. Would Coco be interested in adopting the handsome Russian nobleman? The scenario might have been written by Colette.

Chanel had inherited a grand duke as escort and lover: she was fond of him, but Dimitri could never be more than a casual if decorative substitute for her late great love, Boy Capel. Like the affair with Pierre Reverdy, whom she met during her Russian interlude with Dimitri, or a brief liaison with Stravinsky in 1920, attachments were a temporary distraction from genuine loss. Reverdy drifted out of Chanel's life to become a religious contemplative at a monastery outside Paris. Inevitably, Grand Duke Dimitri took leave of her as well.

To fill whatever vacuum these dead ends left in her, Chanel turned to her work, a total commitment to the dressmaking trade. Her hand was in at every stage from fabric cutting to an occasional turn at the stitching and hems. For the spring and fall salon presentations, Chanel selected the models herself and taught them an unaffected manner of display that would appeal to the "undernourished telephone operator" as well as to the Comtesse de Noailles.

Chanel was well aware of the snob appeal of haute couture, but this was a snobbism that could be exploited beyond the confines of the faubourg St. Honoré. She anticipated the mass marketing of couturier-label garments, the ready-to-wear boom; she had already accepted the challenge of dressing not just the *beau monde* but *tout le monde*.

Out of such ugly-sounding substances as rhodoid, galalithe, and nacrologue, Chanel began to design and market inexpensive costume jewelry, the ideal accompaniment to her plain-spoken elegance in dress. There was no pretense that these baubles were anything but colorfully artificial: it became as acceptable to pin a Chanel costume jewel to an evening dress as to wear one in daytime. The trinkets could be discarded at the next turn of fashion with no great heartache.

The first of the grand couturiers to make perfume an adjunct to his fashion line was Paul Poiret. Chanel became a contender in this field when she discovered Ernest Beaux, the half-French son of the *parfumier* to the court of the czar. At his perfume center in Grasse, Beaux had been experimenting with a product of extraordinary subtlety that endured throughout an evening, yet did not reek of the obvious source odors. With Beaux's formula, and the assistance of a master chemist who had defected from Coty, Chanel launched the product that was to make her name a by-word for perfume.

Once again her timing and instinct were exact. Even the design for the flask was an inspiration. In a simple square-edged bottle, labeled in plain black letters on white, Chanel N° 5, quietly announced itself a classic.

Misia and José-Maria Sert were the constants in Chanel's life: they were there to distract her from brooding despondency; she could confide in Misia and be entertained by José-Maria. Privately, Chanel had little appreciation for José-Maria's artistic talent—he was society's pet decorator and muralist of the period—but she was amused by him and comforted by his exuberant generosity. Early in the Twenties the Serts took Coco on a motor tour of Europe: Sert insisted on paying for every trifle during the trip, took great pains to engage Coco's interest in art, was tireless in the role of good companion. The relationship between Coco and Misia was more complicated. At that time, two people seen constantly together, openly affectionate, were invariably believed to be lovers. Theirs was an intense, almost rival-sibling friendship that endured from one decade to the next—a lifetime alliance based as much on competitiveness as affection. The large irony in their shifting ambivalent friendship was that Misia, having married three times, was envious of Chanel's lovers; Chanel, for all her passionate affairs, would have wanted marriage.

During the continental tour with Misia and José-Maria, Misia introduced Coco to Sergei Diaghilev at a café in Venice. It was doubtful if the great entrepreneur even noticed the dark beauty sitting quietly at Misia's side other than to murmur, "Enchanté." Diaghilev had no great interest in women: Misia was an extraordinary exception. He was troubled and needed to detail his current fiscal difficulties to his dear friend, since Misia had always been his close confidante and occasional savior. (Once when an opening curtain was inexplicably delayed for one of his ballet performances, Diaghilev suddenly appeared in Misia's theater box: "Do you have 20,000 francs? The costumer refuses to allow the curtain to go up until he is paid." Misia immediately sent her chauffeur for a checkbook.)

Diaghilev's present dilemma was this: the London season had been brilliant but a financial disaster: the company was in frightful difficulties. He needed to restage the ever-popular *The Rite of Spring* but could not afford to engage the large orchestra required for Stravinsky's score. Throughout Diaghilev's troubled monologue Misia's companion remained silent.

When Diaghilev returned to Paris, still despondent, he received an unexpected visitor at the Hôtel Continental. It was Coco Chanel, to present him with a check for 300,000 francs. The plans for *The Rite of Spring* could now be successfully consummated—with the proviso that Chanel's gift remain anonymous: Diaghilev was never to speak of the money to anyone or to remind his benefactor of her generosity.

Before the Russian Revolution the favorite café of Menshevik and Bolshevik conspirators had been La Coupole, on the boulevard Montparnasse at place Vavin. Political outcasts like the fiery intellectual Leon Trotsky sat at its tables, fanning the hopes of fellow exiles, while Lenin, awaiting his hour, preferred to play chess at a corner table. Military and social collapse in czarist Russia made possible the Communist upheaval and eventual takeover: civil war sent a new swarm of émigrés to the West, particularly to Paris. Meanwhile, the former colony of conspirators was traveling in the opposite direction in triumph, prepared to direct the new Bolshevik regime.

In Paris the revolutionaries were replaced by the aristocracy, but aristocrats stripped of their privileges and wealth. "We were all suddenly poor," remarked the composer Igor Markevitch. "You wrote a check on the Imperial Bank, but no rubles came." Grand dukes worked as headwaiters, Russian princesses were in demand as governesses, czarist colonels became doormen or taxi drivers, like the "Colonel Taxovich" in Nabokov's *Lolita*: "There were thousands of them playing at that fool's trade." La Coupole was still the preferred haunt of displaced Russians, but White refugees now sat brooding in the wicker chairs so recently abandoned by the Reds.

Seventeen-year-old Boris Kochno, born to the vanquished aristocracy, had escaped Russia by way of Constantinople with only a few volumes of poetry as baggage—and a newspaper photograph of Sergei Pavlovich Diaghilev, the ballet impresario. In Paris the young refugee and his mother were taken in by the painter Sudeikin and his wife, Vera, who happened to be close friends of Diaghilev. For Boris, the compelling interest of being in Paris was the hope of meeting the great director of the Ballets Russes.

Sudeikin knew how wary Diaghilev was of having prodigies thrust upon him (although Kochno was neither dancer nor musician, a prodigy in no way other than showing a sensitivity to music and dance, like Diaghilev himself), so he contrived a scheme whereby the young man would simply appear at Diaghilev's hotel with a message from the painter. Since Diaghilev was attracted to young men, Sudeikin sensed he would be charmed by this one. Boris was carefully coached in how to approach the unpredictable *maître*. The young man memorized a list of answers to questions Diaghilev would surely put to him.

At 3 rue Castiglione, between the place Vendôme and the rue de Rivoli, Kochno found the ultrasmart Hôtel Continental. He was surprised to be allowed by the desk clerk to proceed directly to Diaghilev's suite. As it turned out, Diaghilev was expecting a visitor at precisely that hour, so he had left instructions with the front desk to send the party to him without delay. The valet Beppe met Kochno at the door, then told him to wait. In a moment the great man appeared, his thick figure swathed in a dressing gown, a monocle in one eye, a single forelock of white combed back in his dark hair. He welcomed the young man with unexpected warmth.

Boris Kochno was completely disarmed. None of the careful rehearsals by Sudeikin had prepared him for this cordial encounter. As soon as he launched into the first prepared phrase, Diaghilev changed the subject to Russia, bombarding him with questions in Russian about the country from which Kochno had just fled. A persistent nostalgia for Mother Russia was the fate of every émigré, and Diaghilev was not immune to the deprivation felt by his fellow exiles. While Kochno dredged up recollections of Moscow and St. Petersburg and searched for names that would be familiar to the former director of the Imperial Theaters (Diaghilev was of the same social background as Kochno, descended on "the wrong side of the blanket" from Peter the Great, but had lost his post when he fell out of favor with czarist administrators), Diaghilev stood chewing his tongue, as he did when he was deep in thought. He removed his monocle and stared into the middle distance as if suddenly Russia were as near and vivid as the young man standing before him. Abruptly Diaghilev asked Boris his age.

"I have just turned seventeen."

He then took Boris's hand and said, "We will meet again."

At the next meeting Boris Kochno was appointed secretary to the Ballets Russes. The appointment was vague, his duties undefined. Diaghilev seemed to prefer answering the telephone himself, attending to his own mail. Finally the young man found the courage to ask, "But what is my role?" In French Diaghilev informed him, "A secretary simply makes himself indispensable."

From that moment Boris Kochno made himself indispensable to Sergei Pavlovich and to the Russian ballet.

"I am a charlatan first of all" was Diaghilev's description of himself "—but a charlatan with style. In the second place I am a great charmer; and thirdly, I have no end of cheek." Neither musician nor dancer nor painter nor businessman, Diaghilev managed to be all of these, a genius in bringing all the arts together on stage, and in business substituting charm for money.

It was inevitable that the young composer Igor Markevitch should come to the attention of Sergei Diaghilev. Just as Kochno had made his approach to the *maître* through Sudeikin, Markevitch was placed in Diaghilev's line of vision by the intermediary Alexandrine Troussevitch, an undersecretary to the Ballets Russes. When the sixteen-year-old musical prodigy was presented to Diaghilev, the impresario commented: "He has the look of having just been snatched from the nursery"—but in Russian

Backstage after a Ballets Russes performance of Petrouchka: *(l. to r.) Sergei Grigoriev, the dancer Tamara Karsavina, Diaghilev, the by then hopelessly schizophrenic Nijinsky, and the dancer Serge Lifar.*

Diaghilev issued the command: "Tell him to be at the Grand Hotel with his music tomorrow afternoon at five."

Diaghilev did not keep that first appointment with Igor Markevitch. The period of 1927-28 was one of stress and distraction for Diaghilev: he had lost a series of choreographer-dancers by defection and marriage; there were the usual financial pressures, including unpaid hotel bills that he side-stepped by changing hotels. He was not above thrusting the ballerina Alice Nikitina into the corpulent arms of Lord Rothermere in the hope that the newspaper magnate would then be happy to pour funds into the empty coffers of the Ballets Russes—or encouraging the American oil millionaire Gulbenkian in his pursuit of Spessivetseva for the same reason. (Occasionally these matchmaking schemes backfired so thoroughly that Diaghilev lost both ballerina and patron.) The twentieth anniversary of the Ballets Russes approached; a celebration planned by the company filled Diaghilev with horror: anniversaries only reminded him of his own advancing age.

Also at this time the Ballets Russes had revived Stravinsky's *Petrouchka*, with Lifar dancing the role Nijinksy had made famous in the golden age of the Ballets Russes before the war. In a Machiavellian backstage intrigue, Nijinksy had managed to slip out from under Diaghilev's relentless surveillance to marry a member of the troupe, Romola. By 1919 Nijinsky had lapsed into hopeless schizophrenia, unable to dance or even to function without Romola's aid. It was Diaghilev's hope that if Nijinsky could attend the performance of *Petrouchka*—one of his greatest roles— the experience might shock the dancer to a semblance of sanity. While Romola was away in America, Diaghilev arranged personally to bring Nijinksy to the Opéra where *Petrouchka* was being performed. Nijinsky was installed in Diaghilev's own box: the maestro attempted to elicit some sign of recognition from his former protégé, but Nijinsky did not respond—he was unable to react to the ballet or even to the memory of his own great art.

Igor Markevitch was present the night of the *Petrouchka* revival and the Nijinsky-Diaghilev reunion. It would seem an inauspicious occasion to attract Diaghilev's attention, but the young man was included in the backstage entourage when Nijinksy was photographed with Diaghilev, Karsavina, Grigoriev, Benois—only Markevitch, just beyond the range of the camera lens, does not appear in the haunted photograph.

Alexandrine Troussevitch had known all along that Diaghilev would be attracted to the young composer with his striking borzoi profile, strangely resembling another of Diaghilev's lost loves, Leonide Massine. Although he had failed to show up at his first rendezvous with Markevitch, she was familiar with Diaghilev's character: he would assume indifference in the beginning, then play his cat-and-mouse game with a young boy who interested him.

Another appointment, arranged again by Alexandrine, took place at Colombin's, the *chocolatier*. In this elaborate charade of coquetry, Diaghilev plied the young man with sweets, an extravagant *goûter* intended for a nine-year-old. When Diaghilev was ready to hear Markevitch play, he announced, "We are going to Mlle. Chanel's where we can work quietly."

The music salon at Chanel's *hôtel particulier* was smothered in the odor of tuberose. Diaghilev led Igor to the massive polished Steinway and directed him to play a composition. On those first youthful and derivative pieces Markevitch played, Diaghilev commented: "I have told you to prepare Tomorrow for me, and you are thinking only of Yesterday."

Igor was ready with a return: "I'm not interested in yesterday or today but what is forever." The spirit behind this remark caused Diaghilev to study the young man all the more closely through his monocle.

Markevitch then sang several melodies he had written to poems by Apollinaire. "There," conceded Diaghilev, "you have come upon some happy inspirations. In two or three years we must collaborate on something worthwhile." The impresario was looking at his watch as he said this.

Finally Markevitch played his most recent composition, the finale to his *Sinfonietta*. Throughout this presentation Diaghilev pulled at the flesh of his neck, a habitual gesture of thoughtful agitation.

"Why didn't you play that straight off?"

"It is only a fragment," explained Markevitch. "The work is still unfinished."

"Play it for me again."

Markevitch obliged the maestro by repeating the composition.

"But what led you to write music like that?"

The young man then told of his arrival in Paris the year before, his reactions to the swirl of sound and color seen from his window on the square des Batignolles. He described the emotional impact of an afternoon when he sat transfixed by the panorama at the place du Tertre, fascinated by the movement around him—so fascinated that his tram, number 31, passed several times before he thought of returning home. A theory of motion in life that could be translated into music was beginning to dawn on the sixteen-year-old.

Suddenly Diaghilev realized that the light in the salon had faded. "*Mon Dieu*, I have barely time to dress for the theater." He led Markevitch away from the piano and to the stairs. As the impresario and the boy made their way down the grand staircase, a lovely perfumed apparition was just coming up.

"Ma chère Coco," Diaghilev called to her in passing, "here is a child who promises great things."

● ● ●

Through Diaghilev the young Igor Markevitch was given a passe-partout to the patrons and patronesses of French society who supported the Ballets Russes and commissioned works of music from promising composers. After meeting Coco Chanel—then her equally influential friend, Misia Sert—Markevitch made his debut chez "Tante Winnie" at her imposing mansion on the avenue Henri-Martin.

American-born Winnaretta Singer, now the Princesse Edmond de Polignac, was the woman most likely to consider the young man's possibilities and promote his ambitions, for she took particular interest in composers and was herself a musician of ability and sensitivity. The Princesse de Polignac had financed a number of avant-garde compositions and was prepared to do so again. Markevitch was made welcome to her entourage and almost immediately received a generous commission to write his *Partita*, a concertante that brought the young composer his first success.

Invariably Diaghilev drew his young men into the limelight with one hand and jealously clung to them with the other. Igor was the latest in a series of protégés, all of whom were principal dancers except for Kochno and himself. Fokine, Nijinsky, Massine, Dolin, Lifar, and Balanchine were all great talents enlarged by Diaghilev's efforts and influence, but whose lives and devotion he considered his exclusive property. Kochno and Lifar were Diaghilev's trusted palace guards, two constants in his ménage, but the others had found ways of escape into personal and professional independence—two of them, Nijinsky and Massine, intrigued behind Diaghilev's back to form liaisons with young women, members of the watchful magician's own dance company. There was no fear that Winnaretta would capture the affections of young Markevitch: the older woman's amorous interests lay elsewhere.

CHAPTER NINE

A share in the famous Singer sewing-machine fortune elevated Winnaretta Singer to the aristocracy: she was able to marry the Prince Louis de Scey-Montbéliard in what appeared to be a mutually advantageous wedding of wealth and the bluest of blood.

Winnaretta had been brought to Paris at the age of two; as an adolescent she studied with the academic French painter Felix Barrias until music became the love of her life. She installed a massive pipe organ in her town house in Passy so that she might practice the chorale preludes in Bach's *Das Orgelbüchlein*. A first investment in the arts was her purchase of Manet's *La Lecture*; she came to know the artist, who died when Winnaretta was eighteen. She visited the blind Degas in his testy declining years.

Commissions to fin-de-siècle musicians Chabrier and Fauré brought her into contact with Proust and one of Proust's models for the Baron de Charlus in *Remembrance of Things Past*, Robert de Montesquiou.

Winnaretta's quiet opulence, culturally acceptable credentials, and shrewd generosity made her salon the equal of any French social circle in the rarefied air of the faubourg St. Honoré and the faubourg St. Germain. Her acceptance of the prevailing sexual deviations of the day made her equally acceptable to the night-blooming Proustian set. When she discovered that her own lesbian tendencies had overcome any heterosexual interest she might have imagined for Prince Louis de Scey-Montbéliard, the two parties to the misalliance decided on divorce.

While Winnaretta carried on discreet liaisons with Baronne de Meyer, Dame Ethel Smyth, Romaine Brooks, or Violet Trefusis (the former lover of Vita Sackville-West), her brother Paris followed more closely the tradition of the Singer family patriarch. Isaac Merritt Singer had fathered sixteen illegitimate progeny by three common-law wives in addition to his six legal offspring (Winnaretta and Paris among the latter) and provided for all out of the vast profits from his sewing machine. Paris lived openly with Isadora Duncan as her "Lohengrin" and was the father of one of her two children.

Robert de Montesquiou was able to convince Winnaretta that whatever her sexual inclinations, divorce was a great disadvantage to a woman in society. Soon after, she met the Prince Edmond de Polignac through the awkward circumstance of having been "some American woman" who outbid him at an auction for a Monet he coveted. Later they met formally, and the woman with the Dantesque profile and nasal voice the Prince had "vowed to eternal damnation" became an immediate friend and eventually his wife.

The couple shared a love of the arts, especially of music, and together they were a happy complement as host and hostess of the grand salon on avenue Henri-Martin. Since the Prince de Polignac was homosexual, their affections were not at trial in the marriage bed: they could indulge their divergent passions while maintaining respect and genuine affection for one another.

Edmond was fifty-nine when they married, Winnaretta was twenty-eight. The Prince died before the 1920s arrived, and just as Montesquiou had counseled, a widowed Princesse de Polignac became a substantial and altogether legitimate cornerstone of French society. She was homosexual, but in an age and in a city where sexual inversion excited little notice. Her most intimate friends and frequent guests were either homosexual or bisexual, but her salon and the recipients of her largesse were mixed.

While the Duchesse de Clermont-Tonnerre regretted the age of candlelit dinners in gold lamé rooms, when Proust drank seventeen cups of coffee in her drawing room to calm his asthma, entertainments chez Polignac be-

gan to take precedence over the fading salons of the old guard. The rituals
and privileges of the aristocratic rich were an anachronism in a democratic
age. A global conflict that had begun with the assassination of a prince
and ended with the defeat of a kaiser and the overthrow of a czar had
created a renewed sense of *liberté-égalité-fraternité*. The *beau monde* now
included Picasso, Colette, Stravinsky, and Cocteau—a mélange with origins in music hall, poet's garret, and atelier. The Princesse de Polignac
spared neither money nor taste nor ingenuity in maintaining a guest list of
distinction, but not just distinction of lineage. Artistic accomplishment was
as important a *laissez-passer* to the music salon on avenue Henri-Martin
as blood rank or money.

There were exceptions to Tante Winnie's hospitality. When Vera Sudeikin asked her why she never invited Chanel, Winnaretta replied, "I don't
entertain my tradespeople"—but the real reason may have been that Chanel was a competing patron with her own salon in the same Right Bank
milieu. Or the Princesse might be reluctant to support members of rival
salons—such as Virgil Thomson, who was a favorite of Gertrude Stein—
but only as a diplomatic precaution after a careful assessment of territorial
rights. In her own domain she was preeminent, "the irreplaceable Mae-
cenas," as Poulenc called her.

The twentieth-century revival of baroque music had not yet come about
except in the music room of Winnaretta's mansion. It seemed to her the
days of the great orchestral works were over, so she encouraged composers
like Stravinsky to write works for small orchestra that could be performed
in her own salon.

Winnaretta loved ancient music, but she was not indifferent to the new.
At the turn of the century she had made possible Ravel's *Pavane pour une
infante défunte*. Tryouts for the avant-garde ballets *Le Renard* and *Les
Noces* were held at Winnaretta's soirées before Diaghilev arranged for formal rehearsals on a theater stage. Some of the most advanced compositions of Manuel de Falla, Igor Stravinsky, and the young French musicians
known as Les Six were performed in the Polignac music room. Through a
member of Les Six, Darius Milhaud, Winnaretta met Cole Porter, whom
she commissioned to write a jazz ballet, *Within the Quota*.

Winnaretta's milieu represented a cross-pollination of socialites, syba-
rites, musicians, balletomanes, and the sexually restless. Their rivalries,
feuds, and outbursts of temperament appeared to leave the famous hostess
unperturbed. In truth, she was extremely sensitive to public scandal. Her
own outré behavior took place offstage, in the town house on avenue Henri-
Martin or at the Palazzo Polignac in Venice.

Dedicated to creating an interest in baroque music, the Princesse inevitably sought out the leading exponent of the eighteenth-century repertoire, Wanda Landowska. The Polish harpsichordist sorely tested
Winnaretta's forbearance by having an affair—a seduction for the love of

seduction—with Violet Trefusis, now in exile in Paris and Tante Winnie's own favorite of the moment. Here was a formidable challenge to Winnaretta's innate diplomacy and generosity of spirit—but generosity and diplomacy did prevail. The salon and its princess survived all subterranean intrigues and surface outrages. Possibly the spice of sexual adventuring lent an extra ingredient to that recipe for patronage the Princesse de Polignac subscribed to: social standing, independent wealth, and a need to know and sustain the creatively gifted.

Behind the glacial façade of a Victorian *grande dame*, Winnaretta displayed an unexpected wit. When a rival patron of impeccable bloodlines but declining fortune complained, "My name is as good as Polignac," Winnaretta replied: "Not at the bottom of a check."

If the spirit of Lesbos pervaded the important salons of the 1920s, the lesbian aura was never more evident than at 20 rue Jacob, in the faubourg St.-Germain. Surely the most uninhibited of the Sapphic muses was Natalie Barney, a wealthy American who had resided in France since the turn of the century. Natalie was attractive to men as well as to a veritable harem of women—her great mass of hair held loosely with pins and liable to flow freely as the pins fell. White was her color: soft white flowing gowns by Lanvin and Schiaparelli, a white fox fur piece draped from her shoulder.

As a child, Natalie had hovered in the vicinity of the studio where her adored mother, the portraitist Alice Pike Barney, painted some of the loveliest ladies of Washington society and where Natalie was once called upon to massage the stiff muscles of a weary sitter. This was her first erotic experience: she became adept at the art of massage, her touch described as hypnotic. "Men have skin," Natalie wrote, "but women have flesh— flesh that takes and gives light."

Natalie was so fascinated by her beautiful mother that she lay at night in torment until she received her bedtime kiss, a scene reminiscent of Proust's nightly anticipation of that same maternal benediction and prelude to sleep. Whatever the origin of her deviant sexuality, Natalie became a confirmed and unswerving lesbian, flamboyant in her unorthodoxy. Because of her daily riding in the Bois de Boulogne dressed in masculine attire, with black bow tie and bowler, she became known as the Amazon, a title she assumed with pride.

Like the Princesse de Polignac, Natalie Barney was one of the principal personages of the Belle Epoque who then emerged from the chrysalis of wartime France to flourish in the same grand style during les Années Folles. Also like Winnaretta, Natalie was as French as an American can be. She was perfectly bilingual. Her verses—love poems for the most part—were written in French, for she spoke and wrote in French more often than in English. Literature was the dominant note at Natalie's afternoons, rather than the music that permeated Winnaretta's mansion on the opposite bank.

Natalie cultivated French writers almost exclusively until the wave of literary Americans arrived in France. She then had the privilege of introducing one culture to the other.

It was Ezra Pound's interest in the French recluse Rémy de Gourmont that initially brought him to the door of 20 rue Jacob. In exchange for knowing Gourmont through Miss Barney, Pound brought English and American writers to Natalie's salon. James Joyce, ever on the alert for a possible benefactor, allowed himself to be introduced to Miss Barney by Pound, though he detested salons in particular and society in general. (Natalie was of no material help—she offered her *convives* a generous hospitality and a background of culture, seldom cash—but Joyce met others in her circle who were helpful in the way he most needed.)

Affecting a cape, boots, and cocked hat—or dressed as a shepherd, Renée Vivien as her shepherdess—Natalie would take part in the performances at her own soirées. She arranged for Sapphic pageants or poetry readings, her guests in separate sets: those who came purely for lesbian frolics, those who sought culture exclusively. Transvestite playlets or masquerade balls took place in the drawing room until architects warned Natalie that the floor of her 300-year-old mansion might collapse. On mild summer evenings the gatherings were held outdoors in the rear garden sequestered by the walls of houses on rue Visconti and rue de Seine: "a curtain of ivy over the walls, a huge tree in the courtyard which hung over the house—a lovely rambling garden with its eighteenth-century temple," as described by Natalie's intimate friend Bettina Bergery. The mock Greek temple was called the Temple à l'Amitié, a Mediterranean motif suggestive of the isle of Lesbos and altogether appropriate to the pageants performed on its steps.

Although Mata Hari's prewar belly dances were presented to an all-female audience in the enclosed courtyard, not all the garden rites were restricted to so exclusive a gathering. To a mixed audience Paul Valéry might read his *La Jeune Parque* or Colette preview her 1922 play *La Vagabonde*, with Paul Poiret playing opposite her. Before Virgil Thomson fell in with Gertrude Stein, he was a member of Natalie's salon, and played and sang his own music at the Temple à l'Amitié.

Refreshment at these entertainments was likely to be tea, with cake and sandwiches—only at the end of the Twenties did Natalie see fit to serve champagne. She finally conceded to gin and whiskey "when the Americans came," but drink was not the object of attending Miss Barney's afternoons or soirées. She was at home with those whom society generally excludes: sexual rebels and cultural revolutionaries. The house and its quaint garden—where little sun penetrated, the fountain choked with sea-green plants—was a very special sanctuary for a varied collection of soul mates. Sylvia Beach might gently tease Paul Valéry for his need to frequent Miss Barney's salon, but the poet admitted he wanted to hear the muted sounds of distinguished repartee after a day's grueling thought work, and the friendly clink of teacups in a crowded drawing room.

Whatever good works were accomplished at 20 rue Jacob, the guiding deity of Miss Barney's establishment was Eros. Natalie could never resist a beautiful face and form: she claimed to have been the lover of over forty women—and without being pressed would name names. In her *Souvenirs indiscrets* Natalie tells of her first glimpse of the demimondaine Liane de Pougy riding in her carriage in the Bois de Boulogne. Immediately Natalie determined to seduce one of the most famous courtesans of the Belle Epoque—to save Liane, as she expressed it, from a life of degradation at the hands of men. Against all odds, the young American upstart did seduce the worldly Parisienne: the two women enjoyed a clandestine love affair while concurrently Liane followed the métier of *grande horizontale* for her socially prominent gentlemen.

Another of Natalie's early conquests was the lovely, ephemeral Renée Vivien. Theirs was one of the grand passions of the period just before the Great War, but Natalie was an inconstant lover. Renée suffered from what she considered a series of betrayals. She died, it was said, of love for Natalie—but it would seem that Renée Vivien was already marked for death before she met Natalie, languishing in the midst of life, gradually expiring from an anorexia of the spirit.

The American painter Romaine Brooks was another of Natalie's on-and-off favorites for many years: theirs was as close as any to a stable and continuing relationship, perhaps a reminder of the intimacy and excitement of Alice Pike Barney's atelier—for Romaine was also a portrait painter, specializing in portraits of women. Romaine had weathered a torrid love affair with the Princesse de Polignac and with Natalie managed to make the transition from lover to intimate friend.

Although Romaine detested large gatherings, she consented to serve as cohostess at Natalie's Friday afternoons, or at a Persian dinner (a small boy out of sight behind the skylight scattered flower petals on the guests below), while Natalie flirted with every pretty young thing in sight. Romaine affected masculine dress, her medium-cropped hair tucked into a modified top hat. She painted Natalie in a variety of elegantly transvestite costumes. Besides appearing in Romaine's portraits, Natalie was the model for Evangeline Musset in Djuna Barnes's *Ladies Almanach* and Valerie Seymour in Radclyffe Hall's long-suppressed *Well of Loneliness*.

When Oscar Wilde's niece Dolly appeared at one of Natalie Barney's masques disguised as her uncle, Janet Flanner remarked that her sad equine face was the image of Oscar Wilde's, looking "both important and earnest." Dolly resembled her uncle in other respects, breaking the sexual taboos of the age, risking all in compromising entanglements. She, too, fell in love with the Amazon of rue Jacob.

Despite her consuming passion for women, Natalie found time for support of art and artists. As a reaction against the male-dominated Académie Française, Natalie founded an Académie des Femmes to offer support to women in pursuit of literary careers.

Another of her projects was establishing bursaries to subsidize individual writers, like Valéry. Ezra Pound suggested a venture to relieve T. S. Eliot of his onerous job at Barclay's Bank so that he might devote full time to poetry. Miss Barney was to offer the initial donation, the remaining funds to be subscribed through a society known as Bel Esprit. According to Ernest Hemingway, who was recruited away from Gertrude Stein's rival salon, you either had *bel esprit* or you did not. Pound solicited Hemingway's help in collecting subscriptions. The imprint on the society's stationery was a logo of the Temple à l'Amitié in Natalie Barney's garden, symbol of the spirit behind the enterprise. Hemingway accepted his fundraising obligation with little enthusiasm, but he admired Pound and was willing to assist in the altruistic scheme despite a supercilious attitude about Greek temples in Left Bank gardens and saving poets from banks. When the society collapsed (Eliot escaped his bank job by other means, with the help of an English patron), Hemingway took the money he had put aside for Bel Esprit to the racetrack at Enghien, where he wagered all on a drugged horse in a steeplechase, and lost.

Of Natalie Barney's own verse, Ezra Pound gave mixed notices. Her writing, he thought, was the product of mental laziness, filled with unfinished sentences and broken paragraphs, lit by an occasional sublime comment: the style was elaborately Edwardian. Pound reviewed her 1920 *Pensées d'une Amazone* as a favor but got at the heart of the Amazon's weakness by quoting one of her own lines: "Having got out of life, oh having got out of it perhaps more than it contained."

But Natalie Barney devoted far more energy and enthusiasm to her collection of *intimes* than to her collections of verse. She was completely loyal to her friends, and all forgiving. When Paul Valéry became a member of the Académie Française in 1925, and once in that exalted circle dropped out of Natalie's, she resisted the impulse to comment. Besides, there were so many others for whom she could play hostess: Ford Madox Ford, Djuna Barnes, Anna de Noailles, Sherwood Anderson, Isadora Duncan, Sinclair Lewis, Marie Laurencin—and once, briefly, Marcel Proust. The journalist Morrill Cody said that visiting Natalie Barney's salon may have been a bore but was part of one's education. With his lips poised over Natalie's fingers, Anatole France murmured: "I kiss your hand with sacred terror," but André Gide declined even that formal gesture. "Miss Barney," said Gide, "is one of the few people one ought to see—if one had time."

CHAPTER TEN

By 1924 Dada was dead. At the Galerie Pierre in 1925, Surrealism was launched as the seminal movement of the last half of the Twenties. The show was a great success for the shy Catalan Joan Miró, whose painted dreams set against a lunar landscape were representative of the strange new art.

The culmination of Miró's prewar Montroig period was a large painting entitled *The Farm*, which failed to interest dealers but acquired an underground reputation of its own when it was hung in a Montparnasse café. In 1925 the poet Evan Shipman hoped to buy it, but then learned that his friend Ernest Hemingway wanted to give *The Farm* to Hadley as a birthday gift. Shipman offered to roll dice for the privilege of buying the painting, and Hemingway won—though he did not have the purchase price of 5,000 francs. Meanwhile, the dealer Jacques Viot had received another offer, three times as high as the asking price, but Miró honored the original option to buy. In a frantic scramble to borrow the money, Hemingway and friends went from the Dingo to the Dôme to the Closerie de Lilas soliciting loans. Even Jimmy Charters, the amiable barman of the Dingo, contributed. Thus Ernest succeeded in buying *The Farm*, bearing it home to Hadley in a kind of victory parade: "In the open taxi the wind caught the big canvas as though it were a sail and we made the driver crawl along. At home we hung it and everyone looked at it and was very happy."

For Hemingway, Miró had put into *The Farm* feelings about Spain that he was trying to express in his own attempt at a first novel. He had just come from the celebration of the feast of San Fermín at Pamplona where he had introduced a circle of Montparnasse cronies to bullfighting, just as he had been introduced to the sport by Gertrude Stein. His companions included the humorist Donald Ogden Stewart, who had recently arrived in Paris with sufficient American dollars—in a new surge of inflated value against the failing franc—to underwrite trip expenses for wealthy-impoverished Pat Campbell and Lady Duff Twysden. Truly wealthy Harold Loeb paid his own way. The five friends were to become the principal fictional characters in *The Sun Also Rises*, Hemingway himself as the model for Jake Barnes, the narrator and protagonist. The author exploited the tense relationships and outright hostilities the trip inspired, documenting the fiesta and earlier sequences of Montparnasse life in a fresh and unadorned style that would be the cornerstone of his reputation. Reactions by the living prototypes of the characters in the novel were mixed. Stewart discovered his own quips issuing from a fictional counterpart, Bill Gorton, but was probably less amused to be depicted as an amiable alcoholic. As Brett, Lady Duff Twysden's words and mannerisms were just as carefully recorded, but her complaint was "I never even slept with the bloody bullfighter." In his minor and fatuous role as Braddocks, Ford Madox Ford must have been dismayed, but he kept his annoyance to himself.

Harold Loeb was made miserable by the portrait of himself as Robert Cohn. After he had done so much to further Hemingway's career—admired and respected him as a man and as a writer—to be mirrored as a weak, vain, shallow-minded romantic was a betrayal that soured the remainder of his young life. Hemingway had needed a character to represent everything the new code of the lost generation opposed—if not a villain, at least a disagreeable catalyst-figure—and Harold Loeb was his ruthless choice.

When Hemingway showed the first draft of the novel to Gertrude Stein, it was little more than travelogue and dialogue. "Start over again, and concentrate," said Miss Stein. Hemingway rewrote *The Sun Also Rises* following Miss Stein's advice. Gertrude Stein and Sherwood Anderson were said to have formed Hemingway, "and they were both a little proud and a little ashamed of the work of their minds."

With the left-over energy from having created his remarkable first novel, Hemingway set about writing a lightweight parody called *The Torrents of Spring*. The spoof was written in ten days and was meant as an unflattering takeoff of Sherwood Anderson's style in the 1925 novel *Dark Laughter*. It was the Hemingway method of casting off Gertrude Stein as well, since Anderson was "part of her apparatus." Never again would Gertrude Stein and Ernest Hemingway sit together—he at her feet, she below the Picasso portrait of her—discussing issues literary over crystal glasses of pure fruit *alcools* distilled by the shadow-companion Alice.

1925 was a year of sudden new liaisons. Kitty Cannell—Harold Loeb's fiancée, another maligned character in *The Sun Also Rises*—ran into Pauline Pfeiffer, then working for the couturier Mainbocher. Pauline was leaving Paris to join the Hemingways in Austria for a skiing holiday *à trois* that surprised Kitty, who remembered when Pauline shared her distaste and suspicion of Ernest. The distaste, over a number of months, had turned to love.

Another beginning affair was the burgeoning romance between Chanel and the Duke of Westminster, known as Bend'or. The Duke, reputed to be the wealthiest man in England, was in Paris to escape the ignominy of his divorce trial, which featured a detailed indictment of his extramarital episode with one of many mistresses at the Hôtel de Paris in Monte Carlo.

Chanel could not have failed to notice the "amiable giant" Bend'or lurking about the Théâtre des Champs-Elysées during the rehearsals for *Le Train Bleu* the year before, but at first she was too occupied with costuming to respond openly to Bend'or's interest—an extravagant courtship that included such gestures as sending out-of-season fruit and masses of

Feline and provocative, Josephine Baker came to epitomize the primitive sensuality of the Jazz Age. Her pet leopard, Chiquita, was part of her legend.

flowers, with gems scattered among the strawberries, a diamond hidden in the petals of a rose.

Le Train Bleu was another concoction by Cocteau, this time depicting the seaside sporting life of the Côte d'Azur, with curtain and décor by Picasso and music by Milhaud. Chanel was obliged to create something altogether new to accommodate the gymnast-choreography: she succeeded so admirably that a vogue for sportswear came out of the ballet.

By 1925 Coco Chanel was at the peak of her popularity: this was the year of the Chanel-inspired "little black dress," mass produced in the way of automobiles or, as *Vogue* put it, "the Ford signed by Chanel." Coco was seen at the Longchamp and Auteuil races in the company of the Duke of Westminster and went with him to Deauville for sailing parties on his yacht, *The Flying Cloud*. Bend'or had become the perfect replacement for her one great love, Boy Capel.

Another Duke, but of the Broadway stage musical, Vernon Duke—or Dukelsky, his family name when he left Russia for the United States—was introduced to Diaghilev by Chanel's friend Misia Sert. "Ah," said Diaghilev, "a good-looking composer, how rare." He was obliquely referring to his two adopted "sons," Stravinsky and Prokofiev. When he asked the young man's age, he was delighted to learn that Duke was only twenty. "I don't like men over twenty-five. They lose their adolescent charm and sleep with any woman who gives them the nod. Oh, so you can still blush?"

Despite Diaghilev's horror of jazz and its rhythms assimilated by American composers like Duke, he accepted a Vernon Duke score for the 1925 ballet *Zéphyr et Flore*, presented at the Théâtre de la Gaîté-Lyrique with choreography by Massine and sets by Georges Braque. Massine had just returned to the Ballets Russes under the cloud of having deserted Diaghilev for the ballerina Savina and having formed his own rival company. Diaghilev no longer permitted Massine to call him Serge, but Duke was adopted as Diaghilev's "third son." The filial tie was short-lived. Vernon Duke had his one and only chance with the Ballets Russes for his music to *Zéphyr et Flore*: he was never asked to write another ballet.

Diaghilev resisted all other efforts to allow the American idiom to become incorporated in music for his ballet productions. When Cole Porter was presented to Diaghilev by the Princesse de Polignac, the impresario deliberately avoided the subject of musical comedy. George Gershwin was in and out of Paris, and he also approached Diaghilev, who promised to "think about" using his *Rhapsody in Blue* as a ballet score—with no real intention of doing so.

Vernon Duke was in the audience for a performance of *La Revue Nègre*, the 1925 black import from the United States, when he saw a familiar figure slumped in hiding, inadequately disguised behind a pair of dark glasses, several rows behind his own. The impresario, who professed to despise the growing influence of jazz and the increasing horde of blacks invading Paris, could not resist the sensational Afro-American spectacle. Duke recognized Diaghilev by his "chinchilla" streak, the dyed white forelock of hair.

Even those who were unable to attend performances of *La Revue Nègre* were aware of the star at the Théâtre des Champs-Elysées, Josephine Baker. The slim and sensual mulatto from St. Louis appeared on a poster by Paul Colin that was plastered on every kiosk in Paris. Her slicked-down coiffure—with spit curl like a question mark upside down on her forehead—was imitated by whites and became a verb in French: *Bakerfixer*. Poiret designed a gown for Mademoiselle Ba-kair that brought pink briefly back in fashion, a gown so widely copied it became known as *la robe Joséphine*: her caramel coloring was the inspiration for the sun-tanning craze at Deauville and on the Riviera. The flat accents of Josephine's Americanized French, so repellent to Parisians, were suddenly chic.

At her first performance, slithering snakelike on the back of a huge black performer, Josephine and the jazz dancers of *La Revue* created the first shock waves of the new phenomenon. The primitive rhythms and unrestrained dance movements were a recall to Rousseau's glorification of the noble savage. Black was the color; jazz was suddenly the sound. When *La Revue Nègre* opened, the Jazz Age came to Paris, and the new Pied Piper's magic flute was Sidney Bechet's clarinet.

An exhibition of the new dance the "Char-less-ton" attracted unprecedented crowds to Claridge's on the Champs-Elysées, just as the Charleston Boys were appearing at the Mimosa. So many Parisians wanted to learn the Black Bottom that Orrea Waskae, "Colored American *danseuse*," was teaching the dance to a class of sixty French dancing masters. The traditional *thé-dansant* became Americanized to *un dancing*; it was no longer chic to attend the *bals musettes* in the working-class districts of Paris: the expatriate colonies now patronized black cabarets like *Le Bal Nègre*, on the rue Blomet.

Zclli's and Le Boeuf sur le Toit were soon competing with a new nightclub, Bricktop's, where expatriate Americans mixed with denizens of La Butte, French café society, and celebrities of several worlds. Bricktop herself—the dusky Ada Smith, who dyed her hair orange to touch up her coloring—knew all her regulars by their first names. In Paris, black and white mixed as casually as bohemian and aristocrat. The fashionable invited the black performers Snakehips and Whispering Jack Smith to their parties, or Baby Darling from *La Revue Nègre*, with her new husband, Mr. Legitimus. Cole Porter caused few eyebrows to raise when he invited Bricktop to accompany him to the exclusive Paris Opera Ball, Bricktop wearing the same Molyneux gown as Princess Marina of Greece.

Bricktop was the renowned hostess to the Franco-American cabaret set, and Josephine Baker was the supreme *vedette* of that world. To the French the uninhibited Josephine, with her gold-painted fingernails and celebrated tutu made of bananas, was a creature Baudelaire had invented, or as Anna de Noailles called her, "a pantheress with gold claws"—a symbol of primitive sensuality. For Americans she was the Folies phenomenon, descending on stage from a feathered ball with mirrored interior, half nude, the star of Jazz Age Paris.

Josephine soon learned how to exploit the legend, on stage and off. One theatrical affectation was to keep a snake she called Kiki as part of her ménage, often enough coiled around her neck, a device "to separate the men from the boys." She went walking with her pet leopard Chiquita— the beast's collar changed daily to match the costume of its mistress—on the Champs-Elysées.

During the jazz phase of the Twenties, patrons of Mitchell's, Florence's, or Zelli's risked an encounter with the criminal element of Montmartre: purse snatching and mugging were on the increase. For protection, many black musicians and performers carried arms.

At Florence's in 1928, Mike McKendrick and Sidney Bechet got into an argument, then carried their grievance into the street. Both drew pistols. In the gun battle that followed, neither man was wounded, but a passing Frenchwoman was struck by a stray bullet. Bechet was condemned to eleven months in prison; after serving part of his sentence, he was released, then expelled from France.

The field for jazz players was narrowing, and the welcome was not as ready as in 1925. As black musicians began to monopolize the nightclub circuit, the French imposed countermeasures to assure that half the members of any band would be French nationals. Since jazz was an American phenomenon, French jazzmen were impossible to find. A way of dealing with the new regulations was to employ French musicians to sit in during performances, without playing a note. Those clubs that could afford two bands arranged for separate French and American groups to play alternate sets.

Jazz pianist Henry Crowder came to Europe just as the tighter restrictions and declining employment for ensemble players became prevalent. He had escaped a hardscrabble existence in the American South by working his way North, playing piano at YMCAs—or scrubbing floors, washing dishes, when no other employment turned up—then joined a black jazz quartet known as the Alabamians. A small-time manager got the Alabamians a series of short engagements in Europe, but the gigs trickled out in Venice, and the manager disappeared. While Henry was stranded in Venice, he met Nancy Cunard, who at this stage of her free-floating life had taken up the banner of black rights. She was plainspoken in her defense of racial equality and was able to contribute large sums of money, as well as genuine sympathy, to the cause. Her interest in Henry was no doubt influenced by the color of his skin, but only in part. Nancy, with the insouciant defiance of the rich, took Henry as a lover.

This was 1928: Fascism was on the rise in Italy—the mood in Venice did not match the classic tolerance of France. Wherever Henry Crowder and Nancy Cunard were seen together, black and white fingers interlaced, the shocked Italians reacted. Restaurant personnel were hostile or blatantly insulting: the manager at Henry's hotel suggested that he leave. Finally Nancy took Henry to Paris, where the climate for mixed couples was far more relaxed.

Because of her striking appearance, and by deliberately flaunting her independence, Nancy Cunard had been attracting attention since her adolescent years. Nancy was heiress to the Cunard Line millions of her father, Sir Bache Cunard, and his California-born wife—twenty years younger than himself—Maude Alice Burke, Lady Cunard. When Nancy decided to ignore the mores imposed by upper-class British society, she was following the lead of her mother, who had fallen in love with the conductor Thomas Beecham and lived with him in London.

Nancy was a beauty in the Jazz Age mold: extremely slim, elegant, and to all appearances reserved. William Carlos Williams described her as "straight as any stick, emaciated, holding her head erect, not particularly animated, her blue eyes untroubled, inviolable in her virginity of pure act." Despite the demeanor of distant ice maiden Nancy sometimes assumed, she was sexually attractive to men and women and was herself attracted to both sexes.

During the war Nancy made a single attempt at conventional life by marrying Sydney Fairbairn, the dashing young military officer of the moment. Lady Cunard opposed the alliance, and the marriage may have been as much an act of defiance as an act of love. While Fairbairn was away at the front, Nancy realized that she could not endure the role of wife to him or to any man. She fled to the South of France, ostensibly to recover from a bout of Spanish influenza, but at the same time to agonize over her rash marriage. At the end of World War I Nancy announced to the demobilized officer that she could not remain as his wife: the couple separated but did not divorce until 1925.

While expressing disdain for all that the Twenties cult represented, Nancy Cunard was the archetypal Twenties woman. She bobbed and shingled her hair, wore the short skirts and boyish fashions as if she were the principal model for the new mode; she could be seen in all the stylish cafés and nightclubs with a changing sequence of escorts, extending her long, slim cigarette holder like a symbol of rank. It was Nancy who paid for the drinks, and she could drink throughout a night of party going with no apparent effect. "I never saw her drunk," admitted William Carlos Williams, "—I can imagine she was never quite sober."

A characteristic of the age was the need felt by the wealthy to participate directly in the arts. At the urging of Wyndham Lewis and Ezra Pound—

for reasons more to do with the Cunard millions than the Cunard talent—
Nancy began to write poems. An older mentor, the author George Moore,
encouraged her as well; as a result, a first collection of poems appropri-
ately entitled *Outlaws* came out in 1921.

Moore, rumored to be Lady Cunard's lover before Thomas Beecham
and to have been Nancy's natural father, was as attracted to the daughter
as to the mother. When Moore visited Nancy in Paris, he begged her: "Tell
me about your lovers." On another occasion the elderly gentleman asked
Nancy to show herself to him in the nude—"At least let me see your naked
back." Nancy obliged to that extent, and Moore was able to describe Nancy's back in his 1926 novel, *Ulick and Soracha*.

Whether in fiction or in life, Nancy Cunard became the prototypical I-
don't-care girl of the 1920s. Wealth made it possible for her to lead exactly
the life she chose: to support the talented, to buy her way into print, to
purchase an impecunious lover. Though she invariably picked up the check
at Zelli's, enjoyed Maxim's and Lapérouse, she was more at home at the
obscure demimonde establishment, La Perle. Dinner at La Perle was a ple-
beian 20 francs per person, the food excellent; but it was the outlaw ambience that drew Nancy. Here the working prostitutes convened before they
went on duty. The restaurant was a display case of *papillons de nuit*: Nancy,
a butterfly of another species, was equally attracted to the flame.

Like so many of her set, Nancy was caught up in the fad for Africana
that swept Paris. Fetishes and tribal masks appeared alongside the Surrealist paintings in her collection. She began wearing primitive earrings and
pendants, her slender arms encased in bracelets of carved wood and ivory.
She loved to dance to the new syncopation imported from black America.
Her favorite night spot was the Plantation, with its mural of a Mississippi
steamboat and chalk drawings of darkies on a blackboard. It was at the
Plantation that Crowder got his first job when Nancy brought him back
to Paris, an ironic comment on his situation.

Crowder maintained that Nancy's wealth was not the reason he lived with
her; nevertheless, the Cunard fortune was an irresistible buffer in the pianist's insubstantial existence. In the backlash that followed the Bechet-
McKendrick shooting incident—Crowder had worked with McKendrick—
gigs were scarce, and Crowder was out of work for months at a time.

Nancy may have preferred Crowder's dependence on her. Despite her
generosity in public, she kept her lover on a tight tether, with enough cash
to play craps with his fellow musicians at the Flea Pit. Meanwhile, Nancy
continued her own liberated life of flirtation and sensation and managed
to outrage Crowder more by her lesbian escapades than her affairs with
other men, black and white. Wealth was the means to Nancy's flamboyant
independence, but a way of keeping Crowder from emancipation. She
seemed to want to own a black lover as part of her collection of African

art. "Be more African!" she shrieked at him, and on one occasion struck him across the face with her armload of African bracelets.

The deteriorating situation improved abruptly when Nancy founded the Hours Press in 1928. Here was a way for her to pour energy and time into the arts, as well as money; and by making Crowder her assistant, solve his chronic unemployment. William Bird had given up the Three Mountains Press and was willing to sell his seventeenth-century handpress to Nancy for £300. Just as Virginia Woolf had warned her, out of her own experience with the Hogarth Press, hand-printing was dirty, tiring, and frustrating work, yet the Hours Press turned out to be the most satisfying endeavor Nancy had ever attempted. Not only did she achieve personal fulfillment by learning to become a master printer, but she even managed to turn a profit: the Hours Press doubled her investment within a year. Her old friend George Moore helped launch the press by offering the reprint of his novel *Peronnik the Fool*, and Ezra Pound submitted the unlikely treatise *The Probable Music of Beowulf*. It was difficult to imagine where the profit came from with such items as Norman Douglas's *Report on the Pumice Stone Industry of the Lipari Islands*. The Douglas *Report* represented Nancy's debut as a printer-publisher, and in fact the task of setting the paper in II-point type was a disciplined way of learning the printing trade.

Henry Crowder seemed to share Nancy's enthusiasm for the Hours Press, but when she once too often flung at him the taunt: "Why don't you get a job?" he surprised himself, and Nancy, with the reply "I will." He found a job at Le Bateau Ivre, a way back to jazz piano and a way out of Nancy's world.

CHAPTER ELEVEN

In Harry Crosby's diary were the words, "We who have known war must never forget war. And that is why I have a picture of a soldier's corpse nailed to the door of my library." Crosby was determined to remember not only the war but his own close brush with death on the battlefield: dying was the morbid preoccupation at the center of his life.

He had been one of the gentleman-volunteers for ambulance service in World War I: for his heroism under fire and miraculous survival from an exploding shell, Crosby was awarded the Croix de Guerre. He returned to the United States from wartime France with his citation, a hip flask given to him by his buddies in the Norton-Harjes Ambulance Corps, and a permanently scarred psyche.

It was assumed Harry Crosby would go into banking or take his place alongside other returning veterans of the privileged class, with a seat on the New York Stock Exchange, for he was born into the highest circle of Boston's financial élite: his uncle was J. P. Morgan. But Harry was the family romantic—or ne'er-do-well, as the van Rensselaer-Morgan clan would have it—and he immediately fell in love with a likeminded and rebellious socialite, Polly Peabody. Polly was married, with two children: the scandal of an adulterous liaison would have to be avoided; therefore, J. P. Morgan arranged to have Harry Crosby employed by the family bank in Paris, safely removed from the attractions of Mrs. Peabody. Paris was exactly where Harry most wanted to go—but not particularly to the Morgan bank and certainly not without Polly.

In May 1922 Harry took up the tedious role of apprentice bank manager at number 14 place Vendôme, conveniently located opposite the Ritz Bar. He continued to maintain a long-distance courtship of Polly Peabody through letters: if the family believed the charms of Paris would obliterate Harry's fascination with Polly, they knew nothing of the young man's determined and obsessive nature.

To escape the monotony of high finance, Harry spent as much time as possible at the bar of the Ritz. He lived at the Hôtel Metropolitan on nearby rue Cambon, but for a time he kept a room at the Hôtel Régina. Polly Peabody managed to get away from Boston for a brief clandestine holiday with Harry in this sanctuary on the place des Pyramides.

Meanwhile, he led the free-spending, freewheeling existence of a rake abroad. He was as often at the baccarat tables as he was at his desk at the Morgan bank. He organized a reckless horse-cab race down the Champs-Elysées and came in second. From the windows of the Ritz he tossed champagne bottles at the column on the place Vendôme.

When he could no longer support the enforced separation, Harry boarded the *Aquitania*, bound for New York. Neither Harry's family nor Polly's husband could prevent the inevitable. Peabody agreed to a divorce: Harry and Polly were married and returned to live in Paris in a flat on the rue des Belles-Feuilles in the same neighborhood as the Princesse de Polignac.

Polly's two children from the previous marriage posed a large problem: like many expatriates, Harry could not abide the presence of children or accept a mundane role as parent. He might on an impulse offer six-year-old Polleen a glass of champagne; otherwise, he expected the children to be kept out of his sight. For Polly, this domestic purdah was impossible to maintain. Once when Harry found her playing with the children on the floor just as he entered the flat accompanied by friends, he was so outraged that he steered his friends outside, then disappeared for days. When he did return—with no word spoken about his absence—he presented his wife with an expensive negligée, as much a hint of what he expected of her as a peace offering.

During the months Harry worked at the bank, he often paddled to work in a canoe. The Crosbys had moved from the flat on rue des Belles-Feuilles to an apartment building on the Ile St. Louis, and there he kept the craft tied up at the quai d'Orléans. Mornings he and Polly set off paddling against the barge traffic until they arrived at the Right Bank end of the pont de la Concorde. Harry would step out of the canoe at the quai des Tuileries and walk through the gardens to the place Vendôme while his wife returned upstream to the Ile St. Louis.

The code by which Harry Crosby lived was never regret, never compromise, be in all things extravagant. His actions were determined by impulse: he must seize the moment at any cost; to hold back was to die of ennui.

On the last day of 1923 he bade the Morgan bank adieu. Banking was a denial of his need for total independence of action; he would answer to no one but himself henceforth. In Harry's wide and eclectic reading he had come across a statement by Schopenhauer that he believed applied to himself: "Social rules are made by normal people for normal people, and the man of genius is fundamentally abnormal." Harry knew he was fundamentally abnormal and thought that he might, through writing, discover his genius. Meanwhile, he and Polly could live on the interest from his share of the family wealth.

As Harry's need to make himself into a poet grew into an obsession, Polly began to seek her own place in the arts. She changed her name to Caresse and studied sculpture with Antoine Bourdelle at the Académie de la Grande Chaumière, where she met the other artist-teachers Noguchi, Léger, and Giacometti. Harry was making his friends among the literary set: he went to the races at Chantilly with Hemingway and Dos Passos (both veterans of ambulance corps duty, like himself), and he wrote in his diary, "I would rather have been Joyce than any man alive." Another time he confessed: "Today saw Joyce three times... and worked in me the same emotion as when Lindbergh arrived."

Harry's older cousin was Walter Berry, a long-standing resident of Paris in the exclusive faubourg St. Germain quarter. Walter Berry was a bona fide member of Parisian society that included only the most distinguished Americans, or those with sufficient wealth and a title, like the Princesse de Polignac. Berry was fond of scapegrace Harry and was something of a foster father to him. Alone among members of the family, he encouraged Harry to abandon banking to become a poet.

Walter van Rensselaer Berry lived in an eighteenth-century town house at 53 rue de Varenne, where Edith Wharton had resided before she settled in her country house outside Paris. Berry had been a close friend and companion of Miss Wharton: it was believed that they would surely marry— but actually Berry was a bon vivant, a gallant who preferred younger women and had a weakness for *les grandes horizontales*. Crosby and Berry shared a passion for sexual adventure and books, which may have partly accounted for their unexpected rapport. Harry had access to Berry's exquisite collection of first editions, and through Berry's private library made his first acquaintance with Verlaine, Rimbaud, and Baudelaire, the *poètes maudits* whose sexual and drug-taking excesses were as much an inspiration to Harry as was their poetry. Eventually Harry and Caresse moved into the same rarefied atmosphere of the faubourg St. Germain, to become neighbors at 19 rue de Lille.

In the autumn of 1927 Walter Berry was being treated by Dr. Sergei Voronoff, the famous monkey-gland specialist, in a last effort to revive his failing body and sexual prowess. Berry died in October of that year, and Harry undertook arrangements to have the body cremated. Although Berry's last wishes were that the ashes be scattered, Harry acceded to Edith Wharton's request that the urn be buried in her garden. When he showed up with the urn, he was accompanied by two gendarmes who had come along to make certain the ashes were buried according to French law. Miss Wharton was upset to have the police present during the burial and blamed Harry for the crude intrusion of officialdom during a private memorial service to her dear friend Walter Berry. What Hemingway called Harry's "wonderful gift of carelessness" was in some respects a kind of innocence, but Edith Wharton—author of *The Age of Innocence*—was unforgiving.

Berry's bequest that his library of rare volumes be given to favorite cousin Harry Crosby may have been another source of resentment. Harry was to take possession of the books only after Miss Wharton had made her choice from among them. She dallied over her choice of books from the Berry library, a way of annoying Harry for a time, but in the end she selected only a few sets as a token inheritance and washed her hands of the Crosbys forever after.

Word of the sybaritic pleasures of the Crosby ménage had gotten back to Miss Wharton long before the death of Walter Berry. "Walter's young cousin," she wrote, "turns out to be a sort of half-crazy cad." Edith Wharton would naturally bridle at Polly's change of name to Caresse and disapprove of Caresse's whippet, Narcisse, whose nails were painted gold and whose jeweled collars, like those of Josephine Baker's leopard, were changed daily. Further proof of Harry's "half crazy" way of life was the vast sunken tub the young couple had installed in the 300-year-old house on the rue de Lille. The Crosbys, attired only in dressing gowns and slippers, would receive their guests in the bedroom and soon invite them to join their hosts in the tub, four or more persons at a time, with champagne and caviar sandwiches within casual reach. If the Crosbys came upon a group of art students who attracted them, the students were invited to an impromptu soirée and generously advised to "bring friends." By morning the beds and floors would be encumbered with intermingled bodies, Harry and Caresse somewhere part of the naked Laocoön tangle.

On his own, Harry picked up women as casually as he would pluck a flower for his buttonhole: women were drawn to the handsome, self-assured, free-spending individualist. He believed with Oscar Wilde that "the only way to get rid of a temptation is to yield to it." If he saw a woman who attracted him at a café or in a restaurant, he was quite capable of abandoning his companion of the moment—including his wife—to introduce himself, then walk away with the beautiful stranger.

Caresse was in accord with this free-style sexual contract, which allowed equal freedom to her. But there was more than voluptuous pleasure seeking to their lives: both Harry and Caresse began to produce poetry. Along with their literary ambitions, they had long wanted to be patrons of the arts in a practical way. In 1927 the Crosbys launched the Black Sun Press, not just a vanity-house outlet for their endeavors but a major showcase for the most important writers in Paris at that time. The Black Sun's list of authors included Ernest Hemingway, Archibald MacLeish, Kay Boyle, Ford Madox Ford, and of course Harry's particular idol, James Joyce.

The title of Harry Crosby's first volume of poems, *Red Skeletons*, suggests his characteristically morbid turn of mind. Skeletons fascinated Harry: he had purchased the skeleton of a young girl from a medical supply house, then hung it, draped in a yellow raincoat, from his bookshelves. On the central staircase he had strung up another skeleton, with a contraceptive dangling from its jaws like a tongue.

Harry's verse showed only an occasional gift for expression, and frequently the lines ran to doggerel. Yet he submitted to a grueling session of composition, from nine until noon, then again after lunch until often late at night—an extraordinary discipline inspired by the working habits of James Joyce. The discipline was considerably modified by Harry's addiction to drugs: at this time he was taking opium regularly, in the belief that the drug might help him write his way into the sacred precincts of art.

If Harry's own genius failed to emerge—through drugs, sun worship, or a passion for death—he was more than willing to support the genius of others. Another sun worshiper, D. H. Lawrence, was commissioned to write a work on Harry's obsessional sun theme, to be called *Sun* and paid for in Harry's favorite form of currency, gold. Since Lawrence was in Italy at the time, Harry went to the gare de Lyon with twenty gold coins of $20 each in a Diogenes search for a passenger on the Rome express with an honest face. Just before the train pulled out, Harry found his man, a complete stranger who asked simply, "Is it a bomb?" "No," replied Harry, "gold for a poet." The gold pieces were delivered to Lawrence as planned; the messenger turned out to be the Duke of Argyll.

Harry needed constant stimulus, frequent opportunities for risk, and above all, variety. Every year he and Caresse attended the orgiastic Quatz-

'Arts Bal—once with Caresse riding bareback, and bare breasted, on an elephant rented from "Helen Scott Will Get It For You," an agency Americans turned to for such unlikely items. Harry carried a bag of live snakes and wore a neckpiece of dead pigeons: he distributed his snakes to the nude and gilded students, and one girl was seen to offer a bare nipple to the reptile Harry had given her. But even these outré episodes became routine. Harry hated predictability as much as he loved death.

On a trip to Egypt in 1928 Harry had the soles of his feet tattooed, and Caresse tattooed on the shoulder, with the symbolic black sun. Egypt was a place of hard, bright sun: Harry exposed himself to the burning orb by day and studied Egyptian funerary practices at night. Drugs were easily available in North Africa, and there was an open attitude toward homosexuality that led Harry to yield to that temptation as well, with a shepherd boy from Damascus. This affair no more disturbed Caresse than Harry's heterosexual escapades. He might occasionally wear his wife's lace underthings, not from any perverted inclination but simply because he cared nothing about clothes and had run out of underwear of his own.

Egypt had provided Harry with another piece of wisdom to add to his crazy-quilt philosophy: a statement he picked up from a dervish and transferred to his diary, "My wealth I can measure by the things I can do without." Paris was hardly the place to practice the austerity this maxim implied, yet Harry did manage to divest himself of certain possessions, particularly the valuable editions from Walter Berry's collection he had once so coveted. He might surreptitiously place rare or first editions of Rimbaud and Baudelaire among the tattered secondhand volumes for sale on the bookstalls along the Seine. He could then imagine the delighted excitement of some buyer or bookseller coming across these unexpected treasures, gratis, among the dross.

A simpler life than Paris offered was often the shimmering ideal of the jaded rich. A young Dutch couple, Fran and Mai de Geetere, lived aboard a barge tied up beside the pont Neuf and one day welcomed the Crosbys aboard. Kittens tumbled about on the rusted metal deck, Fran was playing the accordion, and Mai offered the visitors a bowl of cherries—a scene so refreshing to the Crosbys that they began to visit the barge regularly. They brought friends to meet the extraordinary Dutch couple. Fran bartered Holland cheeses, traded sketch portraits for food, did sign painting or any odd job for a living. Since there were no bathing facilities on the barge, the Crosbys offered their new friends the use of their sunken tub at the rue de Lille mansion: each Saturday Fran and Mai arrived with towels, soap, and a change of clothes in a sailor's duffel bag.

Harry and Caresse helped the de Geeteres survive on their subsistence income, bought Fran's sketches, contributed food, delighted to participate even to this limited extent in their lives. When the barge sprung a leak,

Harry offered to pay the overhaul and towing charges. It was as if the wealthy couple had adopted their mirror-image counterpart.

Even as the barge was shipping water, the Crosbys sponsored a drydock party for the towing trip. The vessel was crowded with guests, including the Dolly Sisters, then playing in Paris at the Moulin Rouge—they had come aboard carrying a case of champagne between them. There was Gouda cheese and wine and fruit, the kittens safely out of reach, Fran playing his accordion. The guests danced on as the leaking water of the Seine reached their ankles.

Another celebrated barge party was given by Gerald and Sara Murphy after the opening of the 1923 Ballets Russes production of *Les Noces*. The Murphys had originally wanted to hold the party at the Cirque Médrano, but the director coolly informed them that all of Paris might seem to have become an American colony, but not yet Le Cirque Médrano. Instead, they discovered a *péniche* ordinarily used for official revels of the Chambre des Députés but free on Sundays. The Murphys leased the barge for the first Sunday, June 17, following the presentation of *Les Noces*.

The party was one of those supreme *fêtes* the Murphys would become known for: an affair of careful planning that still allowed for spontaneity and fun. There were some forty guests in all, including the Princesse de Polignac, Igor Stravinsky, Cocteau, Picasso, Chanel, Diaghilev, and the principal dancers from the ballet. Picasso was fascinated with the miniature toys the Murphys had provided instead of floral place settings (the les Halles flower market being closed on Sundays), and Boris Kochno managed to dislodge a wooden laurel wreath from the cciling so that Stravinsky might leap through the vast horseshoe of carved leaves in an awkward balletic rite of spring. The party lasted until dawn, its evanescent spirit, as at any successful party, impossiblc to recall. Afterward guests agreed only that nobody got really drunk, everybody had an amazingly good time, and that the Murphys were an enchanted host and hostess. Gerald claimed that the gift of entertainment originated with Sara: "I helped organize it." Sara insisted: "It wasn't parties that made it such a gay time. There was such affection between everybody. You loved your friends and wanted to see them every day, and usually you did see them every day. It was like a great fair and everybody was so young."

Being young at a time when Paris was a great fair was one of the reasons Harry Crosby had been convinced life would be wasted at the Morgan bank: Gerald Murphy had come to the same conclusion about working in his father's exclusive leather-goods firm, Mark Cross. In 1921 Gerald took Sara and their three children to Paris, ostensibly to study landscape engineering in the city so lavishly endowed with formal gardens. Sara's share of her own family fortune brought in a comfortable $7,000 a year, and Gerald's money from Mark Cross made it possible for the Murphys to settle into a fashionable apartment on the rue Greuze in Passy. Soon after the Murphys arrived in Paris, Gerald was to discover an array of Cubist paintings at the Rosenberg gallery. He lost all interest in landscape engineering from that moment on: "If that's painting, it's what I want to do."

Unlike many well-to-do dilettantes of the era, Gerald Murphy had more than an amateur's passing facility. Natalia Goncharova was his first teacher; his first painting project was to help restore the scenery for *Pulcinella*, along with Dos Passos and other volunteers, when the American colony learned that the Ballets Russes stage sets had been destroyed by fire. This unskilled workman's exercise, done with long-handled brushes from ladders and scaffolds, may have influenced Murphy's subsequent interest in painting on a vast scale. His 12-by-18-foot study of smokestacks and ventilator funnels, *Boatdeck Cunarder*, was accepted by the 1923 Salon des Indépendants over the protest that it was nothing but architectural drawing. Murphy had the support of Fernand Léger, who considered him the only American painter in Paris of any consequence. Like Léger, Murphy was fascinated with artifacts of the twentieth century and painted in the hard, flat colors of ad posters. Even Picasso murmured a rare "C'est beau ça," when he saw Murphy's curtain for the Cole Porter ballet *Within the Quota*. Beneath a Hearst-style headline, UNKNOWN BANKER BUYS ATLANTIC, an upended transatlantic liner was being measured against a skyscraper.

Gerald Murphy had come late to painting, and if he had not come to Paris, he would never have taken up a paintbrush at all. The Yale graduate born to a thriving family business feared that his interest in the arts would be considered neurotic or effeminate in America. But he was aware, even in France, of being a dilettante or part-time artist. The independent income, and a thriving social life, did not correspond to the classic image of a working artist. Léger once suggested to him that a painter could have a comfortable life with little likelihood that his work would be of great importance, but of a difficult life came the only painting of any significance. Murphy might have pointed out their friend Picasso, at least the Picasso of the moment—rich, fashionable, gifted—as a rebuttal to this homily, but he knew his own work was not and never could be first-rate "and the world is too full of second-rate painting." By the mid-Twenties Gerald Murphy decided he would never paint again, and he never did.

This was a time when the Riviera was being rediscovered. Formerly the resort cities of Nice and Cannes thrived in the winter months only, their wedding-cake hotels a hospice for the elderly rich, British tourists, and the infirm. The newcomers—Coco Chanel, Picasso, Cole Porter—were beginning to arrive in the unfashionable summer months, leading the way to undiscovered fishing villages and unpopulated stretches of virgin sand. On the crest of the latest wave, but in their own inimitable style, the Murphys staked out a seaside sanctuary they called Villa America, on the cap d'An-

The Spirit of St. Louis *flying over Paris.*

tibes. Via *le train bleu* the Côte d'Azur had become a kind of overnight suburb of the Parisian social scene, now that the Murphys had transferred their hospitality to the Mediterranean shore.

In the spring of 1925 the Fitzgeralds made their second attempt to live in France, this time "on practically nothing a year." *The Great Gatsby* had just been published to excellent reviews but, in Fitzgerald's opinion, poor sales: the nothing-a-year amounted to the $7,000 he had so far earned from the novel. With their infant daughter, Scottie, the Fitzgeralds sailed on the *Aquitania* to the Mediterranean, then made their way to Paris via Lyon in an automobile they had purchased on the Riviera. The closed car did not suit Zelda's penchant for riding with the wind in her hair, so at a garage in Lyon they had the metal top cut away like a sardine can. They continued driving north until the first spring rain soaked them thoroughly: the topless car had to be abandoned. It was a typical gesture of Scott and Zelda: a decision taken on a momentary impulse, an improvident fling to repent at leisure. The episode was the prelude to their "summer of 1,000 parties and no work."

In Paris they settled into a flat at 14 rue de Tilsitt off one of the busy spokes of the Arc de Triomphe. Despite the impeccable address, the apartment was forbidding, somberly furnished in a mixture of periods one guest called "early Galeries Lafayette." There was, at least, a telephone—or you could get in touch with friends by *pneumatique*, the city-wide vacuum-tube message service. Otherwise you met by chance at the Dôme, American Express, or Zelli's.

The frantic pace of party life left little time for the expatriate parents to concern themselves with their daughter. The Fitzgeralds had high-minded theories of child rearing but turned Scottie over to a series of servants and nannies. On the one occasion anyone ever saw Zelda taking personal care of her daughter, she was bathing Scottie in the bidet.

The friendship between Ernest Hemingway and Scott Fitzgerald was based more on common literary interests than any natural affinity: they admired one another's work and enjoyed one another's company—the enjoyment more on Fitzgerald's side than on Hemingway's—but there was a strain to the relationship from the beginning. At their first meeting in the Dingo Bar, Fitzgerald praised his fellow author in embarrassingly extravagant terms, then lapsed into a kind of drunken paralysis after a single glass of champagne. Hemingway did not think much of a man who could not hold his liquor. As for Zelda, Hemingway thought she was jealous of Scott's writing and would do anything to keep him from his typewriter.

There was some question as to which of the two, Scott or Zelda, led the other into the drunken pranks and party games—kidnaping waiters "to saw in half with a musical saw," splashing through the fountain at l'Observatoire in evening clothes, returning home at dawn from les Halles in a camion loaded with carrots—the escapades that marked their time in Paris, a legendary hedonism, a doomed pursuit of sustained pleasure. A flaw in Fitzgerald's character, according to Hemingway, was Scott's awe of and attraction to the rich. In a hurt letter, Fitzgerald denied any such obsession, despite the evidence from his stories and novels very much concerned with the ethos of affluence. Certainly he was awed by the Old Guard, financial or literary; he was self-conscious about his own middle-American background and sensitive about being outclassed.

Fitzgerald's fascination with the rich led him into the irresistible orbit of Gerald and Sara Murphy and their Riviera coterie. Even the harder-boiled Ernest Hemingway had succumbed to the Murphy charm after having been introduced to them by Dos Passos. In a sense, Gerald and Sara Murphy were the chief witnesses to traumatic breakdowns in both the Hemingway and Fitzgerald marriages.

The Fitzgeralds survived, but barely, Zelda's casual and seemingly innocent flirtation with a dashing young French pilot, Edouard Jozan. While Scott was taking advantage of an exceptional period of productivity, writing most of the day at their rented villa in St. Raphaël, Zelda was on the beach, often surrounded by a group of officers from the nearby base at Fréjus. Zelda's favorite among this circle of bachelor admirers was Jozan, and the Murphys watched with some alarm Zelda's more than passing interest in her tanned and handsome beach companion. "I must say," reported Sara Murphy, "everyone knew about it but Scott." To Scott the situation seemed no more than Zelda's harmless beaux collecting in Montgomery, Alabama, when he was one of the beaux proposing marriage to her. When it dawned on him that Jozan was more than a hopeless admirer of his wife and that Zelda had become seriously attracted to him, there was a scene and an abrupt end to the affair. But neither Scott nor Zelda quite recovered from the episode, and both were sufficiently haunted by the memory of Edouard Jozan to use versions of him in novels: Tommy Barban in Scott's *Tender Is the Night*, and Jacques Chevre-Feuille in Zelda's *Save Me the Waltz*.

The Hemingway break was more serious, leading to a trial separation between Ernest and Hadley and finally to divorce. They had been staying with the Murphys at the Villa America when Bumby came down with whooping cough. In order to spare the Murphy children a dangerous contagion, Ernest and Hadley moved to a smaller villa in the neighborhood. Then Pauline Pfeiffer appeared on the scene: she had had whooping cough as a child, so she offered to join the Hemingways in their quarantine-isolation, an apparently benevolent gesture but one with motives beyond the call of friendship.

"Then, instead of the two of them and their child, there are three of them," wrote Hemingway in *A Moveable Feast*. "First it is stimulating and fun and it goes on that way for a while. All things truly wicked start from an innocence.''

A few months later, when the Hemingway marriage fell apart, Gerald Murphy offered Ernest his atelier on the rue Froidevaux in Paris so that he could set up a separate residence. In later years, Hemingway—with his queer logic—blamed the Murphys for the breakdown of his marriage with Hadley—''Then you have the rich, and nothing is ever as it was again''— and vilified Dos Passos as the ''pilot-fish'' who had led him to the rich.

CHAPTER TWELVE

Harold Stearns had left America in disgust after compiling the volume *Civilization in the United States*. He was just as disillusioned when American civilization pursued him to Paris. He saw the Dôme change from a dingy bistro with a billiard parlor in the back to the favorite tourist café in Montparnasse—the billiard parlor had been eliminated to make room for more Americans. To Ernest Hemingway's dismay his waiter-friend Jean at the Closerie de Lilas had been ordered to shave off his dragoon's mustache and wear a white jacket: the Lilas was being converted to a *bar Americain*. La Coupole had also become an American bar, and Jimmy's and Le Jockey introduced the New York speakeasy ambience to the Boulevard Montparnasse.

The 1927 American Chamber of Commerce estimated that there were 15,000 Americans resident in Paris, but many Americans did not trouble to register with the police: the official estimate was closer to 40,000—or perhaps it just seemed, to the French, there were that many. The American presence was everywhere evident as the transatlantic liners disgorged more and more tourists on the shores of France. These latecomers were not of the same species as those of the earlier migration, at the beginning of the decade. ''With each new shipment of Americans spewed up by the boom the quality fell off,'' wrote Fitzgerald. ''Toward the end there was something sinister about the crazy boatloads.''

Fitzgerald himself did little to enhance the reputation of visiting Americans. Outside a nightclub the drunken author noticed a woman offering a tray of assorted trinkets for sale: he playfully kicked the tray from her hands, the pitiful collection of trivia went flying. Fitzgerald's companions were exasperated with his shameful behavior. ''But I gave her a hundred francs,'' he said. ''Did you see me give her a hundred francs?'' Lawrence Vail, ''King of Bohemia'' (married to heiress Peggy Guggenheim), was arrested for publicly burning a 100-franc note during a café argument.

Americans would never realize how the French secretly felt about them. The childlike behavior and unconscious waste exhibited by visitors from the United States were abhorrent to their Old World hosts. Yankee profligacy and frontier naïveté were qualities that aroused the French to indignation. Yet on the surface there seemed an equilibrium of interests. France was hard up in 1927. The economy was at the point of collapse. Americans were made welcome while the dollars flowed, for there were many Parisians who could profit from the bandwagon American boom. But the rest of France was left brooding and resentful. The Paris *Herald* ran a report on the increasing losses faced by hotels and restaurants in the vicinity of the northeastern battlefields. Sentiment about the late Great War had so dissipated that families of the soldiers who had bled and died in France no longer took Cook's featured tour of Ypres, Verdun, and the Marne. Overseas visitors bypassed the hallowed ground to make a beeline for Maxim's, the Café de la Paix, and the Folies-Bergère.

An outrage that united the French as no other issue could was the recent demand by the United States that France pay its war debt. To the average Frenchman this situation was absurd: in the midst of its gravest financial crisis since the war, France was being dunned for funds borrowed from a rich wartime ally. President Doumergue was obliged to go to Washington to plead poverty to the U.S. Senate—the French press referred to Uncle Sam as Uncle Shylock.

Most Americans did not at first recognize a growing anti-Yankee sentiment. The surliness of service employees was a given of Parisian life—hadn't waiters and taxi drivers *always* been surly? Other indications were more ominous. An editorial in *Paris-Midi* deplored the habit of booing Americans on the street when they were heard to utter a phrase in English. An angry crowd forced the newspaper *Le Matin* to haul down an American flag displayed on the front of the building. A tourist bus was stoned by local residents when it passed through Montmartre.

Now that the Great War was seven years in the distant past, the memory of American doughboy heroes had faded. All the French needed was a single certified American hero to perform the most daring exploit of the century, and their anti-Americanism would reverse overnight.

Two French pilots, Nungesser and Coli, had earlier that year attempted the first flight across the Atlantic: their plane disappeared in the North Atlantic. The tragedy—four American pilots had already been killed in the same attempt—emphasized the danger of intercontinental flying. In the summer of 1927 an air link between Europe and America was still considered an impossible dream.

However, the Brevoort and Lafayette Hotel Group in New York was offering the $25,000 Orteig Prize for the first successful transatlantic flight, and a 25-year-old mail pilot, Charles A. Lindbergh, was determined to set off from New York bound for Paris, nonstop. His plane was a Ryan monoplane of metal superstructure and wooden wings: a consortium of

Missouri businessmen had put up the money to build the machine and named it *The Spirit of St. Louis*.

On May 20, 1927, the Long Island weather reports were as favorable as Lindbergh could expect for the season; it was raining at Roosevelt Field, but clouds were lifting all across the Atlantic. Loaded with enough fuel for forty hours, the plane weighed 5,250 pounds—1,000 pounds more than it had ever carried before—and there was some doubt that it could lift off from the muddy airfield. Lindbergh was up well before dawn with very little sleep behind him to sustain a forty-hour solo venture. Another problem was that the motor, during a warm-up session, could not rev up to full power. The mechanic considered the loss of power a temporary failure due to the weather: "They never rev up on a day like this."

The decision was made; Lindbergh was ready to fly. He had made up half-a-dozen ham sandwiches and a thermos of coffee. He tucked a wishbone in the pocket of his flying jacket, climbed into the cockpit, and adjusted his goggles. "Well, boys, I'm off." Mechanics and helpers had to push on the wing struts to get the plane moving. At takeoff, *The Spirit of St. Louis* skidded through a puddle of water and missed a stretch of telephone line by twenty feet, but Lindbergh was airborne and away. He took a bedraggled kitten along with him for company.

The French had been skeptical all along. In *Paris-Soir* an editorial expressed doubt that a lone flier could stay awake and alert enough "to challenge successfully the dark forces waiting to do battle with him over the Atlantic." Even the Americans, more optimistic by nature, called Lindbergh "The Flying Fool." The flight would have been hazardous under the best of conditions, but Lindbergh was sometimes obliged to fly as low as fifty feet from the surface of the water to avoid great banks of storm. After he had passed Newfoundland, cable reports began coming in from ships that had sighted the low-flying aircraft. Interested parties on both sides of the Atlantic began to take the exploit seriously: at le Bourget airport all planes were ordered grounded until further notice; vessels at sea were advised to keep a sharp lookout. Finally there was a sighting at Dingle Bay, Ireland, then another report from the coast of Cornwall. The news brought on the first wave of mass hysteria.

The romance and risk of Lindbergh's stunt so impressed Harry Crosby that he immediately identified with the Lone Eagle: he would have given his soul to change places with the solitary pilot then flying over the English Channel. His emulation was further encouraged by Caresse's declaration that Harry and Lindy looked alike enough to be brothers, except for Lindbergh's thatch of red hair. As soon as word reached Paris that *The Spirit of St. Louis* had passed over the coast of France at Cherbourg, the Crosbys embarked in their chauffeur-driven limousine along the Route de Flandre leading northward out of Paris. The road was already as crowded

Zelda and F. Scott Fitzgerald with their daughter Scottie on board ship en route to Europe.

with vehicles as when it served as the lifeline for a taxicab army en route to the Battle of the Marne.

Before the Cherbourg sighting, the afternoon crowd at le Bourget had been estimated at 45,000. By the time the Crosbys arrived, there were some 150,000 observers eagerly scanning the sky for the first sign of the monoplane. U.S. Ambassador Myron T. Herrick was waiting for Lindbergh in the control tower with a delegation of French officials. Air space above le Bourget was closed to all traffic in order to keep the skies clear for the single-minded mail pilot from the west.

At twilight kleig lights were trained on the runways; police and airport personnel began to erect barriers to keep the growing crowd at bay. Meanwhile, Lindbergh had twice passed over the Eiffel Tower, but could not locate le Bourget.

"C'est lui!"

At a little past 10:00 P.M. Harry and Caresse Crosby, along with the thousands at the airfield, saw a sudden flash of silver against the moon. "C'est Lindbergh!" Indeed, the frail monoplane was moving in and out of the banked clouds above le Bourget.

The Spirit of St. Louis drifted lower and lower along a flare-lined runway, then made a smooth landing. Lindbergh was prepared to taxi the plane in the direction of the hangars, but at that moment the impatient crowd broke through the police line and spilled over onto the field. There were cries of "Lind-dee, Lin-dee!" as the first enthusiasts reached the aircraft. The Crosbys were unable to approach the center of all this excitement: the plane was completely cut off, surrounded by near riot. Harry and Caresse hovered on the periphery of the crowd, quietly glorying in the triumph of their fellow American.

"Am I here?" asked the dazed pilot as he emerged from the cockpit. "Is this really Paris?"

The wild display on all sides was answer enough. Exhausted by his thirty-three-hour ordeal, Lindbergh was pulled as if by suction into the crowd, hoisted onto eager shoulders, paraded aloft. His headgear was pulled from his head and fell into the crowd: the cap and goggles were recovered by a mechanic, Harry Wheeler, who could no longer reach Lindbergh. A group of French pilots realized they might rescue Lindbergh if Wheeler donned the cap; he did, and was paraded around the field, thus diverting part of the mob, who mistook him for Lindbergh. Meanwhile, the real Lindbergh was freed by a cordon of gendarmes and several French pilots sent to his rescue. It was impossible to present Lindy to his official welcoming committee in the besieged control tower, so the pilots escaped with Lindbergh by driving into Paris for a rendezvous at the Arc de Triomphe. Lindy spoke no French, but under the great arch his companions made known—in broken English—that here, beneath the eternal flame, lay the Unknown Soldier of World War I.

Meanwhile, furious newsmen at le Bourget learned that Lindbergh had been whisked away. A worse revelation was that some unscrupulous United Press correspondent had conspired to tie up all public telephones at le Bourget. In their frustration, a group of newsmen upturned the telephone kiosk occupied by the chief correspondent of the UP, trapping the hapless conniver inside with the wires cut.

The shrewd and equally Machiavellian Hank Wales of the Paris *Herald*, knowing what the situation would be like at le Bourget, had not even ventured to the airport. He cabled a completely fictitious interview with Lindbergh made up of statements Lindy would have made under the circumstances: the scoop earned Wales a $500 bonus.

It took the Crosbys until long past midnight to get back to Paris through the tangle of traffic on the Route de Flandre. Montmartre was packed with celebrants: it was like New Year's Eve in midsummer. Josephine Baker had stopped the show at the Folies to announce that Lindy had made it to Paris. The wildly exultant Crosbys spent the remainder of that historic night toasting the success of the Lone Eagle in champagne.

Lindbergh had been forty hours without sleep. He was driven to Ambassador Herrick's residence at 2 avenue d'Iéna for the luxury of a bath and a meal of bouillon, poached egg, and milk; then to bed by 3:00 A.M., wearing the ambassador's silk pajamas.

While Lindy slept, Herrick assembled an appropriate wardrobe to the measure of the tall, slim pilot—Lindbergh had brought along no change of clothes, no money; he had a passport, but no visa for France. The ambassador would arrange for the inevitable round of receptions: now that Paris was only thirty-three hours from New York, the man who made it possible was an instant celebrity. As long as Lindbergh remained in Paris, the American ambassador would be at his side: the Embassy, and the United States at large, would benefit from the reflected glory of Lindbergh's extraordinary exploit.

The exhausted hero slept till noon. Next day—with his natural tact and a genuine concern—Lindbergh chose to visit Madame Nungesser at 33 faubourg du Temple, a call he put before any official function. Nothing could have endeared him more to the French than to have paid homage to the mother whose son had been lost during a similar attempt to fly the Atlantic.

At a press conference in the Embassy residence, Lindy gracefully submitted to a hail of questions put by international newsmen. To a woman reporter's question about his interest in the opposite sex, he replied, "No, I am not married or engaged, nor have I any prospects of being married or engaged." With all else, Lindy instantly had become the world's most eligible bachelor.

Lindbergh could do no wrong: at those first public appearances his modesty and boyish charm completely won the day. This clear-eyed, clean-living example of American manhood did much to obliterate the image of frivolity and debauch created by the café set.

President Gaston Doumergue presented Lindbergh with the highest decoration France could confer, the cross of the Legion of Honor. At a luncheon given by the Aero Club, Lindbergh was invited to step onto the balcony, bedecked with French and American flags, to greet a cheering mob massed in the square below and spilling into the adjoining streets, a crowd of 50,000. A microphone was placed before him, and Lindy spoke a few carefully chosen words in his first public address—then, at the elaborate French luncheon, drank his first glass of champagne. He went on to the Hôtel de Ville, to be feted in the presence of the mayor of Paris, displayed like some glorious ornament against the backdrop of the medieval town hall: the "Star-Spangled Banner" blared forth, followed by the "Marseillaise." The front page of every newspaper in Paris was filled with the details of Lindbergh's winged victory, column after column devoted to the most celebrated American-in-Paris of all time.

The French love affair with America was to last less than three months. Two anarchists, Nicola Sacco and Bartolomeo Vanzetti, had been convicted of murder and robbery in Dedham, Massachusetts. In what seemed to be a trial representing Boston's upper class versus two hapless Italian immigrants with unpopular political beliefs, the case aroused the French to a passion reminiscent of the Dreyfus Affair. There was evidence that the trial conducted by Judge Thayer had been unfair and his statements outside the courtroom prejudicial. Demands for a new trial had been denied. To the French, and most Europeans, a conservative and repressive court system had condemned the men to death because they were poor, foreign, and proclaimed radical sentiments. National and international pressure for a stay of execution came to nothing. Sacco and Vanzetti were sent to the electric chair on August 22, 1927.

In Paris, news of the execution set off the most alarming riots of the decade. French mobs made the rounds of the cafés where Americans were known to congregate: many U.S. citizens were badly beaten up or at the very least insulted in the street, publicly reviled for the Sacco-Vanzetti deaths. The expatriate colonies of Montmartre and Montparnasse were under siege. The gendarmes and mounted police, who had only recently surrounded the American Embassy to hold back the crowds cheering for Lindbergh, now cordoned off the avenue Gabriel to protect Ambassador Herrick and his diplomatic staff from assault.

Feeling was still running so high by Armistice Day that William L. Shirer was pulled off an assignment to cover Isadora Duncan's funeral in Paris in order to cover the American Legion parade. His editor at the *Chicago*

Tribune was certain there would be demonstrations against the 20,000 former doughboys marching down the Champs-Elysées.

In the late summer of 1927 Isadora Duncan had stepped into a motorcar to go for a drive along the Promenade des Anglais in Nice. As she drove off, she called out to friends, "Adieu, mes amis, je vais à la gloire." As the automobile picked up speed, Isadora's long, trailing scarf—part of the loose-fitting, fluid dress style she had always favored—caught in one of the wheels. She died instantly from a broken neck.

The funeral cortege for Isadora Duncan was made up of only five carriages winding slowly to the Père Lachaise cemetery. The French government ignored the event, although Isadora had been a staunch friend of France: she had rented at her own expense the Metropolitan Opera House in New York to raise funds for France at the outbreak of World War I; she had given up her Château Bellevue, in Neuilly, to serve as a hospital for French wounded. None of Isadora's French friends walked behind the coffin.

Just after the Russian Revolution, Isadora Duncan had established a school of dance in Moscow, and she had married the Russian poet Sergei Esenin: the single imposing floral tribute at her funeral came from Russia: "Le Coeur de Russie Pleure Isadora." The heart of Russia wept for her, but the face of France was turned away.

Since Lindbergh's historic flight, Harry Crosby's death wish entered a new phase: he had himself taken to the air. Along with his friend, the Russian Prince Carageorgovich, Harry began taking flying lessons at Villacoublay. The air-crash death of a fellow student discouraged him not at all.

At this time Harry came to know the French photographer Henri Cartier-Bresson, who spoke to him of what he called "the decisive moment" in photography, the single instant of timing that renders a captured image into a work of art. For Harry, there must be a decisive moment concerning death; he had been reading Nietzsche and was awed by the statement "Die at the right time."

The decisive moment was not yet at hand, but flying exhilarated Harry: the airplane was surely the instrument for a perfect farewell to life. The Crosbys, like so many other wealthy expatriates, kept a second house outside Paris, the Moulin du Soleil—a sanctuary from the frantic, downward-spiraling city life. Harry convinced Caresse to join him in a death pact: when the time came, they would fly above the French woodlands surrounding their country property, then leap from the airplane together. To celebrate this macabre contract, Harry had gravestones prepared for himself and Caresse and erected in the garden at the Moulin du Soleil.

"I never do portraits" was Picasso's stock reply to any such request. The painter's reputation was secure, and growing; he was adamant about refusing commissioned work. But the affluent man-about-town might, on occasion, ignore his own rule and make the proposal himself.

"Mademoiselle, you have an interesting face. I am Pablo Picasso. Please, may I do your portrait?"

The name Picasso meant nothing to the blonde seventeen-year-old, but she was immediately charmed by the man. She had been window-shopping in front of the Galeries Lafayette when the stranger approached her with his blunt introduction. Although Picasso was approaching fifty, he was a dashing gallant in the presence of a lovely young girl like Marie-Thérèse Walter. The flair, finesse, and superhuman vitality that went into his work were just as evident in his seductive personality.

Picasso's paintings of this period show the opposite side to his character: here was the violent misogynist, dismembering his women, then reassembling their faces and forms in cruel distortions. The end to his marriage was in sight; he was restless in the confines of the bourgeois flat on rue La Boétie. His *Femme assise au bord de la mer* of 1929 might well have represented his repulsion to Olga, as theorists put forth; if so, he considered his wife a particularly monstrous form of praying mantis, a creature with sidelong teeth and jaws capable of devouring her mate. Whatever his feelings about Olga, or about women in general, Picasso fell in love with Marie-Thérèse and she with him.

Thus began the most discreet of Picasso's many love affairs. Marie-Thérèse was kept secret from even his closest friends, and certainly from Olga of the unpredictable Russian temperament. Picasso installed his new love in an apartment across the street from his own flat, near enough to the Galerie Simon on adjoining rue d'Astorg to offer an excuse to be with Marie-Thérèse without his wife suspecting the liaison. Although Picasso had already suggested a separation to Olga—a suggestion that triggered a tempestuous scene, though Picasso made no mention of another woman— Marie-Thérèse did not want him to divorce; she was perfectly content to remain in the shadows, an artist's anonymous mistress.

The year 1929 also marked the arrival in Paris of a young Catalan painter who immediately presented himself at Picasso's door. Salvador Dalí intended to visit the three great monuments of France: the palace at Versailles, the Grévin wax museum, and Pablo Picasso. Just as Picasso had done for Miró when that young painter came to him in 1920, he now took the trouble to introduce Dalí to his own dealer, Paul Rosenberg, and to his sometime friend and still a force in art circles, Gertrude Stein.

Also, as if such impulses were cyclical at ten-year intervals, Picasso returned to a Neoclassic style. A wealthy young Swiss, Albert Skira, was casting about for a project to satisfy his mother's insistence that he take on some useful line of endeavor. At first Skira approached Picasso with the idea of illustrating a book on Napoleon that Skira would publish. The Napoleon of modern art was not interested in the other Napoleon. That same summer, while Picasso was visiting Juan-les-Pins, he was waylaid by Skira's determined mother, who asked him to consider illustrations for some other book. By then Skira had thought of producing an illustrated edition of Ovid's *Metamorphoses*. Nothing could have appealed to the painter more than creating plates of Ovid's mythical creatures: the nymphs, satyrs, and minotaurs that were to become a recurrent theme in the Picasso oeuvre. Delighted with his coup, Skira took rooms in the building next door to the Picasso flat. He hovered at the window, awaiting the completion of each new engraving, signaled by Picasso himself, on a clown's antique trumpet blasting down the rue La Boétie.

The parties had become frenetic affairs, as if a last-of-the-wine fete could forever stave off hangover. During the final champagne years, Jean Cocteau had aggressive competition from social climber Elsa Maxwell in creating extravagant backdrops and original guest lists for the frolics of the smart set. Jean Patou's ball was arranged by Elsa Maxwell, the host's town house encased from rooftop to ground floor in silver foil. Scavenger hunts sent socialites scrambling over Paris in search of a Paraguayan flag or Mistinguett's slipper; come-as-you-were parties requested guests to appear dressed as they were when the invitation was received, pajamas and nightgowns predominating. The most original invitations were sent by hairdresser Antoine to inaugurate his new *salon de beauté* and private living quarters on the rue Didier: the building was constructed entirely of Gobain sheet glass, with glass furniture and an interior staircase in pebbled glass—the invitations were engraved on thin sheets of glass, wrapped in parchment, delivered by hand.

The overcrowded *terrasses* on the place Vavin were less a sanctuary of the arts than a tourist stop for new hordes of poseurs. The café circuit still served as a bourse of the rise and fall of fluctuating reputations: Sinclair Lewis hoped to join with the younger generation of writers crowding the Dôme, but the fledgling littérateurs would have none of him; when Lewis stood at his table to make an impassioned point about Flaubert, somebody at an adjoining table shouted, "Sit down, you're a best-seller."

Malcolm Cowley got into a fight with the patron of La Rotonde and was hauled off to the commissariat: he managed to escape fine or imprisonment by a persuasive chorus of witnesses, French and American, who swore the patron was a troublemaker and had swung first. The café set of Montparnasse preferred Gaston, barman and part owner of La Coupole, who was generous, good-natured, and not easily provoked—yet they were drawn to La Rotonde and the Café Sélect, where ugly scenes were more likely to occur.

The great good place of every expatriate's dream was becoming a casualty ward. By 1929 the last wave of visitors to Paris seemed to want the cheap thrill of a ragged and disordered spectacle. The once lithe and glamorous Florence Martin of the Folies-Bergère, now a fading and foulmouthed "Flossie" of the café circuit, was said to have inspired the legend of the two middle-aged American women who drove up in a taxi to the Gypsy Bar, hesitant until Florence Martin entered, raucously drunk, screaming friendly obscenities at Jimmy the barman. One matron in the taxi opened the door to get out, saying to her companion, "This must be the place."

One of Gertrude Stein's young men of 26, surrealist poet René Crevel, wrote to Gertrude and Alice in his quaint English about the last of the nonstop partygoers, Scott and Zelda Fitzgerald: "Curious and poor fellow. A boy. He has a wonderful wife, you know her, I think, but what this young charming and spirituel people has in the hed (tête)? I cannot say, but I want [to] speak about that with you and Miss Touclas."

The rich, like Tom and Daisy Buchanan in *The Great Gatsby*, could retreat "back into their money, or their vast carelessness," but the Fitzgeralds had to keep the party going at all costs. There were gnawing tensions behind the façade of gaiety and excess, not the least of which was that they were broke: Scott had earned $30,000 in 1927, and practically as much in 1928, but he had to borrow money from Scribner's to survive. He considered these loans an advance on his latest novel, *The World's Fair*, which had got off to a false start and would never be completed, though much of the Paris-Riviera background was used in *Tender Is the Night*, published in 1934.

What had been an idyllic interlude for Zelda, with a handsome French pilot on the sands of St. Raphaël, would continue as a recurring nightmare for Scott, who was prey to fears of sexual inadequacy. Whether or not Scott confessed to Hemingway, "Zelda said the way I was built I could never make any woman happy," and whether or not the two men went into the WC at Michaud's like little boys to compare penises, Zelda did once say to Scott she now realized he was homosexual, that he had come home the night before after a drinking spree with Hemingway and murmured in his sleep, "No more, baby."

But Zelda was making other wild assertions in 1929. After a visit to the les Halles flower market she revealed to Scott: "The flowers are talking to me." It could have been another of her cryptic conversational ploys. She once remarked to Gerald and Sara Murphy, "Don't you think Al Jolson is greater than Jesus?"

Gerald Murphy introduced Zelda to Madame Lubov Egorova, former dancer with the Ballets Russes, one of the great ballet teachers in Paris at the time. Zelda had taken ballet lessons briefly as an adolescent; now, at an age when most ballerinas had completed the better part of their careers, she was determined to make herself into a professional dancer. According to Gerald Murphy: "She wanted immediate success. Zelda wanted to dance for the world." When the Murphys went to watch Zelda at practice for a recital, Gerald was embarrassed by her grotesque intensity. "It was really terrible. One held one's breath until it was over. Thank God she couldn't see what she looked like." Zelda recorded her own impression of that time as: "I worked constantly and was terribly superstitious and moody... full of presentiments. Scott drank."

Morley Callaghan had worked on the *Toronto Star* with Ernest Hemingway and was a devotee of the Hemingway mystique: he wrote on the same subjects as his idol, and in the same style. When he brought his wife, Loretto, to Paris in 1929, he was in a sense attempting to relive the Hemingway legend. Callaghan's first impressions of Paris echo Hemingway's original enthusiasm for the city, but at a distance of eight years, seen through the opposite end of a telescope. Callaghan's Paris was the last act of a disintegrating pageant, the tag end instead of the bright beginning of a decade.

The young couple stayed first at the Paris-New York Hotel until the depressing view from their window of a flower-laden hearse parked in the cul-de-sac made them decide to move to the rue de la Santé—with an only slightly less depressing panorama of la Santé's cinder-colored prison walls. Their Paris sojourn was something of a second honeymoon, a leisurely time that began with waking to a summer's day in Paris, then the delight of coffee and steamed milk with croissants. They took a ritual lunch at La Coupole. Later they might stroll along the Champs-Elysées or explore the hard, bright streets around the Opéra, searching for the perfect café to savor the apéritif hour.

At night they went to Zelli's and Bricktop's to dance and passed Le Jockey on the way home, the jazz and cigarette smoke blowing into the street. The Callaghans were doing the things one did in Gay Paree; in truth, they were searching for Hemingway, but the famous writer was not to be found in the famous cabarets. Naturally Callaghan asked Sylvia Beach at Shakespeare and Company to help him get in touch with his former colleague, but Miss Beach had become chary of giving out the addresses of her better-known clients. "You could leave a message," she said, to Callaghan's annoyance. The dilemma solved itself when Hemingway one day came knocking on the Callaghans' door and invited the couple to his apartment on the rue Ferou.

At the end of 1928 Ernest Hemingway's father had committed suicide. Hemingway's mother, at her son's macabre request, sent him the pistol Dr. Hemingway had shot himself with—a grim trophy the writer would brood over in his thirtieth year, 1929. Married to Pauline Pfeiffer now, with money from her generous Uncle Gus and his own expanding income, Hemingway enjoyed a style of life that was a large remove from the place Contrescarpe. The Callaghans were properly impressed with the spacious apartment Ernest and Pauline had taken just off the Luxembourg Gardens, in the shadow of St. Sulpice.

Hemingway's now traditional trip to Pamplona was a far more luxurious excursion than that famous trip in 1925 described in *The Sun Also Rises*: the Hemingways motored down to Spain in their new Ford roadster. Spain, to Hemingway's disgust, had been invaded by American chewing gum and Coca-Cola. He indulged so richly and copiously in the food and wine of the country that he returned to Paris with all the symptoms of gout—he was obliged to go on a diet and drink mineral water only.

The Hemingway acquaintanceship was propitious for the Callaghans: suddenly the young couple were no longer tourists, but had penetrated the inner circle of celebrated expatriates. And Hemingway could indulge the ego satisfaction of having a young writer—new to Paris and open to instruction—dogging his footsteps. Loretto did not get on as well with Pauline Hemingway, who seemed patronizing, especially concerning *la mode* and a milliner she knew but whose name she was reluctant to divulge to Loretto. The two men had more in common. Morley Callaghan had been a collegiate boxer, and Hemingway was anxious to work off the slackness and paunch of the good life.

For Callaghan, some of the allure of his hero dimmed under the stress of a competitive sport. Instead of being instructor to the younger man, as he was in the literary arena, Hemingway found himself being outboxed by the swifter, better-trained Callaghan. Once, when Hemingway's lip was cut by Callaghan's barrage of lefts, Hemingway spat blood directly into the young man's face. They made it up over beers at the Falstaff Bar, where the banter with the English bartender, who had been a professional lightweight fighter, put both men in a better mood.

The flat on the rue de la Santé had to be given up when the Callaghans discovered they were being bitten by bedbugs. But Edward Titus, husband of Helena Rubinstein, offered them the free use of his own apartment. Titus was the new editor of *This Quarter*, an outlet for Callaghan's fiction. With the move to Titus's flat on the rue Delambre, the Callaghans became all the more intimate with café and salon life. They met Gertrude Stein and Scott and Zelda Fitzgerald.

At their first meeting with the Fitzgeralds, Scott stood on his head. When Hemingway heard this, he shrugged and said, "That's Scott." But he asked the Callaghans not to pass on his address to Fitzgerald.

In *That Summer in Paris* Morley Callaghan evokes the small, quiet Miró dressed in his old-fashioned dark suit, striped shirt and bowler hat, acting as timekeeper with great Spanish dignity for one of the Hemingway-Callaghan bouts at the American Club. On another occasion, Fitzgerald was timekeeper and allowed one dramatic round to exceed the two-minute limit. The thickset Hemingway was dumped by his sparring partner during the overtime, and Fitzgerald announced with chagrin that he had carelessly allowed the round to run beyond the limit. Hemingway was furious. He accused Fitzgerald of maliciously allowing the round to run overtime. Fitzgerald was aghast: "He thinks I did it on purpose," he said to Callaghan. It was significant that Hemingway had come to the bout after eating a heavy lunch of lobster thermidor with white burgundy at Prunier's—formerly he would have done his boxing on little more than *poireaux en salade*.

The incident would have gone no farther than the gossip grapevine of Montparnasse had not Isabel Paterson picked up the story for her book column in the New York *Herald Tribune*. Hemingway's growing literary reputation made him Stateside news: unfortunately, Paterson reported that Ernest Hemingway had been knocked out by Morley Callaghan, not just knocked down. With Hemingway's hair-trigger temper and tender ego, the episode grew into a cause célèbre. Morley Callaghan soon realized his friendship with Hemingway was shattered because he had once, inadvertently, toppled the giant.

"There were Americans at night, and day Americans," wrote Zelda Fitzgerald, "and we all had Americans in the bank to buy things with." This was in the autumn of 1929, when Zelda was fifteen pounds underweight, pushing herself to exhaustion at ballet practice. Hemingway had described Zelda's eyes as those of a hawk, and watching her face, "you could see her mind leave the table and go to the night's party and return with her eyes blank as a cat's...." The alternating avidity and blankness in Zelda's face became more pronounced as she lived on the illusion that agents from Diaghilev had come to watch her dance. She awaited an offer from the Ballets Russes when, as it turned out, the agents were actually from the Folies-Bergère, looking for a potential shimmy dancer. Madame Egorova reported a visit with Zelda alone, for tea, when her student's voice and facial expressions shifted bizarrely and Zelda finally dropped to her knees and embraced Madame Egorova's feet. Zelda was beginning to hold on to the sides of the table to get through a meal.

The Fitzgeralds invited Morley and Loretto Callaghan to James Joyce's favorite restaurant, Les Trianons. It was a somber occasion. Joyce did not appear that night; Scott seemed withdrawn, perhaps brooding over his failure to get back to work on *The World's Fair*. Zelda was agitated throughout the meal: "What will we do next?" she kept asking. When she insisted they all go roller-skating, Scott became stern and paternal—strangely, Zelda reverted to a complaisant child. "You're tired," he informed her, then went for a cab. Zelda meekly wished the Callaghans goodnight, then allowed herself to be put into a cab by her husband and sent home, presumably to bed. Morley asked Scott what the trouble was, and Scott replied that Zelda worked far too hard at dance practice.

"Why is she working so hard at it?"

"She wants to have something of her own, be something herself."

Not many months later, just as the decade ended, Zelda's anxiety and depression required her admission to Malmaison, the mental institution just outside Paris where former President Deschanel had been confined exactly ten years earlier. Zelda arrived at Malmaison slightly intoxicated; a week later she abruptly checked herself out of the clinic, against the advice of her physician. When she returned to their apartment in Paris, Scott had been giving a series of parties: Zelda found herself in the midst of a sustained and familiar alcoholic nightmare. Within three weeks her condition was compounded by an inexplicable eczema and recurrent delirium: "There was music that beat behind my forehead and other music that fell into my stomach from a high parabola. . . ." She agreed to submit to treatment at Les Rives de Prangins, near Nyon on Lake Geneva, where her condition was diagnosed as acute schizophrenia. Unlike Nicole Diver in *Tender Is the Night*, Fitzgerald's composite character based on his wife and Sara Murphy, Zelda would never recover from her breakdown.

James Joyce was the most superstitious of men. When Robert McAlmon reported having seen a rat at the Closerie de Lilas, Joyce cried out, "That's bad luck, that's bad luck!" and had to be taken home. Dates and numbers took on extraordinary importance. He would put Sylvia Beach to any amount of trouble to obtain the first bound copy of *Ulysses* by February 2, 1922, the date of his fortieth birthday—or he could turn pale at the realization that he had just asked a guest to dinner who would make thirteen at table.

A Dublin friend, Thomas McGreevy, had called to wangle an introduction to Joyce for a young admirer, Samuel Beckett. Only after McGreevy hung up did Joyce make a mental count of the prospective diners: thirteen! Immediately he got in touch with another guest who could be persuaded to accept an alternate invitation.

At dinner, dressed in a waistcoat of embroidered flowers, Joyce questioned Beckett closely concerning the news and gossip of Dublin. Though living in self-imposed exile, Joyce relentlessly pumped newly arrived Irishmen for information about the home to which he would never return.

Samuel Beckett had just been appointed *lecteur* in English at the prestigious Ecole Normale Supérieure for the 1928-29 academic year. Just out of Trinity College, Dublin, Beckett was uncertain about teaching as a career or following a literary bent of his own. He had of course wanted to meet the celebrated author of *Ulysses*, and McGreevy, his predecessor at l'Ecole Normale, was delighted to bring the two Dubliners together. Joyce and Beckett were twenty-four years apart in age, but Joyce felt an immediate affinity with the hawk-faced young lecturer. In a very short time Beckett found himself with the unexpected role and questionable honor of serving James Joyce as man of all work.

Before Beckett had arrived upon the scene, a series of young men and women of willing disposition filled in as spare-time secretary to Joyce. Both Sylvia Beach and Robert McAlmon felt obliged to do considerable legwork for Joyce, as well as being his publishers. Or any casual acquaintance might be inveigled into rendering service to the master: Philippe Soupault, Surrealist author, remembered being asked by Joyce, "Which way are you going home?"—then discovered he was involved in a complicated, time-consuming errand for Joyce on the opposite side of the city. Because of Joyce's near blindness, and in respect for his genius, any assistance offered to the author was considered an act of homage. But McAlmon, who had assumed the role of spare-time secretary to Joyce prior to Beckett, was disenchanted with the man and his oeuvre. Joyce could be high-handed and infinitely demanding in his attitude toward underlings and patrons alike. If the money McAlmon regularly advanced to Joyce did not arrive when promised, Joyce sent his benefactor blunt little reminders: "I shall be greatly obliged if your monthly cheque arrived punctually." For Joyce's part, McAlmon was far too flippant in his manner: the young man was sadly lacking the respect and subservience Joyce demanded of an acolyte.

When the unpaid assistantship fell to Beckett, he was flattered and eager to be of service. Beckett made himself available to the author's every need or whim: research at the Bibliothèque Nationale, transcriptions at all hours of the day or night, reading aloud to Joyce as the author swabbed his pained eyes following an attack of iritis.

Since Beckett never rose before noon, he arranged to hold seminars with his sole student in the late afternoon, when the two would read Shakespeare together at the Dôme. Descriptions of Beckett at this period vary from "a small redhaired Irishman" (Adolph Hoffmeister) to "a blond beanpole with glasses" (Nino Frank), his eyes alternately colored blue, then green. The most consistent of remembered impressions is the intensity of Beckett's gaze and his profound seriousness. McGreevy called his young friend the Melancholy Irishman, which was close to Joyce's own reference to himself as Melancholy Jesus. Beckett frequented the small Dublin circle of Irish expatriates: Arthur Power, Francis Stuart, Thomas McGreevy, and occasionally mingled with the French Surrealist poets, but he chiefly preferred the company of James Joyce, or his own solitude. He haunted the residence halls on the rue d'Ulm, playing dirges on a flute in the late hours.

His favorite subject of conversation was the philosophic implications of suicide.

Adrienne Monnier spoke of Beckett—as perhaps Beckett thought of himself—as the new Stephen Dedalus, following the Joycean path of "silence, exile, and cunning." Beckett then began to assume the traits of his idol: he pretended to be more nearsighted than he was, holding reading matter very close to his eyes, as Joyce would do; his cigarette dangled carelessly from his fingers, and he crossed his legs in the same fashion. Actually the two men were very alike in character and interests: introverts both, traditionally Irish in their awe of the supernatural. Both men were proficient linguists; they were fascinated scavengers of obscure facts, odd turns of speech, esoteric knowledge.

From the first, Beckett looked up to Joyce as would an adoring son. The two men became as close as Joyce's guarded nature would allow—throughout the friendship they called one another "Mr. Beckett" and "Mr. Joyce." Beckett may have wanted to be the spiritual son to James Joyce, but Joyce had a son, Giorgio, and the only love he had to spare was rationed out to Nora Barnacle, Giorgio, and his daughter, Lucia.

Beckett became so involved with the Joyce family that he decided to forgo his Christmas holiday with family in Dublin in order to be of assistance to Joyce during Nora's hospitalization following a hysterectomy. Joyce was lost without his wife; Beckett felt he could not leave him at that critical time.

A disturbing aspect of Beckett's relationship to the Joyce family was the growing attachment Joyce's daughter felt toward her father's handsome young companion-assistant. Lucia was a graceful, shy creature—attractive except for a slightly cross-eyed squint. This defect was a greatly enlarged deformity in the sensitive girl's mind: she dwelt on the matter of her appearance with all the morbidity of postadolescence. Furthermore, her lonely life in Paris—she was not fluent in French, kept changing schools and languages, was uneasy with every shift of background in her father's nomadic exile—increased an already unstable nature. Lucia was a bundle of complexes and turmoil.

Mildly attracted to Lucia, Beckett treated her with a young man's attention to the young lady of the house—but it was her father he truly cared about and whose attention he sought. With a polite reserve Beckett had learned from Joyce himself, the young man seemed to be paying court to the daughter. Nora and James Joyce observed the one-sided romance develop without realizing how hopeless the affair was to be. Beckett never revealed to the Joyces that he was in love with a girl in Germany, a girl he was determined to marry if she would have him.

The parents considered a match between their daughter and the quiet, intelligent Irishman an ideal alliance. For the first time, the affections of the withdrawn Lucia were aroused: she made no secret of *her* intentions, though the object of her desire might himself show every reluctance. Beckett now tried to avoid seeing Lucia, timing his visits when she would most likely be away—but he did not always succeed. In order to see and be with the admired father, he was continually at risk of a compromising entanglement with the determined daughter.

By now Beckett had become all too aware of Lucia's disturbed and disturbing behavior. Formerly too shy to join in conversation, she now chattered obsessively in company, was nervously animated, childishly hyperactive. Lucia's mind wandered from one subject to the next in no orderly or reasonable pattern: her disconnected monologues reminded Beckett of "the father's mind running rampant in the daughter." Beckett was not alone in his belief that Lucia might be insane. Joyce's translator, Valery Larbaud, had always been convinced that Lucia's bizarre mannerisms indicated neurosis.

Joyce, however, seemed unaware of Lucia's alarming symptoms. The father was consumed by the task of putting together *Finnegans Wake*, distracted by financial worries (*Ulysses* was being pirated in the United States by renegade publisher Samuel Roth), exhausted by overwork and attacks of iritis that left him "literally doubled in two from fatigue and cramp." He was losing the confidence of friends and defenders like Ezra Pound and Wyndham Lewis, who declared *Finnegans Wake* a hopeless puzzle and literary dead end. (Nora's reaction to the work in progress was, "Why don't you write sensible books that people can understand?") Hovering over him was the necessity of another eye operation, his ninth.

Lucia's single psychic outlet was dance. In turn she had attempted drawing lessons, piano, singing, and had given them all up, but from 1926 until 1929 she practiced her dance for as many as six hours daily. A series of teachers that included Jacques Dalcroze and Egorova of the Ballets Russes encouraged her and expressed some acknowledgment of her gifts. In April 1929 Lucia entered an international dance competition at a *bal musette* in Montparnasse, the Bal Bullier. She was much applauded—the audience called for an encore by *l'Irlandaise*—although she did not receive a prize. This was to be Lucia's only moment of glory after three years of intensive study, for she never danced again.

Ezra Pound was briefly back in Paris to look up old friends. Settled in Rapallo now, he was no longer the open, free-spirited iconoclast who became every artist's publicist and friend. Pound's occasional irascibility and incipient paranoia had been fueled by the demagoguery of Benito Mussolini's Fascist regime in Italy. Pound, the long-standing spiritual exile, had at last found sanctuary in a nation that satisfied his most outrageous prejudices.

Ezra Pound joined the Joyce family, along with Samuel Beckett, for dinner at Les Trianons. Here Joyce reigned in unquestionable majesty. The proprietor kept Joyce's customary table on permanent reservation, the head waiter took the trouble to read the entire menu aloud so that the near-blind author did not have to carry eyeglasses or resort to a magnifying glass.

For all his pleasure in dining out, Joyce was no gourmet, but he delighted in entertaining friends whenever he was in funds. He pressed his guests to choose the most expensive items on the menu, while he ate sparingly and would have been as content on a steady diet of canned salmon and boiled lentils. Joyce preferred to drink white wine. The cheapest would do, as long as there was plenty of it.

At dinner Beckett was his usual quiet and modest self, all the more so in the overwhelming presence of Joyce and Pound: to Joyce he showed a characteristic deference, noticeably solicitous toward the older man. Pound interpreted Beckett's manner as that of a sycophant and was to say so later on. He was impatient and rude to Beckett, offering not the slightest interest or customary generosity to a new young literary hopeful. Nor did Pound and Joyce find one another's company agreeable: their views were too divergent now to allow for the easy relationship begun in 1920; they were, despite the polite pretense, no longer friends.

Meanwhile, Beckett was slowly moving away from his total commitment to James Joyce. He had begun to write prose and poetry of his own: his first short story, "Assumption," was published in the same issue of *transition* as his scholarly essay on the Italian influence on James Joyce's work. McGreevy encouraged him to write a poem for the contest sponsored by Nancy Cunard; Beckett completed his entry only minutes before the midnight deadline, then slipped the poem "Whoroscope" under the door of the Hours Press. Nancy Cunard was so impressed with this initial work by an unknown poet that she awarded Beckett the first prize of £10. Later she arranged to meet the prizewinner himself and was further impressed with his "profile of an Aztec eagle." With Nancy Cunard as a patron, Beckett was launched. Three hundred copies of *Whoroscope* were printed as a separate pamphlet by the Hours Press, Beckett's first independently published work.

By now Beckett had wandered out of the exclusive orbit of James Joyce and his family, but Lucia was as much in love with him as ever—and ever more mentally unstable. Finally, she attempted to confront her reluctant lover alone. She invited Samuel to lunch at a Montparnasse restaurant, an invitation Beckett could in no diplomatic way refuse. Instead, he took the precaution of bringing along his student and drinking companion, Georges Pelorson, a deliberate ploy to provide a third-person buffer between himself and Lucia.

When two men, instead of Beckett alone, appeared at the restaurant, Lucia's dismay was evident. Disappointed and melancholy at first, she eventually slipped into a manic stage, became bizarrely agitated, her hands brushing her face in futile gestures that smeared her makeup and disarranged her hair. Neither man dared interrupt her disconnected mono-logue. The luncheon was a Mad Hatter's party, an embarrassment for Beckett and his friend, a disaster for Lucia.

Beckett had no intention of allowing the girl's delusions about him to continue. When next Lucia met him at the door, Beckett blurted out the unhappy truth: the purpose of his call was to see and be with her father. He went on to explain that he did think of her as a friend, with almost brotherly devotion, but that she was not the object of his visits to the Joyce apartment. Lucia was shocked and hurt. When James and Nora Joyce learned of Samuel Beckett's blunt declaration to their daughter, they considered his behavior a low deception. The friendship was over; their door was closed to him. The young Dubliner could never be the foster son of James Joyce he had so wanted to be, and never the son-in-law Joyce intended.

The relationship was not repaired until the Thirties, after Lucia had been diagnosed as schizophrenic and became a patient at Les Rives de Prangins, where Zelda Fitzgerald had been under treatment a few years before.

Chapter Fourteen

The mood in Paris was upbeat. By October 1929 the franc was selling at 25.5 to the dollar, and American dollars were still turning into eminently spendable francs. At the Gaumont Palace Maurice Chevalier was appearing in his first talking picture *La Chanson de Paris*, while the optimistic Emile Coué had carried his own happy song to America: "Every day in every way I am becoming better and better."

Coué's autosuggestion appeared to be having its effect. Following the nasty scandals of the Harding era, Coolidge had served a term of tranquil prosperity, and Hoover had eased into office on the same ticket of rising affluence. Since 1925, with stocks such as Radio, ATT, U.S. Steel, and Montgomery Ward moving ever upward, Paris branches of American brokerage houses were doing unprecedented business. At high tide it was time to get into the swim. Hairdressers and bootblacks listened for market tips from their customers, and cabbies spread the latest word on the hottest issues; everybody borrowed on next month's salary to get in on today's sure thing.

There were noticeable cracks in the Wall Street façade: U.S. business activity was sluggish, unemployment at an unhealthy level; yet speculation grew all the more frantic. In February there had been a brief collapse of stock values. Investors reacted by pushing popular issues to new highs. Bargain hunters were ever poised to swoop in and take up the slack at the first symptoms of slump.

The Federal Reserve cautiously pressured member banks to restrict credit to brokers and to discourage loans that were purely speculative. The warning was ignored. Credit was a staple of the marketplace, as real as currency itself. Since the end of World War I, economic policy had been updated to accommodate Maynard Keynes's theory that potential wealth was a useful correlative to apparent wealth.

The stock market came to represent the great democratic meeting place where J. P. Morgan and his chauffeur both had a piece of Anaconda Copper. The wonder is not so much that his chauffeur was converted to the gospel of unlimited growth but that J. P. Morgan became a true believer: the affluent plunged as recklessly as the financial amateurs. Speculation had become a national pastime. Smaller investors flocked to the mostly unregulated investment trusts being built as pyramids of dubious paper. In the summer of 1929 more than a million shareholders were building the pyramids.

On September 3, six months after Hoover's inauguration, the stock market reached its all-time high. Prices slipped later in September, but this only brought out the bargain hunters in force.

On Tuesday, October 22, a day that became known as Black Tuesday, the frenzy of activity on Wall Street was inexplicable and unprecedented. A dramatic shift of trading patterns took place as six million shares of stock changed hands. For every sell order there was a buyer, but the drop in prices was disastrous. By the next day a torrent of sell orders flooded the trading floor, and by the end of the day the tape was still two hours late with price quotations. Long-dormant fears of ruin had replaced the buoyant optimism of the bulls. After a heady five-year climb, the market plunged backward into the abyss.

By noon on Wednesday, brokers could not keep up with calls to "sell at the market," for they were too busy sending out distress calls for margin coverage to their customers. Prices became impossible to quote: the stock-trading system collapsed into chaos. A messenger boy idly bid a single dollar for White Sewing Machine, quoted at 48 when the market opened, and acquired a block of 100 shares in the absence of any other bid. The trauma was so great that brokers wandered the littered floor like zombies: several whispered to themselves; one man giggled hysterically, and another wept. A consortium of bankers led by J. P. Morgan injected a modicum of hope by ostentatiously buying up large blocks of stock: the market steadied temporarily. But 12,894,650 shares had been sold off in a single session, and the nightmare drop in prices could not be camouflaged. In the sickening slide, the paper gains built up since 1925 had all but vanished by the closing gong at 3:00 P.M. The bankers' consortium discreetly retired from the field. By October 29 investors were fighting to sell. There were still shares of pie in the sky on the market, but not even the bargain hunters were buying. The market hit bottom on November 13: the Coué formula echoed like a bad joke on the floor of the New York Stock Exchange.

A six-hour difference in time isolated the Paris brokerage houses from the Wall Street drama. Telephone lines were jammed: the absence of confirming information from New York only increased the panic of investors living in Paris. The sluggish Paris Bourse had never achieved the scale of U.S. investment activity: French issues were affected only psychologically and superficially, but many Frenchmen of means had succumbed to the American fever and invested in Wall Street as well. They now gathered in large numbers outside the Paris Bourse.

Inside, prices were still recorded on a chalkboard behind the old-fashioned railings, but the Paris Bourse was no help in keeping American investors informed. Hundreds of calls went through to the Paris *Herald* switchboard where extra staff tried to assuage the fears of Americans in Paris during the financial crisis at home. Other groups of Americans joined pockets of French businessmen gathered outside the Banque de Saint-Phalle and the Guaranty Trust, awaiting some mysterious signal of reassurance. The word from home, when it filtered through, was a confirmation of disaster.

Many of the expatriate colony living in France were no longer solvent. They joined the queue at the embassy for emergency funds to return to the United States. The cafés and hotels of Montparnasse emptied out: letters addressed to those who had already left for home piled up in the patrons' mail rack at the Dôme, unread.

The smaller-scale French economy had not shared in the American boom, except obliquely through the hordes of tourists in Paris. France was still a nation of shopkeepers and small farms; gold was the traditional investment of most Frenchmen. Those who did climb on the American bandwagon were also affected by what became known as Le Krach. Maurice Sachs wrote in his diary for October 24: "Nous n'avons plus rien"— "We have nothing left." His mother had suffered a heart attack at the news of the crash; his uncle had committed suicide.

Americans had been the foremost purchasers of French art throughout the Twenties, pushing prices to the same incredible levels as prices on the stock exchange. There were few buyers left in Paris to maintain the unrealistic art prices: galleries on the rue de Seine and rue La Boétie closed down; affluent painters began to move back into the cheap ateliers of another, simpler age. "We don't sell our paintings anymore!" cried André Lhote. "Painting is saved!"

After the years of dissipation, Harry Crosby returned to the United States in December 1929 looking remarkable youthful, apparently in excellent health. His tanned and handsome visage showed little trace of the sexual excess or the drugged and drunken escapades in Paris.

In New York he began to look up acquaintances from the Paris years: Hart Crane, Archibald MacLeish, E. E. Cummings; and he had taken up with an old flame, the now married Josephine Rotch Bigelow. On December 7 Hart Crane gave a party for Harry and Caresse Crosby in his Brooklyn apartment with its view of the famous bridge, the subject of Crane's long poem. Present were Cummings, William Carlos Williams, the Malcolm Cowleys, Walker Evans, the photographer, and a group of homosexual sailors. In the course of the evening someone was shuffling a deck of playing cards; he extended a hand of cards to Harry and told him to pick a card. Calmly Harry crossed himself, predicted he would choose the ace of hearts, then did exactly that. To the others, the random selection of an ace of hearts was a party trick or a coincidence, but the card was of great significance to Harry. He knew something no one else at the party knew.

Before they left that night, the Crosbys invited Hart Crane to join them for dinner three days hence, at the Caviar Restaurant. Also on that date, December 10, Harry had an earlier appointment with his uncle, J. P. Morgan, possibly to discuss the matter of the Crosbys having drawn heavily on capital during the binge years in Paris. The discussion was never held, for Harry did not show up. Nor did he appear at the Caviar Restaurant, where Hart Crane sat waiting with Caresse and her mother-in-law.

When the dinner hour passed, and still no sign of Harry, Caresse thought of calling Harry's friend Stanley Mortimer, who sometimes lent Harry his studio at 1 West 67th Street. Mortimer admitted he had given Harry the key to his studio and agreed to stop by the studio to see if Harry might be there. He did not want to tell Caresse that he was certain Harry had gone to the studio, and with Josephine Bigelow.

The door to the studio was locked from inside, and there was no answer to Mortimer's persistent knocking: by 10:00 P.M. he was obliged to ask the building superintendent to help him break into the studio on the ninth floor.

Two inert bodies, fully clothed, lay across the bed, a .25-caliber Belgian pistol—a sun symbol engraved on its side—dangled from Harry's lifeless hand. A single bullet had passed through Josephine's left temple; in Harry's right temple was an identical bullet hole. Their shoes were off, and on Harry's bare feet were the tattoos he had acquired in North Africa: a Christian cross on the bottom of his right foot, a pagan sun symbol on the left. Josephine was wearing a gay corsage of orchids, and Harry carried with him at the end a whiskey flask, the gift of his fellow corpsmen in the Norton-Harjes Ambulance Service. There was no note.

Hart Crane wrote an elegy for Harry Crosby called "The Cloud Juggler," the last published work before his own suicide in 1932, but E. E. Cummings wrote the epitaph:

2 boston
Dolls; found
with
Holes in each other
's lullaby

Everyone left Paris in August, but Diaghilev fled the city as if it were the source of his personal plague. His body had erupted in running sores: Kochno and Lifar bathed his feverish body with alcohol, changed the dressings on his sores. Dr. Dalimier diagnosed diabetes and placed Diaghilev on a spartan diet: he could take no alcohol whatsoever and was to replace sugar with saccharine. The continental bon vivant could not accept the doctor's regime and would not admit to debility. He gaily cheated on the diet: "But today is *Sunday*," he would say to Kochno as he poured himself a flute of champagne. Dalimier advised Diaghilev to go to Switzerland where a treatment for diabetes by insulin injection had proved successful. Instead, the impresario hastily embarked on the last of his classic Grand Tours, when he introduced the latest of his protégés—in 1929, Igor Markevitch—to the cultural treasures of Europe. Switzerland meant clinics, regime, and hypodermic needles. With his horror of growing old, Diaghilev had always surrounded himself with youth and beauty, hoping to dwell forever removed from all that was associated with sickness, decline, and death.

More than once Diaghilev had presented a copy of Thomas Mann's novella *Death in Venice* to a favored young man on the eve of a trip to the city of canals. Ironically, Igor Markevitch interrupted their tour in Germany to visit family in Switzerland. Diaghilev went to Venice alone.

Meanwhile, Diaghilev's two closest women friends, Coco Chanel and Misia Sert, were cruising the Dalmatian coast with Bend'or, Chanel's latest lover. Both women had reason to hope for distraction from their own unhappy circumstances: Bend'or was being blatantly unfaithful to Coco; Misia's marriage to José-Maria Sert was breaking up.

They put aside their personal dilemmas when a telegram came from Serge Lifar, dictated by Diaghilev: "Am sick, come quickly, Serge."

The Flying Cloud changed course, bound for Venice. As soon as the yacht tied up, Diaghilev's two friends rushed to the Grand Hôtel des Bains where the sick and fading impresario lay in pain. It was shocking to come upon Diaghilev, wasted and colorless, his condition obviously grave. His eyes were animated for the first time as Misia and Coco materialized at his bedside. He was shivering under the blankets, wearing his dinner jacket in bed to keep warm, although the room was suffocatingly hot.

"Oh, how happy I am to see you," he whispered. "I love you in white. Promise me you will always wear white."

These were the last reasonably coherent thoughts he would express. Later in the day he lapsed into delirium and fever and spoke of himself in the past tense while muttering in a disconnected way about the romantic music of Tchaikovsky. "The *Pathétique*, that's what I loved most in my life . . . quick, go hear it and think of me." When asked how he felt, he replied, "I feel drunk."

Misia slipped out quietly to purchase a sweater to replace the unseemly dinner jacket he wore in bed. She found a doctor, a German (the Italian doctors insisted that the patient suffered from rheumatism), and she engaged an English nurse to stand watch in place of the faithful duo, Kochno and Lifar. Suddenly Diaghilev seemed to improve. His temperature was down, he insisted on wearing his plate, he rambled—but hopefully—about a trip to Palermo. Chanel left to rejoin her lover on *The Flying Cloud*; Misia stayed behind to keep company with Lifar and Kochno at Diaghilev's bedside.

On the evening of August 18, Misia returned exhausted to her hotel across the lagoon, the Danieli, while Kochno and Lifar remained with Diaghilev. "They were so white," Diaghilev whispered over and over. "All in white. They were so white." The airy chimera of youth and whiteness hovered about the overheated room. The sick man lapsed into a coma. As soon as the nurse recognized the terminal symptoms, she began packing her valise. Kochno called Misia at the Danieli.

When Misia arrived, she was accompanied by Father Irineus of the Greek Orthodox Church, who had come to administer the last rites for the dying. At dawn Diaghilev's heart ceased to beat. A ray of sunlight struck Diaghilev's forehead; then the hotel room gradually filled with the light of day. Misia was awed by the theatrical spectacle of the lagoon suddenly and gloriously come to life just at the moment of death's visitation, as if the magnificent charlatan had himself arranged the lighting for his adieu.

The private funeral took place among a few close friends assembled in Diaghilev's hotel room. All the currency Diaghilev had carried with him, 6,000 francs, Misia turned over to Lifar and Kochno: she had intended to pay for the funeral and burial by selling her diamond necklace in Venice, but she met Coco Chanel rushing toward her in the Piazza San Marco. Chanel had been overcome with a premonition of Diaghilev's death. At her very first meeting with him, Chanel had offered a generous check to the bankrupt impresario: now, at the end, the gesture was the same. Chanel assumed the last worldly expenses of the man who had forever banked on charm instead of money.

A solemn mass was held for Diaghilev at the Greek Orthodox cathedral in Venice; then the coffin was placed aboard a slim black funeral gondola, its prow carved with gilded angels, the coffin flanked by black-robed priests. The body was borne to the island cemetery of San Michele: Misia Sert and Coco Chanel followed in the first gondola of the floating proces-

Coco Chanel. A shrewd businesswoman, she was the first to design clothes that would appeal to the mass market as well as the beau monde.

sion. At the island Kochno and Lifar were preparing to crawl behind the coffin on their knees to the graveside, but a sharp rebuke from Misia brought them to their feet—she was not quick enough, however, to prevent Lifar's theatrical leap into Diaghilev's open grave. Attendants drew him out of the grave, and while the priests restrained Lifar, mourners filed by dropping flower petals onto the coffin, offering a last homage to the vanished conjurer of the arts, bidding an era farewell.